Statistical Theory

A series of advanced mathematics texts under the editorship of CARL B. ALLENDOERFER

TOPICS IN HIGHER ANALYSIS by Harold K. Crowder and S. W. McCuskey

CONCEPTS IN MODERN ALGEBRA by W. E. Deskins

THEORY AND SOLUTION OF ORDINARY DIFFERENTIAL EQUATIONS by Donald Greenspan

RETRACING ELEMENTARY MATHEMATICS by Leon Henkin, W. Norman Smith, Verne J. Varineau, and Michael J. Walsh

INTRODUCTION TO MATHEMATICAL STATISTICS by Robert V. Hogg and Allen T. Craig

ELEMENTARY MATRIX ALGEBRA, Second Edition, by Franz E. Hohn

METHODS IN ANALYSIS by Jack Indritz

PROJECTIVE AND RELATED GEOMETRIES by Harry Levy

STATISTICAL THEORY by B. W. Lindgren

INTRODUCTION TO PROBABILITY THEORY by James R. McCord, III, and Richard M. Moroney, Jr.

ELEMENTS OF ABSTRACT ALGEBRA by John T. Moore

Statistical Theory

B. W. LINDGREN
Department of Mathematics
Institute of Technology
University of Minnesota

NEW YORK THE MACMILLAN COMPANY
MACMILLAN NEW YORK, LONDON

Second Printing 1963

Library of Congress catalog card number: 62-8161

The Macmillan Company, New York
Collier-Macmillan Canada, Ltd., Galt, Ontario
Divisions of The Crowell-Collier Publishing Company

Printed in the United States of America

Preface

This book is intended as a text for a year's course in the theory of statistics. The minimum mathematical prerequisite is a first course in differential and integral calculus. No formal prerequisite in statistics is assumed, although it is possible that some prior exposure to statistical methods on the part of the reader would make the material more meaningful.

The book has a definite mathematical slant and does not hesitate to introduce the student to mathematics and mathematical notation that may be new to him. But it is not a complete, rigorous, mathematical development of the subject; such a treatment would require much more background and maturity than is assumed here. Mathematically, the level, the spirit, and the degree of completeness of the present work are perhaps comparable to those of a traditional intermediate or advanced calculus course.

It has been my aim to expound clearly and objectively some modern statistical theory, together with the elements of the more "classical" theory of statistics, in a mathematical setting that can be completed and amplified (without being replaced) at a later stage in the student's progress. In view of the probabilistic basis of statistical inference it seems natural to provide in the first four chapters a mathematical study of probability distributions, random variables, and independence, culminating in the Central Limit Theorem. Chapters 5 through 7 present the basic theory of statistical decision-making and its specializations to the problems of estimation and testing of hypotheses. Chapters 9, 10, and 11 apply these concepts to various particular statistical problems.

Anyone teaching from this book will doubtless think of topics that he feels ought to have been included. The field of statistics is tremendous, and its theory cannot be treated exhaustively in one year. However, since there is included more than enough material to keep most students and instructors busy through the year, no apology is offered for the omission or neglect of certain areas. The instructor will also find that the order of topics in a course from this book need not be exactly that followed in the book. For instance, I usually defer the details of multivariate distributions until, say, just prior to Chapter 8. Some skipping about may be necessary in Chapters 9, 10, and 11 because of the press of time.

Advocates of Bayesian statistics will search in vain for an explicit discussion of subjective or personal probability. Although sure that any future revision of this book will take this area into account, I offer as consolation for the present minimum contact with it the possibly lame excuse that the material presented is instructive and useful and will afford the student a reasonably unprejudiced background for a study of the more subtle and still controversial aspects of the theory.

In general I have not used "real" problems with great masses of data because of the likelihood of losing the point being taught in the forest of "real" complications. A problem that can be properly posed in a few lines without such complications is usually not a "real" problem. It seems to me that today's student has ample motivation for statistics in everyday life, and that mathematics and statistical theory are best taught, bit by bit, with simple artificial examples illustrating each bit.

It is of course impossible to detail one's debt to the statistical literature and to existing textbooks in probability and statistics, but readers familiar with the books of Lehmann and Chernoff and Moses (References [12] and [3]) will surely notice their influence here. I wish also to thank and acknowledge my debt to several individuals who have helped me in a variety of ways: Professor I. Richard Savage of the University of Minnesota, Professor Herman Chernoff of Stanford University, Professor Andrew Sterrett of Denison University, Dr. Donald Richter of Bell Telephone Laboratories, and Mr. Patrick Ahern of the University of Minnesota. Miss Shirley Hilsen typed the preliminary version, and students using it have helped by eliminating many errors. I am indebted to the editors of *Biometrika*, *The Annals of Mathematical Statistics*, and the *Journal of the American Statistical Association* for permission to adapt tables for use in this book, and to Professor Sir Ronald A. Fisher, Cambridge, to Dr. Frank Yates, Rothamsted, and to Messrs. Oliver and Boyd, Ltd., Edinburgh, for permission to reprint a portion of Table 2 from their book *Statistical Tables for Biological, Agricultural, and Medical Research.*

B. W. Lindgren

Contents

Statistical Theory

1/Probability Models

We consider an experiment, performed under a given set of conditions. It may be physical, chemical, social, etc. Occasionally an experiment is of such a nature that the outcome of the experiment is uniquely defined by a knowledge of the conditions under which it is performed. But more often than not, the outcome of such an experiment is not so determined, in the sense that when it is repeated under supposedly identical conditions, the outcome is not always the same. This may be because there are factors affecting the outcome which the experimentor is not aware of, or because there are factors he cannot control even though he may be aware of them or because the factors he thinks he can control are really not controlled. Thus the outcome cannot be exactly predicted in terms of ones knowledge of the conditions of the experiment, and we speak of the experiment as an "experiment involving chance," or more simply, as an "experiment of chance."

1.1 Sample Spaces

The possible outcomes of an experiment of chance are considered as objects or mathematical "points," and the collection of such outcomes is called the *sample space* of the experiment. In a given experiment there is some arbitrariness as to just what the sample space is, since there is arbitrariness in what is to be called an outcome, or a "way" in which the experiment turns out. This will be apparent in some of the examples to follow. The point is that in the process of setting up a mathematical model for certain actual experiments, one can proceed in more than one way, depending on his purposes.

1.1.1 Elementary Outcomes. The term *elementary outcome* will be used to denote one of the various ways in which an experiment can terminate, classified according to some scheme that is sufficiently detailed as to permit describing in terms of them any event which is likely to be of interest. It is a flexible designation.

Example 1–1. A coin is tossed. If the coin is a standard coin, its two faces are different and are referred to as "Heads" and "Tails." Although it is conceivable that when the coin falls, it will land on edge or roll into a sewer beyond reach, it is natural and useful to consider that there are two elementary outcomes: Heads up and Tails up. These two outcomes make up the sample space.

Example 1–2. A cube whose six faces are marked with one, two, three, four, five, and six "dots," respectively, is called a *die*. When a die is tossed, it falls (on a flat surface) with one of the six faces turned up. One can think of the outcome of the experiment as these six faces, or as the six numbers giving the numbers of dots on the faces. These six elementary outcomes make up the sample space of the experiment.

Example 1–3. Three coins are tossed. The proper sample space depends again upon what we are interested in. If we are not concerned with which coin is which, but only in the number of coins out of the three which have landed Heads, the list of possible numbers of Heads among the three coins 0, 1, 2, 3 is adequate for our purposes. These four numbers are then the elementary outcomes and make up the sample space.

Example 1–4. A missile is fired at a target on the earth's surface. Because of the uncertainties in the propellant, in the atmospheric conditions, and in the direction of aiming, the result of this experiment cannot be predicted in terms of known or measurable quantities. The experiment is then best considered as an experiment of chance. The landing point of the missile is the elementary outcome of the experiment, and the set of all points on the surface of the earth (perhaps restricted to those lying within a reasonable distance of the target) would make up the sample space. If a rectangular coordinate grid is placed over the target area, assuming a plane surface, the landing point's coordinate representation (x,y) can be identified with the outcome of the experiment. The sample space is thus identified with the collection of all such ordered pairs of coordinate values.

Example 1–5. Four chips marked A, B, C, and D are placed in a container. The chips are mixed, and two are selected from the container. If the selection is done blindly, the outcome is not certain, and the experiment can be considered as an experiment of chance. The elementary outcomes might be thought of as described by listing the particular chips drawn, as follows: AB, AC, AD, BC, BD, CD. These six combinations of two chips from the four make up the sample space.

If the two chips are drawn one at a time and one keeps track of which is drawn first, this order may be important for some reason, and the set of outcomes necessary to keep track of the order would be 12 in number, namely:

$$AB,\ AC,\ AD,\ BC,\ BD,\ CD,\ BA,\ CA,\ DA,\ CB,\ DB,\ DC.$$

Two of these more elementary outcomes involve the letters in any one of the combinations given earlier which did not specify order.

Example 1–6. A certain material is thought of as being composed of tubes or fibers, and each fiber is assumed to be oriented in a certain direction relative to a coordinate system fixed to the material. If a fiber is selected "at random" (or by lot, or blindfolded), the orientation of that fiber could be any one of the infinitely many possible orientations. These possible orientations make up the sample space. This sample space could be identified with the points on a hemisphere (say, of unit radius), a given point on the sphere being associated with the orientation of the vector from the center of the sphere to the point.

1.1.2 Composition of Experiments. It is natural to consider two or more experiments jointly, considering that in many instances it is easier to analyze things by treating a complex experiment as the combination of two or more simpler experiments. If a composite experiment $\mathcal{E}$ is equivalent to the performance first of an experiment $\mathcal{E}_1$, followed by the performance of an experiment $\mathcal{E}_2$, there is a natural way (but not a unique one) of itemizing the outcomes of $\mathcal{E}$ in terms of the outcomes of $\mathcal{E}_1$ and those of $\mathcal{E}_2$. That way is to associate each elementary outcome of $\mathcal{E}_1$ with each elementary outcome of $\mathcal{E}_2$ to obtain what are then by definition the elementary outcomes of the composite experiment. Clearly, if the number of elementary outcomes of $\mathcal{E}_1$ is n_1 and the number of elementary outcomes of $\mathcal{E}_2$ is n_2, the number of elementary outcomes in the composite experiment is the product n_1n_2.

It may be that the elementary outcomes of the composite experiment defined in this way are more "elementary" than is required for a given purpose, but this is no serious objection.

Example 1–7. Consider an experiment consisting of a toss of a coin and a die together. The same effect can be achieved by tossing the coin and then the die, and so we think of the experiment as a composite of those two simpler experiments. The number of elementary outcomes of the composite experiment is 12, considering the two faces of the coin and the six faces of the die as elementary outcomes for the coin and the die, respectively. Denoting Heads by H and Tails by T, the 12 elementary outcomes are:

$$H1, H2, H3, H4, H5, H6, \qquad T1, T2, T3, T4, T5, T6.$$

Example 1–8. Consider again (as in Example 1–5) the drawing of two chips from a container in which are four chips marked A, B, C, and D. The experiment can be performed in two steps: First one chip is drawn, and then from the remaining chips another is drawn. For the first of these operations the obvious elementary outcomes are A, B, C, and D—four in all. The chips available for the second drawing depend on what is drawn first, but whatever is first drawn, the *number* of chips available for the second drawing is three. There are then $4 \cdot 3 = 12$ elementary outcomes in the combined experiment (just those listed at the end of Example 1–5).

If the order of selection happens not to be of interest (so that, for instance, AB is the same as BA), it really is not necessary to have 12 elementary outcomes in the sample space of the composite experiment; but on the other hand there is no harm in having them.

The selection of some objects from a group of objects, as in the above example, is an important kind of composite experiment. Another related kind of experiment is that in which objects are arranged in a *sequence*. If there are n objects, the arrangement can be accomplished by picking one of the n for the first position, then one of the remaining $n - 1$ for the second position, and so on; the number of such arrangements is then $n! = n(n-1)\cdots 3\cdot 2\cdot 1$.

The objects being arranged may not be "distinct" in that some may be, for instance, of the same color. In this case one would not want to call two arrangements different if objects are differently arranged, as long as the color patterns are the same. To count the number of arrangements that are different according to this convention, we reason as follows. The $n!$ distinct arrangement of the n objects can be counted by first counting the number of arrangements that are different according to color and then multiplying this by the number of arrangements for each color scheme. For example, if there are r red objects, b blue objects, and c green objects, we have

$$n! = P\, r!b!c!,$$

where P is the number of different color patterns:

$$P = \frac{n!}{r!\, b!\, c!}.$$

By using this result, we can count the number of elementary outcomes in selecting k from n objects. Indeed, this number is exactly the same as the number of arrangements of n objects, k of which are alike and $n - k$ of which are alike, since doing this arranging is equivalent to selecting k out of n available positions in the sequence in which to place the k objects that are alike. The remaining $n - k$ objects automatically go in the remaining $n - k$ slots. The symbol for the number of these combinations of k out of n objects is $\binom{n}{k}$; it is computed as follows:

$$\binom{n}{k} = \frac{n!}{k!(n-k)!} = \frac{n(n-1)(n-2)\cdots(n-k+1)}{k(k-1)\cdots 3\cdot 2\cdot 1}.$$

This is called a *binomial coefficient*, for reasons that become clear in Problem 1–9.

Example 1–9. From the container with four chips marked *A*, *B*, *C*, and *D*, two are selected. The number of such selections is

$$\binom{4}{2} = \frac{4\cdot 3}{2\cdot 1} = 6.$$

This is also the number of arrangements of two 0's and two 1's:

0011, 0101, 1001, 1010, 1100, 0110,

each of these requiring a choice of two of the four positions in which to put the 0's.

PROBLEMS

1–1. In how many distinct ways can four plus (+) signs and six minus (−) signs be arranged in a row?

1–2. (a) Write out and compare the expressions in factorials for $\binom{10}{3}$ and $\binom{10}{7}$.

(b) Do the same for $\binom{n}{k}$ and $\binom{n}{n-k}$. (c) Compute $\binom{100}{97}$.

1–3. A "decision function" (to be introduced in Chapter 5) assigns to each possible value of a certain variable one of a certian set of actions. If the variable has five possible values and there are three available actions, how many distinct decision functions (or assignments of actions to values) can be constructed?

1–4. A container holds 10 white chips and 20 black chips. An experiment consists of drawing a chip, then another, then another, and then another—keeping track of the colors in the order drawn. How many sample points are there for this experiment? Is the number of sample points different if the chips drawn are replaced each time before the next drawing?

1–5. Each symbol in a sequence of ten symbols is a (+) or a (−). (a) How many distinct sequences are possible? (b) How many sequences have at least eight plus' in them? (c) How many sequences contain exactly five plus' and five minus'? (d) Of the sequences in (c), how many have at least four plus' in a row?

1–6. Three dice are tossed. How many elementary outcomes are there (a) in the most detailed classification of results; (b) if one is interested only in the total number of points thrown; (c) if one is interested in the various combinations of points (such as 2, 3, and 3) but not in which die has which number of points?

1–7. A standard bridge deck contains 52 distinct cards, namely, 2, 3, · · ·, 10, J, Q, K, Ace in each of four "suits": clubs, diamonds, hearts, and spades. Five cards are selected from the deck. (a) How many elementary outcomes are there if we wish to distinguish between two selections that do not consist of the same five cards? (b) What are the appropriate outcomes in the sample space, if we are concerned with only the number of face cards (K, Q, or J) in the selection? (c) How many points are in the sample space if we classify hands only according to whether or not there are any Aces?

1–8. Show that for any positive integer n and positive integer $j \le n$,

$$\binom{n}{j-1} + \binom{n}{j} = \binom{n+1}{j}.$$

1–9. Prove the "binomial theorem":

$$(x + y)^n = \sum_0^n \binom{n}{k} x^k y^{n-k}, \qquad n = 1, 2, \cdots$$

[*Hint:* First verify the result for $n = 1$. Then, assuming it to be true as written for arbitrary n, show by multiplying through both sides by $(x + y)$ that it remains valid for the next integer $n + 1$.]

1–10. Show the following, by expressing each side in terms of factorials:

$$\binom{n}{m}\binom{n-m}{r}\binom{n-m-r}{k-m} = \binom{n}{k+r}\binom{k+r}{k}\binom{k}{m}.$$

Also interpret each side as the number of ways of performing a sequence of selections and deduce the equality from this reasoning.

1–11. Show:

$$\sum_{0}^{r} \binom{n}{k} (-1)^{k+r} = \binom{n-1}{r}.$$

[*Hint:* Let n be fixed and prove by induction on r, first showing the relation to be true for $r = 0$ and then establishing it for r on the assumption that it holds for $r - 1$.]

1–12. Show the following:

(a) $$\sum_{0}^{n} \binom{n}{k} = 2^n, \qquad \text{for } n = 1, 2, \cdots$$

[*Hint:* Substitute $x = 1$ and $y = 1$ in the equation of Problem 1–9.]

(b) $$\sum_{0}^{n-1} (n-k) \binom{n}{k} = \sum_{1}^{n} k \binom{n}{k} = n2^{n-1}.$$

[*Hint:* Substitute $x = 1$ and $y = 1$ in the first derivative with respect to x and the first derivative with respect to y of each side of the equation in Problem 1–9.]

1.1.3 Events. An *event* is any collection of elementary outcomes in the sample space of an experiment of chance. Such a collection may be defined by listing the elementary outcomes that make it up or by giving some property which characterizes or determines the outcomes which make it up. We say that an event E has happened when some one of the outcomes which make it up has happened.

In particular, the set of *all* outcomes in the sample space, that is, the sample space itself, is an event. It is convenient to define as an event the *empty set*, or set containing no outcomes. Such an event is defined by any condition which is not satisfied by any outcome in the sample space.

Example 1–10. Consider again the drawing of two chips from a container with four chips marked A, B, C, and D, and take as the sample space the set of 12 elementary outcomes: AB, AC, AD, BA, BC, BD, CA, CB, CD, DA, DB, DC. (The first letter listed in each case denotes the first chip drawn.) The condition

E: The first chip is A

defines the event E as consisting of the outcomes in the sample space, which are the first three listed, for which the given condition is fulfilled. The condition

F: The first chip is A or B and the second is B or D

defines the set of outcomes consisting of AB, AD, and BD. The condition

G: One of the chips is A

defines the set consisting of AB, AC, AD, BA, CA, DA. The condition

H: Both chips are A

defines the empty set, since no outcomes have this property.

Example 1–11. The number of phone calls coming into a certain exchange during a five-minute period is to be counted. The possible outcomes of this experiment are the integers 0, 1, 2, $\cdots$. An event is then some set of integers. For instance, the condition

$$E\text{: At least four calls come in}$$

defines the set of elementary outcomes which includes all the integers from 4 on up. The event

$$F\text{: At most two calls come in}$$

defines the set of integers (0, 1, 2).

Example 1–12. Consider the sample space of Example 1–6 consisting of the possible orientations of the fibers of a material. These orientations can be described by the colatitude and longitude angles θ and ϕ, where $0 \leq \theta \leq \pi/2$ and $0 \leq \phi < 2\pi$. Events can then be defined in terms of these angles. For instance, the conditions

$$E\text{: } \theta = \frac{3\pi}{8}, \phi = 0, \qquad F\text{: } \theta \leq \frac{\pi}{4}, \qquad G\text{: } 0 \leq \phi < \pi$$

define sets of orientations that are examples of events. If when a fiber is selected, its orientation is $\theta = \pi/8$, $\phi = \pi/2$, one says that "F has happened." For this particular orientation G has also happened, since the condition defining G is also satisfied.

Frequently the same collection of outcomes is defined by two apparently different conditions. If the event E is identical with the event F, we write $E = F$. This means that every outcome in E is also contained in F, and conversely. It also means that the condition defining E implies the condition defining F, and conversely. Thus, to show that two conditions define the same event, it suffices to show that each outcome satisfying one condition also satisfies the other, and conversely.

1.1.4 Complements, Intersections, and Unions. Events can be composed or combined or operated on to form new events in many ways. The *union* of two events, also called their *sum*, is defined as the event consisting of any outcomes in either event making up the union (or in both). The operation of set union, which is commutative, corresponds to the logical conjunction "or." The sumbol $+$ and the symbol $\cup$ have both been used to denote a set union:

$$E \cup F = E + F = \{E \text{ or } F\} = \{\text{set of outcomes in either } E \text{ or } F\}.$$

The intersection of two events, also called their *product*, is defined as the event that is the set of outcomes which lie in both of the two events (as the name "intersection" implies). If an outcome occurs which satisfies condition E and also condition F, the outcome lies in the intersection. The operation of set intersection corresponds to the logical conjunction " and." The symbol $\cap$ has been used to indicate set intersection, as has ordinary product notation:

$$E \cap F = EF = \{E \text{ and } F\} = \{\text{set of outcomes in both } E \text{ and } F\}.$$

If EF is the empty set (that is, if no outcomes satisfy both conditions E and F), the events E and F are said to be *disjoint*, or sometimes *mutually exclusive*.

The *difference* $E - F$ is defined as the event consisting of those outcomes which lie in E but do not lie in F. The *complement* of an event E, here denoted by $\bar{E}$, is the event described by saying that E has not occurred. That is, if the event consisting of all the outcomes is called S, the complement of E is the event $S - E$.

It is helpful to have the picture of these concepts provided by the "Venn diagram." In such a diagram a set of outcomes is symbolized by a region in the plane. For instance, events E, F, and G might be represented by points within the circle, rectangle, and triangle, respectively, in Figure 1–1.

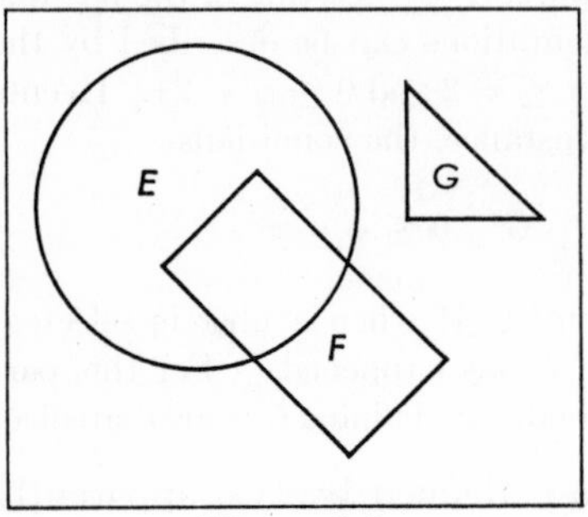

Figure 1–1

In Figure 1–1 the events E and G are disjoint, having no common points, as are F and G. The sets of outcomes called EF, $E + F$, $E - F$, and $\bar{E}$ are as pictured in Figure 1–2. Observe that EF and $E - F$ are disjoint and that their union is E.

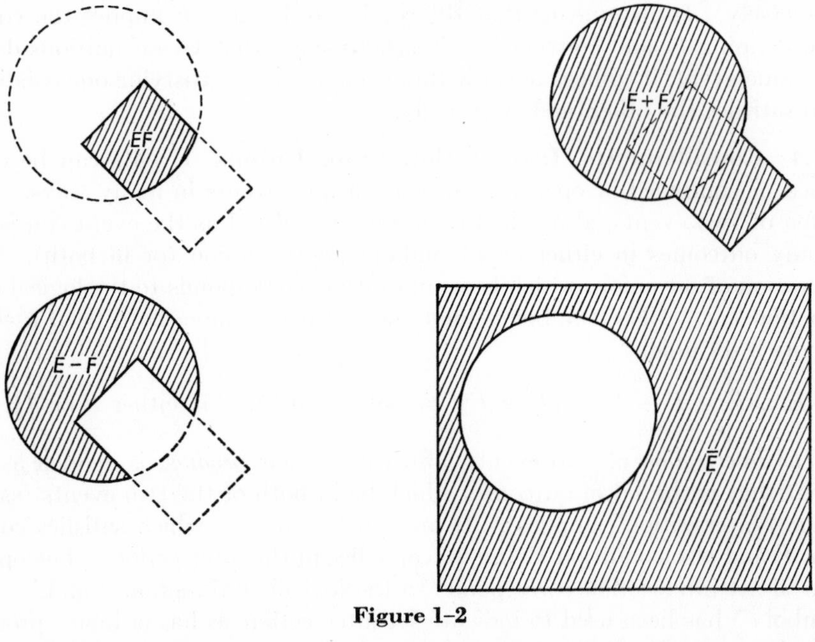

Figure 1–2

Example 1–13. A card is drawn from a standard deck of cards (defined in Problem 1–7). The sample space S consists of the 52 cards in the deck, any one of which might be drawn. (These are perhaps the most elementary outcomes one can conceive of here, and there might well be instances in which a less fine classification of results would be adequate.) Consider the following events:

E: The card drawn is a spade;
F: The card drawn is a Jack;
G: The card drawn is a face card.

Then, for example, $E + F$ is the set of cards consisting of all the spades plus the other three Jacks. The event $E - F$ is the set consisting of all the spades except the Jack. The event FG is identical with F. The event $S - E$ is the set consisting of all the hearts, diamonds, and clubs. The event $(E + G) - F$ is the set consisting of all the spades except the Jack together with the remaining three Queens and three Kings.

Example 1–14. A pointer is spun horizontally about a pivot, and a scale is marked around the circle traced by its tip, from 0 to 1, the 1 being identified with the 0. The experiment consists of spinning the pointer once and allowing it to come to rest. The corresponding sample space may be taken to be the set of stopping points, that is, the set of real numbers on the scale from 0 to 1. Consider the following events, where X denotes the stopping point:

$$E:\ 0.5 < X < 0.8, \qquad F:\ X > 0.6, \qquad G:\ X < 0.4.$$

The event $E + F$ is the set defined by $0.5 < X < 1$. The intersection EF is the set defined by $0.6 < X < 0.8$. The event $\bar{G}$ is the set defined by $X \geq 0.4$. The difference $E - F$ is the set defined by $0.5 < X \leq 0.6$.

The notions of set union and intersection are easier to define for infinitely many sets than are the addition and multiplication of infinitely many numbers. If $E_1, E_2, \cdots$ are events, their union $\bigcup E_i$ is defined as the event consisting of all outcomes that belong to any one or more of the E_i. Their intersection $\bigcap E_i$ is the set of all outcomes that belong to every E_i.

Example 1–15. Let a sample space consist of the set of real numbers and let E_n denote the interval $(A - 1/n, A + 1/n)$. The only number in all these intervals (for $n = 1, 2, \cdots$) is the number A. The set consisting of this one number is therefore the intersection $\bigcap E_n$. Notice that the complement of this intersection is the union of the complements:

$$\overline{\bigcap E_n} = \overline{\{A\}} = \bigcup \bar{E}_n$$

For, if a point is in some one or more of the complements, it is not A; and if a point is not A, then for a sufficiently large n, it is not in E_n. (This is true not only for this example, but in general.)

A *family* of events (technical names: Borel field, σ-algebra) is a collection of events such that the whole sample space, complements, and countable unions of events of the family are also in the family. Such a family would necessarily contain the empty set, differences of events, and countable intersections of events. If a sample space is finite, the collection of all sets of outcomes is always a family of events. In any sample space the two events that are the whole sample space and the empty set constitute a family.

Example 1–16. In the spinning pointer example (1–14), it is reasonable to want to include intervals (a,b) in any family of events that is to be useful. The family must then contain, in addition to intervals, sets that are considerably more complicated than intervals. For instance, the complement of (a,b) is the union of $[0,a]$ and $[b,1]$. The intersection of the intervals $(0.2 - 1/n, 0.2 + 1/n)$, $n = 1, 2, \cdots$, is the single point 0.2. The union of (a,b) with the set consisting of the single point b is the half-open interval $(a,b]$; and so on.

1.1.5 Random Variables and Random Vectors.

In constructing a model for an experiment of chance, we have introduced the notion of a *sample space*, or collection of possible outcomes of the experiment, and a *family* of events, or sets of outcomes. Before completing the model construction with the notion of probability of an event, we define what is called a *random variable.*

The outcomes of experiments can be varied in nature. They can be readings on a scale; sets of coordinates of points; descriptions such as Heads and Tails, or defective and nondefective; characteristics of an agricultural product; orientations of a force; velocities of a gas particle; numbers of people in a waiting line; groups of people selected from a "population" or larger group; etc. This list suggests that often the outcome of an experiment is numerical—a number or an ordered set of numbers. When the outcome is not itself a number, it is very common that some numerical characteristic of the outcome is of interest. Such a numerical characteristic termed is named "random variable"; it assigns a number to each outcome of the experiment.

Let Ω denote a sample space and let ω denote an elementary outcome in Ω. Assume that a certain family of events is specified.

Definition. A random variable is a real valued (measurable)[1] function $X(\omega)$ defined on a sample space Ω with a given family of events.

(A function $X(\omega)$ on a sample space Ω is said to be measurable if for each real number c the event defined by the inequality $X(\omega) \leq c$ belongs to the given family of events. If the sample space is finite, every function on it is measurable with respect to the family of all subsets of the space.)

Sometimes it is convenient to code the outcomes of an experiment with numbers; such a coding is an example of a random variable. Sometimes the outcome ω of an experiment is itself a real number; in this case the assignment $X(\omega) = \omega$ is a natural random variable to consider.

[1]The concept of measurability is needed when spaces with a continuum of points are studied. We shall not concern ourselves with this technical question of measurability; the functions arising in practice are invariably measurable, and considerable ingenuity is required to construct a *non*measurable function. For practical purposes, then, the word "measurable" in the definition of a random variable can be ignored.

It may be that several numerical characteristics of an outcome are of interest. A vector function on the outcome space Ω:

$$(X_1(\omega), X_2(\omega), \cdots, X_n(\omega))$$

will be called a *random vector.* (Again, a requirement of measurability is necessary for mathematical rigor.) Each component of a random vector, is of course, a random variable.

It is often desired to compute the value of some function $y = g(x)$ for each value x of a random variable $X(\omega)$. The value of y is then random, and we denote this new random variable by $Y = g(X(\omega))$. A function of several random variables

$$Z = h(X_1(\omega), \cdots, X_n(\omega))$$

is also a random variable, since it provides an assignment of a number to each outcome ω. Several functions of several random variables define a random vector:

$$\begin{cases} U_1(\omega) = k_1(X_1(\omega), \cdots, X_n(\omega)) \\ \quad\vdots \\ U_m(\omega) = k_m(X_1(\omega), \cdots, X_n(\omega)). \end{cases}$$

An event is defined by a condition on the values of a random variable. For example, the condition $X(\omega) \leq c$ is satisfied by some outcomes and not by others; those for which it is satisfied make up an event, which we shall often speak of as "the event $X(\omega) \leq c$."

The term *random variable* refers to the function $X(\omega)$ in the mathematical model, although it is common practice to speak of the physical (or other) quantity being represented by the model as a random variable. Actually, the physical quantity being represented in the model is not necessarily intrinsically random; the randomness is in the mathematical model set up to represent it. Yet, it is commonly said that certain physical quantities "are" random variables, meaning by this that the mathematical model of a random variable usefully represents the physical situation.

Example 1–17. A die of the usual variety is tossed, and the face that lands "up" is considered to be the outcome. There are six possible outcomes—the six faces, identified with different numbers of dots. The function

$$X(\omega) = \text{the number of dots on the upturned face}$$

assigns an integer to each of the six outcomes and is a random variable.

Example 1–18. A coin is tossed, with possible outcomes H and T. Consider the assignment or coding:

$$X(\omega) = \begin{cases} 1, & \text{if } \omega \text{ is } H, \\ 0, & \text{if } \omega \text{ is } T. \end{cases}$$

This is a random variable—a very simple one—taking on one of only two possible values.

Example 1–19. A missile is fired at a target, and we denote by ω the landing point. Consider the quantity

$$R(\omega) = \text{distance from } \omega \text{ to the target.}$$

This is a random variable, a numerical quantity depending for its value on an experiment of chance. Also, each of the coordinates of the landing point in some convenient coordinate system would be a random variable, a function of the landing point. The pair of coordinates would be called a *random vector.*

Example 1–20. The resistance in a certain resistor, nominally 100 ohms, is measured. The result of the measurement (even for a given resistor) can be thought of as a random variable, variation being introduced through the measurement process. Further variation would be introduced if we thought of the resistor as one pulled from a pile of "100 ohm" resistors, whose resistances are not alike owing to uncontrolled variations in the manufacturing process. Here we have an experiment in which the outcome ω is itself a number, and the quantity $X(\omega) = \omega$ is a random variable. Another random variable that might be of interest is the deviation, $Y(\omega) = \omega - 100$, about the nominal resistance.

Example 1–21. Two individuals A and B toss a coin alternately, infinitely often. The sample points or outcomes ω are infinite sequences of H's and T's. Some of the random variables that might be of interest are

$$\begin{aligned} X(\omega) &= \text{the number of tosses before } A \text{ and } B \text{ are first even} \\ &\quad\ \text{in the number of Heads each has thrown;} \\ Y(\omega) &= \text{the proportion of the time in which } A \text{ leads } B; \\ Z(\omega) &= 1 \text{ or } 0, \text{ according as the third toss is } H \text{ or } T. \end{aligned}$$

Example 1–22. In Example 1–12 the sample space of an experiment was considered to be composed of orientations (of a fiber) in space. The colatitude and longitude coordinates associated naturally with each orientation, or with each point on the unit hemisphere used to represent the orientations, are random variables: $\theta(\omega)$ and $\phi(\omega)$. Together they constitute a random vector: $(\theta(\omega), \phi(\omega))$. Any function of these coordinates would define yet another random variable.

Example 1–23. From a group (or "population") of 1000 people a person is to be drawn by lot. Since the precise person ω who will de drawn cannot be foretold, the selection is an experiment of chance. The possible outcomes can be taken to be the various people who might be drawn. Any numerical characteristic of the person drawn, say his weight, $W(\omega)$, is a random variable. A set of numerical characteristics, such as his weight, height, age, and blood pressure, would be a random vector: $(W(\omega), H(\omega), A(\omega), B(\omega))$.

PROBLEMS

1–13. An experiment consists of tossing two dice. In terms of the usual 36 elementary outcomes, list the outcomes in the following events:

(a) A: The sum is divisible by 4.
(b) B: Both numbers are even.
(c) C: The numbers on the dice are equal.
(d) D: The numbers differ by at least 4.

(e) AB (g) $B - A$

(f) $C + D$ (h) $\overline{(A + B)}$

1–14. Show the following for any events E, F, and G in a sample space S:

(a) $E - F = E\overline{F}$ (d) $\overline{(EF)} = \overline{E} + \overline{F}$

(b) $EF + E\overline{F} = E$ (e) $\overline{(E + F)} = \overline{E}\,\overline{F}$

(c) $E = SE$ (f) $E(F + G) = EF + EG$

1–15. Five cards are selected from a standard bridge deck (Problem 1–7). Let the elementary outcomes of this experiment be all possible selections of 5 cards from the 52. Determine the number of elementary outcomes in each of the following events:

(a) The hand contains exactly one "pair." (A pair consists of two cards of the same denomination; for example, two Kings. The other three cards in the hand are to be of three different denominations.)

(b) The hand contains two pairs of different denominations and a fifth card of still a different denomination.

(c) The hand contains two of one denomination and three of another denomination.

(d) The hand contains three of one denomination, but the other two do not form a pair.

(e) The hand consists of five cards, all of the same suit.

1–16. The outcomes of a certain experiment are the points in a plane, each identified by its rectangular coordinates (x,y). Sketch the events defined by the following conditions on the coordinates:

(a) $x^2 + y^2 = 1$ (d) $|x - y| \leq 2$ (g) $(b) + (c)$

(b) $x^2 + y^2 \leq 1$ (e) $2x \leq y$ (h) $(f) - (b)$

(c) $x + y > 3$ (f) $|x| < 1$ and $|y| < 1$ (i) $(f) \cap (e)$

1–17. Let ω denote the outcome (x,y) in the experiment of Problem 1–16. Let $X(\omega) = x$, $Y(\omega) = y$, and $R(\omega) = \sqrt{x^2 + y^2}$. Sketch the events defined by the following conditions:

(a) $X(\omega) \leq 2$ (c) $|Y(\omega)| = 1$ (e) $Y(\omega) > X^2(\omega)$

(b) $R(\omega) > 3$ (d) $R(\omega) = Y(\omega)$ (f) $|X(\omega) - 2| > 1$

1–18. Let ω denote the outcome of the toss of a die, and let $X(\omega)$ have the value 1 if the number of dots is odd, and the value 0 if the number of dots is even. What are the events $X(\omega) \leq c$ for various values of c?

1.2 Probability Spaces

We are about to embark on the study of probability models—mathematical models for experiments of chance. A probability model consists of a sample space, a family of events, and an assignment of a number to each event of the family. This number assigned to a given event is to be its "probability." Whether what is represented by this number is an objective thing (a property of the experiment only) or is subjective and personal is an interesting question that we shall not take up at this point. (The reader concerned about this matter should consult Reference[1] [16] and references given there.) For the present we conceive of the probability of an event as the proportion of possible sets of conditions which lead to the event.

For example, a container holds one white and nine black beads, and we are about to draw one "at random," that is, reach in blindly and fumble around for one of the beads. Because of the preponderance of black beads, most people would bet that the bead drawn will be black, even if only one bead is drawn and if the stakes are not too high. To go a step further, no doubt most people would be more willing to bet on black if it were known that there were 99 black beads and 1 white bead. In either case we should be forced to admit that white is a possibility, but would insist that somehow white is not very likely. So we assign the number 0.9 as the probability of the event "black" in the first case, and the number 0.99 in the second.

Such an experiment is found, upon performing it repeatedly, to have the interesting property that the proportion of black beads drawn in a large number of such random selections from the same group of beads is approximately the same as the proportion of black beads available; that is, the same as the proportion of circumstances which lead to selection of a black bead. We shall find that the mathematical model to be studied has also such a property.

1.2.1 Axioms. The specification of probabilities of events cannot be completely arbitrary and still be consistent. It has been found that the following axioms both agree with intuition and provide a consistent model. Let Ω denote the sample space of an experiment, and let E and E_i denote events in the family being considered. A probability $P(E)$ is then specified for each event E in such a way that the following properties hold:

(1) $$P(\Omega) = 1,$$

(2) $$0 \leq P(E) \leq 1,$$

(3) $$P(\cup E_i) = P(E_1) + P(E_2) + \cdots,$$ provided $E_1, E_2, \cdots$ are pairwise disjoint.

The sample space together with an assignment of probability satisfying the above axioms to each event in a family of events is called a *probability space.* The assignment of probability to events is referred to as a *probability distribution.*

One easy consequence of these axioms follows from the fact that E and $\bar{E}$ are disjoint and $E + \bar{E} = \Omega$:

$$P(\bar{E}) = P(\Omega) - P(E) = 1 - P(E).$$

In particular, the complement of the empty set is Ω, and therefore the probability assigned the empty set is 0.

[1]Numbers in brackets refer to the numbers in the list of References, page 389.

The following less obvious consequences will also be found useful. If $E_1, E_2, \cdots$ is a "descending" sequence of sets (each contained in the preceding), then

$$P(\cap E_n) = \lim_{n \to \infty} P(E_n) \qquad \text{(descending sequence)},$$

and if $E_1, E_2, \cdots$ is an "ascending" sequence (each contained in the one following), then

$$P(\cup E_n) = \lim_{n \to \infty} P(E_n) \qquad \text{(ascending sequence)}.$$

To deduce the latter result, we first note that

$$E_n = E_1 + (E_2 - E_1) + \cdots + (E_n - E_{n-1}).$$

Since the terms on the right are pairwise disjoint,

$$P(\cup E_n) = \lim_{n \to \infty} [P(E_1) + \cdots + P(E_n - E_{n-1})] = \lim_{n \to \infty} P(E_n).$$

The result stated for descending sequences now follows from this, since an intersection is the complement of the union of the complements.

Example 1–24. A die is tossed; the face that lands up, identified by the number of dots on the face, is the outcome. There are six outcomes and so the most complete family of events comprises $2^6 = 64$ events, since in forming an event, each outcome is either included or not included. One possible assignment of a number to each event is the proportion of the total number of outcomes included in the event. For instance, the event E: An even number of points thrown is made up of the three outcomes 2, 4, and 6; it would be assigned the number $1/2$ as its probability. Also, an event consisting of a single outcome would be given the probability $1/6$. The outcomes are then "equally likely" in this model.

Example 1–25. Consider again the spinning pointer of Example 1–14. The elementary outcomes are the numbers on the interval [0,1], and we consider a family of events that includes all subintervals of [0,1].

Setting up a probability model requires that, subject to the axioms, we assign probabilities to each event in the family. This would appear to be a formidable task, but we state without proof that there is a smallest family containing the intervals in [0,1] and that the probabilities of events in this family are determined by an assignment of probabilities to the *intervals*. (Cf. Reference [13], page 59 and 103.) That is, the setup job is finished when a probability is assigned to each interval $[a,b]$.

Although mathematically arbitrary (subject to the axioms), the assignment of probability should be based on intuition, experience, or some theoretical consideration, if it is to have any hope of successfully representing the actual physical situation—in this instance, the spinning pointer. Here, intuition suggests that no regions should be more likely than others of the same size, and so a natural model to try out is one in which the probability of an interval is proportional to its width:

$$P[a,b] = k(b - a).$$

Since $P[0,1]$ must be 1, we choose $k = 1$.

An event made up of two disjoint intervals has, then, the sum of their probabilities as its probability:

$$P([0.1,0.3] + [0.4,0.9]) = 0.2 + 0.5 = 0.7.$$

An event consisting of a single point (say, 0.2) has as its probability the limit of the probabilities of a sequence of intervals containing and closing down on 0.2:

$$P(0.2) = \lim_{n\to\infty} P\left[0.2 - \frac{1}{n}, 0.2 + \frac{1}{n}\right] = \lim_{n\to\infty} \frac{2}{n} = 0.$$

It should be emphasized that in these examples we have not proved that the probabilities are the given ones; rather, we *define* probabilities—set up a model, which may or may not reflect the characteristics of the real situation. Hopefully, it does. Sometimes, as in the above examples, intuition will suggest how to set up a reasonable and useful model, including the numbers to use as probabilities. More often than not, one's only approach to a model is through the uncertain channel of performance of the experiment. Reasoning from the resulting data to the model is the process of "statistical inference."

1.2.2 The Addition Law. Axiom (3) in the set of axioms (§1.2.1) for a probability assignment furnishes an "addition law" for disjoint events:

$$P(E + F) = P(E) + P(F) \qquad (E \text{ and } F \text{ disjoint}).$$

It is useful to have an extension of this law to cover the more general case in which the events in question are not necessarily disjoint.

The desired extension is obtained by applying axiom (3) to a decomposition of the sum $E + F$ into three mutually exclusive parts:

$$E + F = EF + E\bar{F} + \bar{E}F.$$

Axiom (3) now says that

$$P(E + F) = P(EF) + P(E\bar{F}) + P(\bar{E}F).$$

Then, since

$$P(E) = P(EF + E\bar{F}) = P(EF) + P(E\bar{F}),$$

or

$$P(E\bar{F}) = P(E) - P(EF),$$

and similarly

$$P(\bar{E}F) = P(F) - P(EF),$$

it follows that

$$P(E + F) = P(E) + P(F) - P(EF).$$

This general addition law holds for any events E and F and reduces to the simpler law for disjoint events when EF is the empty set, in which case $P(EF) = 0$.

Example 1–26. Let E and F denote the events "spade" and "face card," respectively, in the experiment of drawing a card from a standard bridge deck. Then $P(E) = 13/52$, $P(F) = 12/52$, and $P(EF) = 3/52$. Therefore,

$$P(\text{spade or face card}) = \frac{13}{52} + \frac{12}{52} - \frac{3}{52} = \frac{22}{52}.$$

1.2.3 The Discrete Case. In setting up a probability model on a sample space with a finite or countably infinite number of outcomes, it suffices to define a probability for each of the individual outcomes, such that the total of the assigned probabilities is 1. Axiom (3) then requires that the probability of an event E be computed as the sum of the probabilities assigned to the individual outcomes that make it up:

$$P(E) = \sum_{\omega \text{ in } E} P(\omega).$$

Example 1–27. Consider the 12 outcomes of selecting two chips from chips A, B, C, and D in a container. One way of assigning probability to these outcomes is to make them equally probable, giving $1/12$ to each. With this model we have, for instance,

$$P(A \text{ drawn first}) = P(AB) + P(AC) + P(AD) = \frac{3}{12}.$$

Similarly, the probability that the selection includes A or B (or both) is

$$\begin{aligned} P(A \text{ or } B \text{ drawn}) &= 1 - P(\text{only } C \text{ and } D \text{ drawn}) \\ &= 1 - \left[P(CD) + P(DC)\right] = \frac{5}{6}. \end{aligned}$$

Example 1–28. A coin is tossed until Heads first appears. It will be seen later that a natural way to assign probabilities to the (countably infinitely many) elementary outcomes 1, 2, 3, ⋯ is as follows:

$$P(k \text{ tosses required}) = \left(\frac{1}{2}\right)^k, \qquad k = 1, 2, \cdots$$

Using the formula for the sum of a geometric series, we see that the assigned probabilities total 1:

$$\tfrac{1}{2} + \tfrac{1}{4} + \tfrac{1}{8} + \cdots = 1.$$

The probability that, say, the first Heads will appear in three or fewer tosses is

$$P(1, 2, \text{ or } 3 \text{ tosses required}) = \tfrac{1}{2} + \tfrac{1}{4} + \tfrac{1}{8} = \tfrac{7}{8}.$$

The probability that an even number of tosses is required is

$$P(2 \text{ or } 4 \text{ or } 6 \text{ or } \cdots) = \tfrac{1}{4} + \tfrac{1}{16} + \tfrac{1}{64} + \cdots = \tfrac{1}{3}.$$

And so on.

PROBLEMS

1–19. (a) Show that if event A is contained in event B, $P(A) \leq P(B)$.

(b) Show that $P(A) = \sum P(AE_n)$, where the E_n's are mutually disjoint and $\bigcup E_n = \Omega$.

1–20. A card is to be drawn from a standard bridge deck. Let the 52 cards be assigned equal probabilities, and determine the probabilities of the following events:

(a) The card is a spade.
(b) The card is a face card.
(c) The card is a spade or a face card.
(d) The card is not an ace or a heart.

1–21. The outcomes of an experiment are the nine pairs of numbers (x,y) where x and y are integers from 1 to 3. Suppose that the probability 1/6 is assigned to any outcome in which $x = y$ and 1/12 to any other outcome. Determine the probabilities of the following events:

(a) $x = 2$ (c) $x = 2$ or $y = 1$ (e) $y > 1$
(b) $y = 1$ (d) $x + y \leq 4$ (f) $|x - y| = 1$.

1.2.4 A Priori Models in Finite Discrete Cases. There is an important class of experiments in which the appropriate probability model is strongly suggested by intuition. These are sometimes called *a priori* models, being set up without actual experimentation, although such actual experience usually bears out the usefulness of the model. In such a situation there are finitely many possible outcomes (the sample space is finite); and there are reasons, often geometrical, to believe that one outcome ought to have the "same chance of occurring" as any other. With such a conviction one sets up a model in which equal probabilities are assigned to the outcomes. If there are n outcomes, each is given probability $1/n$.

In one type of problem in this category the experiment consists of tossing a symmetrical object—a coin, a cube, or any other regular polyhedron. The object lands on one of its sides, and these sides are then the elementary outcomes. The geometrical symmetry suggests that no side should be weighted more than any other; hence they are assigned equal weights or probabilities. The spinning of a roulette wheel and the spinning of the cylinder of a revolver are also experiments in which one would be loathe to assign unequal weights, again primarily because of geometrical symmetries.

Another type of experiment in this category is that in which a certain number of objects are selected blindly from a finite collection of objects. There are $\binom{N}{n}$ distinct selections of n from N objects, and in the model suggested by intuition these combinations are decreed equally likely. The probability $1/\binom{N}{n}$ is assigned to each selection. The objects are said to be "selected at random" when this model is applicable. Whether an actual bunch of n from N objects can be selected in such a way that this model is applicable is indeed a moot question. At any rate it is usually a good idea to mix or shuffle the objects before making a selection. The phrase "random selection," sometimes used to describe the outcome of such an experiment, refers to the manner in which the selection is made, not to the specific bunch of objects drawn.

In a model in which the outcomes are equally probable, the probability of an event E is just the ratio of the number of outcomes in E to the total number of outcomes in the experiment.

Example 1–29. Two chips are selected at random from a container that holds four white and three black chips. This means that the probability $1/\binom{7}{2} = 1/21$ is assigned to each of the 21 possible selections. The probability of an event is, then, just the number of outcomes in the event times 1/21, the probability common to the outcomes. For instance,

$$P(\text{both chips are white}) = \frac{1}{21}\,(\text{number of selections in which both chips are white})$$

$$= \frac{1}{21}\binom{4}{2} = \frac{2}{7}.$$

Example 1–30. The four faces of a regular tetrahedron are marked for identification. When it is tossed, one of these faces is down. Taking the four faces as the elementary outcomes, the symmetry of the tetrahedron suggests that the appropriate model is an assignment of 1/4 as the probability of each elementary outcome.

1.2.5 Nondiscrete Cases. Assignment of probabilities to the individual elementary outcomes does not adequately prescribe a probability model for a sample space which is uncountably infinite. In most such cases the probabilities assigned to individual outcomes should be zero, whereas the probability of an event made up of such outcomes may not be zero. In particular, the probability assigned to the whole sample space is to be unity. Direct assignment of probabilities to events by some means is required.

Nondiscrete cases usually arise when the sample space is (1) a set of ordinary real numbers, such as the interval $[0,1]$ or the whole real line $(-\infty, \infty)$; (2) a set of points in a plane—either a two-dimensional set such as the points within a circle or some set of points constituting a curve in the plane; (3) a set of points in a three-dimensional space—either a three-dimensional set such as the set of points in a certain cube or a two-dimensional set such as a portion of a given surface, or a one-dimensional set of points on a curve; or (4) a set of points in a space of higher dimension than three. At least in cases (1), (2), and (3), the total probability 1 can be visualized as a unit glob of mass—or paint, in the case of areas and curves—which must be distributed over the sample space in some way. It is spread thickly to indicate regions of high probability; thinly, over regions that are not so likely. Lumps are left at any single points that have positive probability; this introduces discreteness, and a model with *only* lumps is a discrete model.

The "unit glob" with which we start is three-dimensional if the sample space is three-dimensional; it is two-dimensional (to be spread like an infinitely thin coat of paint) if the sample space is a surface; and it is one-dimensional (like thin paint on a wire) if the sample space is a curve. If there is no "lumpiness" or discreteness in the model, one can describe the way probability is distributed in terms of a *density*, using this term in the common physical sense. According to this usage, the density of a distribution or smear at a point is the limiting ratio of the amount of material (probability) spread in a tiny region of appropriate dimension about the point to the length or area or volume of the region (whichever is appropriate) as this region shrinks to zero in all directions.

Such a density is a point function—a number defined at each point—and has the property that its integral over any region gives the amount of material (probability) in that region:

$$\text{Mass in region } E = \int_E (\text{mass density function})\, dR,$$

where dR denotes the element of length, area, or volume, depending on the dimensionality of the mass distribution.

A mass distribution that has constant density is called *uniform*. In such a distribution the amount of mass in a region is proportional to the measure (length, area, or volume) of the region, since the constant density factors out of the integral. This is the kind of distribution considered in Example 1–25, in which instance the density function is 1 over the sample space [0,1] and the probability of a subinterval is the length of the subinterval. A uniform distribution of probability can be defined only over a finite portion of an n-dimensional space because the total probability is finite; the probability assigned to an event is proportional to its "size" (length, area, etc.), a quantity that satisfies the additivity axiom.

In a general probability distribution of continuous type, the probability of an event is an "area-like" measure which permits different weightings for different portions of the sample space.

Example 1–31. In Examples 1–6 and 1–12 we considered the orientation of a randomly chosen fiber of a material. To express the notion that there are no preferred orientations for a certain material under given conditions, probability could be defined as follows: Any event defined by the condition that the orientation vector falls in a certain solid angle A is assigned a probability proportional to the size of the solid angle, that is, proportional to the area on the unit hemisphere determined by the solid angle. In order that the total probability be 1, then, we define

$$P(A) = \frac{1}{2\pi}\,(\text{area subtended by } A \text{ on a unit hemisphere}).$$

The event $0 \leq \phi \leq \pi/4$ (where ϕ is the longitude coordinate of the orientation) consists of points on one-eighth of the hemisphere; its probability is 1/8 in this model.

Example 1–32. A consequence of Maxwell's law in physics states that the probability density function for the speed of a molecule of an ideal gas is

$$f(v) = (\text{const.})\ v^2 \exp(-hmv^2).$$

The constant multiplier is determined so that the area under the graph of $f(v)$, which is the integral of $f(v)$, is unity. (The numbers h and m are physical constants.) The probability that the speed of a molecule falls in a set E is, then,

$$P(E) = \int_E f(v)\, dv.$$

PROBLEMS

1–22. The order on the ballot of the names of six candidates for three municipal judgeships is determined in such a way that all orders are equally likely. What is the probability that the names of three already in office (the incumbents) will appear at the head of the list?

1–23. A committee of three is chosen at random from five men and five women. What is the probability that (a) the committee will consist of all men or all women? (b) at least one man and at least one woman are on the committee? (c) at least one man is on the committee?

1–24. A lot of 20 articles is to be accepted or rejected on the basis of inspection of four out of the lot drawn at random. If it is decided to accept the lot when at most one of the four inspected articles is defective, but otherwise to reject the lot, what is the probability of rejecting a lot that is only 10 per cent defective?

1–25. Determine the probabilities for the various selections of five cards in Problem 1–15, assuming that these are random selections.

1–26. Consider an experiment whose outcomes are positive numbers. Given that the distribution of probability is described by a density function that at any positive number x is e^{-x}, compute the probability that (a) the outcome exceeds 2; (b) the outcome is at most 1; (c) the outcome lies between 1 and 2.

1–27. Consider an experiment whose outcomes are the points in the square bounded by $x = 0$, $y = 0$, $x = 2$, and $y = 2$ in the xy-plane. If probability is distributed uniformly over this sample space, determine probabilities of each of the following events:

(a) $x + y < 2$	(d) $x^2 + y^2 > 1$	(g) $\lvert x - y \rvert < 1$
(b) $x + y < 1$	(e) $x > 1$ and $y < \frac{3}{2}$	(h) $x - y < 1$
(c) $x > \frac{1}{2}$	(f) $x > 1$ or $y > 1$	(i) $x - y > 2$

1–28. Let the sample space of an experiment consist of the points within the unit cube defined by $0 \le x \le 1$, $0 \le y \le 1$, $0 \le z \le 1$. Assuming probability to be uniformly spread throughout the cube, determine the probability of the event consisting of those points (x,y,z) such that $x + y + z \le 1$.

1.3 Dependence and Independence

Perhaps the feature of probability theory which most distinguishes it from the study of mass distributions is the concept of independence. To handle situations which often arise, it is necessary to have some means of dealing with the effect of one experiment on a subsequent experiment when the results of the second are determined in part by the performance of the first. Conversely, in a situation in which two experiments have *no* effect on each other, the significance of this independence in the appropriate probability model is of interest.

1.3.1 Conditional Probability. The probability model that best represents a given experiment depends in part on such information as might be available about the outcome. If complete information is available about the outcome, no probability model is needed, but there are many instances in which partial information is available which should alter the probabilities from what would be appropriate in the absence of that information. For instance, if it is known that the outcome of the toss of a die is not a four, five, or six, it would be futile to bet on any of these outcomes. Further, one should be more willing to bet on a three with this added information than without it.

Knowing something about the result of an experiment of chance usually means that a smaller sample space is adequate—some of the elementary outcomes are eliminated by what is known. Having certain information is equivalent to knowing that some event F has occurred, and the elementary outcomes in F can be considered as constituting a new sample space. In this new sample space, probability is redefined so that the total probability in F is 1 but other probabilities are in the same proportions as before. If F is a condition whose probability is nonzero, and for any event E in F, we define

$$P(E|F) = \frac{P(E)}{P(F)} \qquad (E \text{ contained in } F,\ P(F) \neq 0),$$

which is read: "the probability of E, given F." This definition yields a probability on the events of the new sample space F which satisfies the axioms for a probability space. (This should be and easily is verified.)

The way to define the conditional probability of an event E not entirely contained in the conditioning event F is clear when it is realized that since the outcomes in E which are not in F cannot occur, what is wanted is the conditional probability of EF:

$$P(E|F) = P(EF|F) = \frac{P(EF)}{P(F)} \qquad (P(F) \neq 0).$$

The earlier formula is a special case of this.

Example 1–33. A card is drawn at random from a standard bridge deck, and we are informed only that it is a face card. What is the probability that it is (1) a Jack? (2) a Heart?

A Jack is a face card; so,

$$P(\text{Jack}\,|\,\text{face card}) = \frac{P(\text{Jack})}{P(\text{face card})} = \frac{1/13}{3/13} = \frac{1}{3}.$$

A Heart is not necessarily a face card, and therefore

$$P(\text{Heart}\,|\,\text{face card}) = \frac{P(\text{Heart and face card})}{P(\text{face card})} = \frac{3/52}{12/52} = \frac{1}{4};$$

that is, one-fourth of the face cards are Hearts, and one-third of the face cards are Jacks.

The relation defining conditional probability can be rewritten in the form of a useful "multiplication law":

$$P(EF) = P(E|F)\,P(F).$$

This is valid (Problem 1–30) even when $P(F) = 0$, no matter how $P(E|F)$ might be defined. The multiplication law can be extended (Problem 1–32) to rules of the form

$$P(EFGH\cdots) = P(E)\,P(F|E)\,P(G|EF)\,P(H|EFG)\cdots,$$

at least for a finite number of events.

Such multiplication laws are useful in constructing a probability model for a *composite* experiment. Suppose that an experiment $\mathcal{E}$ consists of performing an experiment $\mathcal{E}_1$ and then performing an experiment $\mathcal{E}_2$. Suppose further that $\mathcal{E}_1$ has m equally likely elementary outcomes and that for each of these $\mathcal{E}_2$ has n equally likely elementary outcomes; let these be denoted by $u_1, \cdots, u_m$ and $v_1, \cdots, v_n$, respectively. The elementary outcomes in the composite experiment are the mn distinct pairs u_j and v_k. From the multiplication law we have

$$P(u_j \text{ and then } v_k) = P(u_j)\,P(v_k|u_j) = \frac{1}{m}\cdot\frac{1}{n} = \frac{1}{mn},$$

and so the elementary outcomes of the composite experiment are equally likely.

Example 1–34. A coin is tossed three times. There are two elementary outcomes for each toss, and therefore $2 \cdot 2 \cdot 2 = 8$ elementary outcomes for the composite experiment, namely:

$$HHH,\ HHT,\ HTH,\ THH,\ TTH,\ THT,\ HTT,\ TTT.$$

Assuming heads and tails to be equally likely in each toss, these eight outcomes have each the probability 1/8.

Example 1–35. A bowl contains 8 white chips and 12 black chips. A chip is drawn at random, and then another chip is drawn at random from the remaining chips. What is the probability that (1) the first is black and the second white? (2) One chip is black and the other white?

To compute the probability (1) use the model for random selection at each drawing, assigning equal probabilities to the available chips:

$$\begin{aligned} P(\text{1st black and 2nd white}) &= P(\text{1st black})\, P(\text{2nd white} \mid \text{1st black}) \\ &= \frac{12}{20} \cdot \frac{8}{19}. \end{aligned}$$

The probability (2) is now computed, using the addition law:

$$\begin{aligned} P(\text{one black and one white}) &= P(\text{1st black and 2nd white}) \\ &\quad + P(\text{1st white and 2nd black}) \\ &= \frac{12}{20} \cdot \frac{8}{19} + \frac{8}{20} \cdot \frac{12}{19}. \end{aligned}$$

This number is equal to $\binom{12}{1}\binom{8}{1} \Big/ \binom{20}{2}$, the probability of obtaining 1 white and 1 black chip in a selection of 2 from the 20 chips when equal probabilities are assigned to the $\binom{20}{2}$ distinct selections in the experiment we have previously defined as drawing at random a sample of 2 chips from the 20. Thus it is that (as concerns events that can be described without reference to the order of selection) probabilities computed from this definition of random selection of two are identical with those computed from the multiplication law and the definition of random selection of one. It does not matter, then, whether the chips are taken from the bowl one at a time or drawn together.

Example 1–36. From a bowl containing 8 white and 12 black chips, one is drawn at random, another is drawn at random from what is left, a third from what is left after the first two are removed, and so on until five chips have been drawn. What is the probability that the chips, in the order drawn, are white, black, black, white, and black?

By using the multiplication rule we have

$$\begin{aligned} P(WBBWB) &= P(W)\, P(B \mid W)\, P(B \mid WB)\, P(W \mid WBB)\, P(B \mid WBBW) \\ &= \frac{8}{20} \cdot \frac{12}{19} \cdot \frac{11}{18} \cdot \frac{7}{17} \cdot \frac{10}{16}. \end{aligned}$$

(The factor $P(W \mid WBB)$, for instance, means here the probability that on the fourth drawing a white chip is obtained, given that the first chip was white, the second black, and the third black.) It is to be noticed that this probability of $(WBBWB)$ just computed is equal to the following:

$$\frac{\binom{8}{2}\binom{12}{3}}{\binom{20}{5}\binom{5}{3}} = \frac{8 \cdot 7 \cdot 12 \cdot 11 \cdot 10 \cdot 5 \cdot 4 \cdot 3 \cdot 2 \cdot 1 \cdot 3 \cdot 2 \cdot 1}{2 \cdot 1 \cdot 3 \cdot 2 \cdot 1 \cdot 20 \cdot 19 \cdot 18 \cdot 17 \cdot 16 \cdot 5 \cdot 4 \cdot 3}.$$

If the scheme apparent in writing down this expression were quite general, it would follow that the various orderings of two white and three black chips among the five drawings would have equal probabilities. That the scheme is general can be shown by induction, using the multiplication law. Rather than write out the general proof, let us demonstrate that if in the case at hand the scheme is assumed to be correct for a selection of four chips, it also works for five:

$$P(WBBWB) = P(WBBW)\,P(B|WBBW)$$

$$= \frac{\binom{8}{2}\binom{12}{2}}{\binom{20}{4}\binom{4}{2}} \cdot \frac{10}{16} = \frac{\binom{8}{2}\binom{12}{3}}{\binom{20}{5}\binom{5}{3}}.$$

The general argument would be analogous. The net result is that—if we are interested only in the number of white and the number of black chips drawn—the chips can be drawn one at a time or in a bunch; the probability model is the same. For example,

$$P(\text{2 whites and 3 blacks among 5}) = \frac{\binom{8}{2}\binom{12}{3}}{\binom{20}{5}} = \binom{5}{3} \cdot \frac{\binom{8}{2}\binom{12}{3}}{\binom{20}{5}\binom{5}{3}},$$

computed either as the number of different orderings of two white and three black results times the probability for any one ordering, or on the assumption that the $\binom{20}{5}$ different selections of five are equally likely.

It is interesting to notice that the probability of EF can be expressed with either E or F as the condition in the multiplication law:

$$P(EF) = P(E)\,P(F|E) = P(F)\,P(E|F).$$

This implies that

$$P(E|F) = \frac{P(E)\,P(F|E)}{P(F)}.$$

This is readily extended (Problem 1–34) to Bayes' theorem:

$$P(A_i|F) = \frac{P(A_i)\,P(F|A_i)}{P(A_1)P(F|A_1) + \cdots + P(A_n)P(F|A_n)},$$

where $A_1, \cdots, A_n$ are disjoint events whose union is the whole sample space.

Example 1–37. Two machines in a certain plant turn out 10 and 90 per cent, respectively, of the total production of a certain type of article. Suppose the probability that the first machine turns out a defective article is 0.01 and that the second machine turns out a defective article is 0.05. What is the probability that an article taken at random from a day's production was made by the first machine, given that it is defective?

We apply Bayes' theorem, with F the condition that an article is defective, A_1 the condition that it was made by machine 1, and A_2 the condition that it was made by machine 2:

$$\begin{aligned} P(\text{made by machine } 1 \mid \text{defective}) &= P(A_1 \mid \text{F}) \\ &= \frac{P(A_1)P(F \mid A_1)}{P(A_1)P(F \mid A_1) + P(A_2)P(F \mid A_2)} \\ &= \frac{0.10 \times 0.01}{0.10 \times 0.01 + 0.90 \times 0.05} = \frac{1}{46}. \end{aligned}$$

PROBLEMS

1–29. (a) Determine the probability that a die lands 4, given that the outcome is even. (b) Determine the probability that it lands 6, given that the outcome is divisible by 3.

1–30. (a) Show that if $P(F) = 0$, then $P(EF) = 0$.
(b) Show that $P(AC \mid B) = P(A \mid BC)P(C \mid B)$.

1–31. Two cards are drawn at random from a standard bridge deck. Determine the probability that (a) they are both face cards, given that they are of the same suit; (b) they are both face cards; (c) both are Hearts, given that both are red. (Hearts and Diamonds are red.)

1–32. Show that $P(EFG) = P(E)\ P(F \mid E)\ P(G \mid EF)$.

1–33. The outcomes of an experiment are real numbers, and the distribution of probability is continuous with the density

$$\frac{1/\pi}{1 + x^2}$$

at the number x. Determine (a) the probability that the outcome exceeds 1, given that it is a positive number; (b) the probability that it is positive, given that it is on the interval $(-1,1)$.

1–34. Let $A_1, A_2, \cdots$ be a sequence of pairwise disjoint events whose union is the whole sample space of an experiment of chance. (a) Show that

$$P(E) = \sum_i P(E \mid A_i)P(A_i).$$

(b) Show that

$$P(A_i \mid E) = \frac{P(A_i)P(E \mid A_i)}{P(A_1)P(E \mid A_1) + P(A_2)P(E \mid A_2) + \cdots}.$$

1–35. A bowl contains M black and $N - M$ white chips; n chips are drawn one at a time at random (without replacing any). Let P_n denote the proposition that the probability of each sequence of n chip colors consisting of k blacks and $n - k$ whites is given by the formula

$$\frac{\binom{M}{k}\binom{N-M}{n-k}}{\binom{N}{n}\binom{n}{k}} \qquad \text{for } k = 0, 1, \cdots, n.$$

Show (a) P_1, and (b) that P_n implies P_{n+1}, using the multiplication rule as illustrated in Example 1–35.

1.3.2 Independent Events. It may happen that a conditional probability is independent of the condition, in this sense:

$$P(E|F) = P(E).$$

If this is the case, then also

$$P(F|E) = \frac{P(F)\,P(E|F)}{P(E)} = P(F),$$

and the events E and F are said to be *independent*. These conditions, and hence the independence of E and F, are equivalent to the condition

$$P(EF) = P(E)P(F).$$

This condition automatically holds if either $P(E)$ or $P(F)$ is zero, and hence an event of zero probability is independent of any other event.

Example 1–38. A card is drawn at random from a standard bridge deck. Consider the events

E: The card is a Heart,
F: The card is a face card.

It is seen that $P(E) = 1/4$ and $P(F) = 3/13$. Further,

$$\begin{aligned} P(EF) &= P(\text{card is a Heart and a face card}) \\ &= \tfrac{3}{52} = \tfrac{1}{4} \cdot \tfrac{3}{13} = P(E)P(F). \end{aligned}$$

Hence E and F are independent events. Whether or not a card drawn is a Heart is independent of whether or not it is a face card.

The notion of independence is extended to more than two events as follows: Events $E_1, E_2, \cdots, E_n$ are said to be independent if for any subset of k events $E_{i_1}, \ldots, E_{i_k}$, the following factorization holds:

$$P(E_{i_1}E_{i_2}\cdots E_{i_k}) = P(E_{i_1})\,P(E_{i_2})\cdots P(E_{i_k}).$$

This definition may appear to be unnecessarily complicated. Yet, if all we required for independence was the simpler condition that the events be pairwise independent (shown in Example 1–39 to be not equivalent to the above), we could not necessarily conclude, for instance, that EF and G are independent when E, F, and G are independent. Further, the simple requirement that $P(E_1\cdots E_n) = P(E_1)\cdots P(E_n)$ would not even guarantee pairwise independence, as seen in Problem 1–40.

Example 1–39. The outcomes of an experiment of chance are the four points in three-dimensional space with rectangular coordinates (1,0,0), (0,1,0), (0,0,1), and (1,1,1). Let probability be distributed equally among these four outcomes and consider the events:

E: The first coordinate is 1;
F: The second coordinate is 1;
G: The third coordinate is 1.

It is easy to verify the following:

$$P(EF) = \tfrac{1}{4} = P(E)P(F),$$
$$P(EG) = \tfrac{1}{4} = P(E)P(G),$$
$$P(FG) = \tfrac{1}{4} = P(F)P(G),$$

showing that the events E, F, and G are pairwise independent. However, they are not independent, since

$$P(EFG) = P(\text{each coordinate is 1}) = \tfrac{1}{4},$$

whereas

$$P(E)P(F)P(G) = \tfrac{1}{8}.$$

That we should not want to call E, F, and G independent in this instance is evident from the following computation:

$$P(EF \mid G) = \frac{P(EFG)}{P(G)} = \frac{1}{2}.$$

$$P(EF) = \frac{1}{4}.$$

The probability assigned to EF depends on whether or not G has occurred.

1.3.3 Independent Experiments. Consider a probability model for an experiment $\mathcal{E}$, which is composed of two simpler experiments $\mathcal{E}_1$ followed by $\mathcal{E}_2$. If in this model every event relating to $\mathcal{E}_1$ only is independent of every event relating to $\mathcal{E}_2$ only, the experiments $\mathcal{E}_1$ and $\mathcal{E}_2$ are called *independent experiments*.

Example 1–40. In Example 1–34 the eight elementary outcomes of an experiment consisting of three tosses of a coin were assigned equal probabilities, 1/8 to each. The experiment can be thought of as being composed of experiment $\mathcal{E}_1$, the first toss, of $\mathcal{E}_2$, the second toss, and of $\mathcal{E}_3$, the third toss. The number of events for each experiment is very small, and one can easily verify that for any events E_1, E_2, and E_3 giving conditions on the outcomes of $\mathcal{E}_1$, $\mathcal{E}_2$, and $\mathcal{E}_3$, respectively, the condition for independence holds. For instance,

$$\begin{aligned} P(\text{1st toss } H, \text{2nd toss } T) &= P(HTH \text{ or } HTT) \\ &= \tfrac{1}{8} + \tfrac{1}{8} \\ &= P(\text{1st toss } H)\ P(\text{2nd toss } T). \end{aligned}$$

In the model that assigns equal probabilities to the eight elementary outcomes, the individual tosses are independent experiments.

In constructing a probability model for an experiment composed of simpler experiments, the notion that these constituent experiments are independent is built into the probability model by using the multiplication property defining independent events. That is, any event of the form EF, where E

relates to one subexperiment and F to another, is assigned the probability $P(E)P(F)$, and so on.

Example 1-41. A coin is tossed and then a die. There are 12 elementary outcomes in this experiment, each consisting of one of the two outcomes for the coin toss and one of the six outcomes for the toss of the die. The probability assigned to an elementary outcome of the composite experiment must be $(1/6)(1/2) = 1/12$, if the toss of the coin and the toss of the die are to be independent experiments.

If experiments are independent it is not essential that they be performed in a certain order, since neither the product $P(E)P(F)$ nor the probabilities in the product involve or depend on this order. Tossing a coin three times is equivalent, then, to tossing three coins once if the tosses are independent.

PROBLEMS

1-36. A certain type of device is used to shut off a flow when a container is filled to a certain depth; its "reliability" (probability that it works when it should) is assumed to be 0.9. A second type of shutoff device is placed "in parallel," that is, so that the flow is shut off if *either* device works; the reliability of this second device is assumed to be 0.7. What is the reliability of the combination? What is the probability that when the depth is reached, just one of the devices will work? (Assume that the devices operate independently.)

1-37. A certain device consists of four parts so connected that the device works only if all four parts work, where "works" means operates successfully in a certain mission. If the probability that each part individually works is 0.9, what is the probability that the device works? (Assume independence.)

1-38. In ten tosses of a coin what is the probability of the following sequence of results, assuming independent tosses: $H, T, H, H, T, T, T, H, T, T$?

1-39. Show the following: (a) If A and B are independent events, then A and $\bar{B}$ are independent. (b) If A, B, and C are independent events, then A, B, and $\bar{C}$ are independent. (c) If $P(AB) = 0$, but $P(A)$ and $P(B)$ are not zero, then A and B are not independent.

1-40. Probability is assigned to five points in a three-dimensional space as given in the following table:

(x,y,z)	(1,1,1)	(1,1,0)	(1,0,1)	(0,1,1)	(0,0,0)
Probability	$\frac{1}{8}$	$\frac{3}{16}$	$\frac{3}{16}$	$\frac{3}{16}$	$\frac{5}{16}$

Let E, F, and G be the events $x = 1$, $y = 1$, and $z = 1$, respectively, and show that

$$P(EFG) = P(E)P(F)P(G).$$

Show also that E, F, and G are *not* pairwise independent.

1-41. Two teams are to play a series of games for the best four out of seven games; as soon as one team wins four games, the series ends. The probability that team A wins over team B is assumed to be 0.5 if the game is played on team B's field, and 0.7 if the game is played on team A's field. The first two games are to be played on team B's field, the next three on team A's field, and the last two (if the series runs that long) on team B's field. What is the probability that team A wins the series in four games? In five games? What is the probability that the series does not run to six games?

2/ *Univariate Distributions*

In this chapter we study the distribution of probability associated with a single random variable $X(\omega)$ defined on a probability space Ω. A random variable was defined in Chapter 1 as a function taking each outcome of an experiment of chance into a real number—it is a "mapping" of the sample space into the space of real numbers. It may well be that not all real numbers are possible values of a given random variable, but if, once and for all, the set of all reals is adopted as the space of values, all cases are covered. It will be found that a random variable induces a distribution of probability in this space of values, a *univariate distribution.* It is this distribution and the special characteristics associated with the nature of the space of values which are the center of attention. The chapter will close with a discussion of several important parametric classes of univariate probability models.

2.1 Distribution of Probability in the Space of Values

Since a random variable attaches a real number to each outcome of an experiment of chance, it is natural to describe the result of the experiment in terms of that number. Indeed, any condition on the value of a random variable defines an event in the sample space consisting of those outcomes for whose attached numbers the condition is fulfilled.

Example 2–1. In firing at a target, a random variable of interest is the amount of miss $R(\omega)$, where ω is the landing point of the missile. The condition $R(\omega) < 2$ defines the event consisting of all those landing points within two units of the target. The condition $R(\omega) = 5$ defines the event consisting of those landing points at a distance five units from the target.

Because of a technicality arising in certain cases, it is not possible to insist on considering every conceivable condition on the values of a random variable—and fortunately not necessary. In practice, it is found that the "Borel sets," the sets in the smallest family of sets of real numbers containing the semi-infinite intervals $(-\infty, x]$, is sufficiently inclusive. (Cf. Example 1–25.) This family includes finite intervals: open, (a,b); closed, $[a,b]$; or half-open,

$(a,b]$ or $[a,b)$. It also includes single points, semi-infinite intervals (x, ∞), the whole set of reals, and the empty set.

A random variable $X(\omega)$ was defined so that any event in Ω, corresponding under $X(\omega)$ to one of this family of Borel sets of real numbers, is automatically one of the family of events that are assigned probabilities in Ω. Each such set E of real numbers, then, can be assigned a probability equal to the probability of the set of outcomes ω for which $X(\omega)$ is in E:

$$P[X(\omega) \text{ falls in } E] = P^{\Omega}[\text{set of } \omega \text{ such that } X(\omega) \text{ is in } E].$$

In this way probability is transferred from Ω to $(-\infty, \infty)$, the space of values of $X(\omega)$. We say that the probability distribution in Ω *induces* a probability distribution in $(-\infty, \infty)$.

Really, before calling this measure on sets of real numbers a probability distribution one should verify that the axioms for a probability space are satisfied. Let $\mathcal{X}$ denote the outcome space $(-\infty, \infty)$ together with the induced probabilities on its Borel sets. Then, clearly,

$$\begin{aligned} P(\mathcal{X}) = P(-\infty, \infty) &= P(\text{set of } \omega \text{ such that } -\infty < X(\omega) < \infty) \\ &= P(\Omega) = 1, \end{aligned}$$

and similarly the probability of an empty set is zero. The additivity property follows from the set identity:

$$\begin{aligned} &\{\text{All } \omega \text{ such that } X(\omega) \text{ is in } \cup E_i\} \\ &\qquad = \cup \{\text{all } \omega \text{ such that } X(\omega) \text{ is in } E_i\}. \end{aligned}$$

When the attention is focused on the probability space $\mathcal{X}$, the dependence of the random variable $X(\omega)$ on the outcome ω is often suppressed, and one speaks of the event "X in E." The probability of this event is indicated variously as follows:

$$P(E) = P(X \text{ in } E) = P^{\mathcal{X}}(X \text{ in } E) = P^{\Omega}(X(\omega) \text{ in } E),$$

the superscript being employed only when there is some reason to emphasize the space whose probability distribution is being used.

Example 2–2. Consider the random variable $X(\omega)$ which takes the value 1 or the value 0 according as ω is Heads or Tails in the toss of a coin. Using the usual model for an "unbiased" coin, in which Heads and Tails are considered equally likely, we find that the induced distribution in the space of values assigns probability 1/2 to the value 0 and also to the value 1, and probability 0 to any other values or any set of values not containing 0 or 1. A set of reals containing 0 but not 1 is assigned probability 1/2, and a set containing both 0 and 1 is assigned probability 1.

Exactly the same probability space results from considering the random variable $Y(\omega)$ which takes on the value 1 or the value 0 according as an "unbiased" die shows an odd or an even number of points.

It is seen in Example 2–2 that different random variables can induce the same distribution of probability in the space of reals. Indeed, given any random variable $X(\omega)$ the induced distribution in the space $\mathfrak{X}$ can be obtained by considering $\mathfrak{X}$ itself as the sample space and by taking the random variable $X(x) = x$, where x is a number in $\mathfrak{X}$. In particular, if the sample space is initially the set of real numbers, the distribution induced by the random variable $X(x) = x$ is exactly the initial distribution.

Example 2–3. An experiment consists of operating a light bulb until it fails. The result of the experiment is described by the life of the bulb in hours. This number of hours is the outcome of the experiment, and it is a real number x. The function $X(x) = x$ is a random variable that induces in the set of real numbers precisely the probability distribution of the original experiment.

2.1.1 The Distribution Function. A random variable $X(\omega)$ defines a probability for each semi-infinite interval $(-\infty,\lambda]$:

$$P(-\infty,\lambda] = P^{\Omega}(-\infty < X(\omega) \leq \lambda) = P(X \leq \lambda).$$

This probability depends on the right-hand end point λ. It is a *function* of λ. It is called the *distribution function* of the random variable X, or of the probability distribution on $(-\infty,\infty)$ induced by $X(\omega)$. (Some call it the *cumulative distribution function* and then shorten this name to c.d.f.)

One of the inadequacies of traditional functional notation is that the same notation is used for a whole function, $f(x)$, as is used for the specific value of the function corresponding to x. When referring to a whole function (that is, to the *rule* for associating values of one variable with those of another), the particular letter employed within the parentheses is not significant: $f(y)$ denotes the same functional relationship as $f(x)$; perhaps a better notation would be $f(\cdot)$. The x or y used is a "dummy" variable in that $f(x)$ means that a certain operation is to be performed on whatever number x is "plugged" in. Thus, if we denote a distribution function by $F(\lambda)$, we have

$$F(\lambda) = P(X \leq \lambda), \quad F(x) = P(X \leq x), \quad F(q) = P(X \leq q), \quad \text{etc.,}$$

but the *function* $F(\cdot)$ is the same in each case as long as the same X and probability distribution are used in each case. A different distribution function results from using a different random variable; if more than one random variable is involved in a problem, we shall usually use a subscript to identify the various distribution functions:

$$F_X(\lambda) = P(X \leq \lambda), \quad F_Y(\lambda) = P(Y \leq \lambda), \quad \text{etc.}$$

Here the function $F_X(\cdot)$ defines a relationship different from that defined by $F_Y(\cdot)$, and it makes no difference that we might use the same dummy variable in defining both.

Of course we shall continue to use the traditional interpretation that, for instance, $F(4)$ denotes the particular value of the function $F(\cdot)$ obtained from performing the functional operation on the number 4:

$$F_X(4) = P(X \leq 4).$$

Example 2–4. In Example 1–25 a model was adopted for the spinning pointer with the scale [0,1] at its tip, a probability model in which the probability of an interval of real numbers on [0,1] was defined to be its length. The distribution function for the random variable X, the number at which the pointer stops, is then

$$F(\lambda) = P(X \leq \lambda) = P(0 \leq X \leq \lambda) = \lambda, \quad \text{for } 0 \leq \lambda \leq 1.$$

For $\lambda < 0$ this probability is zero, and for $\lambda > 1$, it is 1. This distribution function is shown in Figure 2–1.

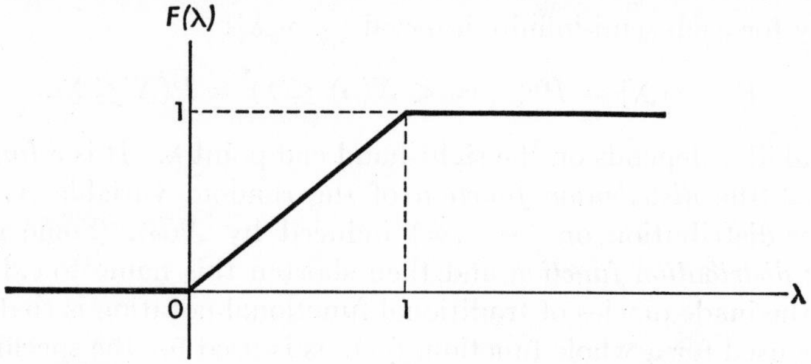

Figure 2–1 Distribution function for Example 2–4

A distribution function $F(x)$ enjoys the following basic properties as a result of its being a probability in a probability space:

(a) $$0 \leq F(x) \leq 1;$$
(b) $$F(-\infty) = 0, \quad F(\infty) = 1;$$
(c) $$F(x) \leq F(y), \quad \text{whenever } x < y;$$
(d) $$\lim_{y \to x^+} F(y) = F(x).$$

The first two of these properties are immediate; the third is true because the interval $(-\infty, x]$ is contained in the interval $(-\infty, y]$ whenever $x < y$. Condition (d), that $F(x)$ is continuous from the right at each point x, follows from a condition for continuity in terms of sequences: A function $F(x)$ is continuous at $x = a$ if and only if for any sequence $x_1, x_2, \cdots$ with limit a, the corresponding functional values $F(x_1), F(x_2), \cdots$ have limit $F(a)$. If, then, $y_1, y_2, \cdots$ is a sequence of values approaching x from the right, the interval $(-\infty, x]$ is the intersection of the intervals $(-\infty, y_n]$, so that

$$P(-\infty, x] = P(\cap(-\infty, y_n]) = \lim_{n \to \infty} F(y_n).$$

(The sequence $\{y_n\}$ can be taken to be monotonic—steadily decreasing—so that the sequence of intervals $(-\infty, y_n]$ is a descending sequence of sets.) The distribution functions in the example above and the examples to follow should be examined for the validity of these properties.

Example 2–5. Consider the random variable θ defined to be the colatitude coordinate of the random orientation of a fiber, as in Example 1–31, page 20. Assuming probability to be distributed uniformly over all orientations, as discussed in that example, it follows that the distribution function of θ is

$$\begin{aligned} F_\theta(\lambda) &= P(\theta \leq \lambda) \\ &= \frac{\text{area of portion of unit sphere where } \theta \leq \lambda}{\text{area of unit hemisphere}} \\ &= \frac{2\pi(1 - \cos \lambda)}{2\pi} = 1 - \cos \lambda, \quad \text{for } 0 \leq \lambda \leq \frac{\pi}{2}. \end{aligned}$$

Similarly, for the random variable ϕ defined to be the longitude coordinate, we find the distribution function

$$\begin{aligned} F_\phi(\mu) = P(\phi \leq \mu) &= \frac{\text{area of wedge of width } \mu}{\text{area of hemisphere}} \\ &= \frac{\mu}{2\pi}, \quad 0 \leq \mu < 2\pi. \end{aligned}$$

The areas in these computations are shown in Figure 2–2 and the distribution functions in Figure 2–3.

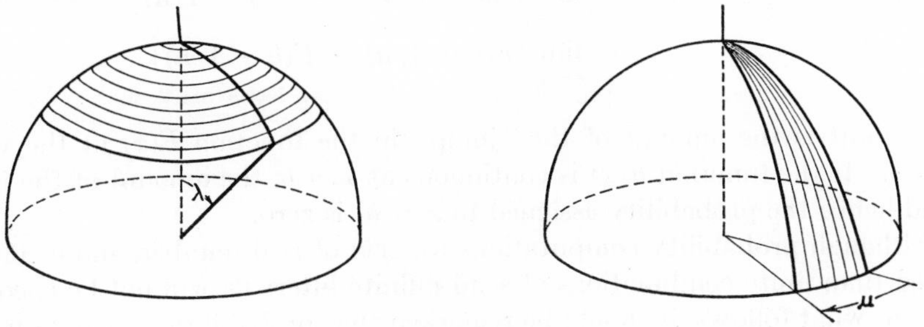

Figure 2–2

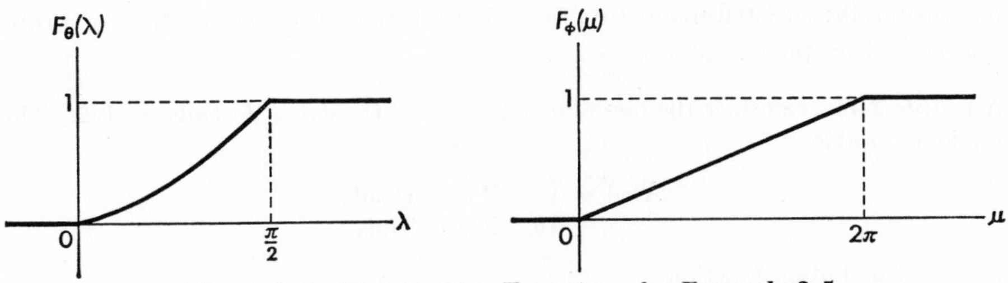

Figure 2–3 Distribution Functions for Example 2–5

Probabilities for sets of real numbers that are expressible in terms of semi-infinite intervals can be given in terms of the distribution function. The probability of the interval $(a,b]$, which is the set $(-\infty,b]$ minus the set $(-\infty,a]$, is thus expressed as

$$P(X \text{ in } (a,b]) = P(X \leq b) - P(X \leq a) = F(b) - F(a),$$

where $F(x)$ is the distribution function of the random variable X. It is seen that the amount of increase in $F(x)$ over the interval from a to b is the probability of the interval. A closed interval can be expressed as a half-open interval plus the left end point; hence,

$$P(X \text{ in } [a,b]) = P(X \leq b) - P(X \leq a) + P(X = a).$$

Similarly, for an open interval,

$$P(X \text{ in } (a,b)) = P(X \leq b) - P(X \leq a) - P(X = b).$$

Since a single point may be expressed as the intersection of a decreasing sequence of intervals containing it, its probability can be expressed in terms of the distribution function as follows:

$$\begin{aligned} P(X = b) &= P(\cap(b - 1/n, b + 1/n]) \\ &= \lim_{n\to\infty} P(b - 1/n < X \leq b + 1/n) \\ &= \lim_{n\to\infty} [F(b + 1/n) - F(b - 1/n)] \end{aligned}$$

This limit is the amount of the "jump" in the function $F(x)$ at the value $x = b$. If the function $F(x)$ is continuous at $x = b$, the amount of the jump (and hence the probability assigned to $x = b$) is zero.

Although probability computations for sets of real numbers more complicated than finite combinations of semi-infinite intervals will not be encountered in what follows, it should be remarked that probabilities are determined by the distribution function for all Borel sets of real numbers. In this sense the probability distribution function characterizes the distribution of probability in the space $\mathcal{X}$ of values.

Example 2–6. Consider the toss of a coin, with $P(\text{Heads}) = P(\text{Tails}) = 1/2$. The random variable

$$X(\omega) = \begin{cases} 1, & \text{if } \omega = \text{Heads} \\ 0, & \text{if } \omega = \text{Tails} \end{cases}$$

has the distribution function

$$F(x) = \begin{cases} 0, & \text{for } x < 0 \\ 0.5, & \text{for } 0 \leq x < 1 \\ 1, & \text{for } x \geq 1. \end{cases}$$

This is pictured in Figure 2–4. Notice that the amount of the jump in $F(x)$ at $x = 0$ is the probability assigned to the value 0, and the amount of the jump at $x = 1$ is the probability assigned to 1. The function does not rise at any other point or over any other interval, since any interval not containing 0 or 1 has probability 0.

2.1.2 Percentiles. A distribution function is sometimes expressible as a simple algebraic or other "elementary" function, but frequently it is not so expressible and cannot be evaluated by using ordinary tables of powers, logarithms, exponential functions, or trigonometric functions. New tables may be required, and for the distribution functions of many useful probability models such tables have been constructed. Some of these are included in the Appendix.

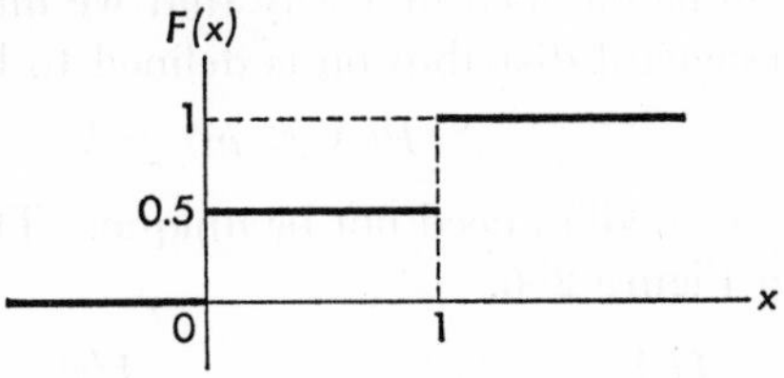

Figure 2–4

A distribution function can be tabled by giving its values corresponding to a set of given, conveniently spaced values of the independent variable. Table I (Appendix) is constructed in this way. On the other hand, the distribution function can be specified by giving the values of the independent variable corresponding to conveniently chosen values of the function. Table II is of this type.

If a distribution function rises steadily from the value 0 to the value 1, with no jumps or intervals of constancy in between, there is for each p on $[0,1]$ a unique value x_p having the property that

$$P(X \leq x_p) = p.$$

This is called a *percentile* (or a fractile, or a quantile) of the distribution of the random variable X. For instance, $x_{.05}$ is called the fifth percentile and is that value of x such that the probability is 0.05 that X will not exceed it. Figure 2–5 illustrates the seventieth percentile of a distribution function.

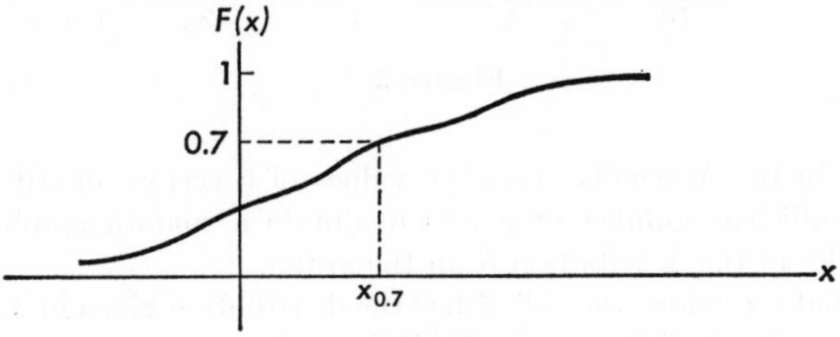

Figure 2–5

Particular percentiles are given special names; the twenty-fifth, fiftieth and seventy-fifth percentiles are called, respectively, the *first quartile*, the, *median*, and the *third quartile* of the distribution. The tenth percentile of the distribution is sometimes called the *first decile*, and so on.

If a distribution function does not increase steadily but has horizontal portions or jumps, the above definition of a percentile is not adequate. It can be patched in a way that we illustrate with the median. The median of a general distribution is defined to be any number m satisfying the relations

$$P(X \leq m) \geq \tfrac{1}{2} \quad \text{and} \quad P(X \geq m) \geq \tfrac{1}{2}.$$

The median need not be unique. The three possible situations are illustrated in Figure 2–6.

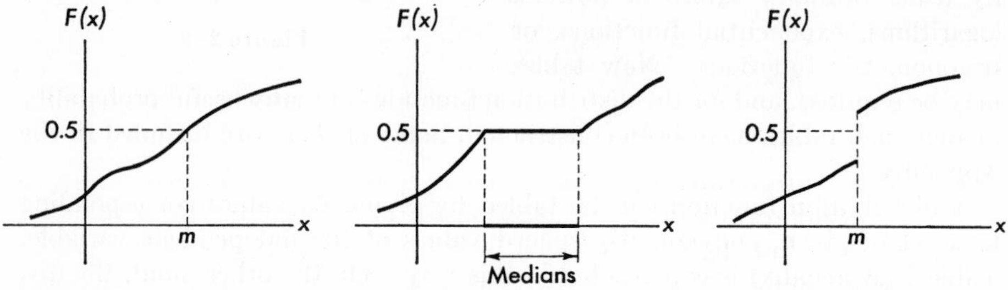

Figure 2–6

PROBLEMS

2–1. A random variable X has the distribution function shown in the accompanying sketch, Figure 2–7.
Determine the following: (a) $P(X = 1/2)$; (b) $P(X = 1)$; (c) $P(X < 1)$; (d) $P(X \leq 1)$; (e) $P(X > 2)$; (f) $P(1/2 < X < 5/2)$.

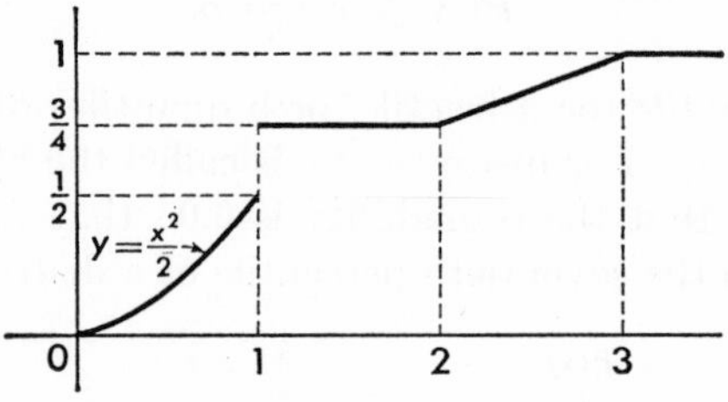

Figure 2–7

2–2. Table I in the Appendix gives the values of a certain distribution function. Plot a sufficient number of points to obtain a smooth graph, and estimate the deciles of the distribution from the graph.

2–3. Given that a random variable Z has the distribution given in Table I (Appendix), compute the following probabilities:

(a) $P(Z < 1.4)$
(b) $P(-0.3 < Z < 1.4)$
(c) $P(Z > 2)$
(d) $P(|Z| > 3)$
(e) $P(|Z - 1| < 2)$
(f) $P(Z^2 < 2)$

2–4. A random variable X has the following distribution function:

$$F(x) = \begin{cases} 1 - 0.75e^{-x}, & \text{if } x \geq 0 \\ 0, & \text{if } x < 0. \end{cases}$$

Determine the following: (a) $P(X > 2)$; (b) $P(X \leq 0)$; (c) $P(X = 0)$; (d) $P(X = 2)$.

2–5. Each horizontal line in Table II (Appendix) gives percentiles of a member of a certain class of distribution functions. Plot the distribution function for "five degrees of freedom" (that is, using the fifth line in the table). From the graph, estimate the following (in which X denotes a random variable with this distribution):

(a) the fortieth percentile
(b) $P(X > 8)$
(c) $P(|X - 5| < 2)$
(d) $P(X < 3)$.

2.1.3 Two Important Classes of Distributions. It is convenient to identify two important classes of distribution, one containing those distributions in which probability is assigned in discrete amounts at isolated points, and another containing those distributions that do not "lump" probability at individual points but rather "smear" it out over an interval of values. Distributions in these classes are called, respectively, *discrete* and *continuous*. This classification is not exhaustive; there are certainly distributions that are neither all discrete nor all continuous. (Cf. Problem 2-4).

A random variable $X(\omega)$ that can assume only a finite or countably infinite set of different values is called a *discrete* random variable, and its distribution is said to be a discrete distribution in the space of values. The distribution function can rise only on this at most countably infinite set of values, and it must therefore jump a nonzero amount at one of these values at least; between these values it is constant. The distribution and the distribution function are then characterized by the probabilities assigned to the individual values in the set of possible values:

$$p_i = P(X = x_i),$$

where x_i is one of the list of possible values, $x_1, x_2, \cdots$.

Example 2–7. Three chips are drawn together at random from a bowl containing five chips numbered 1, 2, 3, 4, and 5. There are ten possible outcomes in this experiment:

123, 124, 125, 134, 135, 145, 234, 235, 245, 345,

each having probability 1/10. Let $X(\omega)$ denote the *sum* of the numbers on the chips in outcome ω. The values of X corresponding to the above list of outcomes are, respectively,

6, 7, 8, 8, 9, 10, 9, 10, 11, 12.

The possible values of $X(\omega)$ and the corresponding probabilities for those values are then as follows:

x_i	6	7	8	9	10	11	12
p_i	0.1	0.1	0.2	0.2	0.2	0.1	0.1

The distribution function is that shown in Figure 2–8.

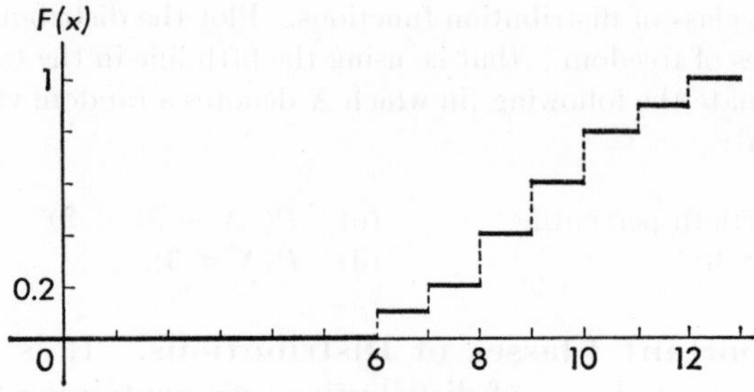

Figure 2–8

Example 2–8. In packaging a certain product it is desired that at least 8 ounces be included in each package. For certain purposes, then, one might be interested only in whether a package contained less than 8 ounces, or 8 ounces or more. Thinking of the possible weights of packages as the points ω in the sample space, we introduce the random variable

$$X(\omega) = \begin{cases} 1, & \text{if } \omega < 8 \text{ oz.} \\ 0, & \text{if } \omega \geq 8 \text{ oz.} \end{cases}$$

That is, 1 corresponds to a "defective" package and 0 to a "nondefective" one. The random variable X can take on just the values 0 and 1, and the corresponding probabilities are determined by the distribution of probability in the sample space:

$$\begin{aligned} P(X = 0) &= P^{\Omega}(\omega \geq 8) = P(\text{package weighs 8 oz. or more}), \\ P(X = 1) &= P^{\Omega}(\omega < 8) = P(\text{package weighs less than 8 oz.}). \end{aligned}$$

Example 2–9. The lengths of "10-foot" sections of pipe are measured in inches to the nearest inch. Here, even though the length might be thought of as assuming any of a continuum of possible values, the round-off process introduces discreteness into the set of values. The only possible values of the *measured* lengths are

$$\ldots,\quad 118,\quad 119,\quad 120,\quad 121,\quad 122,\quad \ldots,$$

and each value in this list has a corresponding probability—the probability that, in measuring, a length is rounded off to that value. More precise measurements of length would lead to possible values that are more numerous but nonetheless discrete (even should the precision be carried to, say, ten decimal places). Of course a discrete model involving lengths to ten decimal places would be more complicated to deal with than the idealization of a continuous model. But even though we have a continuous model in mind, data must be recorded discretely.

If the distribution function of a random variable is a continuous function, no single value can have a nonzero probability because a continuous function has no jumps. It turns out, however, that useful probability models involve distribution functions that, if continuous, are also differentiable except possibly at a finite number of points.[1] A random variable and the corresponding distribution are called *continuous* if the distribution function is continuous and has a derivative at each point with the possible exception of a finite number of points.

The derivative of a distribution function $F_X(\lambda)$ is called the *density function* of the distribution; it will be denoted by $f(\lambda)$ or by $f_X(\lambda)$ when clarity requires specific reference to the random variable:

$$f_X(\lambda) = \frac{d}{d\lambda} F_X(\lambda) = \frac{d}{d\lambda} P(X \leq \lambda).$$

Examination of the increment quotient defining $f_X(\lambda)$ shows that it is a density in the sense explained in Chapter 1, page 20. For positive h, for instance,

$$f_X(\lambda) = \lim_{h \to 0^+} \frac{P(\lambda < X \leq \lambda + h)}{h}.$$

A derivative, and hence $f(\lambda)$, is a "differential coefficient":

$$dF(\lambda) = f(\lambda)\, d\lambda.$$

This differential of $P(X \leq \lambda)$ can be used, for small $d\lambda$, to approximate an increment in $P(X \leq \lambda)$ corresponding to an increment in λ from λ to $\lambda + d\lambda$:

$$f(\lambda)\, d\lambda \doteq P(X \leq \lambda + d\lambda) - P(X \leq \lambda) = P(\lambda < X \leq d\lambda).$$

The term *probability element* is sometimes used for this differential.

One of the properties of a function which is differentiable except at a finite number of points is that it is the integral of its derivative (cf. the reference cited in footnote 1):

$$F(x) = \int_{-\infty}^{x} f(\lambda)\, d\lambda.$$

From this it follows that

$$P(a < X < b) = \int_a^b f(\lambda)\, d\lambda.$$

---

[1]In more advanced presentations the term *continuous* is used to describe the case in which the distribution function is "absolutely continuous." Functions satisfying the condition we have given are absolutely continuous but not necessarily conversely. See, for example, Titchmarsh, *The Theory of Functions*, 2nd ed., London, 1939, for a discussion of absolute continuity and the equivalent condition in terms of differentiability "almost everywhere."

(Notice that since single points have zero probability, the probabilities of the intervals (a,b), $[a,b]$, $(a,b]$, and $[a,b)$ are all the same.) A definite integral can be interpreted geometrically as an area, and Figure 2–9 shows $F_X(\lambda)$ exhibited as an area. Figure 2–10 shows $P(a < X < b)$, and Figure 2–11 illustrates the probability element.

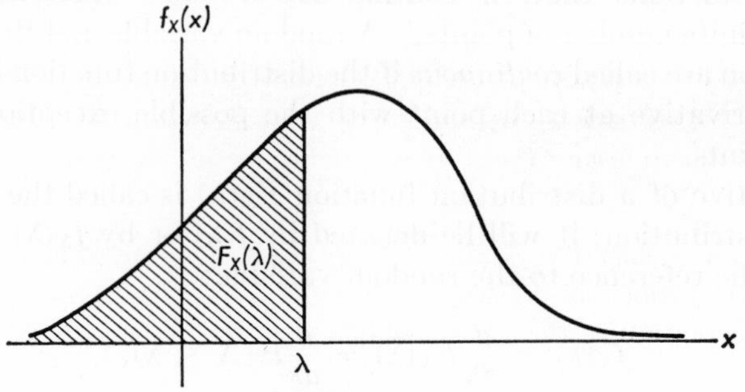

Figure 2–9

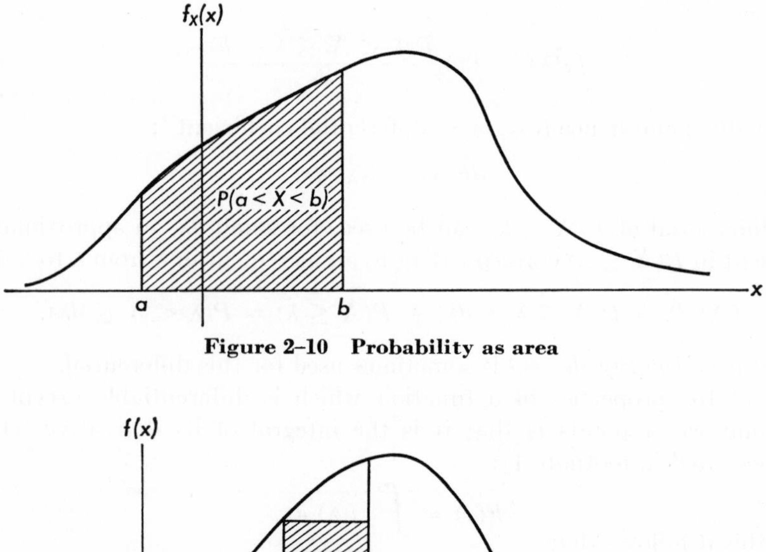

Figure 2–10 Probability as area

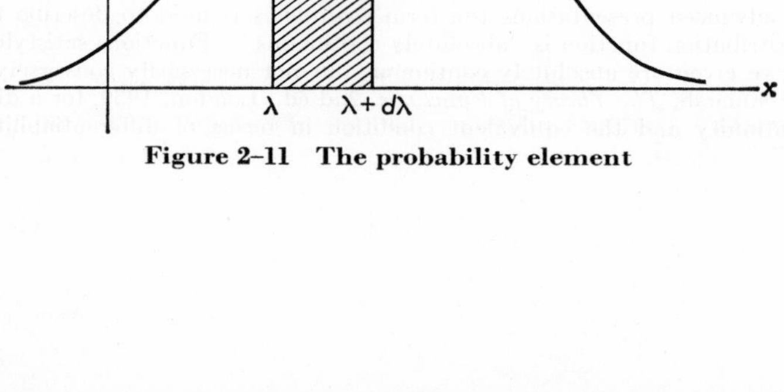

Figure 2–11 The probability element

The density function of a continuous random variable satisfies the following basic properties as a consequence of its being the derivative of a distribution function:

(a) $$f(x) \geq 0,$$

(b) $$\int_{-\infty}^{\infty} f(x)\,dx = 1.$$

The first of these is a result of the nondecreasing character of a distribution function, and the second is equivalent to the condition $F(\infty) = 1$, expressing the fact that an assignment of probability is "normalized" to have a unit total.

Example 2–10. Consider the random variables θ and ϕ, the spherical coordinates of a random orientation, as defined in Example 2–5. The density functions are obtained by differentiating the corresponding distribution functions given in that example:

$$f_\theta(\lambda) = \frac{d}{d\lambda}(1 - \cos\lambda) = \sin\lambda, \quad \text{for } 0 < \lambda < \frac{\pi}{2},$$

$$f_\phi(\mu) = \frac{d}{d\mu}\left(\frac{\mu}{2\pi}\right) = \frac{1}{2\pi}, \quad \text{for } 0 < \mu < 2\pi.$$

(Outside the indicated ranges the densities are zero.) The graphs of these density functions are shown in Figure 2–12.

The distribution functions can be recovered from the density functions by integration. For instance,

$$F_\theta(x) = \int_{-\infty}^{x} f_\theta(\lambda)\,d\lambda = \begin{cases} 0, & \text{for } x < 0, \\ \int_0^x \sin\lambda\,d\lambda, & \text{for } 0 < x < \frac{\pi}{2}, \\ 1, & \text{for } x > \frac{\pi}{2}. \end{cases}$$

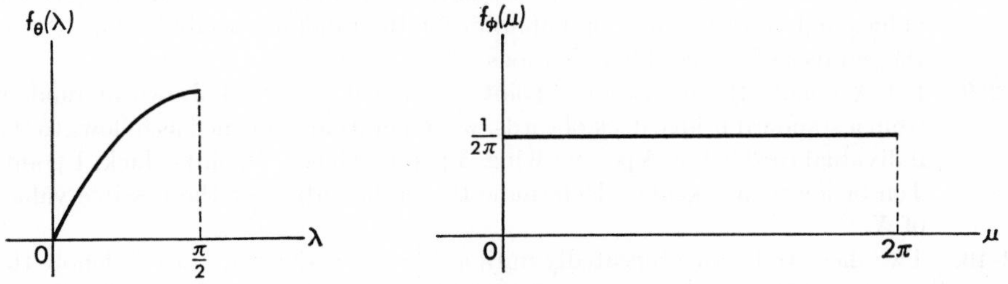

Figure 2–12

Although most of the probability models one meets in applications involve random variables that are either of the discrete type or of the continuous type, occasionally the need arises for a model in which the random variable is neither discrete nor continuous. One such instance is discussed in the following example.

Example 2–11. A model used in describing the life of an electron tube in a certain type of use involves the following distribution function for this life:

$$F(x) = \begin{cases} 1 - R_0 e^{-kx}, & \text{for } x \geq 0, \\ 0, & \text{for } x < 0. \end{cases}$$

This is shown in Figure 2–13. It is seen here that there is a jump in the amount $1 - R_0$ at $x = 0$, indicating a probability $1 - R_0$ that a tube taken from the shelf is bad to begin with, or a probability R_0 (possibly less than 1) that the tube is good. The quantity

$$R(x) = P(\text{tube life exceeds } x) = 1 - F(x) = R_0 e^{-kx}$$

is called the *reliability* of the tube in a mission of x time units, and R_0 might then be termed the *initial reliability*.

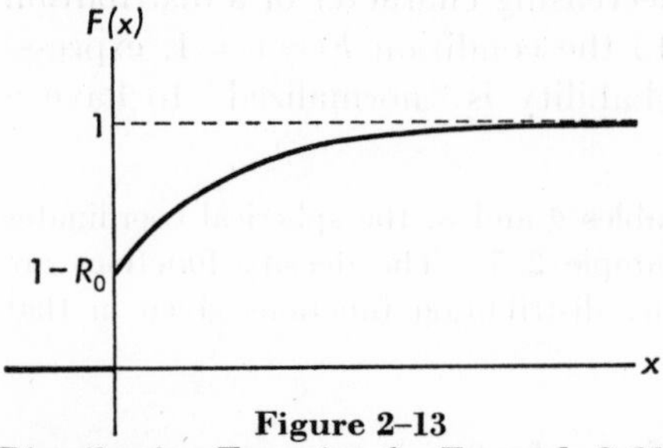

Figure 2–13
Distribution Function for Example 2–11

PROBLEMS

2–6. Two articles among ten articles in a lot are defective. Determine the possible values and the corresponding probabilities for the random variables X, the number of defectives in a random selection of one article from the lot, and Y, the number of defective articles in a random selection of four.

2–7. Five electron tubes in a box are to be tested one at a time until the one defective tube among the five is located. Determine the possible values and the corresponding probabilities for the random variable defined to be the number of tests required.

2–8. A tester is to identify three cigarettes of three different brands and is told to assign the brand name A to one, and the name B to another, and the name C to the third. Suppose that he cannot really tell the difference by smoking the cigarettes and assigns the three names at random. Determine the possible values and corresponding probabilities for the random variable defined to be the number of correct identifications.

2–9. Let X denote the number of "points" assigned to a card drawn at random from a standard bridge deck of cards, when points are assigned as follows to the individual cards: Ace, 4 points; King, 3 points; Queen, 2 points; Jack, 1 point; Ten or lower, no points. Determine the probabilities for the possible values of X.

2–10. Two dice are thrown repeatedly until a "seven" is thrown. Let X denote the number of throws necessary, and determine the probability distribution for X.

2–11. As in Example 2–7, three chips are drawn together at random from a bowl containing five chips numbered 1, 2, 3, 4, and 5. Let Y denote the smallest of the three numbers drawn and R the largest number drawn minus the smallest. Determine the distributions of probability for Y and R. Compute also $P(Y \leq 2)$ and $P(R > 2)$.

2–12. A random variable X has the distribution function $F(x) = x^2$ for x on $[0,1]$, 0 for x on $(-\infty,0)$, and 1 for $x \geq 1$. First observe that this distribution is of the continuous type and then determine the density function of the distribution.

2–13. A random variable X has the distribution function

$$F(x) = \frac{1}{\pi}\left(\frac{\pi}{2} + \text{arc tan } x\right),$$

where the value of arc tan x is taken to be that on the range from $-\pi/2$ to $\pi/2$. Determine the density function, the third quartile of the distribution, and the probability that $|X| < 1$.

2–14. A random variable X has the density function

$$f(x) = \begin{cases} 1 - |x|, & \text{for } |x| < 1, \\ 0, & \text{elsewhere.} \end{cases}$$

Determine and sketch the distribution function of X. Compute also $P(X > 0)$ and $P(|X| > 1/2)$. Interpret these with respect to both the graph of the density function and the graph of the distribution function.

2–15. Show that if $f(a - x) = f(a + x)$, so that the graph of $f(x)$ is symmetrical about the ordinate $x = a$, then the median of the distribution with density function $f(x)$ is a.

2.1.4 Specifying a Distribution. When a probability model is constructed by defining a probability space Ω, with outcomes, events, and probabilities as discussed in Chapter 1, there is induced a corresponding distribution of probability in the space of values of any random variable on Ω. Because the interest is most often centered in the distribution in the space of values, it is convenient to be able to construct a probability model in that space directly. This can be done in general by specifying a function $F(x)$ to be used as the distribution function; that is, to be used as the probability of the interval $(-\infty,x]$. Thus $F(x)$ assigns probability directly to all such semi-infinite intervals and indirectly (through the addition law) to complements, countable unions, and countable intersections.

Not just any function $F(x)$ will serve to define probabilities, since there are certain conditions to be satisfied—the probability axioms. It was seen in §2.1.1 that a distribution function induced by a probability distribution given in Ω satisfies the following conditions:

(a) $0 \leq F(x) \leq 1,$

(b) $F(-\infty) = 0, \quad F(\infty) = 1,$

(c) $F(x) \leq F(y), \quad \text{whenever } x < y,$

(d) $\lim_{y \to x^+} F(y) = F(x).$

It happens that these conditions are sufficient to ensure that a function $F(x)$ which satisfies them defines a probability distribution on $(-\infty,\infty)$, taking $P(-\infty < X \leq x) = F(x)$. (Cf. Reference [4], page 53, for a proof of this.)

For the case of a discrete random variable $X(\omega)$, an alternative method of specifying a probability distribution is to give a probability for each of its possible values,

$$p_i = P(X = x_i),$$

in such a way that the total of such probabilities is 1, each p_i being a number on [0,1].

The probability distribution for a continuous random variable can be set up by specifying a density function $f(x)$. This can be any integrable function satisfying the properties

(i) $$f(x) \geq 0,$$

(ii) $$\int_{-\infty}^{\infty} f(x)\,dx = 1.$$

Defining from this the function

$$F(x) = \int_{-\infty}^{x} f(u)\,du,$$

one obtains a distribution function, a function satisfying the properties (a) through (d) above.

Example 2–12. Consider the function defined as follows:

$$f(x) = \begin{cases} 1 - x/2, & \text{for } 0 < x < 2, \\ 0, & \text{for } x < 0 \text{ or } x > 2. \end{cases}$$

This function is non-negative, and

$$\int_{-\infty}^{\infty} f(x)\,dx = \int_{0}^{2} \left(1 - \frac{x}{2}\right) dx = 1.$$

It therefore serves to define a probability distribution on $(-\infty, \infty)$. The corresponding distribution function is its integral:

$$F(x) = \int_{-\infty}^{x} f(u)\,du = \begin{cases} 0, & \text{for } x < 0, \\ x - \frac{1}{4}x^2, & \text{for } 0 \leq x \leq 2, \\ 1, & \text{for } x > 2. \end{cases}$$

2.1.5 Functions of a Random Variable. It was seen in §1.1.5 that a function $y = g(x)$ serves to define a random variable $Y(\omega)$ in terms of $X(\omega)$:

$$Y = Y(\omega) = g(X(\omega)).$$

The point or outcome ω is mapped by $X(\omega)$ into a real number x, and this point in turn is mapped by $g(x)$ into another real number y. The space of values of Y is again the set of real numbers $(-\infty, \infty)$, and the mapping provided by $g(x)$ can be used to transfer probability from the space $\mathfrak{X}$ of X-values into the space $\mathcal{Y}$ of Y-values. Thus,

$$P(Y \text{ in } E) = P^{\mathfrak{X}}(g(X) \text{ in } E) = P^{\Omega}[g(X(\omega)) \text{ in } E].$$

In particular,

$$P(Y \leq y) = P^{\mathfrak{X}}(g(X) \leq y) = P^{\Omega}[g(X(\omega)) \leq y],$$

and this defines the distribution function of Y in terms of either the probability distribution in $\mathfrak{X}$ or the probability distribution in Ω.

Example 2–13. Let the random variable X have the probability distribution defined by the following distribution function:

$$F(x) = \begin{cases} 1 - e^{-x}, & \text{for } x \geq 0, \\ 0, & \text{for } x < 0. \end{cases}$$

This is a non-negative random variable, all its probability being distributed over non-negative numbers. Consider now, for each non-negative x, the quantity $y = \sqrt{x}$. This relationship defines a new random variable $Y = \sqrt{X}$, with distribution function:

$$F_Y(\lambda) = P(Y \leq \lambda) = P(\sqrt{X} \leq \lambda) = P(X \leq \lambda^2)$$
$$= F_X(\lambda^2) = 1 - e^{-\lambda^2},$$

for $\lambda \geq 0$. If $\lambda < 0$, $P(Y \leq \lambda) = 0$. The density function of Y can then be computed by differentiation:

$$f_Y(\lambda) = \frac{d}{d\lambda}(1 - e^{-\lambda^2}) = 2\lambda e^{-\lambda^2}, \quad \text{for } \lambda > 0.$$

Example 2–14. Consider the discrete random variable X with probability distribution defined by the following table of probabilities:

x_i	-1	0	1
p_i	0.3	0.4	0.3

Suppose one is interested in the random variable $X^2 - 1 = Y$. That is, for each value x of the random variable X, we compute $x^2 - 1$. The value $x = -1$ is mapped into the value $y = 0$; the value $x = 0$, into $y = -1$; and the value $x = 1$, into $y = 0$. Thus Y takes on fewer values than X, the two values $x = 1$ and $x = -1$ being mapped into the single value $y = 0$. The probabilities assigned to $x = 1$ and $x = -1$ are then both given to $y = 0$, and the complete probability table for Y is as follows:

y_j	-1	0
$P(Y = y_j)$	0.4	0.6

Similarly, the random variable $Z = |X|$ takes on just the two values 0 and 1, according to the following probability table:

z_k	0	1
$P(Z = z_k)$	0.4	0.6

Example 2–15. Let $Y = aX + b$ for certain constants a and b, with $a > 0$. The distribution function of Y can be expressed in terms of the distribution function of X as follows:

$$F_Y(\lambda) = P(aX + b \leq \lambda) = P\left(X \leq \frac{\lambda - b}{a}\right)$$
$$= F_X\left(\frac{\lambda - b}{a}\right).$$

If X is a continuous random variable, so is Y, and the density function of Y can be obtained from the density function of X:

$$f_Y(\lambda) = \frac{d}{d\lambda} F_X\left(\frac{\lambda - b}{a}\right) = \frac{1}{a} f_X\left(\frac{\lambda - b}{a}\right).$$

If $a < 0$, a similar relation holds, and by combining the two results, one obtains

$$f_{aX+b}(\lambda) = \frac{1}{|a|} f_X\left(\frac{\lambda - b}{a}\right).$$

The technique of the Example 2–15 extends to any strictly monotonic functional relationship. Let $g(x)$ have the property that $g(x) < g(x')$ whenever $x < x'$; the function $g(x)$ is then said to be strictly monotonically increasing. If $g(x)$ is continuous, there is a unique inverse $x = g^{-1}(y)$ for each y such that $g(g^{-1}(y)) = y$ and $g^{-1}(g(x)) = x$. Then

$$P(Y \leq \lambda) = P(g(X) \leq \lambda) = P(X \leq g^{-1}(\lambda)) = F_X(g^{-1}(\lambda)).$$

If X is continuous, so is Y, with density

$$f_Y(\lambda) = \frac{d}{d\lambda} P(Y < \lambda) = \frac{d}{d\lambda} F_X(g^{-1}(\lambda))$$
$$= f_X(g^{-1}(\lambda)) \frac{d}{d\lambda} g^{-1}(\lambda).$$

Interpretation of this result in terms of "probability elements" may be helpful. If $y = g(x)$ and the differential dy corresponds to the differential dx (see Figure 2–14), these differentials are related as follows:

$$dx = \frac{1}{g'(x)}\, dy,$$

so that

$$P^Y(dy) = P^X(dx) = f_X(x)\, dx = f_X(x) \frac{1}{g'(x)}\, dy.$$

The coefficient of dy is then the density of Y and is the result obtained above, since dy/dx is the reciprocal of dx/dy.

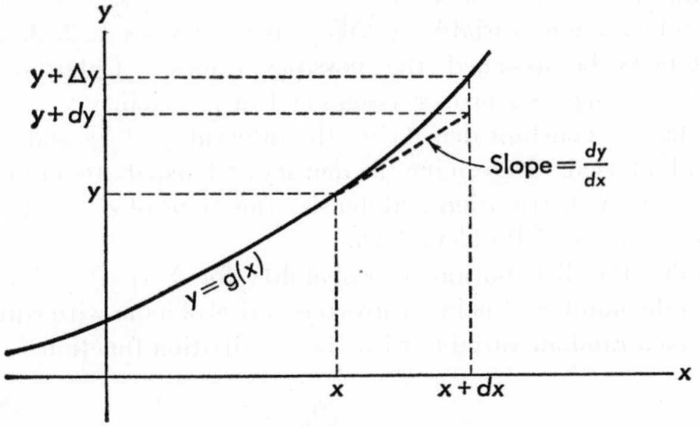

Figure 2–14

If $g(x)$ does not have a unique inverse, which would be the case if it were not always increasing or always decreasing, the various inverses must be accounted for. The following example shows how this can be done in one instance.

Example 2–16. Let X have the density function $[\pi(1 + x^2)]^{-1}$ and let $Y = X^2$. Then

$$P(Y \leq \lambda) = P(X^2 \leq \lambda) = P(-\sqrt{\lambda} \leq X \leq +\sqrt{\lambda})$$
$$= F_X(\sqrt{\lambda}) - F_X(-\sqrt{\lambda}).$$

Differentiating, we obtain

$$f_Y(\lambda) = \frac{d}{d\lambda} P(Y \leq \lambda) = f_X(\sqrt{\lambda}) \frac{1}{2\sqrt{\lambda}} - f_X(-\sqrt{\lambda}) \frac{-1}{2\sqrt{\lambda}}$$
$$= \frac{1/\sqrt{\lambda}}{\pi(1 + \lambda)}.$$

This holds for $\lambda > 0$, both the distribution and density functions of Y being 0 for $\lambda < 0$.

PROBLEMS

2–16. Determine in each case the value of the constant k such that the given function is a density function:

(a) $f(x) = \begin{cases} kx, & \text{for } 0 < x < 2 \\ 0, & \text{for } x < 0 \text{ or } x > 2 \end{cases}$

(b) $f(x) = \begin{cases} kx(1 - x), & \text{for } 0 < x < 1 \\ 0, & \text{for } x < 0 \text{ or } x > 1 \end{cases}$

Determine and sketch the corresponding distribution functions.

2-17. Can ke^{-x} be used as a density function if k is suitably chosen?

2-18. Can $ke^{-|x|}$ be used as a density function? If so, determine k and the corresponding distribution function.

2-19. A discrete random variable X takes on the values 1, 2, 3, ... Can equal probabilities be assigned the possible values? Determine K such that $P(X = j) = Kp^j$ is a proper assignment of probability.

2-20. Let X have a constant density on the interval $[-1,1]$, and zero density outside that interval. Determine the density and distribution functions of $Y = X^2$.

2-21. Determine the distribution and density functions of $Z = |X|$, where X is the random variable of Problem 2-20.

2-22. Determine the distribution of probability for $Y = X^2 - 7X + 10$, where X denotes the number of points thrown in a toss of a die with equally likely faces.

2-23. Let X be a random variable with the distribution function

$$F(x) = \begin{cases} 0, & x < 0 \\ x^2, & 0 \leq x \leq 1 \\ 1, & x > 1. \end{cases}$$

Determine the distribution function of $Y = X^2$.

2-24. Let the distribution function $F(x)$ of a random variable X be strictly monotonic, and determine the distribution function of the random variable $Y = F(X)$.

2-25. Let X have the strictly monotonic distribution function $F(x)$, and let $G(x)$ be another strictly monotonically increasing function. Show that the random variable $G^{-1}(F(X))$ has the distribution function $G(x)$. (The function $G^{-1}(u)$ is the inverse of the function $G(x)$, having the property $G^{-1}(G(x)) = x$.)

2.2 Expectation

There is a close analogy between the notions of probability distribution and distribution of mass. In particular, the distribution of probability in the space $(-\infty, \infty)$ of values of a random variable is analogous to a distribution of a finite amount of mass along a line—a linear mass distribution. If $M(x)$ is defined to be the amount of mass to the left of, or at, the point x, the quantity $M(\infty)$ is the total mass, and the proportion $M(x)/M(\infty)$ has the properties of a probability distribution function. A discrete probability distribution would correspond to a discrete mass distribution; for example, to beads situated on an infinitely thin, stiff wire at points whose coordinates are the possible values of the random variable, the mass of a bead being proportional to the probability of the corresponding value. A continuous probability distribution is analogous to a straight wire of variable density, the mass density at any point being proportional to the probability density at that point. Indeed, a mass density is computed from a mass distribution function $M(x)$ exactly as a probability density is computed from a probability distribution function, that is, by differentiation.

The average that is to be defined now is the analogue in a probability distribution on $(-\infty, \infty)$ of the *center of gravity* of the corresponding mass distribution. It is a measure that describes the location or centering of the distribution. (It is not the only measure of location; the median, for example, defined in §2.1.2, is also a measure of location. The median seems to have little application to mass distributions, but in that case would be the point such that half the total mass is on either side of it.) In the case of a probability distribution, the "center of gravity" will be called the *expectation*, the *expected value*, the *mean*, the *mean value*, or sometimes just the *average value*.

The expectation of a random variable will first be defined for the discrete case and then extended to the general case by a limiting process.

2.2.1 The Discrete Case. Consider a discrete random variable X with possible values $x_1, x_2, \cdots$ and corresponding probabilities $p_1, p_2, \cdots$. The expected value of X is then defined to be the following weighted sum of its values:

$$E(X) = \sum_i x_i p_i.$$

The symbol μ or the more specific μ_X will also be used for expectation. The weights are just the probabilities, and this weighted sum is the analogue of the first moment of a mass distribution. Since the probabilities p_i are "proportions," their sum being 1, the expected value is actually on *average* first moment. It corresponds to the formula

$$\text{Center of gravity} = \frac{\sum x_i m_i}{\sum m_i}$$

for a distribution of masses $m_1, m_2, \cdots$, at points $x_1, x_2, \ldots$.

Example 2–17. Let X be 0 or 1 according as a coin falls Tails or Heads. Assuming

$$P(\text{Heads}) = P(\text{Tails}) = 1/2,$$

we have

$$E(X) = 1 \cdot P(X = 1) + 0 \cdot P(X = 0) = 1/2.$$

It is immediately evident that the "expected" value of X need not be one of its possible values.

Examples 2–18. A coin is tossed repeatedly until Heads appears; let X denote the number of necessary tosses. The possible values of X are the positive integers $1, 2, \cdots$, and for a fair coin the probability function is

$$\begin{aligned} P(X = k) &= P(\text{1st Heads on } k\text{th toss}) \\ &= (\tfrac{1}{2})^k. \end{aligned}$$

The expectation is then

$$E(X) = \sum_1^\infty kP(X = k) = \sum_1^\infty k(\tfrac{1}{2})^k = 2.$$

PROBLEMS

2–26. Compute the expected value of X and of Y in Problem 2–6.

2–27. Compute the expected number of required tests in locating the one bad tube among five, in Problem 2–7.

2–28. Compute the expected number of correct identifications by the cigarette tester in Problem 2–8.

2–29. Compute the expected number of points assigned to a card drawn at random from a deck of cards, as in Problem 2–9.

2–30. Compute $E(X)$ in Problem 2–10.

2–31. Compute $E(Y)$ and $E(R)$ in Problem 2–11.

2.2.2 The General Definition. Let Ω denote the sample space of an experiment of chance, let $P^{\Omega}(E)$ denote the probability of an event E in the sample space, and let $X(\omega)$ or X denote a random variable defined on Ω.

We assume first that in the space $\mathcal{X}$ of values of X, all the probability is assigned to a finite interval $[a,b]$. We divide this interval by means of partition points x_i:

$$a = x_0 < x_1 < x_2 < \cdots < x_n = b.$$

If we round off all the values of X in the interval $(x_{i-1},x_i]$ to the value x_i, the result is a discrete random variable (an approximation to X) with expected value

$$\sum_{i=1}^{n} x_i P^{\Omega}(x_{i-1} < X(\omega) \leq x_i).$$

The expected value of X is then defined as the limit, if it exists, of such expressions over all partitions of $[a,b]$. That is, if there is a number I such that the approximating sum above can be made arbitrarily close to I by taking a sufficiently fine partition,[2] this number I is the limit of the approximating sums and defines the expected value of X:

$$E(X) = \lim \sum_{i=1}^{n} x_i P^{\Omega}(x_{i-1} < X(\omega) \leq x_i).$$

This is actually an *integral* (a "Lebesgue integral," as opposed to the "Riemann integral" of elementary calculus), and an integral notation is occasionally convenient:

$$\lim \sum_{i=1}^{n} x_i P^{\Omega}(x_{i-1} < g(\omega) \leq x_i) = \int_{\Omega} g(\omega)\, dP^{\Omega}.$$

Thus,

$$E(X(\omega)) = \int_{\Omega} X(\omega)\, dP^{\Omega}.$$

[2]More precisely, the condition would be that corresponding to $\epsilon > 0$ there exists a $\delta > 0$ such that the approximating sum differs from I by less than ϵ if only the maximum subinterval length in the partition is less than δ.

When the range of values of $X(\omega)$ is not finite, the expectation is first defined for a truncated variable:

$$X_{AB}(\omega) = \begin{cases} B, & \text{if } X(\omega) > B, \\ X(\omega), & \text{if } A < X(\omega) \le B, \\ A, & \text{if } X(\omega) \le A, \end{cases}$$

and then for $X(\omega)$ by a limiting process:

$$E(X) = \lim_{\substack{A \to -\infty \\ B \to \infty}} E(X_{AB}).$$

It was shown in §2.1 that a random variable induces in the space of its values a probability distribution, according to the relation:

$$P^{\mathcal{X}}(A) = P^{\Omega}(X(\omega) \text{ falls in } A).$$

The expected value of $X(\omega)$ is really dependent only on this distribution of probability in $\mathcal{X}$; this follows from the fact that

$$P^{\Omega}(x_{i-1} < X(\omega) \le x_i) = P^{\mathcal{X}}(x_{i-1} < x \le x_i).$$

For, then we have

$$E[X(\omega)] = \lim \sum_{i=1}^{n} x_i P^{\mathcal{X}}(x_{i-1} < x \le x_i) = \int_{\mathcal{X}} x \, dP^{\mathcal{X}}.$$

Computation of an expectation as a limit of a sum is not feasible, but fortunately other means are at hand. Indeed, recalling that the probability of a small interval $(x_{i-1}, x_i]$ is approximately $f(x_i)$ times the width of the interval, in the continuous case, we should not be surprised to find that $E(X)$ reduces to an ordinary integral in that case. We shall not prove here the necessary theorems but rather base our computations on the following results:[3]

1. If the integral on the right exists (as an improper Riemann-Stieltjes integral),

$$\int_{\mathcal{X}} g(x) \, dP^{\mathcal{X}} = \int_{-\infty}^{\infty} g(x) \, dF_X(x),$$

where $F_X(x)$ is the distribution function defined by $P^{\mathcal{X}}$, namely, $P^{\mathcal{X}}(X \le x)$.

2. If X is a continuous random variable with density $f_X(x)$,

$$\int_{-\infty}^{\infty} g(x) \, dF_X(x) = \int_{-\infty}^{\infty} g(x) f_X(x) \, dx.$$

[3]These results are discussed in Reference [4], §7.4–7.5. Results (2) and (3) are discussed also in Franklin, *Treatise on Advanced Calculus*, Wiley, New York, 1940, Chapter 8. The Riemann-Stieltjes integral is defined much as is the ordinary Riemann integral except that the interval length $x_i - x_{i-1}$ in the approximating sums is replaced by $g(x_i) - g(x_{i-1})$ for a given "integrator function" $g(x)$:

$$\int_a^b f(x) \, dg(x) = \lim \sum_{i=1}^{n} f(\xi_i)[g(x_i) - g(x_{i-1})],$$

where ξ_i is a point on $[x_{i-1}, x_i]$ and the limit is taken over partitions of $[a,b]$.

3. If X is a discrete random variable with $p_i = P(X = x_i)$,

$$\int_{-\infty}^{\infty} g(x)\, dF_X(x) = \sum_i g(x_i)p_i.$$

These results provide the necessary means of computation of the expected value of a random variable:

$$E(X) = \int_{-\infty}^{\infty} x\, dF_X(x).$$

In the discrete case this reduces to the expression given in the preceding section:

$$E(X) = \sum_i x_i P(X = x_i) \qquad \text{(discrete case)},$$

and in the continuous case to

$$E(X) = \int_{-\infty}^{\infty} x f_X(x)\, dx \qquad \text{(continuous case)}.$$

Example 2–19. Let X be non-negative, with distribution function $1 - \exp(-x)$ for $x \geq 0$. The corresponding density function is $f_X(x) = \exp(-x)$ for $x > 0$, and the expected value of X is then

$$E(X) = \int_0^{\infty} xe^{-x}\, dx = 1.$$

Example 2–20. Let X have the distribution function $1 - 0.8\exp(-x)$, for $x \geq 0$ (and zero for $x < 0$). This defines a special case of the distribution in Example 2–11; there is a jump of 0.2 at $x = 0$, and from there on the distribution is continuous with density $0.8\exp(-x)$. The expectation is computed by calculating separately the moments of the discrete and continuous parts and adding these together:

$$E(X) = 0 \cdot P(X = 0) + \int_0^{\infty} 0.8xe^{-x}\, dx = 0.8.$$

An expected value may fail to exist as a finite limit if too much probability is assigned to large values of the random variable. Because, in considering the integrals over an infinite range, we take limits as a finite range is extended to $+\infty$ and to $-\infty$ independently, there is no provision for cancellation of large positive and large negative moments. That is, integrals must converge absolutely in order for an expectation, as defined, to be finite.

Example 2–21. Consider the density function

$$f(x) = \frac{1}{\pi(x^2 + 1)}.$$

Since

$$\lim_{A \to \infty} \int_0^A \frac{x}{\pi(x^2 + 1)}\, dx = \lim_{A \to \infty} \frac{1}{2\pi} \log(A^2 + 1) = \infty,$$

we say that the expectation is undefined for this distribution. Even though the total area under the graph of $f(x)$ is finite, there is too much probability in the tails for the integral to remain convergent when the additional factor x is inserted.

PROBLEMS

2–32. Compute $E(X)$ for the random variable X in Problem 2–12.
2–33. Compute $E(X)$ for the random variable X in Problem 2–14.
2–34. Compute the expected values of θ and ϕ in Example 2–10.
2–35. Let $f(x)$ be the density function of a random variable X, and assume that $f(x)$ is symmetrical about the value $x = k$. That is, assume that $f(k + x) = f(k - x)$ for all x. Show that if $E(X)$ exists, it is equal to k.
2–36. Determine the expected value of a random variable with density function $K \exp(-x^2)$.

2.2.3 Functions of a Random Variable. If $Y = g(X)$, which is short for $Y(\omega) = g(X(\omega))$, the expected value of Y can be expressed as an integral over Ω, as an integral over $\mathcal{Y}$, or as an integral over $\mathcal{X}$, using the notation of §2.1.5. We defined in that section the probability of any set of real numbers —values of Y—as follows:

$$P^{\mathcal{Y}}(B) = P^{\mathcal{X}}(g(X) \text{ in } B) = P^{\Omega}(g(X(\omega)) \text{ in } B).$$

Consequently,

$$P^{\Omega}(y_{i-1} < g(X(\omega)) \leq y_i) = P^{\mathcal{X}}(y_{i-1} < g(x) \leq y_i) = P^{\mathcal{Y}}(y_{i-1} < y \leq y_i).$$

It then follows that

$$\begin{aligned} E[g(X(\omega))] &= \lim \textstyle\sum y_i P^{\Omega}(y_{i-1} < g(X(\omega)) \leq y_i) = \displaystyle\int_{\Omega} g(X(\omega))\, dP^{\Omega} \\ &= \lim \textstyle\sum y_i P^{\mathcal{X}}(y_{i-1} < g(x) \leq y_i) = \displaystyle\int_{\mathcal{X}} g(x)\, dP^{\mathcal{X}} \\ &= \lim \textstyle\sum y_i P^{\mathcal{Y}}(y_{i-1} < y \leq y_i) = \displaystyle\int_{\mathcal{Y}} y\, dP^{\mathcal{Y}}. \end{aligned}$$

Applying the computation formula of result (1) on page 53 to the last two integrals, we obtain:

$$E(Y) = E[g(X(\omega))] = \int_{-\infty}^{\infty} y\, dF_Y(y) = \int_{-\infty}^{\infty} g(x)\, dF_X(x).$$

The latter integral provides what we shall find to be a useful method of calculation which avoids the computation of the distribution function of Y. Using results (2) and (3) of page 53, we obtain further:

$$E(Y) = \sum_j y_j P(Y = y_j) = \sum_i g(x_i) P(X = x_i),$$

for the discrete case, and

$$E(Y) = \int_{-\infty}^{\infty} y f_Y(y)\, dy = \int_{-\infty}^{\infty} g(x) f_X(x)\, dx,$$

for the continuous case.

Example 2–22. A cube has its six sides colored Red, White, Blue, Green, Yellow, and Violet. It is assumed that these six sides are equally likely to show, when the cube is tossed. That is, we consider a probability space with elementary outcomes R, W, B, G, Y, V and probabilities 1/6 for each of these outcomes; this space is Ω.

Consider now the random variable that assigns the number 1 to R and W, the number 2 to G and B, and the number 3 to Y and V:

$$\begin{aligned} X(R) &= X(W) = 1; \\ X(G) &= X(B) = 2; \\ X(Y) &= X(V) = 3 \end{aligned}$$

The space $\mathcal{X}$ of values of $X(\omega)$ can be thought of as consisting of the numbers 1, 2, and 3, each with probability 1/3, the distribution induced by $X(\omega)$ from that on Ω.

Next let $Y = (X - 2)^2$. The values $X = 1$ and $X = 3$ give rise to $Y = 1$; the value $X = 2$, to $Y = 0$. Thus $\mathcal{Y}$ consists of the values 1 and 0 with probabilities 2/3 and 1/3, respectively. There are then three possible computations of

$$E(Y) = E[(X - 2)^2] = E[(X(\omega) - 2)^2].$$

Using the distribution on Ω:

$$\tfrac{1}{6}\,[X(R) - 2]^2 + \cdots + \tfrac{1}{6}\,[X(V) - 2]^2 = \tfrac{2}{3};$$

using the distribution on $\mathcal{X}$:

$$\tfrac{1}{3}\,(1 - 2)^2 + \tfrac{1}{3}\,(2 - 2)^2 + \tfrac{1}{3}\,(3 - 2)^2 = \tfrac{2}{3};$$

or, using the distribution on $\mathcal{Y}$:

$$1 \cdot \tfrac{2}{3} + 0 \cdot \tfrac{1}{3} = \tfrac{2}{3}.$$

Following the mappings and transfers of probability makes it clear in this example that the computations are equivalent.

Example 2–23. Let X have the distribution function

$$F_X(x) = \begin{cases} 0, & x < 0, \\ x, & 0 \le x \le 1, \\ 1, & x > 1. \end{cases}$$

(This was the model used for the spinning pointer, Example 2–4.) Consider now the random variable $Y = \sqrt{X}$, the positive square root of X. The distribution function of Y can be computed from the distribution function of X:

$$F_Y(y) = P(\sqrt{X} \le y) = P(X \le y^2) = \begin{cases} 0, & y < 0, \\ y^2, & 0 \le y \le 1, \\ 1, & y > 1. \end{cases}$$

Observe that $\sqrt{X} \leq y$ is equivalent to $X \leq y^2$ because only the positive square root is considered. The expected value of Y can be computed in either of two ways: from the distribution of Y as just computed or from the distribution of X. That is,

$$E(Y) = \int_{-\infty}^{\infty} y f_Y(y)\, dy = \int_0^1 y \cdot 2y\, dy = \tfrac{2}{3},$$

or

$$E(Y) = E(\sqrt{X}) = \int_{-\infty}^{\infty} \sqrt{x} f_X(x)\, dx = \int_0^1 \sqrt{x}\, dx = \tfrac{2}{3}.$$

2.2.4 Properties of Expectations. A random variable is called *simple* if it takes on only a finite set of values, and the expectation of a simple random variable is especially easy to express. If $X(\omega)$ defined on Ω takes on the values $x_1, \ldots, x_k$ with probabilities $p_1, \ldots, p_k$, then

$$E[X(\omega)] = \sum_{i=1}^{k} x_i p_i.$$

Simple random variables are important because, first, theorems are usually easy to establish for simple random variables, and second, all useful random variables can be expressed as limits of sequences of simple random variables. It is a fact that will not be established here (cf. Reference [13], page 107) that the class of functions $X(\omega)$ so expressible is precisely the class of "measurable" functions to which the term *random variable* is restricted.

Thus, properties of random variables are often proved by first proving them for simple random variables and then expressing more general random variables as limits of sequences of simple ones. For instance, if $X(\omega)$ and $Y(\omega)$ are simple random variables, we can readily establish that

$$E[X(\omega) + Y(\omega)] = E[X(\omega)] + E[Y(\omega)].$$

For, if the values of X are $x_1, \ldots, x_k$ with probabilities $p_1, \ldots, p_k$, and the values of Y are $y_1, \ldots, y_m$ with probabilities $q_m, \ldots, q_m$, the values of $X + Y$ are $x_i + y_j$ for all possible pairings of values of X and of Y. So $X + Y$ is a simple random variable with expectation

$$\begin{aligned} E(X + Y) &= \sum_{i=1}^{k} \sum_{j=1}^{m} (x_i + y_j) P(X = x_i \text{ and } Y = y_j) \\ &= \sum_{i=1}^{k} x_i \sum_{j=1}^{m} P(X = x_i \text{ and } Y = y_j) \\ &\qquad + \sum_{j=1}^{m} y_j \sum_{i=1}^{k} P(X = x_i \text{ and } Y = y_j) \\ &= \sum_{i=1}^{k} x_i P(X = x_i) + \sum_{j=1}^{m} y_j P(Y = y_j) \\ &= E[X(\omega)] + E[Y(\omega)]. \end{aligned}$$

By expressing arbitrary random variables as limits of sequences of elementary random variables, this additivity condition can be extended to the general case with the following kind of manipulation:

$$\begin{aligned} E(X + Y) = E[\lim (X_n + Y_n)] &= \lim E(X_n + Y_n) \\ &= \lim E(X_n) + \lim E(Y_n) \\ &= E(X) + E(Y). \end{aligned}$$

To carry this through, it is necessary to know that $\lim E(X_n) = E(\lim X_n)$, a point we do not take up. (Cf. Reference [13], §7.1 and §7.2.)

It is possible in similar fashion to show that $E(aX) = aE(X)$ for any constant a. Combining this property of homogeneity with the above additivity property, we obtain the *linearity* of the expectation

$$E[aX + bY] = aE(X) + bE(Y).$$

This property of an ordinary (Riemann) integral is usually discussed in calculus; that it holds for the integral called *expectation*, we have shown for simple random variables, and we shall assume that it is valid in general.

Another useful property of expectations is this:

$$P[X(\omega) \geq 0] = 1 \quad \text{implies} \quad E[X(\omega)] \geq 0.$$

This property is immediately clear from the definition of expectation. The only terms one would need to include in the approximating sums are those corresponding to positive partition points x_i, and so all of the approximating sums and the limit would be non-negative. Using this property together with the additivity of the expectation yields the following:

$$P[X(\omega) \leq Y(\omega)] = 1 \quad \text{implies} \quad E[X(\omega)] \leq E[Y(\omega)].$$

For, if $X \leq Y$, the random variable $Y - X \geq 0$, and therefore $E(Y - X) = E(Y) - E(X) \geq 0$.

Another useful property of expectations is obtained by observing that since $X \leq |X|$ and $-X \leq |X|$,

$$E(X) \leq E(|X|) \qquad \text{and} \qquad E(-X) = -E(X) \leq E(|X|).$$

These inequalities together imply that

$$|E(X)| \leq E(|X|).$$

Example 2–24. Denoting $E(X)$ by μ, we have from the linearity property:

$$E(X - \mu) = E(X) + E(-\mu) = E(X) - E(\mu).$$

A constant is a simple random variable that is extremely simple, and its expectation is that constant; hence, $E(\mu) = \mu$, and therefore

$$E(X - \mu) = 0.$$

In terms of the analogy between mass and probability, this result corresponds to the fact that the "first moment" of a mass distribution about its center of gravity is zero; the center of gravity is the balance point.

PROBLEMS

2–37. Let X have a constant density function over $[-1,1]$, with zero density outside that interval. Determine $E(X^2)$ in two ways. (Cf. Problem 2–20.)

2–38. Compute $E(|X|)$ for the random variable X of Problem 2–37.

2–39. Let θ denote the colatitude coordinate of Example 2–10, page 43, and compute $E(\cos\theta)$ in two ways. Compute also $E(\cos^2\theta)$.

2–40. Let X be a discrete random variable with the distribution of X in Example 2–18, page 51, and try to compute $E(2^X)$.

2–41. Show that $E(AX) = AE(X)$, where A is a constant and X is a simple random variable.

2–42. Three chips are drawn from a bowl containing five chips numbered 1, 2, 3, 4, 5. The probability space Ω consists of the ten distinct outcomes, each with probability 1/10. Let $X(\omega)$ denote the smallest and $Y(\omega)$ the largest of the numbers drawn. Show by direct computation of each of the expectations that

$$E[X(\omega) + Y(\omega)] = E[X(\omega)] + E[Y(\omega)].$$

2–43. For any set A of real numbers define $I_A(x) = 1$ for x in A and 0 for x not in A. Show that

$$P(A) = E[I_A(X)] = \int_A dF_X(x).$$

2–44. Show that if $P(A) = 0$, then for any $g(x)$ defined (and finite) over A:

$$\int_A g(x)\, dF_X(x) = E[I_A(X)g(X)] = 0.$$

2.3 Moments and Generating Functions

The quantity $E[(X - b)^k]$, when it exists, is called the *kth moment* of the random variable X (or of its distribution) about the point b. In particular, then, the expectation of a random variable is its first moment about $x = 0$, and the first moment of a random variable about its expectation was seen in Example 2–24 to be zero. The first moment of a distribution corresponds to its center of gravity and is therefore a measure of "centering" or "location" of a distribution.

Moments of a distribution about its expectation are called *central* moments. The second central moment, in particular, is called the *variance* of the distribution, written either var X or σ_X^2:

$$\text{var } X = \sigma_X^2 = E[(X - E(X))^2].$$

Second moments about other points can be expressed in terms of the variance; to see this, we first write

$$\begin{aligned} E[(X-a)^2] &= E[(X - \mu + \mu - a)^2] \\ &= E[(X-\mu)^2] + 2(\mu - a)E(X - \mu) + (\mu - a)^2, \end{aligned}$$

using the fact that $(\mu - a)$ is a constant. If $\mu = E(X)$, then $E(X - \mu) = 0$, and the first term on the right is var X:

$$E[(X - a)^2] = \text{var } X + (\mu - a)^2.$$

Since the second term on the right is non-negative, this second moment about a is always at least as large as var X. The variance is then the smallest second moment, a fact that will be exploited repeatedly.

The second moment relation just derived is referred to as the "parallel axis theorem," after its counterpart in the case of a mass distribution. A special case, $a = 0$, is very handy:

$$E(X^2) = \text{var } X + [E(X)]^2,$$

or equivalently

$$\text{var } X = E(X^2) - [E(X)]^2.$$

Notice that the mean of the square is not usually equal to the square of the mean; the difference is var X.

The transformation $Y = aX + b$, called *linear*, combines a change of scale and a translation. Since $E(Y) = aE(X) + b$, it follows that

$$\text{var } Y = E[(aX + b - aE(X) - b)^2] = a^2E[(X - E(X))^2] = a^2 \text{ var } X.$$

The variance is a measure of spread or dispersion in a distribution. If probability 1 is concentrated at a single value, the variance of the distribution is zero. If probability is spread over a wide range, the variance is large.

Since the variance is an expected square, the units of the variance are the square of the units of X. For example, if X is a number of inches, the units of var X are square inches. To obtain a measure of dispersion with the same units as X, one defines the *standard deviation* as the positive square root of the variance:

$$\sigma_X = \sqrt{\sigma_X^2}.$$

Clearly, if $Y = aX + b$, $\sigma_Y = |a|\sigma_X$.

The term *absolute* moment is used to describe $E(|X - a|^k)$. The first absolute moment, $E(|X - a|)$, is sometimes used as a measure of dispersion of probability. It is not so simple to work with mathematically as the variance. It is shown in Problem 2–54 that the first absolute moment is smallest about the distribution median.

Example 2–25. Consider a continuous random variable X with the density function $\exp(-x)$ for $x > 0$ (and zero for $x < 0$). The expected square is

$$E(X^2) = \int_0^\infty x^2 e^{-x}\, dx = 2,$$

and the expected value,

$$E(X) = \int_0^\infty xe^{-x}\,dx = 1.$$

The variance is therefore $2 - 1^2 = 1$. The median of the distribution is log 2, and the first absolute moment about this value is

$$\begin{aligned} E(|X - \log 2|) &= \int_0^{\log 2} (\log 2 - x)e^{-x}\,dx + \int_{\log 2}^\infty (x - \log 2)e^{-x}\,dx \\ &= \log 2. \end{aligned}$$

2.3.1 The Chebyshev and Related Inequalities. The Chebyshev inequality is a useful theoretical tool as well as a relation that shows in just what sense the variance of a distribution measures the dispersion of probability. It follows from the basic inequality we consider first.

Basic Inequality. If $h(x) \geq 0$ for all x, and if for all x in a set A,

$$h(x) \geq b > 0,$$

then

$$P(X \text{ in } A) \leq \frac{1}{b} E[h(X)].$$

The proof of this inequality is as follows: The integral that expresses $E[h(X)]$ is broken into two parts:

$$E[h(X)] = \int_A h(x)\,dF_X(x) + \int_{\bar{A}} h(x)\,dF_X(x).$$

If the second term is dropped, the right-hand side becomes smaller—or certainly no greater than before; if in the first term $h(x)$ is replaced by b, which is less than or equal to $h(x)$ on A, again the right-hand side does not increase. Hence,

$$E[h(X)] \geq b\int_A dF_X(x) = bP(X \text{ in } A).$$

Upon dividing by b, we obtain the basic inequality.

The basic inequality is used to obtain Chebyshev's inequality by an appropriate choice of $h(x)$ and A. Let $h(x) = (x - \mu)^2$, which is non-negative, and let A denote the set of x's such that $|x - \mu| \geq c$. Then,

$$P(|X - \mu| \geq c) \leq \frac{1}{c^2} E(X - \mu)^2 = \frac{\sigma^2}{c^2}$$

This is known as Chebyshev's inequality.

Example 2–26. If Z has the distribution function of Table I, in which the mean is zero and the variance 1, we have

$$P(|Z - \mu_Z| \geq 3\sigma_Z) = 1 - P(-3 < Z < 3) \doteq 0.0026,$$

which is certainly less than $(1/3)^2 = 1/9$.

Example 2–27. If X takes on the values 1 and -1, each with probability 1/2, we find $E(X) = 0$ and var $X = 1$. Then

$$P(|X - \mu_X| \geq \sigma_X) = 1 - P(-1 < X < 1) = 1,$$

which shows that in general the inequality cannot be improved without imposing restrictions on the distribution in addition to existence of the variance.

Example 2–28. The following result is occasionally useful: If $E(X) = E(X^2) = 0$, the $P(X = 0) = 1$. This follows from the Chebyshev inequality: for any integer n we have

$$P\left(|X| > \frac{1}{n}\right) \leq n^2 E(X^2) = 0,$$

and therefore

$$P(|X| > 0) = \lim_{n\to\infty} P\left(|X| > \frac{1}{n}\right) = 0.$$

Clearly, also, if $E(X) = K$ and var $X = 0$, then $X = K$ with probability 1. [To obtain this, set $Y = X - E(X)$.] Thus a variance of zero really does mean that probability is not spread at all but concentrated in a single point.

PROBLEMS

2–45. Compute the variance of X and the variance of Y in Problem 2–6.
2–46. Compute the variance of Y and the variance of R in Problem 2–11.
2–47. Compute the variance of X in Problem 2–12.
2–48. Compute the variance of X in Problem 2–14.
2–49. Compute the variance of X in Example 2–20, page 54.
2–50. Let X have mean μ and variance σ^2. Show the following:
(a) The "standardizing" transformation $Y = (X - \mu)/\sigma$ yields a random variable with zero mean and unit variance.
(b) $E[(X - \mu)^3] = E(X^3) - 3\mu\sigma^2 - \mu^3$.
2–51. The random variable X takes on the possible values $-a$, 0, and $+a$ with probabilities 1/8, 3/4, and 1/8, respectively. Compute $P(|X| \geq 2\sigma)$ and compare with the bound for this probability given by Chebyshev's inequality.
2–52. For the family of "chi-square" distributions whose percentiles are given in Table II, the mean is the number of "degrees of freedom" and the variance is twice that number. Compute $P(|X - 4| > 8)$ for the case of four degrees of freedom, and compare this result with the bound given by Chebyshev's inequality.

2–53. Show that if $0 < K < \sigma_X$, then $P(|X| > K) > 0$. [*Hint:* Use the fact that $\sigma_X^2 \leq E(X^2)$, splitting the integral expression for $E(X^2)$ into two terms, one an integral over $|x| \leq K$ and one over $|x| > K$, to show that

$$\int_{|x|>K} x^2\, dF(x) > 0.$$

Then use Problem 2–44.]

2–54. Show that $E(|X - a|)$ is a minimum when a is the median of the distribution of the continuous variable X. [*Hint:* Write this expectation as an integral, break it into two parts (over $x \leq a$ and $x > a$), and then minimize by setting the derivative with respect to a equal to zero.

2.3.2 Moment Generating Functions. The *moment generating function* of the distribution of a random variable X is formally defined as follows:

$$\psi(t) = E(e^{tX}) = \int_{-\infty}^{\infty} e^{tx}\, dF_X(x).$$

This expected value depends on the choice of t. For $t = 0$, it always exists: $\psi(0) = 1$. For some distributions it exists for all t, and for others, only for a limited range of values of t.

Replacing the exponential function by its power series expansion and then interchanging summation and integration, we obtain:

$$\psi(t) = \int_{-\infty}^{\infty} \sum_{k=0}^{\infty} \frac{(tx)^k}{k!}\, dF(x) = \sum_{k=0}^{\infty} \frac{t^k}{k!} \int_{-\infty}^{\infty} x^k\, dF(x)$$

$$= \sum_{k=0}^{\infty} E(X^k) \frac{t^k}{k!}.$$

In cases in which the interchange is permitted, then, the kth moment of a distribution about $x = 0$ is the coefficient of $t^k/k!$ in the series expansion of the moment generating function:

$$E(X^k) = \psi^{(k)}(0).$$

This is the usual Maclaurin expansion coefficient, but it can also be seen to be correct by differentiating[1] $\psi(t)$, k times:

$$\frac{d^k}{dt^k}\{E(e^{tX})\} = E(X^k e^{tX})$$

and substituting $t = 0$.

Example 2–29. Consider the random variable X which takes the value 1 with probability p and the value 0 with probability $q = 1 - p$. In this case the moments are readily calculated directly:

$$E(X^k) = 1^k \cdot p + 0^k \cdot q = p \qquad (k = 1,2,\ldots).$$

[1]Differentiating inside $E(\cdot)$ is really differentiating under an integral sign, which is permitted when the derivative of the integrand exists and is bounded by an integrable function (cf. Reference [13], page 126).

The moment generating function is

$$\begin{aligned}\psi(t) = E(e^{tX}) &= e^{t\cdot 1}p + e^{t\cdot 0}q = pe^{t} + q \\ &= p\left(1 + \frac{t}{1!} + \frac{t^2}{2!} + \cdots\right) + q \\ &= 1 + p\frac{t}{1!} + p\frac{t^2}{2!} + \cdots\end{aligned}$$

The coefficients of $t^k/k!$ are indeed the moments $E(X^k)$.

Example 2–30. Consider the distribution for X defined by

$$F(x) = \begin{cases} 0, & \text{for } x < 0 \\ 1 - \dfrac{e^{-x}}{4}, & \text{for } x \geq 0. \end{cases}$$

This has a jump of 3/4 at $x = 0$, indicating that $P(X = 0)$ is 3/4 and that $P(X > 0)$ is 1/4. The moment generating function is

$$\begin{aligned}\psi(t) &= \frac{3}{4}e^{t\cdot 0} + \int_0^\infty e^{tx}\cdot\frac{e^{-x}}{4}\,dx = \frac{3}{4} + \frac{1}{4}(1-t)^{-1} \\ &= 1 + \frac{1}{4}t + \frac{1}{2}\frac{t^2}{2!} + \frac{3}{2}\frac{t^3}{3!} + \cdots\end{aligned}$$

From this we can read $E(X) = 1/4$, $E(X^2) = 1/2$, and so on. The variance can then be computed from these:

$$\text{var } X = E(X^2) - [E(X)^2] = \tfrac{1}{2} - \tfrac{1}{16} = \tfrac{7}{16}.$$

The integral and the power series involved here are convergent only for $|t| < 1$, but of course it is only necessary to have $\psi(t)$ defined in a neighborhood of $t = 0$.

Another type of generating function yields what are called the *factorial moments:*

$$E[X(X-1)(X-2)\cdots(X-k+1)].$$

The generating function for these moments is

$$\eta(t) = E(t^X) = \int_{-\infty}^{\infty} t^x\,dF(x).$$

Differentiating k times under the integral sign (when this is permitted), one finds

$$\eta^{(k)}(1) = \left.\frac{d^k}{dt^k}E(t^X)\right|_{t=1} = E[X(X-1)\cdots(X-k+1)].$$

The variance can be computed from the first two factorial moments:

$$\text{var } X = E[X(X-1)] + E(X) - [E(X)]^2.$$

The moment generating and the factorial moment generating functions are related:

$$\eta(t) = E(t^X) = E(e^{X \log t}) = \psi(\log t).$$

Which one to use is often a matter of convenience, depending on the form of the distribution. Sometimes the factor t^x is readily combined with $dF(x)$, and sometimes e^{tx} is easier to handle.

Example 2–31. Consider again (as in Example 2–29) the distribution that puts probability p at $x = 1$ and probability $q = 1 - p$ at $x = 0$. For this distribution,

$$\eta(t) = t^1 \cdot p + t^0 \cdot q = pt + q.$$

Then $\eta'(t) = p$, and all higher derivatives are zero. Thus $E(X) = p$ and $E(X^2 - X) = 0$, so that

$$\text{var } X = 0 + p - p^2 = pq.$$

2.3.3 The Characteristic Function. Closely related to the moment generating functions of the preceding section is the *characteristic function* of a distribution:

$$\begin{aligned}\phi(t) = E(e^{itX}) &= \int_{-\infty}^{\infty} e^{itx} dF(x) \\ &= \int_{-\infty}^{\infty} \cos tx \, dF(x) + i \int_{-\infty}^{\infty} \sin tx \, dF(x).\end{aligned}$$

These integrands are bounded (and continuous) for all t, and the integrals therefore always exists. This is the reason why characteristic functions are used in preference to moment generating functions, which may or may not exist, in the mathematics of probability theory.

Formally, of course, $\phi(t) = \psi(it)$, and so the characteristic function also "generates moments":

$$E(X^k) = i^{-k}\phi^{(k)}(0),$$

provided these moments exist. However, the major use of the characteristic function is in connection with sums of independent random variables, to be taken up in Chapter 4.

In using characteristic functions, one or more of the following theorems are called upon; we shall simply state these, referring for proofs to References [15], pages 400 ff., and [4], pages 93 ff.

1. If $x - h$ and $x + h$ are any two points of continuity of $F(x)$, its increment over $(x - h, x + h)$ is given by the *inversion formula:*

$$F(x + h) - F(x - h) = \lim_{T \to \infty} \frac{1}{\pi} \int_{-T}^{T} \frac{\sin ht}{t} e^{-itx}\phi(t) \, dt.$$

2. To each characteristic function there corresponds a unique distribution function having that characteristic function.

3. If distribution functions $\{F_n(x)\}$ converge to a distribution function $F(x)$ for all x at which F is continuous, the functions $\{\phi_n(t)\}$ converge to the characteristic function of $F(x)$. Conversely, if the characteristic functions $\{\phi_n(t)\}$ converge at each t to $\phi(t)$ which is continuous at $t = 0$, then $\phi(t)$ is a characteristic function, and the corresponding distribution functions $\{F_n(x)\}$ converge to the distribution function determined by $\phi(t)$.

4. If $E(|X|^k)$ exists, so does $E(|X|^j)$ for $j = 0, 1, \ldots, k - 1$, and

$$\phi(t) = 1 + E(X)(it) + E(X^2)\frac{(it)^2}{2!} + \cdots + E(X^k)\frac{(it)^k}{k!} + o(t^k),$$

where $o(u)$ denotes a function such that $o(u)/u \to 0$ as $u \to 0$.

The fact that there is an inversion formula, (1), implies the uniqueness property (2). Other equivalent inversion formulas are used; cf. Reference [15], pages 400 ff. Property (3) is referred to as the "continuity theorem" for characteristic functions. Property (4) relates existence of moments to the smoothness of the characteristic function.

Example 2–32. Consider again the density function of Example 2–21:

$$f(x) = \frac{1}{\pi(1 + x^2)}.$$

The characteristic function of the distribution defined by this density is

$$\phi(t) = \frac{1}{\pi}\int_{-\infty}^{\infty} \frac{\cos tx}{1 + x^2}\,dx + \frac{i}{\pi}\int_{-\infty}^{\infty} \frac{\sin tx}{1 + x^2}\,dx = e^{-|t|}.$$

(The evaluation of these integrals is not elementary, but their values can be found in tables of definite integrals.) This characteristic function is not differentiable at $t = 0$, corresponding to the fact that not even the first moment of the distribution exists.

PROBLEMS

2–55. A random variable X takes the value k with probability 1 and any other value with probability 0. Determine the moment generating function and from it the moments about 0. Determine also the variance and the third moment about the mean.

2–56. Compute the moment generating function of the distribution defined by the density function

$$f(x) = xe^{-x}, \quad x > 0.$$

Expand it in a power series and read the moments.

2–57. Compute the factorial moment generating function of the discrete distribution defined by the probability function

$$P(X = k) = p(1 - p)^k, \quad k = 0, 1, \ldots,$$

where $0 < p < 1$. Show that $E(1) = 1$, $E(X) = (1 - p)/p$, and var $X = (1 - p)/p^2$.

2–58. Express the characteristic function of the random variable $Y = aX + b$ in terms of the characteristic function of X.

2–59. Show that if X is discrete with possible values 0, 1, 2,..., the coefficient of t^k in the series expansion of the factorial moment generating function is $P(X = k)$.

2–60. Determine the characteristic function of the family of distributions defined by the density function

$$f(x;a,m) = \frac{a/\pi}{(x - m)^2 + a^2}.$$

(Use the result of Example 2–32.)

2–61. Use the "basic inequality" of §2.3.1, with suitably chosen $h(x)$ and A, to show that $P(X \leq 0) \leq E(e^{tX})$ for $t < 0$.

2.4 Some Useful Discrete Models

In this section are presented certain discrete probability distributions in one dimension which find frequent application. They are really *classes* of distributions, the probability functions of the distributions in a given class being expressed by a single formula containing one or more "parameters." The assignment of specific values to the parameters defines a specific distribution in the class. The parameters serve to "index" the class.

2.4.1 The Bernoulli Distribution. Aside from the "singular" distribution, which assigns all probability to a single value, the simplest distribution is that in which probability is assigned to just two values. Without loss of generality we can take these two values to be 0 and 1. A random variable X that takes on only the values 0 and 1 is said to be a Bernoulli variable. Its probability function is quite simple:

k	$P(X = k)$
0	$1 - p$
1	p

The choice of a value for the parameter p on the range $0 \leq p \leq 1$ determines a particular member of the class of Bernoulli distributions. The probability function can also be expressed by a convenient formula:

$$P(X = k) = p^k(1 - p)^{1-k}, \quad \text{for } k = 0, 1.$$

The expectation of any function $g(\cdot)$ of a Bernoulli random variable is the sum of two terms:

$$E[g(X)] = g(1)p + g(0)(1 - p).$$

In particular the kth moment about 0, for $k = 1, 2, \ldots,$ is

$$E(X^k) = p,$$

and the moment generating function is

$$\begin{aligned}\psi(t) = E(e^{tX}) &= e^t p + (1 - p)\\ &= 1 + pt + p\frac{t^2}{2!} + \cdots\\ &= \sum_{k=0}^{\infty} E(X^k)\frac{t^k}{k!}.\end{aligned}$$

Any experiment of chance with just two possible outcomes can be coded so that one outcome is given the value 0, and the other, the value 1. Some examples of such experiments are these: A coin falls Heads or Tails; an innoculation takes or does not take; a product is acceptable or defective; a person is male or female; a roulette wheel stops on black or does not stop on black; a team wins or loses a game; and so on.

2.4.2 The Binomial Distribution. A Bernoulli experiment (one with just two possible outcomes) is performed a certain finite number of times in such a way that no one performance or more affect the results of any others. These are called *independent trials* of the Bernoulli experiment. The random variable of interest is the number of times the experiment results in a given one of the two possible outcomes.

To be more specific, let the two outcomes be H and T, with probabilities p and $1 - p$, respectively, and let H be assigned the number 1 and T the number 0. Let X denote the number of H's among the n independent trials —which is also the sum of the 0's and 1's attached to the outcomes of the trials. The values that X can assume are 0, 1, 2, ..., n, and probabilities for these values are computed as follows.

Consider the value $X = k$, resulting when k H's occur among the n trials. These k H's together with $n - k$ T's can occur in any of

$$\frac{n!}{k!(n-k)!} = \binom{n}{k}$$

distinct orderings in the sequence of n trials. The probability for each such ordering is the product (to incorporate the assumed independence) of k p's and $n - k$ q's: $p^k q^{n-k}$, (where $q = 1 - p$). Adding these $\binom{n}{k}$ probabilities, all alike, we obtain the result

$$P(X = k) = \binom{n}{k} p^k q^{n-k}, \qquad k = 0, 1, \ldots, n.$$

Being probabilities for the $n + 1$ possible values of X, these quantities must add up to 1, and that they do is apparent directly from the binomial theorem:

$$\sum_{k=0}^{n} P(X = k) = \sum_{k=0}^{n} \binom{n}{k} p^k q^{n-k} = (p + q)^n = 1^n = 1.$$

The factorial moment generating function of a *binomial distribution*, as the distribution of probability just defined is called, is easily obtained as follows:

$$\eta(t) = E(t^X) = \sum_{k=0}^{n} t^k \binom{n}{k} p^k q^{n-k}$$
$$= \sum_{k=0}^{n} \binom{n}{k} (pt)^k q^{n-k} = (pt + q)^n.$$

The mean and variance can be computed from the first two factorial moments, $\eta'(1)$ and $\eta''(1)$. They are, respectively,

$$E(X) = np \qquad \text{and} \qquad \operatorname{var} X = npq.$$

Example 2–33. Let X denote the number of sixes thrown in 12 tosses of a die. Assuming independence, the "binomial formula" derived above gives

$$P(X = k) = \binom{12}{k}\left(\frac{1}{6}\right)^k\left(\frac{5}{6}\right)^{12-k},$$

since p, the probability of a six in a single toss, is 1/6. The expected number of sixes is

$$E(X) = np = 12 \cdot \tfrac{1}{6} = 2.$$

The variance of the distribution is $npq = 5/3$. The probability of any event described in terms of X can be computed as a suitable sum of binomial probabilities. For instance,

$$P(\text{at least 3 sixes}) = 1 - P(\text{2 or fewer sixes})$$
$$= 1 - \left[\binom{12}{2}\left(\frac{1}{6}\right)^2\left(\frac{5}{6}\right)^{10} + \binom{12}{1}\left(\frac{1}{6}\right)^1\left(\frac{5}{6}\right)^{11} + \binom{12}{0}\left(\frac{1}{6}\right)^0\left(\frac{5}{6}\right)^{12}\right]$$
$$\doteq 0.32.$$

PROBLEMS

2–62. A random variable takes on the values a and b with probabilities p and $1\text{-}p$, respectively. Express this variable as a linear function of a Bernoulli variable and determine its mean, variance, and moment generating function.

2–63. Let X have a probability distribution defined by the density $f(x) = [\pi(1 + x^2)]^{-1}$. Let $Y = 1$ if $X \geq 1$ and $Y = 0$ if $X < 1$. What is the distribution of Y?

2–64. A person attempts predicting the fall of a coin in each of several independent tosses. If he really has no clairvoyant powers and is only guessing, what is the probability that he will predict correctly in four out of four successive trials? In eight or more out of ten successive trials? In at most two out of ten trials?

2–65. The reliability (probability of successful functioning) of a certain automatic cut-off device is assumed to be 11/12. What is the reliability of a system consisting of four such devices so arranged that any one or more would operate properly when necessary?

2–66. Determine the reliability of a certain piece of equipment which consists of four components, each having reliability 0.9, so arranged that each component must work if the equipment is to work.

2–67. Determine the mean and variance of a random variable which is binomially distributed with parameters $n = 100$ and $p = 0.2$.

2–68. What is the expected number of Heads when ten coins are tossed?

2–69. A random variable X is binomially distributed with mean 3 and variance 2. Compute $P(X = 7)$.

2–70. Determine the probability that all of five articles taken from a production line are good, given that the probability of a defective article's being produced is .1. What is the probability that at most one of five has a defect? What is the average number of defective in a lot of 50 articles?

2–71. Carry through the details of the computation of the mean and variance of a binomial distribution from the factorial moment generating function.

2–72. Determine the rth factorial moment of a binomial distribution.

2.4.3 The Hypergeometric Distribution. Closely related to the binomial distribution is the *hypergeometric distribution*. Again one is concerned with the occurrence of some event A or its complement B when an experiment is performed, but in place of independence of trials there is a certain kind of dependence. To be specific, the hypergeometric model arises when the ingredient Bernoulli trials consist of drawing an object from a collection of objects of two kinds, A and B. The drawing is repeated n times, but rather than replace each object drawn before drawing the next, which would result in the binomial model, one makes each selection *from what is left* after the preceding drawings, without replacement. The results of the drawings are clearly not independent.

One might think at first that since drawings are made from different collections, the trials are not identical; but the fact is that they are identical. (Saying that trials or experiments are identical means that the distribution of probability is the same each time, not that the outcomes of different trials are necessarily the same.) When each trial or drawing is considered by itself, the drawing might just as well be from the whole collection initially available, if no information is at hand concerning the results of the previous trials. Thus the absolute probability of the result A in any trial (as opposed to a conditional probability that might be computed, given certain information about earlier trials) is the same as for any other trial. If among N objects there are M of type A, this probability of A is M/N for each trial; the probability of type B is, of course, $1 - M/N = (N - M)/N$.

Example 2–34. Four balls are drawn at random, in succession without replacement, from three black balls and seven white balls in a container. The probability that the third ball drawn is black is 3/10, with no information on the outcomes of the first two trials:

$$\begin{aligned} P(\text{3rd ball black}) &= P(WWB) + P(WBB) + P(BWB) + P(BBB) \\ &= \tfrac{7}{10}\,\tfrac{6}{9}\,\tfrac{3}{8} + \tfrac{7}{10}\,\tfrac{3}{9}\,\tfrac{2}{8} + \tfrac{3}{10}\,\tfrac{7}{9}\,\tfrac{2}{8} + \tfrac{3}{10}\,\tfrac{2}{9}\,\tfrac{1}{8} = \tfrac{3}{10}. \end{aligned}$$

The random variable of interest (the random variable whose distribution is called *hypergeometric*) is the number of objects drawn with property A among the n drawn. Since this variable does not take into account the order in which the objects appear, it is immaterial whether the objects are actually drawn one at a time at random, without replacement, or drawn at random in a bunch. (This matter was discussed in Example 1-36 and Problem 1-35.) The probability function for a hypergeometric random variable X, the number of A's drawn in a bunch of n objects taken from N objects of which M are A's, is as follows:

$$P(X = k) = P(k\ A\text{'s among the } n \text{ drawn}) = \frac{\binom{M}{k}\binom{N-M}{n-k}}{\binom{N}{n}}.$$

This formula holds for all possible values of k. The list of possible values runs from the larger of 0 and $n - (N - M)$ through the integers up to the smaller of n and M, since there could be no more A's or B's drawn than there are in the entire initial collection of N objects. However, since for $r > N$,

$$(N)_r \equiv N(N-1)\cdots 2\cdot 1\cdot 0\cdot(-1)\cdots = 0,$$

it makes sense to define

$$\binom{N}{r} = 0, \quad \text{for } r > N,$$

and with this convention, the formula given above for $P(X = k)$ can be used for any integer from 0 on up, being automatically zero where it must be zero.

The sum of the hypergeometric probabilities must be 1, and this does not require proof, but it is interesting to observe that it can be verified directly by using the binomial theorem. Showing that the sum is 1 is equivalent to showing that

$$\sum_0^N \binom{M}{k}\binom{N-M}{n-k} = \binom{N}{n},$$

and this is seen as follows:

$$\begin{aligned}\sum_0^N \binom{N}{n} t^n &= (1+t)^N = (1+t)^{N-M}(1+t)^M \\ &= \sum_{r=0}^N \binom{N-M}{r} t^r \sum_{s=0}^N \binom{M}{s} t^s \\ &= \sum_{s=0}^N \sum_{r=0}^{N-s} \binom{N-M}{r}\binom{M}{s} t^{r+s} \\ &= \sum_{k=0}^N \sum_{n=k}^N \binom{N-M}{n-k}\binom{M}{k} t^n \\ &= \sum_{n=0}^N \left\{\sum_{k=0}^N \binom{N-M}{n-k}\binom{M}{k}\right\} t^n.\end{aligned}$$

The desired equality is obtained upon equating the coefficients of the various powers of t.

The expected value of a hypergeometric random variable can be computed directly or as a special case of the factorial moment. In the following computation of the rth factorial moment, this notation is used:

$$p(k;N,M,n) = \frac{\binom{M}{k}\binom{N-M}{n-k}}{\binom{N}{n}} = P(X = k),$$

and again $(k)_r$ for the product of r consecutive integers starting with k and going down: $k(k-1)\cdots(k-r+1)$. The rth factorial moment is then

$$E[(X)_r] = \sum_{k=r}^{N}(k)_r\,p(k;N,M,n) = \sum_{k=r}^{N}(k)_r\frac{\binom{N-M}{n-k}\binom{M}{k}}{\binom{N}{n}}.$$

By using the identity

$$(k)_r\binom{M}{k} = (M)_r\binom{M-r}{k-r},$$

one obtains

$$\begin{aligned}\sum_{k=r}^{N}(k)_r\binom{N-M}{n-k}\binom{M}{k} &= \sum_{k=r}^{N}(M)_r\binom{M-r}{k-r}\binom{N-M}{n-k}\\ &= (M)_r\sum_{j=0}^{N}\binom{M-r}{j}\binom{(N-r)-(M-r)}{(n-r)-j}\\ &= (M)_r\binom{N-r}{n-r}\sum_{j=0}^{N}p(j;N-r,M-r,n-r)\\ &= (M)_r\binom{N-r}{n-r} = \frac{(M)_r(n)_r\binom{N}{n}}{(N)_r}.\end{aligned}$$

Thus,

$$E[(X)_r] = \frac{(M)_r(n)_r}{(N)_r}.$$

In particular, for $r = 1$,

$$E(X) = \frac{nM}{N};$$

and for $r = 2$,

$$E[X(X-1)] = \frac{M(M-1)n(n-1)}{N(N-1)}.$$

From these moments the variance can be computed:

$$\begin{aligned}\text{var } X &= E[X(X-1)] + E(X) - [E(X)]^2 \\ &= \frac{M(M-1)n(n-1)}{N(N-1)} + n\frac{M}{N} - \left(n\frac{M}{N}\right)^2 \\ &= n\frac{M}{N}\frac{N-M}{N}\frac{N-n}{N-1} = npq\frac{N-n}{N-1},\end{aligned}$$

where $p = M/N$, the probability of A for a single trial, and $p + q = 1$.

Example 2–35. A lot of ten contains three defective and seven good articles. Suppose that four articles are drawn from the lot at random, but without replacement, and that we are interested in X, the number of defective articles among the four drawn. The probability function for X is

$$p(k;10,3,4) = \frac{\binom{3}{k}\binom{7}{4-k}}{\binom{10}{4}}.$$

In the following table are given the values of this function for the possible values $k = 0, 1, 2,$ and 3, as well as computations needed for determining the expectation and variance:

k	$30p(k)$	$30kp(k)$	$30k^2p(k)$
0	5	0	0
1	15	15	15
2	9	18	36
3	1	3	9
	30	36	60

From this we compute

$$E(X) = \frac{36}{30} = 4 \cdot \frac{3}{10},$$

and

$$\text{var } X = \frac{60}{30} - \left(\frac{36}{30}\right)^2 = \frac{14}{25} = 4 \cdot \frac{3}{10} \cdot \frac{7}{10} \cdot \frac{10-4}{10-1}.$$

These direct computations lead to the same results as the formulas, as should of course be expected.

It is apparent from the nature of the situation that if one increases the size N of the collection of objects from which the drawings are made, holding the ratio of M to N fixed at some value $M/N = p$, the distribution of the number of A's in a given number of trials tends to the binomial distribution. The larger the N, the less the proportion of the two types of objects is altered when one object is removed. The approach of the hypergeometric to the binomial probabilities is readily seen as follows:

$$\frac{\binom{M}{k}\binom{N-M}{n-k}}{\binom{N}{n}} = \frac{(M)_k(N-M)_{n-k}n!}{k!(n-k)!(N)_n}$$

$$= \frac{M}{N}\frac{M-1}{N-1}\cdots\frac{M-k+1}{N-k+1}\frac{N-M}{N-k}\cdots\frac{N-M-n+k+1}{N-n+1}\binom{n}{k}$$

$$\to p\cdot p\cdots p\cdot q\cdots q\binom{n}{k} = p^k q^{n-k}\binom{n}{k}$$

The usefulness of the approach of the hypergeometric to the binomial distribution lies in the possiblity of estimating a hypergeometric probability with an easier-to-compute binomial probability, when the number of objects drawn is considerably less than the number available. From a practical point of view, it is important to know "how fast" the hypergeometric distribution tends to the binomial. To give some hint of this, the calculations in the next example are presented.

Example 2–36. Presented in the table below are hypergeometric probabilities of 0, 1, 2, 3, 4, and 5 "defectives" in a selection of ten articles from populations of sizes $N = 50$, 100, 200, and ∞, half of which are defective. The last, $N = \infty$, is really the binomial case for $n = 10$ and $p = 0.5$.

k	$N = 50$	$N = 100$	$N = 200$	$N = \infty$ (Binomial)
0	.0003	.0006	.0008	.0010
1	.0050	.0072	.0085	.0098
2	.0316	.0380	.0410	.0439
3	.1076	.1131	.1153	.1172
4	.2181	.2114	.2082	.2051
5	.2748	.2539	.2525	.2461

2.4.4 The Geometric Distribution. Also stemming from a Bernoulli distribution is the *geometric distribution.* In a sequence of independent Bernoulli trials with probability p for H and probability $1 - p$ for T, let

$$X = \text{number of } T\text{'s preceding the first } H.$$

Using the multiplication rule, one finds (for $0 < p \leq 1$):

$$P(X = k) = p(1-p)^k \qquad k = 0, 1, 2, \ldots.$$

These total 1, as is readily seen directly, the quantities $p, p(1-p), \cdots$ forming a geometric progression:

$$\sum_{k=0}^{\infty} p(1-p)^k = p[1 + (1-p) + (1-p)^2 + \cdots]$$
$$= \frac{p}{1-(1-p)} = 1.$$

The factorial moment generating function of X is

$$\eta(t) = E(t^X) = p\sum_0^{\infty} t^k(1-p)^k = \frac{p}{1-t(1-p)}.$$

From this or directly from the definition one can compute the rth factorial moment:

$$E[(X)_r] = E[X(X-1)\cdots(X-r+1)] = r!\left(\frac{1-p}{p}\right)^r.$$

Example 2–37. Let X denote the number of tosses of a die prior to the toss in which a two or a three first appears. Since the probability of a two or a three in a single toss is 1/3, the probability function of X is

$$P(X = k) = \frac{1}{3}\left(\frac{2}{3}\right)^k \qquad k = 0, 1, 2, \cdots.$$

The expected value is

$$E(X) = \frac{1-p}{p} = 2.$$

PROBLEMS

2–73. Five beads are drawn together from a bowl containing four white and seven black beads. Let X denote the number of white beads among the five drawn and determine the probability function of X. Using this, compute the mean and variance directly, and then check the results using the formulas.

2–74. Given that 10 of 100 objects are defective, determine the probability that three out of five drawn at random are defective. Compare this with the probability that three out of five drawn are defective, if the five are drawn one at a time, with replacement and mixing after each drawing. (Compare also the labor involved in the two computations.)

2–75. What is the expected number of Aces drawn in a bridge hand of 13 cards? (The deck contains 52 cards, of which 4 are Aces.) What is the expected number of face cards? (There are 12 face cards in the deck.)

2–76. In a population of 10,000 voters, 45 per cent favor a certain proposal. What is the probability that among ten voters chosen at random, without replacement, six or more favor the proposal?

2–77. Show that for fixed n and fixed $M/N = p$, the rth factorial moment of a hypergeometric distribution tends to that of a binomial distribution with parameters n and p, as N becomes infinite.

2–78. Of 20 cups of coffee, 15 are brewed in the usual way and 5 are made from instant coffee. After tasting all 20 cups, a taster selects 5 which he thinks are the ones made from instant coffee. What is the probability that if his selection is random (made by "pure chance"), exactly k of the 5 he selects are made from instant coffee?

2–79. Let X have a hypergeometric distribution with parameters N, n, and M. Let $P(X = k)$ be denoted by $p(k;M)$. Show that if $M' > M$,

$$\frac{p(k;M)}{p(k;M')} \geq \frac{p(k+1;M)}{p(k+1;M')}.$$

(Express each probability in terms of factorials and start canceling.)

2–80. A die is cast repeatedly until a six shows. What is the expected number of throws necessary?

2–81. Two dice are cast repeatedly. What is the expected number of casts required to obtain a seven? To obtain a 7 or an 11?

2–82. A bowl contains three white and seven black beads. Beads are drawn one at a time without replacement. Determine the distribution of the number of black beads drawn before a white bead is first drawn, and compare this with the distribution that would be correct if the beads were replaced after each drawing.

2–83. From the factorial moment generating function obtain the formula for the variance of a random variable with the geometric distribution.

2–84. Beads are drawn one at a time, without replacement, from a bowl with three white and seven black beads. Determine the distribution of the number of drawings required to get all the white beads.

2.4.5 The Poisson Distribution. A distribution of probability among the values $k = 0, 1, 2, \ldots$ is defined, for any given $m > 0$, by the formula

$$p(k) = e^{-m}\frac{m^k}{k!},$$

since $p(k) \geq 0$ and

$$\sum_{k=0}^{\infty} p(k) = e^{-m}\sum_{k=0}^{\infty}\frac{m^k}{k!} = e^{-m}e^{m} = 1.$$

This distribution is called the *Poisson distribution*, with parameter m. A random variable having this distribution is called a *Poisson random variable.*

For the moment deferring consideration of situations that involve this Poisson model, we can determine the moments of the distribution from the factorial moment generating function:

$$\eta(t) = E(t^X) = \sum_{k=0}^{\infty} t^k p(k) = e^{-m}\sum_{k=0}^{\infty}\frac{(tm)^k}{k!} = e^{m(t-1)}.$$

Differentiating r times,

$$\eta^{(r)}(t) = m^r e^{m(t-1)},$$

we obtain

$$E[(X)_r] = \eta^{(r)}(1) = m^r.$$

In particular, for $r = 1$, this yields

$$E(X) = m,$$

and for $r = 2$,

$$E[X(X-1)] = m^2.$$

The variance is then

$$\begin{aligned} \operatorname{var} X &= E[X(X-1)] + E(X) - [E(X)]^2 \\ &= m^2 + m - m^2 = m. \end{aligned}$$

It is seen that the parameter m which indexes the various members of the Poisson family of distributions happens to be both the expectation and the variance.

The Poisson distribution is applicable in many situations in which some kind of "event" or "change of state" or "flaw" or "failure" occurs, in a manner thought of intuitively as "at random," in time or over distances or areas or volumes. In the following discussion the generic term *changes* will be used, and they will be considered as occurring randomly in time.

It will now be shown that the Poisson distribution describes the number of changes on a given interval when these changes satisfy the following *Poisson postulates;* in these let $P_n(t)$ denote the probability of n changes in an interval of width t:

1. Events concerning changes in nonoverlapping intervals are independent.
2. The probability of a given number of changes in an interval depends on the size of the interval but not on its location.
3. There is a constant λ such that

$$\frac{P_1(h) - \lambda h}{h} \to 0 \quad \text{as } h \to 0.$$

4. For $n = 2, 3, \ldots,$

$$\frac{P_n(h)}{h} \to 0 \quad \text{as } h \to 0.$$

It is convenient to have the following notation: The symbol $o(h)$ is used to represent *any* function of h that "goes to zero faster than h" in this sense:

$$\lim_{h \to 0} \frac{o(h)}{h} = 0.$$

The same $o(h)$ is used for possibly different functions of h, provided they have this property. In terms of this notation, postulates (3) and (4) can be rewritten in the following equivalent form:

3. $P_1(h) = \lambda h + o(h)$,
4. $P_n(h) = o(h)$ for $n = 2, 3, \ldots.$

Expressed roughly, these last postulates state that the probability of a change in a small interval is approximately proportional to the width of the interval if the interval is small, and that the occurrence of more than one change in a small interval is quite unlikely. It is, of course, clear that the probability of a change cannot be proportional to the width of the interval for large intervals, since probability is bounded above by 1. For small intervals, however, halving the size of the interval approximately halves the probability of finding a change there.

A family of differential equations for the probabilities $P_n(t)$ is obtained as follows: It is first observed that if n changes occur in the interval $(0,t+h)$, these n changes will be divided between the intervals $(0,t)$ and $(t,t+h)$ in one of $n+1$ mutually exclusive ways, with $0, 1, \cdots,$ or n changes in $(0,t)$ and the remainder in $(t,t+h)$. Hence,

$$\begin{aligned} P_n(t+h) &= P(n \text{ changes in } (0,t+h)) \\ &= P(n \text{ changes in } (0,t) \text{ and none in } (t,t+h)) \\ &\quad + P(n-1 \text{ changes in } (0,t) \text{ and } 1 \text{ in } (t,t+h)) \\ &\quad + \cdots + P(0 \text{ changes in } (0,t) \text{ and } n \text{ in } (t,t+h)). \end{aligned}$$

By using the independence given by postulate (1) to factor these probabilities, one obtains for $n > 0$:

$$\begin{aligned} P_n(t+h) &= P_n(t)[1 - \lambda h - o(h)] + P_{n-1}(t)[\lambda h + o(h)] \\ &\quad + P_{n-2}(t)o(h) + \cdots + P_0(t)o(h); \end{aligned}$$

and for $n = 0$:

$$P_0(t+h) = P_0(t)[1 - \lambda h - o(h)].$$

Since any finite linear combination of functions $o(h)$ is again $o(h)$, one finds upon transposing $P_n(t)$, dividing by h, and taking the limit as $h \to 0$:

$$\begin{cases} P'_n(t) = -\lambda P_n(t) + \lambda P_{n-1}(t) & \text{for } n > 0, \\ P'_0(t) = -\lambda P_0(t). \end{cases}$$

The appropriate initial conditions are clearly $P_0(0) = 1$ and $P_n(0) = 0$ for $n > 0$.

The differential equation and the initial condition for $P_0(t)$ easily imply that

$$P_0(t) = e^{-\lambda t}.$$

Substituting this and $n = 1$ in the other differential equation yields

$$P'_1(t) + \lambda P_1(t) = \lambda e^{-\lambda t}.$$

By multiplying by $e^{\lambda t}$ and integrating, one obtains

$$e^{\lambda t} P_1(t) = \lambda t + \text{constant}.$$

The initial condition $P_1(0) = 0$ then implies

$$P_1(t) = \lambda t e^{-\lambda t}.$$

The probability $P_2(t)$ is found similarly by using this result for $P_1(t)$ and $n = 2$; and so on. Induction on n shows that

$$P_n(t) = e^{-\lambda t}\frac{(\lambda t)^n}{n!}.$$

This is the Poisson formula given earlier with parameter $m = \lambda t$. It is the probability function for the random variable X, the number of changes in an interval of width t. The expectation of this random variable, or the expected number of changes in an interval of width t, is the parameter λt. This shows that λ can be interpreted as the expected number of changes in a unit interval.

Example 2–38. Customers enter a waiting line "at random" at a rate of four per minute. Assuming that the number entering the line in any given time interval has a Poisson distribution, we can determine, say, the probability that at least one customer enters the line in a given half-minute interval. Taking a minute as the unit of time, we have $\lambda = 4$, and hence the average number of arrivals per half-minute is $\lambda/2 = 2$. Therefore,

$$\begin{aligned} &P(\text{at least one arrival in a half-minute interval}) \\ &\qquad = 1 - P(\text{none arrive in a half-minute interval}) \\ &\qquad = 1 - e^{-\lambda t}\frac{(\lambda t)^0}{0!} = 1 - e^{-2} \doteq 0.865. \end{aligned}$$

In addition to serving as the model for numerous random variables arising in practice, the Poisson distribution is useful as a tool for approximating binomial probabilities in a certain extreme case. It will be shown now that the formula for binomial probabilities goes over into a Poisson formula as the n and p in the binomial distribution approach, respectively, ∞ and 0 in such a way that np remains fixed. The binomial formula can be written as follows:

$$\binom{n}{k} p^k q^{n-k} = \frac{n}{n}\frac{n-1}{n}\cdots\frac{n-k+1}{n}\frac{(np)^k}{k!}(1-p)^{-k}(1-p)^n.$$

The first k factors on the right all approach 1, the next factor remains fixed, and the next one tends to 1. The final factor is treated as follows:

$$(1-p)^n = [(1-p)^{-1/p}]^{-np},$$

the desired limit then being

$$\lim_{\substack{p\to 0\\ np \text{ fixed}}} (1-p)^n = \left\{\lim_{p\to 0}(1-p)^{-1/p}\right\}^{-np} = e^{-np}.$$

By multiplying the limits of the various factors together, one obtains the limit of the product:

$$\lim_{\substack{n\to\infty\\ np \text{ fixed}}} \binom{n}{k} p^k q^{n-k} = e^{-np}\frac{(np)^k}{k!}.$$

The impact of this result is that the probability $\binom{n}{k} p^k q^{n-k}$ in a binomial distribution can be approximated by a Poisson probability $e^{-np}(np)^k/k!$ when n is "large" and p is "small." The sizes of n and p for which this approximation is feasible depends, of course, on the degree of approximation required. The example below will give some indication of the success of the approximation.

Example 2–39. In the table below are given values of the probability function for each of two binomial distributions, one in which $n = 10$ and $p = 0.1$, and the other in which $n = 20$ and $p = 0.05$. In each case $np = 1$, and the Poisson approximations using $\lambda t = np = 1$ are also given. (The table is clearly not quite complete.)

k	Poisson, $m = 1$	Binomial (10, .1)	Binomial (20, .05)
0	.368	.349	.358
1	.368	.387	.377
2	.184	.194	.187
3	.061	.057	.060
4	.015	.011	.013
5	.0031	.0015	.0022

PROBLEMS

2–85. Weak spots occur in a certain manufactured tape on the average of one per 1000 feet. Assuming a Poisson distribution of the number of weak spots in a given length of tape, what is the probability that (a) a 2400-foot roll will have at most two defects? (b) A 1200-foot roll will have no defects? (c) In a box of five 1200-foot rolls, two have just one defect and the other three have none?

2–86. Given that X has a Poisson distribution with variance 1, calculate $P(X = 2)$.

2–87. A Geiger counter records on the average of 40 counts per minute when in the neighborhood of a certain weakly radioactive substance. Determine the probability that (a) there will be two counts in a 6-second period. (b) There will be k counts in a T-second period.

2–88. Telephone calls are being placed through a certain exchange at random times on the average of four per minute. Assuming a Poisson law, determine the probability that in a 15-second interval there are three or more calls.

2–89. Flaws in the plating of large sheets of metal occur at random on the average of one in a section of area 10 square feet. What is the probability that a sheet 5 feet by 8 feet will have no flaws? At most one flaw?

2–90. Show directly that the Poisson formula obtained for $P_n(t)$ does satisfy postulates (3) and (4) which were used in deriving it.

2–91. A certain machine manufactures bolts and turns out defective bolts on the average of one per 200 bolts. They are packaged in boxes of 50. Determine the probability that a box has at most one defective bolt. Determine also the probability that of the 100 boxes in a carton, no box has more than one defective bolt.

2–92. Given that 1500 out of 50,000 people in a certain city are watching a certain television program, what is the probability that of 200 people called at random fewer than four are watching the program?

2–93. A man holds 5 tickets in a lottery in which 1000 tickets are sold. Ten tickets are to be drawn for prizes. What is the probability that the man wins at least one prize?

2.5 Continuous Cases

The families of continuous distributions to be taken up here are among those that find most frequent application as probability models for experiments. There are many other important continuous distributions, which are important because of their use in describing characteristics of samples; their consideration will be deferred until their significance will be more apparent.

2.5.1 The Uniform Distribution. The notion of a uniform distribution of probability over a sample space was discussed in Chapter 1; the word "uniform" refers to the constancy of the density of the distribution. It will be said that a random variable X has a uniform distribution, or is uniformly distributed, if the induced probability distribution in its space of values is continuous with constant density on some finite interval:

$$f(x) = \begin{cases} \dfrac{1}{(b-a)}, & \text{if } a < x < b \\ 0, & \text{if } x < a \quad \text{or} \quad x > b. \end{cases}$$

With this density, the distribution assigns to any interval included in $[a,b]$ a probability proportional to the length of the interval.

The distribution function of a uniform distribution, obtained by integration of the above density, is a "ramp" function:

$$F(x) = \begin{cases} 0, & \text{if } x < a \\ \dfrac{x-a}{b-a}, & \text{if } a \le x \le b \\ 1, & \text{if } x > b. \end{cases}$$

Because the uniform distribution is symmetric about the midpoint of the interval over which probability is spread, it follows (by Problem 2–35) that this midpoint value is the expected value as well as the median:

$$E(X) = \text{median} = \frac{a+b}{2}.$$

The expected square of a uniformly distributed variable is

$$E(X^2) = \int_a^b x^2 \frac{dx}{b-a} = \frac{b^3 - a^3}{3(b-a)},$$

and from this the variance is found to be

$$\text{var } X = E(X^2) - [E(X)]^2 = \frac{(b-a)^2}{12}.$$

The moment generating function is also readily computed:

$$\psi(t) = E(e^{tX}) = \int_a^b e^{tx} \frac{dx}{b-a} = \frac{e^{tb} - e^{ta}}{t(b-a)}$$

$$= 1 + \frac{(b+a)}{2}t + \frac{b^3 - a^3}{3(b-a)}\frac{t^2}{2!}$$

$$+ \cdots + \frac{b^{n+1} - a^{n+1}}{(n+1)(b-a)}\frac{t^n}{n!} + \cdots.$$

Example 2–40. It was shown in Problem 2–24 that if X has a strictly monotonic distribution function $F(x)$, the distribution function of the random variable $F(X) = Y$ is

$$P(Y \leq y) = P[F(X) \leq y] = P[X \leq F^{-1}(y)] = y,$$

for $0 \leq y \leq 1$. That is, Y is uniformly distributed on $[0,1]$. This is actually correct even if $F(x)$ has horizontal portions; for, if x_y denotes the largest of the inverse values of $F(x)$, then

$$P(Y \leq y) = P[F(X) \leq y] = P(X \leq x_y) = F(x_y) = y.$$

Example 2–41. Let changes occur according to the Poisson law, and consider a fixed interval, say, the interval $[0,1]$. Consider the time T at which a change occurs, given that exactly one change occurs on the interval. For $0 \leq t \leq 1$,

$$P(T \leq t \,|\, \text{one change in } [0,1]) = \frac{P(T \leq t \text{ and one change in } [0,1])}{P(\text{one change in } [0,1])}$$

$$= \frac{P(\text{one change in } [0,t] \text{ and none in } [t,1])}{P(\text{one change in } [0,1])}$$

$$= \frac{\lambda t e^{-\lambda t} e^{-\lambda(1-t)}}{\lambda e^{-\lambda}} = t.$$

Thus, the location of the change given that there is exactly one is uniformly distributed on the interval.

2.5.2 The Negative Exponential Distribution. The probability distribution on positive real numbers defined by the distribution function

$$F(x) = 1 - \exp(-\lambda x), \quad \text{for } x > 0,$$

where $\lambda > 0$, is referred to as a negative exponential (or a Laplace or an exponential) distribution with parameter λ. The corresponding density function is the derivative of $F(x)$:

$$f(x) = \lambda e^{-\lambda x}, \qquad x > 0.$$

The moment generating function, defined for $|t| < \lambda$, is then

$$\psi(t) = E(e^{tX}) = \int_0^\infty e^{tx}(\lambda e^{-\lambda x})\,dx$$
$$= \lambda \int_0^\infty e^{-(\lambda - t)x}\,dx$$
$$= \frac{\lambda}{\lambda - t} = \sum_0^\infty \left(\frac{1}{\lambda}\right)^k t^k.$$

Therefore the kth moment about 0 is

$$E(X^k) = \frac{k!}{\lambda^k}.$$

The mean and variance are then

$$E(X) = \frac{1}{\lambda} \quad \text{and} \quad \text{var } X = \frac{1}{\lambda^2}.$$

Many applications of this distribution are concerned with events occurring according to a Poisson law, when it is the distribution of the time between successive "changes." For, consider such a Poisson process with an average of λ changes per unit time, and denote by L the time from one particular change to the next. Then, for $x > 0$,

$$P(L < x) = 1 - P(L > x) = 1 - P(\text{no changes in } x \text{ time units})$$
$$= 1 - e^{-\lambda x},$$

which is the negative exponential distribution function, as claimed.

Example 2–42. Suppose that the life L of a certain type of electron tube in a given environment has a negative exponential distribution with mean life 100 hours. Suppose further that such a tube is observed to be operating after 80 hours. What is the distribution of its future life, $L - 80$?

What is wanted here is a *conditional* probability that $L - 80 \le x$, given that $L > 80$:

$$P(L \le 80 + x | L > 80) = \frac{P(80 < L \le 80 + x)}{P(L > 80)}$$
$$= \frac{F_L(80 + x) - F_L(80)}{1 - F_L(80)} = 1 - e^{-0.01x}.$$

Thus the distribution of future life is the same as the initial distribution of L. For such tubes, an old tube is as good as a new one, and replacing tubes that are operating is of no advantage!

It is interesting to observe that the negative exponential distribution is a continuous analogue of the geometric distribution. Schematically, the relationship can be represented this way:

Geometric : binomial = negative exponential : Poisson.

In the Poisson case there are "changes" occurring intermittently; the Poisson distribution describes the number of such changes in a given interval, and the negative exponential is the distribution of the spacing between such changes. On the other side, one imagines an indefinite sequence of Bernoulli trials, with "Heads" occurring intermittently, each corresponding to a "change"; the binomial distribution describes the number of "Heads" in a given "interval" (which is now a given number of trials), and the geometric distribution gives the "spacing" between successive "Heads," where the spacing is measured as a certain number of trials.

2.5.3 The Cauchy Distribution. The function $1/(1 + x^2)$ is non-negative and has finite area π between its graph and the x-axis. Hence, the function

$$f(x) = \frac{1}{\pi(1 + x^2)}$$

can serve as the density function in a probability model. A random variable X having such a distribution is called a *Cauchy random variable.* The distribution function is the indefinite integral:

$$\begin{aligned} F(x) = P(X \leq x) &= \int_{-\infty}^{x} \frac{du}{\pi(1 + u^2)} \\ &= \frac{[\text{arc tan } x - \text{arc tan}(-\infty)]}{\pi} \\ &= \frac{(\text{arc tan } x + \pi/2)}{\pi}. \end{aligned}$$

The characteristic function of the distribution can be shown to be

$$\phi(t) = E(e^{itX}) = \int_{-\infty}^{\infty} \frac{\cos tx + i \sin tx}{\pi(1 + x^2)}\, dx = e^{-|t|},$$

(cf. Example 2–32, page 66). This function is not differentiable at $t = 0$, and so the moments cannot be obtained by differentiating it. Indeed, no moments of the form $E(X^k)$, $k = 1, 2, \ldots$, exists, since, for example,

$$\int_{-\infty}^{\infty} \frac{x\, dx}{\pi(1 + x^2)}$$

is not a convergent integral.

The median of the distribution exists, of course, and is 0 because of the symmetry about that value. A more general Cauchy-type distribution with median M and first quartile $M - b$ is defined by the density

$$f(x) = \frac{b}{\pi[b^2 + (x - M)^2]}.$$

A random variable with this density is linearly related to a random variable with the particular Cauchy density given first, in which $M = 0$ and $b = 1$.

PROBLEMS

2–94. Let θ be uniformly distributed on $[-\pi/2,\pi/2]$. Determine (a) the mean and variance of θ; (b) the probability that $|\theta| > \pi/4$; (c) the expected value of $\cos\theta$.

2–95. Let X be uniformly distributed over the set of values consisting of the two intervals $[0,1]$ and $[2,3]$. Sketch the distribution function and determine the median, mean, and variance of the distribution.

2–96. Determine the probability that arc tan $X < 1/2$, where X has the Cauchy distribution with median zero and third quartile 1.

2–97. Show that the Cauchy variable with median M and third quartile $M + b$ is linearly related to a Cauchy variable with median M' and third quartile $M' + b'$.

2–98. Determine the median of the negative exponential distribution.

2–99. Customers join a waiting line according to the Poisson law, with an average time between arrivals of 2 minutes.

(a) What is the probability that 5 minutes will elapse with no customers arriving?

(b) What is the probability that in a 5-minute interval at most two customers arrive?

2–100. In a certain electronic device there are ten tubes each having a life distribution that is negative exponential with mean 50 hours. The device fails if any one of the tubes fails, and when it fails, the tube that has caused the failure is replaced and the device turned on again. Determine the distribution of the time from one failure of the device to the next, assuming that tubes fail independently of one another.

2–101. Let the times between failures of a certain device have a common distribution function $F(x)$; the probability of successful operation (no failures) for a period t is called the *reliability* of the device:

$$R(t) = 1 - F(t).$$

The *hazard* is defined in terms of reliability:

$$H(t) = -\frac{d}{dt}[\log R(t)].$$

(This can be interpreted as the rate of "dying" among many such systems relative to the number still operating.) Show that if the hazard is constant, the distribution of system life (or time between failures) is the negative exponential, and conversely.

2–102. Show that if the times between successive "events" have the negative exponential distribution with parameter λ, then

$$P(\text{one or more events in } h) = \lambda h + o(h).$$

2.5.4 The Normal Distribution. Perhaps the most exploited of probability models are those called *normal*, or *Gaussian*. The *standard* normal distribution is defined by the probability density

$$f(x) = \frac{1}{\sqrt{2\pi}}\exp\left(\frac{-x^2}{2}\right) \qquad -\infty < x < \infty.$$

This is non-negative, and its graph encloses with the x-axis a finite area. That this area is 1 with the constant multiplier used is seen from the following computation. Let

$$I = \int_{-\infty}^{\infty} \exp\left(\frac{-x^2}{2}\right) dx,$$

and compute the square:

$$I^2 = \int_{-\infty}^{\infty} \exp\left(\frac{-x^2}{2}\right) dx \int_{-\infty}^{\infty} \exp\left(\frac{-y^2}{2}\right) dy$$

$$= \int_{-\infty}^{\infty} \int_{-\infty}^{\infty} \exp\left(\frac{-(x^2 + y^2)}{2}\right) dx\, dy$$

$$= \int_{0}^{2\pi} \int_{0}^{\infty} \exp\left(\frac{-r^2}{2}\right) r\, dr\, d\theta = 2\pi.$$

(The change of variables to polar coordinates in this improper double integral can be justified.)

The standard normal distribution function is the indefinite integral of the above density function:

$$N(x) = \frac{1}{\sqrt{2\pi}} \int_{-\infty}^{x} \exp\left(\frac{-u^2}{2}\right) du.$$

Values of this function are tabulated in Table I (Appendix).

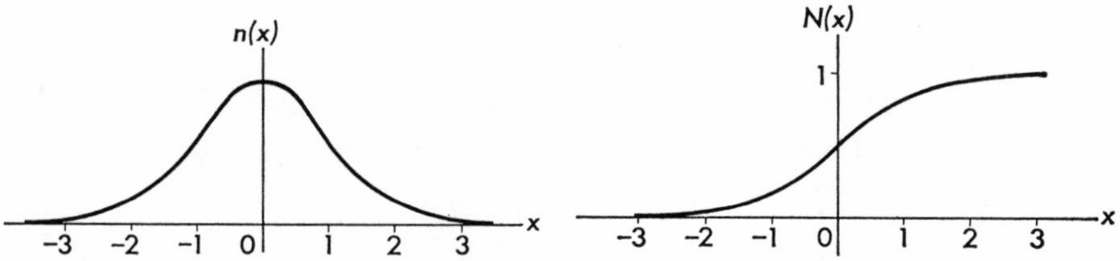

Figure 2–15

The moment generating function of a standard normal distribution exists and is computed as follows, using the device of completing the square:

$$\psi(t) = \frac{1}{\sqrt{2\pi}} \int_{-\infty}^{\infty} \exp\left(tx - \frac{x^2}{2}\right) dx$$

$$\frac{1}{\sqrt{2\pi}} \int_{-\infty}^{\infty} \exp\left[\frac{-(x^2 - 2tx + t^2)}{2} + \frac{t^2}{2}\right] dx$$

$$= \frac{1}{\sqrt{2\pi}} \exp\left(\frac{t^2}{2}\right) \int_{-\infty}^{\infty} \exp\left[\frac{-(x - t)^2}{2}\right] dx = \exp\left(\frac{t^2}{2}\right).$$

Expanding this one obtains

$$\psi(t) = \sum_0^\infty \frac{(t^2/2)^k}{k!} = \sum_0^\infty \frac{(2k)!}{2^k k!} \frac{t^{2k}}{(2k)!},$$

from which it is seen that odd-order moments about 0 vanish, while the moment of even-order $2k$ is

$$\frac{(2k)!}{2^k k!} = (2k-1)(2k-3)\cdots 5\cdot 3\cdot 1, \qquad k = 1, 2, \ldots.$$

In particular the mean is zero and the variance 1. The description "standard" is therefore consistent with the previous use of the term to indicate a variable with zero mean and unit variance.

More generally, a normally distributed random variable is defined to be one that can be obtained from a standard normal variable by a linear transformation (change of scale and translation). Thus, if Z is standard normal, any variable of the form

$$X = aZ + b$$

(for $a \neq 0$) is said to be normally distributed. It follows at once that

$$E(X) = b \qquad \text{and} \qquad \text{var } X = a^2.$$

If a should happen to be negative, one can write

$$X = (-a)(-Z) + b,$$

where $-Z$ is again standard normal because of the symmetry of the density function. So, without loss of generality, let $a > 0$, and the relation between X and Z can then be written

$$X = \sigma Z + \mu,$$

where μ and σ are the mean and standard deviation, respectively, of X.

Probabilities for a normally distributed X can be computed from the standard normal table. For,

$$P(X \le x) = P(\sigma Z + \mu \le x) = P\left(Z \le \frac{x-\mu}{\sigma}\right) = N\left(\frac{x-\mu}{\sigma}\right).$$

Thus, to determine the distribution function of X at the value x, one subtracts the mean from x, divides by the standard deviation, and looks in the standard normal table (Table I) opposite $(x-\mu)/\sigma$ (which is the distance from μ to x measured in standard deviation units). Just one table is needed for the whole family of normal distributions.

The density function of a general normal random variable X is the derivative of its distribution function:

$$f_X(x) = \frac{d}{dx} P(X \leq x) = \frac{d}{dx} N\left(\frac{x-\mu}{\sigma}\right)$$
$$= \frac{1}{\sqrt{2\pi}\,\sigma} \exp\left[\frac{-(x-\mu)^2}{2\sigma^2}\right].$$

To indicate that the distribution of X is normal with mean μ and variance σ^2, we shall sometimes write

$$X \stackrel{d}{=} \mathcal{N}(\mu,\sigma^2).$$

Example 2–43. If $X \stackrel{d}{=} \mathcal{N}(10,4)$, the density function of X is

$$f(x) = \frac{1}{2\sqrt{2\pi}} \exp\left[\frac{-(x-10)^2}{8}\right].$$

To see how probabilities are computed, consider

$$P(|X-9| > 1).$$

This is computed by expressing the event $|X - 9| > 1$ in terms of the distribution function and obtaining values of the distribution function from the standard normal table:

$$\begin{aligned} P(|X-9| > 1) &= 1 - P(|X-9| < 1) \\ &= 1 - P(8 < X < 10) \\ &= 1 - [F_X(10) - F_X(8)] \\ &= 1 - N\left(\frac{10-10}{2}\right) + N\left(\frac{8-10}{2}\right) \\ &\doteq 1 - 0.5 + 0.1587 = 0.6587. \end{aligned}$$

It should be pointed out that every function of the form

$$(\text{Constant}) \exp\left[\frac{-(x-h)^2}{k}\right]$$

can be used as the density function of a normal distribution if the constant multiplier is properly chosen. Set $h = \mu$ and $k = 2\sigma^2$, and let $X = \sigma Z + \mu$, where Z is standard normal; this variable X then has the given function as its density function.

Example 2–44. Suppose that a density function is of the form

$$(\text{Constant}) \exp[-3(x-1)^2].$$

This is of the normal type, with $\mu = 1$ and $2\sigma^2 = 1/3$, or $\sigma^2 = 1/6$. The constant multiplier is then

$$\frac{1}{\sqrt{2\pi}\sigma} = \frac{1}{\sqrt{2\pi(1/6)}} = \sqrt{\frac{3}{\pi}}.$$

The moment generating function of a general normal distribution is readily obtained from that of the standard normal distribution. If $X = \sigma Z + \mu$, where Z is standard normal,

$$\begin{aligned}\psi_X(t) &= E(e^{tX}) = E(e^{t[\sigma Z+\mu]}) = e^{\mu t}E(e^{\sigma t Z}) \\ &= e^{\mu t}\psi_Z(\sigma t) = \exp(\mu t + \tfrac{1}{2}\sigma^2 t^2).\end{aligned}$$

The characteristic function is then

$$\phi_X(t) = \psi_X(it) = \exp(i\mu t - \tfrac{1}{2}\sigma^2 t^2).$$

The central moments of a general normal distribution are expressible in terms of the variance. Again writing $X = \sigma Z + \mu$, we have

$$E[(X-\mu)^{2k}] = \sigma^{2k}E(Z^{2k}) = (2k-1)(2k-3)\cdots 3\cdot 1\sigma^{2k},$$

for $k = 1, 2, \ldots$. The odd order moments about the mean are all zero.

2.5.5 The Lognormal Distribution. The random variable X is said to have a *lognormal* distribution if $\log X$ is normally distributed; that is, if X is of the form e^Y, where Y is normal. Because of this functional dependence on a normal random variable, the various pertinent properties of a lognormal distribution may be deduced from properties of a normal distribution. In particular, the density function of X is obtained as follows. Let $X = e^Y$, where $Y \overset{d}{=} \mathcal{N}(\mu,\sigma^2)$. Then

$$\begin{aligned}f_X(x) &= \frac{d}{dx}P(e^Y \le x) = \frac{d}{dx}F_Y(\log x) \\ &= \frac{1}{x}f_Y(\log x) = \frac{1}{x\sqrt{2\pi}\,\sigma}\exp\left[\frac{-(\log x-\mu)^2}{2\sigma^2}\right],\end{aligned}$$

provided $x > 0$. If $x < 0$, $P(e^Y \le x) = 0$, and so $f_X(x) = 0$. Thus the distribution of X is confined to the positive real axis.

The kth moment of X about zero is expressible in terms of the moment generating function of $\log X$:

$$E(X^k) = E(e^{kY}) = \psi_Y(k) = \exp(k\mu + \tfrac{1}{2}\sigma^2 k^2).$$

In particular,

$$E(X) = \exp(\mu + \tfrac{1}{2}\sigma^2),$$

and

$$\operatorname{var} X = E(X^2) - [E(X)]^2 = (\exp \sigma^2 - 1)\exp(2\mu + \sigma^2).$$

The median of X is that number M such that $P(X < M) = \frac{1}{2}$, or in terms of Y, such that

$$P(e^Y < M) = \tfrac{1}{2} \quad \text{or} \quad P(Y < \log M) = \tfrac{1}{2}.$$

Clearly, then, $\log M = \mu$, and therefore the median is $M = e^\mu$.

The lognormal distribution finds application in a wide variety of fields: physics, engineering, economics, biology, astronomy, sociology, and even philology. It is used as the distribution of incomes, of household size, of particle size, body weight, results of endurance tests, and so on. (Cf. J. Aitchison and J. A. C. Brown, *The Lognormal Distribution*, Cambridge University Press, New York, 1957.)

PROBLEMS

2–103. Show that if Z has a normal distribution with zero mean, so does $-Z$.

2–104. Given that X is normal with mean 10 and variance 4, compute

$$P(|X - 10| > 3).$$

2–105. Given that X is normally distributed with mean 10 and that $P(X > 12) = 0.1587$, determine $P(9 < X < 11)$.

2–106. Given that X is normal with mean 30 and variance 25, compute

$$\text{(a) } P(X > 27), \qquad \text{(b) } P(|X - 28| < 2).$$

2–107. Determine the first and third quartiles (that is, the twenty-fifth and seventy-fifth percentiles) of a standard normal distribution. From these determine the first and third quartiles of a normal distribution with mean 10 and variance 4.

2–108. Suppose that in tabulating observations on a normal random variable with mean 10 and variance 4, the range of possible values is divided into ten parts by the points 6, 7, . . ., 14. (The first "class interval" goes from $-\infty$ to 6, the next from 6 to 7, etc.) Determine the probabilities of each interval.

2–109. Using characteristic functions, show that if X is normal, so is $Y = aX + b$ for any constants a and b, with $a \neq 0$.

2–110. Determine the density function and expectation of the random variable $|X - \mu|$, where X is normal with mean μ and variance σ^2.

2–111. Show that if X is log-normal, so is X^r.

2–112. It is found that in a certain rock-crushing process, the "diameters" d of the crushed rocks have approximately a lognormal distribution, with mean diameter 1.5 inches and standard deviation 0.3 inch.

(a) What percentage of rocks would have diameters exceeding 2 inches? Less than 1 inch?

(b) Assuming rock weights to be proportional to d^3, what is the expected weight of a rock (in terms of the constant of proportionality)?

3 / Several Random Variables

Several random variables must be considered simultaneously in many contexts. There may be a vector of real values assigned to each elementary outcome ω of an experiment. For instance, if ω denotes a randomly drawn person, one might be interested in $(X(\omega), Y(\omega), Z(\omega))$, where X is the height, Y the weight, and Z the age of the person drawn. In some cases the sample space itself may be an n-dimensional space, as in the example of the landing point of a projectile fired at a target. In fact, even when the basic experiment of interest is itself essentially one-dimensional, one is forced to consider multidimensional concepts in analyzing a composite experiment that consists of performing the given experiment several times.

To be sure, each coordinate or component of a random vector is a random variable, being a function defined on the underlying chance experiment or space of outcomes, and as such, has a univariate distribution. However, in examining the several coordinates simultaneously or jointly, new considerations arise. It is these which are studied in this chapter. To cushion the introduction of new ideas, the important case of two variables is treated first, and then the notions are extended to the case of any finite number of variables. The terms *bivariate* and *multivariate*, respectively, are used to describe these situations.

3.1 Bivariate Distributions

A two-dimensional random vector is a function $(X(\omega), Y(\omega))$ defined on a probability space Ω. The "values" of this function are vectors, or geometrically, points (x,y) in the plane. A random vector induces a probability distribution in the plane of "values" as follows:

$$P(S) = P^{\Omega}[(X(\omega),\ Y(\omega)) \text{ lies in } S],$$

where S is a given set[1] of points in the plane.

[1]The set S should be one of the family (Borel field) of sets generated by semi-infinite rectangles of the form $\{x \leq A \text{ and } y \leq B\}$. Functions on Ω to be considered as random vectors would be restricted to those having the property that the ω-set for which $(X(\omega), Y(\omega))$ lies in S is in the family of sets assigned probability in Ω (the measurability property).

As in the univariate case it may happen that the basic probability space Ω is *itself* the space of "values." That is, the elementary outcome ω may be itself a vector or point (ω_1, ω_2), and in such a case it is artificial to distinguish between the functional values and the points ω which lead to them. In any case, the distribution of primary interest is that in the space of vector values, and so we shall usually drop any reference to the underlying probability space Ω, writing for the random vector simply (X, Y).

Again two general types of distribution stand out: the *discrete* type, with probability concentrated in lumps at isolated points, and the *continuous* type, in which probability is spread over a region, no single points or curves having any positive probability. Again, however, these two types do not include all useful models. For instance, a bivariate distribution might be continuous in one variable and discrete in the other, or be otherwise concentrated along lines or curves in the plane. Also, a distribution can include discrete lumps at isolated points, concentrations along curves, and smears over regions of the plane.

In the case of a discrete distribution it is again convenient to work in terms of a *probability function:*

$$p(x,y) = P(X = x \text{ and } Y = y).$$

This may be specified directly, or it may be defined indirectly by a distribution of probability on an underlying space Ω. The possible outcomes (x,y) are sometimes presented in a rectangular tabulation, all possible values of X along the top margin, say, and all possible values of Y along the left margin; the probability for each pair (x,y) is entered under the x and across from the y. The probabilities must, of course, total 1.

Example 3–1. Three balls numbered from 1 to 3 are placed in a container. Two balls are drawn, one at a time at random, without replacement. Let

$$X = \text{number of the first ball drawn,}$$
$$Y = \text{number of the second ball drawn.}$$

The outcomes are pairs of numbers (x,y). The possible values of X as well as the possible values of Y are 1, 2, and 3. The probabilities for the various possible combinations are easily computed to be those given in the following table:

$Y \backslash X$	1	2	3
1	0	$\frac{1}{6}$	$\frac{1}{6}$
2	$\frac{1}{6}$	0	$\frac{1}{6}$
3	$\frac{1}{6}$	$\frac{1}{6}$	0

The probability of any event concerning (X, Y) can be computed from this table. For instance,

$$P(\text{number drawn first is smaller than number drawn second})$$
$$= P(X < Y) = P[(1,2), (1,3), \text{ or } (2,3)]$$
$$= \tfrac{1}{6} + \tfrac{1}{6} + \tfrac{1}{6} = \tfrac{1}{2}.$$

A continuous bivariate distribution can be defined by specifying a non-negative integrable function $f(x,y)$ whose integral over the whole plane is 1. This function serves as a *density function*. The probability of a set S of points (x,y) is given by the integral of the density function over that set:

$$P(S) = \int_S\int f(x,y)\, dA,$$

where dA denotes the area element in this double integral. Geometrically, the integral can be interpreted as the volume under the surface $z = f(x,y)$ above the xy plane and within the cylinder with base S. A distribution defined by a density is a continuous distribution; for, if S is a curve or a discrete set of points, the double integral over S is zero.

Example 3–2. Consider the density function

$$f(x,y) = \begin{cases} 1, & \text{if } 0 < x < 1 \text{ and } 0 < y < 1, \\ 0, & \text{elsewhere.} \end{cases}$$

The integral of this function over the whole plane is 1, being just its integral over the region where it is not zero, namely, over the unit square. The probability assigned to any set contained in the unit square is the area of that set (the base) times 1 (the altitude). The distribution is said to be *uniform* on the unit square.

In the case of a distribution that is to be, say, continuous in X and discrete in Y, one would find useful a function $f(x,y)$ which is a density in x and a probability in y, such that

$$P(X \text{ in } A \text{ and } Y \text{ in } B) = \sum_{y \text{ in } B} \int_A f(x,y)\, dx.$$

We shall not have occasion to discuss such models.

The *distribution function* of the joint distribution of (X, Y) is defined as follows:

$$F(x,y) = P(X \le x \text{ and } Y \le y).$$

If probability is initially given in a sample space Ω, or if it is specified by means of a density function or a probability function, the distribution function is determined by such initial specification. For example, if there is given a joint density function $f(x,y)$, the corresponding joint distribution function is

$$F(x,y) = \int_{-\infty}^{x} \int_{-\infty}^{y} f(u,v)\, dv\, du.$$

The density function can then be recovered from $F(x,y)$ by successive differentiation:

$$f(x,y) = \frac{\partial^2}{\partial x\, \partial y} F(x,y).$$

So, in general, one defines the density function (if it is not given at the outset) as this mixed second-order partial derivative of $F(x,y)$, when it exists. The density function is thus the limiting ratio of the amount of probability in a small rectangle divided by the area of the rectangle, as the rectangle narrows down to the single point (x,y).

Example 3–3. Consider again the uniform distribution of probability on the surface of a unit hemisphere, used in Examples 1–31 and 2–5 to represent the random orientation of fibers of a material. Let θ and ϕ denote the colatitude and longitude angles, respectively, with $0 \le \theta \le \pi/2$ and $0 \le \phi < 2\pi$. The joint distribution function of θ and ϕ is the following probability:

$$\begin{aligned} F(\lambda,\mu) &= P(\theta \le \lambda \text{ and } \phi \le \mu) \\ &= \text{fraction of the area of the hemisphere in which } \theta \le \lambda \text{ and } \phi \le \mu \\ &= \frac{1}{2\pi} \int_0^\mu \int_0^\lambda \sin\theta\, d\theta\, d\phi = \frac{\mu}{2\pi}(1 - \cos\lambda). \end{aligned}$$

Differentiating this with respect to μ and then with respect to λ, we find the density function to be

$$f(\lambda,\mu) = \frac{1}{2\pi} \sin\lambda \qquad \text{for } 0 < \lambda < \frac{\pi}{2},\quad 0 < \mu < 2\pi.$$

(The area of the portion of the hemisphere in which the given inequalities hold was computed as a surface integral, the element of surface area being given in spherical coordinates by $\sin\theta\ d\theta\ d\phi$.)

If one chooses to set up a bivariate model by specifying the distribution function, his choice of function is subject to certain conditions. It can be shown that if the following conditions are satisfied by a function $F(x,y)$, it can be used as a distribution function and determines a probability distribution in the plane:

1. $F(x,\infty)$ and $F(\infty,y)$ are one-dimensional distributions in x and y, respectively.
2. $F(-\infty,y) = F(x,-\infty) = 0$.
3. $F(a + h,b + k) - F(a + h,b) - F(a,b + k) + F(a,b) \ge 0$ for all a,b,h,k.

With the interpretation of $F(x,y)$ as $P(X \le x \text{ and } Y \le y)$, condition (3) simply ensures that the probability assigned to any rectangle is not negative. These conditions are easily checked in cases in which probabilities are initially specified by some other means—from the density function or from probability in an underlying space Ω. In case the density is given, condition

(3) is a simple consequence of the non-negativity of the density function. Conversely, starting with $F(x,y)$, condition (3) states that the numerator of the ratio whose limit is the partial derivative which defines the density function, and hence that limit, should be non-negative.

3.1.1 Functions of Two Random Variables. For each possible value (x,y) of a random vector (X, Y) it may be of interest to compute some function $z = g(x,y)$. This functional relationship defines a random variable $Z(\omega) = g[X(\omega), Y(\omega)]$, or in less cumbersome notation, $Z = g(X, Y)$. Probability is thereby transferred from the xy plane to the space $\mathcal{Z}$ of values of Z:

$$P^{\mathcal{Z}}(Z \text{ in } C) = P[g(X,Y) \text{ in } C],$$

the latter being computed either as a probability in the plane or from an underlying distribution in Ω.

The distribution function of Z is then

$$F_Z(z) = P(Z \leq z) = P[g(X,Y) \leq z],$$

and if $E(Z)$ exists, it can be computed from $F_Z(z)$:

$$E(Z) = \lim \sum z_i P(z_{i-1} < Z \leq z_i) = \int_{-\infty}^{\infty} z \, dF_Z(z).$$

It can also be computed from the distribution of (X, Y) without going through the step of obtaining explicitly $F_Z(z)$:

$$E(Z) = \lim \sum z_i P^{xy}(z_{i-1} \leq g(X,Y) \leq z_i) = \iint_{xy\text{-plane}} g(x,y) \, dP^{xy},$$

where P^{xy} refers to the probability distribution in the xyplane. This last integral can be computed in the continuous case in terms of the joint density function:

$$E[g(X,Y)] = \int_{-\infty}^{\infty} \int_{-\infty}^{\infty} g(x,y) \, f(x,y) \, dx \, dy,$$

and in the discrete case in terms of the probability function:

$$E[g(X,Y)] = \sum_i \sum_j g(x_i,y_j) \, p(x_i,y_j).$$

Example 3–4. Consider the uniform distribution on the unit square, discussed in Example 3–2, as the joint distribution of (X, Y). Let $Z = X + Y$. The distribution function of Z is easily computed geometrically:

$$F_Z(z) = P(Z \leq z) = \begin{cases} 0, & \text{if } z < 0 \\ \frac{1}{2}z^2, & \text{if } 0 \leq z \leq 1, \\ 1 - \frac{1}{2}(2 - z)^2, & \text{if } 1 \leq z \leq 2, \\ 1, & \text{if } z > 2. \end{cases}$$

(Since the density function is indentically 1 on the unit square, an event has a probability equal to the area of its overlap of the unit square, as shown in Figure 3–1.)

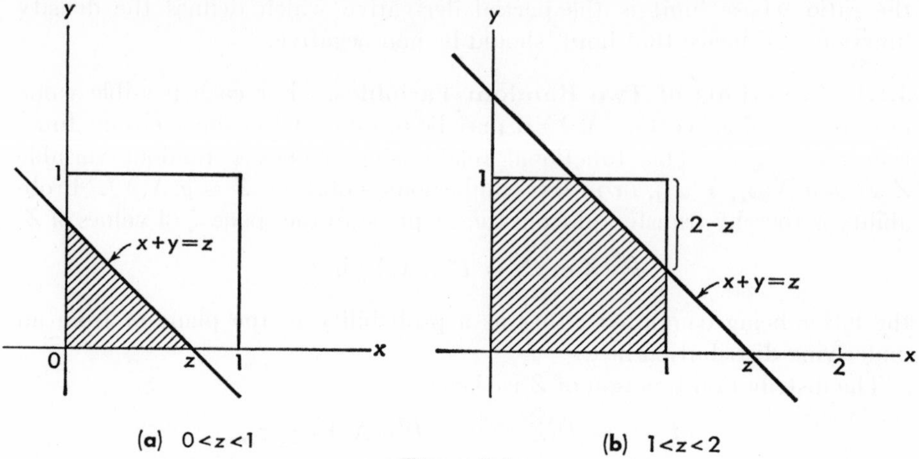

Figure 3–1

The expected value of Z can be computed from this distribution function or directly from the initial distribution in the xy plane:

$$E(X + Y) = \int_0^1 \int_0^1 (x + y)\, dx\, dy = 1.$$

Example 3–5. Consider the random orientation (θ,ϕ), with density function

$$f_{\theta,\phi}(\lambda,\mu) = \frac{(\sin \lambda)}{2\pi}$$

for $0 \leq \lambda \leq \pi/2$, $0 \leq \mu < 2\pi$. If this represents the direction of a random force with constant magnitude K, the component of force along $\lambda = \pi/2$, $\mu = 0$ is given by $K \sin \theta \cos \phi$. The expected value of this component is

$$E(K \sin \theta \cos \phi) = K \int_0^{\pi/2} \int_0^{2\pi} \sin \lambda \cos \mu \frac{\sin \lambda}{2\pi}\, d\mu\, d\lambda = 0,$$

and the variance is then the expected square:

$$E(K^2 \sin^2 \theta \cos^2 \phi) = K^2 \int_0^{\pi/2} \int_0^{2\pi} \sin^2 \lambda \cos^2 \mu \frac{\sin \lambda}{2\pi}\, d\mu\, d\lambda = \frac{K^2}{3}.$$

PROBLEMS

3–1. Let X be the number of 5's and Y the number of 6's that turn up in a single toss of two dice. Construct a table of probabilities for this bivariate distribution. From it determine

(a) The probability that $X + Y$ is at least 1.
(b) The probability table for the random variable $Z = X + Y$.
(c) The expected value of $X^2 + Y^2$.

3–2. A Bernoulli experiment with outcomes A and B is performed repeatedly, with $P(A) = p$, $P(B) = 1 - p$. Let X denote the number of the trial in which A first appears, and Y the number of the trial in which B first appears. Construct the probability table for (X, Y) and determine the probability that only A or only B appears in the first three trials.

3–3. A random point (X, Y) is distributed uniformly (that is, with constant density function) on the square whose vertices are (1,1), (−1,1), (1,−1), and (−1,−1). Determine the probabilities of these events:

(a) $X^2 + Y^2 < 1$ (c) $|X + Y| < 2$

(b) $2X - Y > 0$ (d) $|X - Y| < 1/2$.

3–4. Show that the following is not a distribution function:

$$F(x,y) = \begin{cases} 1 - e^{-x-y}, & \text{if } x > 0 \text{ and } y > 0, \\ 0, & \text{otherwise.} \end{cases}$$

3–5. Show that

$$F(x,y) = \begin{cases} (1 - e^{-x})(1 - e^{-y}), & \text{if } x > 0 \text{ and } y > 0, \\ 0, & \text{otherwise,} \end{cases}$$

does have the properties of a distribution function, and compute (a) the corresponding density function; (b) $P(X < 1)$; (c) $P(X + Y \leq 2)$; (d) $P(X > Y)$.

3–6. Let (X, Y) have the distribution function of Problem 3–5.

(a) Determine the distribution function of $Z = X + Y$.

(b) Compute the expected product $E(XY)$.

3–7. Let (X, Y) have the distribution of probability given in Problem 3–3. Determine the distribution function of

(a) $Z = X + Y$.

(b) $W = \max(X, Y)$, the larger of X and Y. [*Hint:* $W \leq w$ if and only if both X and Y are no larger than w.]

3–8. Let $f(x,y)$ be proportional to $\exp[-(x^2 - 2xy + 2y^2)]$. Determine the proportionality constant so that $f(x,y)$ is a density function. Compute $E(XY - Y^2)$, where (X, Y) has the joint density $f(x,y)$.

3.1.2 Marginal Distributions. Some particularly simple examples of functions of (x,y) are the "coordinate functions": $g(x,y) = x$ and $h(x,y) = y$. That is, each coordinate of a random point (X, Y) is a random variable, with a distribution determined by the joint distribution of (X, Y). Thus the distribution function of the random coordinate X is

$$F_X(x) = P(X \leq x) = P(X \leq x \text{ and } Y \leq \infty) = F(x, \infty).$$

Similarly,

$$F_Y(y) = P(X \leq \infty \text{ and } Y \leq y) = F(\infty, y).$$

In terminology motivated by the rectangular display of bivariate probabilities in the discrete case, the distribution of X alone and the distribution of Y alone are often called *marginal* distributions, and their distribution functions are called marginal distribution *functions*. (This terminology does not alter the fact that they are distributions in the usual sense but refers to their origin.)

In the discrete case the marginal probability function of X is

$$p_X(x_i) = \sum_{\text{all } y_j} p(x_i, y_j),$$

a corresponding relation for Y being immediate. The probabilities for the values of X in the top margin are obtained by summing the probabilities in the columns.

Example 3–6. Summing the columns and rows of the bivariate table of Example 3–1 one obtains the marginal probabilities as follows:

y_j \ x_i	1	2	3	$p(y_j)$
1	0	$\frac{1}{6}$	$\frac{1}{6}$	$\frac{1}{3}$
2	$\frac{1}{6}$	0	$\frac{1}{6}$	$\frac{1}{3}$
3	$\frac{1}{6}$	$\frac{1}{6}$	0	$\frac{1}{3}$
$p(x_i)$	$\frac{1}{3}$	$\frac{1}{3}$	$\frac{1}{3}$	1

(The distributions for X and Y here are identical, as might be expected. For, in speaking of the distribution of Y, say, one refers to the number on the second ball drawn, with no information at hand as to what was drawn first.)

In the continuous case the marginal distribution function is an integral of the joint density function:

$$F_X(x) = F(x, \infty) = \int_{-\infty}^{x} \int_{-\infty}^{\infty} f(u,y)\, dy\, du.$$

The density of the marginal distribution is the derivative

$$f_X(x) = \frac{d}{dx} F_X(x) = \int_{-\infty}^{\infty} f(x,y)\, dy.$$

Geometrically interpreted, the density of X at $x = k$ is given by the area of the cross-section at $x = k$ of the solid region under the surface that represents $f(x,y)$.

Example 3–7. It was seen in Problem 3–5 that the function $\exp(-x - y)$ for $x > 0$ and $y > 0$ is a density function. If (X, Y) has the joint distribution defined by this density, the marginal density function for X is

$$f_X(x) = \int_0^{\infty} e^{-x-y}\, dy = e^{-x}, \qquad x > 0,$$

and similarly $f_Y(y) = \exp(-y)$, for $y > 0$. That is, the marginal distributions are negative exponential.

3.1.3 Conditional Distributions. In general a "conditional" distribution function of a random variable X, given an event E of positive probability, is the conditional probability:

$$F(x \mid E) = P(X \leq x \mid E) = \frac{P(X \leq x \text{ and } E)}{P(E)}.$$

When studying the relation between two random variables, it is of interest to consider probabilities for one variable conditioned by information concerning the other; for instance,

$$P(X \leq x \mid Y \text{ in } B) = \frac{P(X \leq x \text{ and } Y \text{ in } B)}{P(Y \text{ in } B)},$$

which is defined if $P(Y \text{ in } B)$ is not zero. This conditional probability has the properties of a distribution function, and it is called the conditional distribution function of X, given that Y is in B. If such a distribution function is defined for each B_i of a sequence of disjoint events $\{B_i\}$ whose union is the whole y space, then

$$\begin{aligned} F_X(x) &= P(X \leq x) = P(X \leq x \text{ and } Y \leq \infty) \\ &= \sum_i P(X \leq x \mid Y \text{ in } B_i)\, P(B_i). \end{aligned}$$

Introducing the conditional expectation,

$$E(X \mid Y \text{ in } B) = \int_{-\infty}^{\infty} x\, dP(X \leq x \mid Y \text{ in } B),$$

we have this relation:

$$\begin{aligned} E(X) &= \sum_i \int_{-\infty}^{\infty} x\, dP(X \leq x \mid Y \text{ in } B_i) P(B_i) \\ &= \sum_i E(X \mid Y \text{ in } B_i) P(B_i). \end{aligned}$$

It is also desirable to have a conditional distribution defined for X when the condition is of the type $Y = k$; that is, to serve as the model in a situation in which the value of Y is known. This conditional distribution is defined as above if the given value of Y has positive probability; but in case Y is continuous, the probability that $Y = k$ is always zero, and the above definition does not apply. Unfortunately, a rigorous development in this situation is not possible with the mathematical tools that are being assumed.[2] About the best that can be done here is to state as fact that there is an essentially unique quantity $Q(A,y)$ having the property that

$$P(X \text{ in } A \text{ and } Y \text{ in } B) = \int_B Q(A,y) f_Y(y)\, dy.$$

[2] A rigorous treatment is available, for example, in Reference [12], page 39 ff.

(This corresponds to a property that holds when the conditioning event has positive probability.) A quantity having this property can be exhibited:

$$P(X \text{ in } A \text{ and } Y \text{ in } B) = \int_B \int_A f(x,y)\,dx\,dy$$

$$= \int_B \left\{ \int_A \frac{f(x,y)}{f_Y(y)}\,dx \right\} f_Y(y)\,dy.$$

The Q is the quantity in braces, and it is this which is taken as defining the conditional probability:

$$P(X \text{ in } A \mid Y = y) = \int_A \frac{f(x,y)}{f_Y(y)}\,dx.$$

The integrand is then the conditional *density* function of X given $Y = y$:

$$f(x \mid Y = y) = \frac{f(x,y)}{f_Y(y)}.$$

This is intuitively very appealing. For a given y, the function $f(x \mid Y = y)$ varies with x just as $f(x,y)$ does along the cross-section at the given y, except that the total area under the cross-section graph is made to be 1 by dividing $f(x,y)$ at each point by the area of the cross-section, $f_Y(y)$.

Since the conditional distribution of X given $Y = y$ is a probability distribution, moments of the conditional distribution are defined. For instance, the conditional mean of X, given $Y = y$, is

$$E(X \mid Y = y) = \int_{-\infty}^{\infty} x\, f(x \mid Y = y)\,dx.$$

The value of this depends on the value y, which defines the condition; and as a function of y, the conditional mean given $Y = y$ is called the *regression function* of X on Y. The regression function of Y on X would, of course, be $E(Y|X = x)$.

Example 3–8. Consider a uniform distribution on the triangle bounded by $x = 0$, $y = 0$, and $x + y = 1$. The density of this distribution is

$$f(x,y) = \begin{cases} 2, & \text{if } x + y \le 1,\ x \ge 0, \text{ and } y \ge 0, \\ 0, & \text{otherwise.} \end{cases}$$

Then

$$f_X(x) = \int_{-\infty}^{\infty} f(x,y)\,dy = \int_0^{1-x} 2dy = 2(1 - x),$$

for $0 \le x \le 1$. In terms of this, the conditional density can be computed:

$$f(y|X = x) = \frac{f(x,y)}{f_X(x)} = \frac{2}{2(1 - x)} = \frac{1}{1 - x}, \qquad 0 < y \le 1 - x.$$

That is, the conditional distribution of Y, given $X = x$, is uniform on $[0,1 - x]$. The cross-sections of $f(x,y)$ at any given x are of constant height, although the intervals over which they extend vary with x (cf. Figure 3–2).

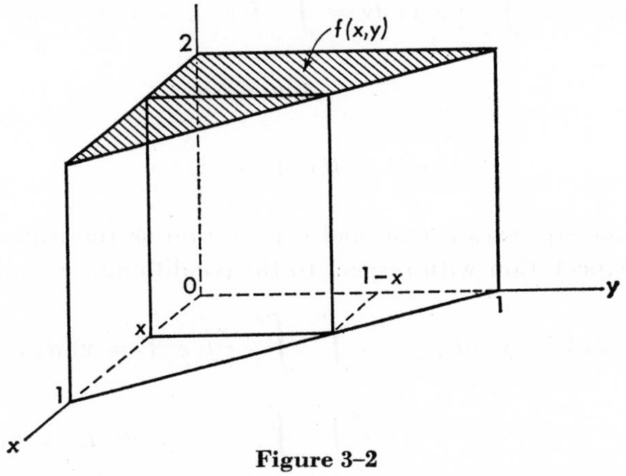

Figure 3–2

Example 3–9. Consider the density $\exp(-x - y)$, x and y positive, discussed in Example 3–7. The conditional density of X is

$$f(x \mid Y = y) = \frac{e^{-x-y}}{e^{-y}} = e^{-x}, \qquad x > 0.$$

This happens to be independent of the condition, a phenomenon to be considered more in detail in the next section. The graphs of the various distribution functions here are shown in Figure 3–3, with scales altered to bring infinity into view.

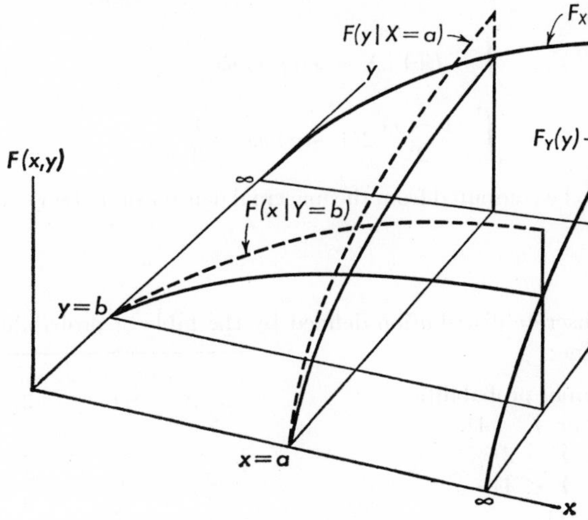

Figure 3–3

Some further relations are useful. One is an expression for a marginal density as an expectation of a conditional density:

$$f_X(x) = \int_{-\infty}^{\infty} f(x,y)\, dy = \int_{-\infty}^{\infty} f(x \mid Y = y)\, f_Y(y)\, dy$$

$$= E[g(x, Y)],$$

where

$$g(x,y) = f(x \mid Y = y).$$

Another relation expresses a marginal expectation as the expected value of a conditional expectation with respect to the conditioning variable:

$$\int_{-\infty}^{\infty} E(X \mid Y = y)\, dF_Y(y) = \int_{-\infty}^{\infty}\int_{-\infty}^{\infty} x\, f(x \mid Y = y)\, dx\, f_Y(y)\, dy$$

$$= \int_{-\infty}^{\infty}\int_{-\infty}^{\infty} x\, f(x,y)\, dy\, dx = E(X).$$

This will sometimes be written as follows:

$$E(X) = E_Y[E(X \mid Y)].$$

Similar formulas and computations hold in the discrete case.

Example 3–10. In Example 3–8, in which (X, Y) is distributed uniformly over a certain triangle, the conditional distribution of Y, given $X = x$, was found to be uniform on $[0,1 - x]$. The conditional mean $E(Y \mid X = x)$ is then the midpoint, $(1 - x)/2$, and

$$E(Y) = \int_{-\infty}^{\infty} E(Y \mid X = x) f_X(x)\, dx$$

$$= \int_0^1 \frac{(1 - x)}{2}\, 2(1 - x)\, dx = \frac{1}{3}.$$

This can, of course, also be computed from the marginal density of Y, $f_Y(y) = 2(1 - y)$, $0 \le y \le 1$.

PROBLEMS

3–9. Consider the discrete distribution defined by the table of probabilities shown here. Determine:

(a) The marginal probabilities.
(b) $P(X = 2 \text{ or } Y = 4)$.
(c) $P(X = 2 \mid Y = 2)$.
(d) $P(X = 1 \mid Y < 4)$.
(e) $E(Y \mid X = 1)$.
(f) $E(X \mid Y > 2)$.

Y \ X	1	2	3
2	$\frac{1}{12}$	$\frac{1}{6}$	$\frac{1}{12}$
3	$\frac{1}{6}$	0	$\frac{1}{6}$
4	0	$\frac{1}{3}$	0

3–10. Let (X, Y) be uniformly distributed over the region $x^2 + y^2 \leq 4$. Compute the following:

(a) $P(Y > kX)$.
(b) $f_X(x)$
(c) $f(x \mid Y = 1)$
(d) $P(|X| < 1 \text{ given } Y = 0.5)$.
(e) The distribution function of $X^2 + Y^2$.
(f) The distribution function of $\sqrt{X^2 + Y^2}$.

3–11. Consider the density function

$$f_{X,Y}(x,y) = \frac{1}{\pi} \exp[-(x^2 - 2xy + 2y^2)].$$

Compute (a) $f_X(x)$; (b) $f(x \mid Y = y)$; (c) $E(X \mid Y = y)$; (d) $E(Y \mid X = x)$.

3–12. Let the joint density function of (X, Y) be $(4xy)^{-1/2}$ for $0 < x < 1$ and

$$0 < y < x,$$

and 0 outside that triangle. Determine (a) the marginal density function of X; (b) the conditional density function of Y, given $X = 1/4$.

3–13. Show: $\displaystyle\int_{-\infty}^{\infty} P(X \text{ in } A \mid Y = y)\, f_Y(y)\, dy = P(X \text{ in } A)$.

3–14. Write out for the discrete case what is involved in the formula $E(X) = E[E(X \mid Y)]$.

3–15. Consider disjoint events $E_1, E_2, \ldots$ such that $\sum E_i = A$. Show that

$$E(X \mid A) = \sum_k E(X \mid AE_k) P(E_k \mid A).$$

3–16. Let $h(x) \geq 0$ and suppose that $h(x) \geq b > 0$ for x in B. Use the result of Problem 3–15, with x replaced by $h(x)$ (taking A as the whole x space and $E_1 = B$, $E_2 = \bar{B}$), to show that $E[h(X)] \geq bP(X \text{ in } B)$. [This provides another proof of the "basic inequality" of §2.3.1.]

3.1.4 Independence. It can happen (as in Example 3-9) that the conditional distribution of one variable, given a value of the other, is independent of that value:

$$P(X \text{ in } A \mid Y = y) = P(X \text{ in } A).$$

If this be the case, then for any A and B,

$$\begin{aligned} P(X \text{ in } A \text{ and } Y \text{ in } B) &= \int_B P(X \text{ in } A)\, dF_Y(y) \\ &= P(X \text{ in } A) \int_B dF_Y(y) \\ &= P(X \text{ in } A) P(Y \text{ in } B). \end{aligned}$$

Then, according to a definition of Chapter 1, the experiment that consists of observing a value of X and the experiment that consists of observing a value of Y are independent experiments; we now say that X and Y are *independent random variables*.

Since the above factorization must be valid for all events A and B, it must in particular be valid for $\{X \le x\}$ and $\{Y \le y\}$; using these for A and B, respectively, one obtains:

$$F(x,y) = F_X(x)F_Y(y),$$

and in the continuous case (upon differentiation):

$$f(x,y) = f_X(x)f_Y(y).$$

In the discrete case, taking $A = \{X = x\}$ and $B = \{Y = y\}$ yields:

$$p(x,y) = p_X(x)p_Y(y).$$

It is then clear, upon integrating and summing, respectively, that these relations for the density functions and for the probability functions would each imply that $P(X \text{ in } A \text{ and } Y \text{ in } B)$ factors, as in the definition of independence. That is, the various factorization conditions are equivalent, and it is a matter of indifference which is taken as the definition.

Example 3–11. Let (X, Y) have the joint density $\exp(-x - y)$ for positive x and y. As seen in Example 3–7, the marginal density for X is $\exp(-x)$, and for Y (by symmetry) it is $\exp(-y)$. The product of these *is* the joint density function, and therefore the variables X and Y are independent.

Example 3–12. The uniform distribution on the triangle bounded by $x + y \le 1$, $x \ge 0$, and $y \ge 0$, discussed in Example 3–8, does *not* have the factorization property, since the marginal densities are $2(1 - x)$ and $2(1 - y)$, whereas $f(x,y)$ is either 0 or 2. This is sufficient to establish dependence (or lack of independence), but it is noted also that the conditional density function computed in Example 3–8 is not independent of the condition.

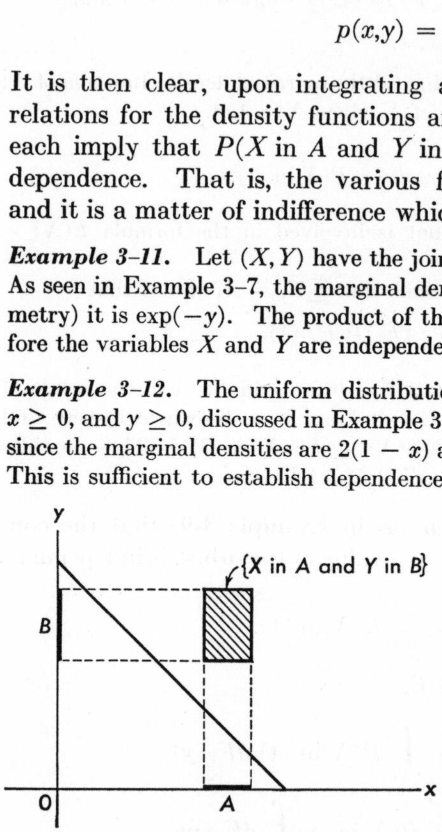

Figure 3–4

In this instance the dependence of X and Y can be deduced without any calculation at all if it is noticed, for example, that the shaded rectangle $\{X \text{ in } A \text{ and } Y \text{ in } B\}$ in Figure 3–4 has zero probability, but the sides $\{X \text{ in } A\}$ and $\{Y \text{ in } B\}$ do not have zero probabilities in the marginal distributions (the latter obtained by projecting the probability onto the corresponding axis).

The reasoning used in Example 3-12 shows that in general the region in the plane where the joint density is not zero must "factor"—that is, it must be a rectangle, possibly infinite, with sides along the coordinate axes corresponding to the regions of values of X and Y where the marginal densities are not zero—if X and Y are to be independent.

Although not generally the case, it is true for independent random variables that the marginal distributions determine the joint distribution. To construct a bivariate model with independence, it is only necessary to multiply together the marginal distribution functions to obtain the joint distribution function (or the marginal densities to obtain the joint density).

Example 3–13. Suppose that X and Y are each standard normal random variables, and that it is desired to consider the bivariate distribution in which X and Y are independent. The joint density function for (X, Y) is formed by multiplying together the density functions for X and Y:

$$\begin{aligned} f_{X,Y}(u,v) &= \frac{1}{\sqrt{2\pi}} \exp\left(\frac{-u^2}{2}\right) \frac{1}{\sqrt{2\pi}} \exp\left(\frac{-v^2}{2}\right) \\ &= \frac{1}{2\pi} \exp\left(\frac{-[u^2+v^2]}{2}\right). \end{aligned}$$

If $Z = g(X)$ and $W = h(Y)$, the random variables Z and W have a joint probability distribution determined by that of X and Y. In particular, it is often convenient to know that if X and Y are independent, so are $g(X)$ and $h(Y)$. For, if A' denotes the set of values of X such that $g(X)$ is in A, and B' denotes the set of values of Y such that $h(Y)$ is in B, then

$$\begin{aligned} P[g(X) \text{ in } A \text{ and } h(Y) \text{ in } B] &= P(X \text{ in } A' \text{ and } Y \text{ in } B') \\ &= P(X \text{ in } A')P(Y \text{ in } B') \\ &= P[g(X) \text{ in } A]P[h(Y) \text{ in } B]. \end{aligned}$$

Another important property is that independence of X and Y implies a factorization of the expected product of $g(X)$ and $h(Y)$:

$$\begin{aligned} E[g(X)h(Y)] &= \int_{-\infty}^{\infty} \int_{-\infty}^{\infty} g(x)h(y)f_X(x)f_Y(y)\, dx\, dy \\ &= \int_{-\infty}^{\infty} g(x)f_X(x)\, dx \int_{-\infty}^{\infty} h(y)f_Y(y)\, dy \\ &= E[g(X)]E[h(Y)]. \end{aligned}$$

Example 3–14. The random coordinates (θ,ϕ) of a random orientation, with joint density given in Example 3–5, are independent, since that joint density function is the product of the marginal densities as computed in Example 2–10. Therefore the expectation in Example 3–5 could be computed this way:

$$E(K \sin \theta \cos \phi) = KE(\sin \theta)\, E(\cos \phi) = 0.$$

Example 3–15. Consider the sum Z of independent random variables X and Y. The characteristic function of the sum can be computed in terms of the characteristic functions of the summands:

$$\begin{aligned} \phi_Z(t) = E[\exp(it[X+Y])] &= E[\exp(itX)]\, E[\exp(itY)] \\ &= \phi_X(t)\, \phi_Y(t). \end{aligned}$$

A similar relation holds for moment generating functions when they exist.

PROBLEMS

3–17. Let X and Y be independent random variables, each normally distributed with mean 0 and variance 2.
(a) Write out the joint density function.
(b) Determine the distribution function of $W = \sqrt{X^2 + Y^2}$.
(c) Determine the distribution density function of the angle θ between the positive x-axis and the ray from (0,0) to (X, Y). (Let $0 \leq \theta < 2\pi$.)

3–18. Let X and Y be independent random variables, each with the negative exponential distribution with mean 1/2. Write out the joint density function and compute $P(X + Y \leq z)$ for a given constant z.

3–19. Let U and V be independent random variables, each having the distribution of W in Problem 3–17(b). Compute $P(aU > bV)$.

3–20. Show that the X and Y in Problem 3–10 are not independent.

3–21. Suppose that the times between successive "events" have independent, identical, negative exponential distributions with mean $1/\lambda$. Show that P(more than one event in h) $= o(h)$ as $h \to 0$. [*Hint:* Write this probability as $P(X + Y \leq h)$ and use a modification of Problem 3–18.]

3–22. Show that although the coordinates θ and ϕ in Example 3–14 are independent, the rectangular components $K \sin \theta \cos \phi$ and $K \sin \theta \sin \phi$ are not independent.

3.1.5 Moments and Moment Generation. In addition to the usual moments of the marginal distributions of X and Y, there is now the possibility of "mixed moments":

$$E[(X - a)^r(Y - b)^s].$$

Of particular importance is the second-order mixed moment:

$$E[(X - a)(Y - b)] = E(XY) - aE(Y) - bE(X) + ab.$$

Taking a and b to be the expected values of X and Y, respectively,

$$E[(X - \mu_X)(Y - \mu_Y)] = E(XY) - E(X)E(Y).$$

This is called the *covariance* of X and Y, and will be denoted either by $\text{cov}(X, Y)$ or by σ_{XY}. It was shown in §3.1.4 that if X and Y are independent, $E(XY) = E(X)E(Y)$, and in this case the covariance would vanish. The converse of this implication is tempting but false, for the next example shows that the covariance can vanish without independence.

Example 3–16. Consider the discrete joint distribution of (X, Y) defined by the following table of probabilities:

Y \ X	6	8	10
1	0.2	0	0.2
2	0	0.2	0
3	0.2	0	0.2

The expectation of X is 8 and that of Y is 2. The expected product XY is

$$\begin{aligned} E(XY) &= (1 \times 6) \times 0.2 + (3 \times 6) \times 0.2 + (2 \times 8) \times 0.2 + (1 \times 10) \times 0.2 + \\ &\quad (3 \times 10) \times 0.2 \\ &= 80 \times 0.2 = 16. \end{aligned}$$

This is the same as $E(X)E(Y)$, and therefore the covariance of X and Y is zero—a consequence of the symmetry of the distribution about the mean point (8,2).

The characteristic function of a bivariate distribution of (X, Y) is defined to be

$$\phi(s,t) = E(e^{isX+itY}).$$

It becomes clear upon formal differentiation under the integration $E(\cdot)$ that when such manipulations are valid, moments are obtained as follows:

$$E(X^hY^k) = i^{-h-k}\frac{\partial^{h+k}}{\partial s^h\,\partial t^k}\phi(s,t)\bigg|_{s=t=0}.$$

For independent X and Y the joint characteristic function reduces to the product of the marginal characteristic functions:

$$\phi(s,t) = E(e^{isX+itY}) = E(e^{isX})E(e^{itY}) = \phi_X(s)\phi_Y(t).$$

3.1.6 The Correlation Coefficient. A covariance can be thought of as a measure of "coherence" between two random variables. Being the average product of deviations about the means it suggests, when it is large and positive, that X and Y tend to be large together and small together; when it is large numerically but negative, that X tends to be large when Y is small and conversely; when it is zero, that positive products appear about as often as negative products in the average, so that if X is large, Y may be either large or small.

One might then ask: "Is a covariance of, say, 17 considered large?" To answer this, it is necessary to know how large a covariance can be. The matter is settled by the inequality:

$$|\sigma_{XY}| \leq \sigma_X\sigma_Y.$$

To prove this inequality, consider the non-negative random variable $(U-kV)^2$ for some real constant k. Its expectation is non-negative for all choices of k:

$$0 \leq E[(U - kV)^2] = k^2E(V^2) - 2kE(UV) + E(U^2).$$

The last expression is, then, a non-negative quadratic function of k, and its discriminant must as a result be nonpositive:

$$[E(UV)]^2 - E(U^2)E(V^2) \leq 0.$$

This is a form of the *Schwarz inequality*; setting $U = X - E(X)$ and $V = Y - E(Y)$ yields the desired result.

Since the extreme values of the covariance depend on the variances, it is natural to introduce a unit-free quantity that does not—the *correlation coefficient:*

$$\rho_{XY} = \frac{\sigma_{XY}}{\sigma_X \sigma_Y}.$$

According to the Schwarz inequality this is numerically no larger than 1:

$$-1 \leq \rho_{XY} \leq 1.$$

Further, it is insensitive to the scale of measurement. For, when the x and y scales are changed, the standard deviations in the denominator are multiplied by the corresponding scale factors and cancel the factors that appear in the covariance. And since the covariance and the variance are both based on differences, neither do translations affect the correlation coefficient. That is, since

$$\text{var}(aX + b) = a^2 \text{ var } X, \qquad \text{var}(cY + d) = c^2 \text{ var } Y,$$

and

$$\text{cov}(aX + b, cY + d) = ac \text{ cov}(X, Y),$$

it follows that the correlation of $aX + b$ and $cY + d$ is the same as that of X and Y.

Examining more closely the derivation above of Schwarz' inequality, we can see the significance of the extreme cases $\rho = \pm 1$. If $\rho^2 = 1$, the discriminant of the quadratic in k must be zero, and the quadratic has exactly one zero. That is, there is a value of k such that $E[(U - kV)^2] = 0$; and this can happen only if $U = kV$ with probability 1 (according to Example 2–28), which means that X and Y are linearly related with probability 1. It is easy to see that $+1$ corresponds to a positive k and -1 to a negative k.

In Example 3–16 it was seen that X and Y need not be independent if they are uncorrelated (that is, if $\rho = 0$). This means that the dependence involved in two variables' being large together and small together is not the only kind of dependence encountered. But if X and Y *are* independent, it follows that $\rho = 0$; they must be uncorrelated or "incoherent."

Writing out the formula for the correlation coefficient in a finite discrete case is suggestive in terms of solid analytic geometry: If (X, Y) is one of the points $(x_1,y_1), \ldots, (x_n,y_n)$, with $E(X) = E(Y) = 0$, then

$$\rho_{XY} = \frac{\sum x_i y_i p(x_i,y_i)}{\sqrt{\sum x_i^2 p_X(x_i)}\ \sqrt{\sum y_i^2 p_Y(y_i)}}.$$

Except for the probability weighting factors, this is the formula for the cosine of the angle between the two vectors $(x_1, \ldots, x_n)$ and $(y_1, \cdots, y_n)$. When this cosine is 1 or -1, the vectors are parallel in the same or opposite directions, respectively; the components of the vectors are then in proportion, so that $Y = kX$. If the cosine is zero, the vectors are perpendicular.

Example 3–17. Consider the density function

$$f(x,y) = \begin{cases} 8xy, & \text{if } 0 \le x \le y \le 1, \\ 0, & \text{otherwise.} \end{cases}$$

The marginal density functions are $4x(1 - x^2)$ and $4y^3$, each defined on $[0,1]$. From these can be computed the means and variances: $E(X) = 8/15$, $E(Y) = 4/5$, var $X = 11/225$, and var $Y = 2/75$. For the covariance we need

$$E(XY) = \int_0^1 \int_0^y xy\; 8xy\; dx\; dy = \frac{4}{9};$$

and then

$$\rho_{XY} = \frac{E(XY) - E(X)E(Y)}{\sqrt{(\text{var } X)(\text{var } Y)}} = \frac{4/9 - 32/75}{\sqrt{(2/75)(11/225)}} = \frac{4}{\sqrt{66}}.$$

PROBLEMS

3–23. Show that $\text{cov}(X,Y) = E(XY) - E(X)\,E(Y)$.

3–24. Determine the covariance for the discrete distribution whose probability table is shown.

Y \ X	−1	0	1
0	0.1	0.1	0.1
2	0.1	0.2	0.1
4	0.1	0.1	0.1

3–25. Consider the random orientation (θ,ϕ) with joint density function $f_{\theta,\phi}(\lambda,\mu) = (\sin \lambda)/2\pi$. Show that $[\cos \phi \sin \theta]$ and $[\sin \phi \sin \theta]$ are uncorrelated, even though (as shown in Problem 3–22) they are not independent.

3–26. Show the following: (a) If X and Y have means both zero, the random variables $X - Y$ and $X + Y$ are uncorrelated if and only if var X = var Y. (b) If $\rho_{XY} = \pm 1$, the variance of the random variable $X + Y$ is $(\sigma_X \pm \sigma_Y)^2$.

3–27. Compute the coefficient of correlation in the bivariate distribution with density $f(x,y) = 2$ for $x + y \le 1$, $x \ge 0$, and $y \ge 0$.

3–28. Use the Schwarz inequality to show that if $E(X^2)$ is finite, so is $E(X)$.

3.1.7 Transformations. To bring out the similarities between transformations in one dimension and transformations in two dimensions and thereby make the latter seem more natural, we review some of the facts concerning the former. Let the transformation defined by the continuously differentiable function $y = g(x)$ carry the region R of x values into the region S of y values. If

$$\frac{dy}{dx} = g'(x) \neq 0$$

for all x in R, the transformation is monotonic—the graph of $y = g(x)$ is steadily increasing or steadily decreasing. For each y in S, then, there is a unique x in R, called $g^{-1}(y)$, such that $g(g^{-1}(y)) = y$. The function $g^{-1}(y)$ is the *inverse* function, and this is differentiable with derivative

$$\frac{dg^{-1}(y)}{dy} = \frac{dx}{dy} = \frac{1}{dy/dx} = \frac{1}{g'(x)}.$$

The differential coefficient dy/dx provides a change-in-length factor from dx to $dy = (dy/dx)\,dx$, and dx/dy similarly provides the change factor in going from dy to $dx = (dx/dy)\,dy$. A definite integral is transformed as follows:

$$\int_R h(x)\,dx = \int_S h(g^{-1}(y))\,\frac{dx}{dy}\,dy,$$

in which, of course, dx/dy represents the function of y obtained by differentiating $g^{-1}(y)$. If X is a random variable with density function $f_X(x)$, the random variable $Y = g(X)$ has the density function

$$f_Y(y) = f_X(g^{-1}(y))\left|\frac{dx}{dy}\right|.$$

Going now to two dimensions, we state without proofs (found in books on advanced calculus) the corresponding facts about a transformation

$$\begin{cases} u = g(x,y) \\ v = h(x,y) \end{cases}$$

which takes a region R of points in the xy plane into a region S of points in the uv plane. It is assumed that g and h are continuously differentiable. The quantity that plays the role of the derivative is now the Jacobian of the transformation:

$$\frac{\partial(u,v)}{\partial(x,y)} = \begin{vmatrix} \dfrac{\partial u}{\partial x} & \dfrac{\partial u}{\partial y} \\[2ex] \dfrac{\partial v}{\partial x} & \dfrac{\partial v}{\partial y} \end{vmatrix}.$$

If this is not zero over R, there is a unique inverse transformation

$$\begin{cases} x = G(u,v) \\ y = H(u,v) \end{cases}$$

which takes each point (u,v) of S into a unique point (x,y) in R such that

$$\begin{cases} g(G(u,v),H(u,v)) = u \\ h(G(u,v),H(u,v)) = v, \end{cases}$$

these again being identities in (u,v). Further, the Jacobian of the inverse transformation is the reciprocal of the Jacobian of the direct one:

$$\frac{\partial(x,y)}{\partial(u,v)} = \left(\frac{\partial(u,v)}{\partial(x,y)}\right)^{-1}.$$

The Jacobian is the factor needed for conversion of area elements, and the change of variables in a double integral is accomplished this way:

$$\int_R\int f(x,y)\,dx\,dy = \int_S\int f[G(u,v),H(u,v)]\left|\frac{\partial(x,y)}{\partial(u,v)}\right|du\,dv.$$

where S, is the image of the region R under the transformation.

If (x,y) is a possible value of the random vector (X,Y), the transformation being considered defines the new random vector (U,V) with

$$\begin{cases} U = g(X,Y) \\ V = h(X,Y). \end{cases}$$

This transformation induces a probability distribution in the uv plane as follows: If S is a set in the uv plane and R is the set of all points in the xy plane that have "images" in S under the transformation, then

$$P[(U,V) \text{ in } S] = P[(X,Y) \text{ in } R].$$

If the distribution of (X,Y) is of the continuous type, the probability of S can be expressed as an integral over R:

$$\begin{aligned} P[(U,V) \text{ in } S] &= \int_R\int f_{X,Y}(x,y)\,dx\,dy \\ &= \int_S\int f_{X,Y}(G(u,v),H(u,v))\left|\frac{\partial(x,y)}{\partial(u,v)}\right|du\,dv, \end{aligned}$$

where $f_{X,Y}(x,y)$ is the joint density function of (X,Y). Since this relation holds for each event S in the uv plane, the density of (U,V) is the integrand function of the uv-integral:

$$f_{U,V}(u,v) = f_{X,Y}(G(u,v),H(u,v))\left|\frac{\partial(x,y)}{\partial(u,v)}\right|.$$

That is, to obtain the density of (U,V), solve the transformation equations for x and y in terms of u and v, substitute for x and y in the joint density of X and Y, and multiply by the absolute value of the Jacobian of (x,y) with respect to (u,v). [Equivalently one can divide by the absolute value of the Jacobian of (u,v) with respect to (x,y).]

Example 3–18. Let R denote the rectangular region in the plane of (λ,μ) defined by the inequalities $0 < \lambda < \pi/2$, $0 \leq \mu < 2\pi$, and consider the transformation to the (x,y) plane defined by

$$x = \sin\lambda\cos\mu, \qquad y = \sin\lambda\sin\mu.$$

The region R is mapped into the interior of the unit circle in the xy plane, which is then the region S shown in Figure 3–5.

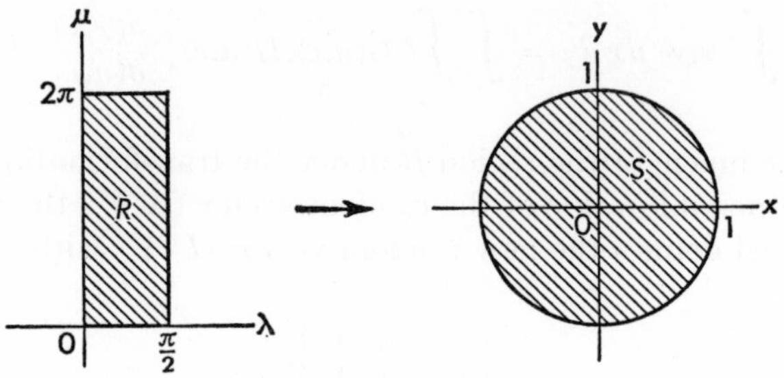

Figure 3–5

The random vector (θ,ϕ) defined on R with density $(\sin\lambda)/2\pi$ (as discussed in Example 3–5) is transformed into (X, Y), where

$$X = \sin\theta\cos\phi, \qquad Y = \sin\theta\sin\phi.$$

The density function of (X, Y) is easily written down, using the inverse transformation,

$$\begin{cases} \lambda = \sin^{-1}\sqrt{x^2 + y^2} \\ \mu = \tan^{-1}(y/x). \end{cases}$$

It is

$$\begin{aligned} f_{X,Y}(x,y) &= f_{\theta,\phi}(\sin^{-1}\sqrt{x^2+y^2}, \tan^{-1}(y/x))\,\frac{1}{\sin\lambda\cos\lambda} \\ &= \frac{1/2\pi}{\sqrt{1-(x^2+y^2)}}, \end{aligned}$$

which holds for $x^2 + y^2 < 1$, or in S. The factor $[\sin\lambda\cos\lambda]^{-1}$ is the Jacobian of (λ,μ) with respect to (x,y), or the reciprocal of

$$\frac{\partial(x,y)}{\partial(\lambda,\mu)} = \begin{vmatrix} \cos\lambda\cos\mu & -\sin\lambda\sin\mu \\ \cos\lambda\sin\mu & \sin\lambda\cos\mu \end{vmatrix}.$$

We shall be especially interested in *linear* transformations:

$$\begin{cases} u = ax + by \\ v = cx + dy, \end{cases}$$

and we now apply the results discussed above to this particular type of transformation. The Jacobian of a linear transformation is just the determinant of the coefficients:

$$\frac{\partial(u,v)}{\partial(x,y)} = \begin{vmatrix} a & b \\ c & d \end{vmatrix} = ad - bc = \Delta.$$

If Δ vanishes, the coefficients a and b are proportional to c and d, which means that v is a multiple of u. This degenerate case is ruled out when it is assumed that the Jacobian of the transformation does not vanish. If it does not vanish, then, there is a unique inverse:

$$\begin{cases} x = Au + Bv \\ y = Cu + Dv, \end{cases}$$

where $A = d/\Delta$, $B = -b/\Delta$, $C = -c/\Delta$, and $D = a/\Delta$. The Jacobian of the inverse transformation is

$$\frac{\partial(x,y)}{\partial(u,v)} = \begin{vmatrix} A & B \\ C & D \end{vmatrix} = AD - BC = \frac{1}{\Delta}.$$

Given a continuous bivariate distribution for the random vector (X, Y), the induced distribution of (U, V) defined by

$$\begin{cases} U = aX + bY \\ V = cX + dY \end{cases}$$

has the joint density function

$$f_{U,V}(u,v) = \frac{1}{|\Delta|} f_{X,Y}(Au + Bv,\ Cu + Dv).$$

Example 3–19. If X and Y are independent, each having a negative exponential distribution with unit mean, the joint density function of (X, Y) is

$$f_{X,Y}(x,y) = \exp(-x - y), \qquad x > 0,\ y > 0.$$

Consider now the random vector (U, V) where

$$\begin{cases} U = X + Y \\ V = X - Y. \end{cases}$$

The Jacobian of the transformation is $\Delta = -2$, and the inverse transformation is given by

$$\begin{cases} X = \frac{1}{2}(U + V) \\ Y = \frac{1}{2}(U - V). \end{cases}$$

The first quadrant, which is the region in which the density of (X, Y) is positive, is transformed into the region S between the bisectors of the first and fourth quadrants of the uv plane, as shown in Figure 3-6.

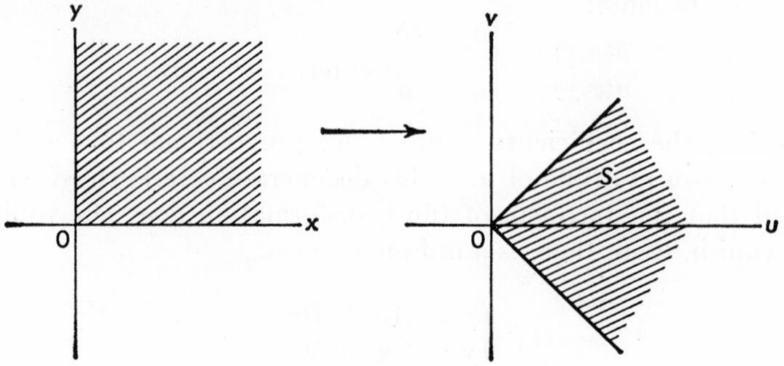

Figure 3-6

The joint density function of (U,V) is

$$f_{U,V}(u,v) = \tfrac{1}{2}e^{-u}, \quad \text{for } (u,v) \text{ in } S.$$

Incidentally, the computation of the marginal density of U yields the density of the sum $X + Y$, which is U:

$$f_{X+Y}(u) = f_U(u) = \int_{-\infty}^{\infty} f_{U,V}(u,v)\,dv$$
$$= \tfrac{1}{2}\int_{-u}^{u} e^{-u}\,dv = ue^{-u}, \qquad u > 0.$$

Similarly, the marginal density of V is the density of $X - Y$:

$$f_V(v) = \int_{-\infty}^{\infty} f_{U,V}(u,v)\,du = \tfrac{1}{2}\int_{|v|}^{\infty} e^{-u}\,du = \tfrac{1}{2}e^{-|v|}.$$

3.1.8 The Bivariate Normal Distribution. A particular class of multivariate models of considerable importance is the family of multivariate normal distributions. This family will be discussed in §3.2.4; at this point only the *bi*variate case is treated.

A random vector (X, Y) is said to have a *bivariate normal* distribution if X and Y can each be expressed linearly in terms of two independent, standard normal variables U and V:

$$\begin{cases} X = aU + bV + h \\ Y = cU + dV + k. \end{cases}$$

The moments of (X, Y) can be expressed in terms of the constants in this transformation, as follows:

$$\mu_X = E(X) = h, \qquad \mu_Y = E(Y) = k$$
$$\sigma_X^2 = \text{var } X = \text{var}(aU + bV) = a^2 + b^2,$$
$$\sigma_Y^2 = \text{var } Y = \text{var}(cU + dV) = c^2 + d^2,$$
$$\sigma_{XY} = \text{cov}(X, Y) = \text{cov}(aU + bV, cU + dV) = ac + bd.$$

Further,

$$\Delta^2 = (ad - bc)^2 = (a^2 + b^2)(c^2 + d^2) - (ac + bd)^2$$
$$= \sigma_X{}^2\sigma_Y{}^2(1 - \rho^2),$$

where ρ denotes the correlation coefficient of (X,Y), defined in §3.1.6.

If $\Delta = 0$, or $ad = bc$, then $\rho = \pm 1$ and X and Y are linearly related (with probability 1). In this case the distribution would be singular, all the probability being concentrated on the line representing the linear relation; the density would not exist. The distribution would be essentially univariate rather than bivariate.

In the strictly bivariate case, with $ad \neq bc$, there is a density function, which will now be derived. The joint density function of (U, V) is the product of two standard normal densities:

$$f_{U,V}(u,v) = \frac{1}{2\pi}\exp[-\tfrac{1}{2}(u^2 + v^2)].$$

Since $X - h$ and $Y - k$ are given by a linear transformation on (U, V), their joint density is written down as a special case of the general formula obtained earlier:

$$f_{X-h,Y-k}(r,s) = \frac{1}{|ad - bc|}\exp\{-\tfrac{1}{2}[(Ar + Bs)^2 + (Cr + Ds)^2]\},$$

where, as before, $A = d/\Delta$, $B = -b/\Delta$, $C = -c/\Delta$, $D = a/\Delta$, and $\Delta = ad - bc$. The quantity in brackets in the exponent of the above density function can then be written

$$\frac{1}{\Delta^2}[(d^2 + c^2)r^2 - 2(db + ca)rs + (b^2 + a^2)s^2]$$
$$= \frac{1}{1 - \rho^2}\left\{\frac{r^2}{\sigma_X{}^2} - 2\rho\frac{rs}{\sigma_X\sigma_Y} + \frac{s^2}{\sigma_Y{}^2}\right\}.$$

Finally, then, (using the result of Problem 3–30):

$$f_{X,Y}(x,y) = \frac{1}{2\pi\sigma_X\sigma_Y\sqrt{1 - \rho^2}}\exp(-\tfrac{1}{2}Q),$$

where

$$Q = \frac{1}{1 - \rho^2}\left\{\frac{(x - h)^2}{\sigma_X{}^2} - 2\rho\frac{(x - h)(y - k)}{\sigma_X\sigma_Y} + \frac{(y - k)^2}{\sigma_Y{}^2}\right\}.$$

It is instructive to express things in terms of the second moment matrix M:

$$M = \begin{pmatrix}\sigma_X{}^2 & \sigma_{XY} \\ \sigma_{XY} & \sigma_Y{}^2\end{pmatrix} = \begin{pmatrix}a^2 + b^2 & ac + bd \\ ac + ba & c^2 + d^2\end{pmatrix}.$$

(See Problem 3–32 for definitions and exercise in manipulation.) The inverse matrix is

$$M^{-1} = \frac{1}{\det M}\begin{pmatrix} c^2 + d^2 & -(ac + bd) \\ -(ac + bd) & a^2 + b^2 \end{pmatrix},$$

where

$$\det M = \begin{vmatrix} a^2 + b^2 & ac + bd \\ ac + bd & c^2 + d^2 \end{vmatrix} = (ad - bc)^2 = \Delta^2.$$

In terms of these, the quantity Q in the density function of (X, Y) can be written

$$Q = (x - h \quad y - k)\, M^{-1}\begin{pmatrix} x - h \\ y - k \end{pmatrix}.$$

It is clear that the inverse of the transformation used above can be used to transform a density function of the form derived into that of independent, standard normal U and V. That is, any bivariate distribution having a density function of the form derived is bivariate normal. Indeed, any function that is an exponential function with a negative definite (cf. Problem 3–33) quadratic exponent can, with proper choice of constant multiplier, serve as the density function of a bivariate normal distribution. The requirement that the exponent be negative definite ensures (by Problem 3–33) that what would be interpreted as var X and var Y are positive, and that det M > 0, which in turn implies that $\rho^2 < 1$.

Example 3–20. Let X and Y have means 0 and 2 and variances 10 and 4, respectively, and let $\text{cov}(X, Y) = 6$. The second-moment matrix M is then

$$M = \begin{pmatrix} 10 & 6 \\ 6 & 4 \end{pmatrix},$$

with determinant $\det M = 40 - 36 = 4$. The inverse is

$$M^{-1} = \frac{1}{4}\begin{pmatrix} 4 & -6 \\ -6 & 10 \end{pmatrix},$$

and now the density function can be written out:

$$f(x,y) = \frac{1}{2\pi\sqrt{4}} \exp\left\{-\frac{1}{2}\left[x^2 - 3x(y-2) + \frac{5}{2}(y-2)^2\right]\right\}.$$

PROBLEMS

3–29. Show that the transformation $u = x$, $v = x - y$ has a unique inverse, by solving for x and y. Determine the Jacobian of the transformation and of the inverse. Determine the image of the first quadrant of the xy plane under this transformation. Determine the inverse images of the u-axis and the v-axis.

3–30. Discuss the geometric significance of the transformation $x' = x + h$, $y' = y + k$, for given constants h and k. Determine the joint density function of (X', Y') induced by this transformation on the variables (X, Y) with joint density $f(x,y)$.

3–31. Let X and Y be independent, standard, normal random variables. Let $U = X$ and $V = X/Y$, and determine the joint density of (U,V). From this obtain the density of $X/Y = V$.

3–32. The "product" of two-by-two matrices is defined as follows:

$$\begin{pmatrix} a & b \\ c & d \end{pmatrix}\begin{pmatrix} e & f \\ g & h \end{pmatrix} = \begin{pmatrix} ae + bg & af + bh \\ ce + dg & cf + dh \end{pmatrix},$$

with analogous definitions for products involving one-by-two and two-by-one matrices. Given

$$\boldsymbol{x} = \begin{pmatrix} x_1 \\ x_2 \end{pmatrix}, \qquad \boldsymbol{x}' = (x_1 \quad x_2),$$

$$\boldsymbol{A} = \begin{pmatrix} 3 & 2 \\ -1 & 1 \end{pmatrix}, \qquad \boldsymbol{B} = \begin{pmatrix} 2 \\ 5 \end{pmatrix},$$

(a) Determine a matrix $\boldsymbol{A}^{-1}$ with the property $\boldsymbol{A}\boldsymbol{A}^{-1} = \boldsymbol{I} = \boldsymbol{A}^{-1}\boldsymbol{A}$, where

$$\boldsymbol{I} = \begin{pmatrix} 1 & 0 \\ 0 & 1 \end{pmatrix},$$

and equality of two matrices means that they agree element by element.

(b) Show that $\boldsymbol{IC} = \boldsymbol{CI} = \boldsymbol{C}$ for any two-by-two matrix $\boldsymbol{C}$.

(c) Compute the matrices $\boldsymbol{Ax}$, $\boldsymbol{x}'\boldsymbol{A}$, $\boldsymbol{AB}$, $\boldsymbol{x}'\boldsymbol{Ax}$, $\boldsymbol{A}^{-1}\boldsymbol{B}$.

(d) Write out the equations $\boldsymbol{Ax} = \boldsymbol{B}$ and show that $\boldsymbol{x} = \boldsymbol{A}^{-1}\boldsymbol{B}$ is a solution.

3–33. Show that the quadratic form $Q(x_1,x_2) = ax_1^2 + 2bx_1x_2 + cx_2^2$ can be written as

$$Q(x_1,x_2) = \boldsymbol{x}'\begin{pmatrix} a & b \\ b & c \end{pmatrix}\boldsymbol{x}.$$

Show also that $Q(x_1,x_2) > 0$ for all $\boldsymbol{x} \neq \boldsymbol{0}$ if and only if $a > 0$ and $ac - b^2 > 0$. (Such a Q is called *positive definite*.)

3–34. Write out the density function of the normally distributed (X, Y) with means $(0,4)$ and moment matrix

$$\boldsymbol{M} = \begin{pmatrix} 1 & 2 \\ 2 & 9 \end{pmatrix}.$$

3–35. A certain bivariate normal density is given by

$$f(x,y) = (\text{constant}) \exp(-x^2 - xy + 2y^2).$$

Determine the first and second moments and the proper constant multiplier.

3–36. The "level curves" of a surface $z = f(x,y)$ are the curves in the xy plane defined by $f(x,y) =$ constant. (Familiar examples of these are the "contour lines" or lines of constant elevation on a map.) Determine the level curves of the joint density function of the distribution in Problem 3–34, and also those of the density function of a pair of independent normal variables.

3–37. It is shown in analytic geometry that the rotation transformation

$$\begin{cases} x = u\cos\theta - v\sin\theta \\ y = u\sin\theta + v\cos\theta \end{cases}$$

reduces $ax^2 + 2bxy + cy^2$ to the form $a'u^2 + b'v^2$ if θ is chosen such that $\cot 2\theta = (a - c)/2b$. Use this fact to show that, given an arbitrary nonsingular bivariate normal distribution, there is a linear transformation that results in a distribution with independent components. Interpret this geometrically in terms of level curves.

3–38. Determine the characteristic function $E[\exp(isX + itY)]$ of normal (X,Y) by expressing X and Y in terms of independent, standard, normal (U,V). Show that it can be expressed in the form $\exp(-\frac{1}{2}Q)$, where Q is a quadratic form in (s,t) with matrix M (the matrix of second moments).

3–39. Show that if (X, Y) is bivariate normal, then
(a) any (Z, W) linearly related to (X, Y) is also bivariate normal.
(b) The marginal distributions of any bivariate normal distribution are normal.
(c) A linear function $AX + BY + C$ is normal.

3.2 Multivariate Distributions

We turn next to the simultaneous consideration of several random variables. A random vector is defined to be a vector-valued function

$$(X_1(\omega), \ldots, X_n(\omega))$$

defined on a probability space Ω. As usual the reminder of the dependence on ω will be dropped, and the vector will be written $(X_1, \ldots, X_n)$. The "values" of an n-dimensional vector function are points $(x_1, \ldots, x_n)$ in n space, and probability for sets in that space is carried over from Ω:

$$P(S) = P^{\Omega}[(X_1(\omega), \ldots, X_n(\omega)) \text{ lies in } S].$$

It may be that Ω is itself n-dimensional, with $\omega = (\omega_1, \cdots, \omega_n)$, and that the random vector of interest is the outcome ω itself:

$$(X_1(\omega), \ldots, X_n(\omega)) = (\omega_1, \ldots, \omega_n) = \omega.$$

In any case there is defined a probability distribution function

$$F(x_1, \ldots, x_n) = P(X_1 \le x_1, \ldots, X_n \le x_n),$$

called the *joint* distribution function of $(X_1, \ldots, X_n)$. This function satisfies conditions similar to those given for the two-dimensional case in the preceding section—conditions that would have to be satisfied by a function one might wish to adopt as a distribution function in setting up a model.

A *continuous* distribution results from a direct assignment of probability in the space of vector values by means of a *density* function. Such a function is non-negative, and its integral over the whole n-dimensional space is 1:

$$\int_{-\infty}^{\infty} \cdots \int_{-\infty}^{\infty} f(x_1, \ldots, x_n)\, dx_1 \cdots dx_n = 1.$$

The probablity of a region R is given by the integral of the density function over that region:

$$P[(X_1, \ldots, X_n) \text{ in } R] = \int \cdots \int_R f(x_1, \ldots, x_n)\, dx_1 \cdots dx_n.$$

In particular, the joint distribution function is expressed in terms of the density function as follows:

$$F(x_1, \ldots, x_n) = \int_{-\infty}^{x_n} \cdots \int_{-\infty}^{x_1} f(u_1, \ldots, u_n)\, du_1 \cdots du_n.$$

Conversely, given a distribution function for $(X_1, \cdots, X_n)$ which is a continuous function and has a sufficiently smooth nth-order mixed partial derivative with respect to $x_1 \cdots$, and x_n, that partial derivative is a density function:

$$\frac{\partial^n}{\partial x_1 \cdots \partial x_n} F(x_1, \ldots, x_n) = f(x_1, \ldots, x_n),$$

whose integral, as above, gives back the distribution function.

A probability measure of *discrete* type in the space of vector values can be defined by assigning certain non-negative numbers to some countable set of points so that the sum of assigned values is 1.

A distribution need not fall into one of the two categories of distributions that possess density functions or which are discrete, but these do include the most important models.

Given any function of n variables $g(x_1, \ldots, x_n)$, the composite function

$$g[X_1(\omega), \ldots, X_n(\omega)]$$

defines a random variable (call it Z) written

$$Z = g(X_1, \ldots, X_n).$$

The expected value of this variable can be expressed as an ω integral:

$$E[g(X_1, \ldots, X_n)] = \int_\Omega g[X_1(\omega), \ldots, X_n(\omega)]\, dP^\Omega,$$

or, if the distribution function $F_Z(z)$ of Z is known, as

$$E(Z) = \int_{-\infty}^{\infty} z\, dF_Z(z).$$

More often than not, however, it is convenient to compute $E(Z)$ in terms of the multivariate distribution of $(X_1, \ldots, X_n)$. In the continuous case, for example,

$$E[g(X_1, \ldots, X_n)] = \int_{-\infty}^{\infty} \cdots \int_{-\infty}^{\infty} g(x_1, \ldots, x_n)f(x_1, \ldots, x_n)\, dx_1 \cdots dx_n.$$

Happily, the result is the same when using any of these computations. (This is a generalization of the ideas discussed in detail in §2.2.3.)

The joint characteristic function of $(X_1, \ldots, X_n)$ is defined to be

$$\phi(t_1, \ldots, t_n) = E[\exp(it_1X_1 + \cdots + it_nX_n)].$$

As in the one- and two-dimensional cases, the derivatives of this function evaluated at $t_1 = \cdots = t_n = 0$ give rise to the various moments of the joint distribution, if these moments exist.

3.2.1 Marginal and Conditional Distributions. Any single coordinate X_i of a random vector is surely a random variable (a real valued function on a probability space) and as such has a distribution, called its *marginal distribution.* The corresponding marginal distribution function is

$$F_{X_i}(\lambda) = P(X_i \leq \lambda) = F(\infty, \ldots, \infty, \lambda, \infty, \ldots, \infty),$$

the λ appearing in the ith position in the joint distribution function. When there are more than two components, however, there are marginal distributions that are themselves multivariate; for instance,

$$F_{X_1,X_2}(u,v) = P(X_1 \leq u, X_2 \leq v) = F(u,v,\infty, \ldots, \infty).$$

Clearly, every distribution function must have the property that if any arguments are allowed to go to ∞, the resulting function of the remaining variables is again a distribution function.

The characteristic function of the marginal distribution of any subset of random variables is obtained by setting $t_i = 0$ for the i corresponding to the variables not considered. For example, in the case of four random variables (X_1,X_2,X_3,X_4),

$$\begin{aligned}\phi_{X_1,X_2}(t_1,t_2) &= E[\exp(it_1X_1 + it_2X_2)] \\ &= E[\exp(it_1X_1 + it_2X_2 + 0X_3 + 0X_4)] \\ &= \phi_{X_1,X_2,X_3,X_4}(t_1,t_2,0,0).\end{aligned}$$

It is helpful to regard the marginal distribution of a set of variables as the *projection* of the "mass", in a joint distribution of *all* the variables, onto the subspace of the set of variables in the marginal distribution. For example, the joint distribution of (X,Y) is the projection onto the xy plane of the joint distribution of (X,Y,Z); if a distribution is uniform over a solid sphere, the projection onto the xy plane will cover a circle and be thick near the center of the circle and very thin around the edge.

Example 3–21. Consider a uniform distribution of probability throughout the unit sphere $x^2 + y^2 + z^2 \leq 1$. In projecting this distribution onto the xy plane, we find the probability of a set S of points (x,y) to be the volume within the sphere and the cylinder of base S, divided by the total of the sphere. For example,

$$P(X > 0 \text{ and } Y > 0) = P(\text{quarter of the unit sphere}) = \tfrac{1}{4}.$$

The distribution of Z is obtained by projecting the probability all onto the z-axis. For example,

$$\begin{aligned} P(Z \leq \lambda) &= \frac{\text{volume of sphere below the plane } z = \lambda}{\text{volume of the sphere}} \\ &= \frac{1}{4}(2 + 3\lambda - \lambda^3), \quad \text{for } -1 < \lambda < 1. \end{aligned}$$

The marginal density function of Z is then the derivative

$$f_Z(\lambda) = \tfrac{3}{4}(1 - \lambda^2), \qquad -1 < \lambda < 1.$$

Conditional distributions are defined just as in the bivariate case. In general, if the condition is that certain components have given values, the conditional density (in the continuous case) is the joint density of all components divided by the joint marginal density of those components with the given values—with those particular given values used wherever the corresponding dummy variables appear.

Example 3–22. Given the distribution of (X,Y,Z) as in Example 3–21, the joint conditional density of X and Y, given $Z = k$, would be

$$f(x,y|Z = k) = \frac{f(x,y,k)}{f_Z(k)} = \frac{1}{\pi(1 - k^2)},$$

for $x^2 + y^2 \leq 1 - k^2$. That is, this conditional density is uniform in the circle of radius $\sqrt{1 - k^2}$. The result is clear geometrically, for the conditional density on the plane $z = k$ varies just as does the joint density on that cross-section, the division by $f_Z(k)$ furnishing a normalization so that the total conditional probability is 1.

As in the bivariate case, the condition for *independence* of the random variables $(X_1, \ldots, X_n)$ can be expressed in several ways:

(1) $f(x_1, \ldots, x_n) = f_{X_1}(x_1) \cdots f_{X_n}(x_n)$,

(2) $F(x_1, \ldots, x_n) = F_{X_1}(x_1) \cdots F_{X_n}(x_n)$,

(3) $P(X_1 \text{ in } A_1, \ldots, X_n \text{ in } A_n) = P(X_1 \text{ in } A_1) \cdots P(X_n \text{ in } A_n)$,
for any choice of events $A_1, \ldots, A_n$.

In (1) the f denotes either the density functions, in the continuous case, or the probabilities of the indicated values, in the discrete case. These conditions are equivalent, and any one of them can be taken to be the definition of independence.

Again it is true that if $X_1, \ldots,$ and X_n are independent random variables, so are $g_1(X_1), \ldots,$ and $g_n(X_n)$. And as before, this implies in particular that the joint characteristic function of independent random variables factors into the product of the characteristic functions of the marginal distributions

$$\phi(t_1, \ldots, t_n) = \phi_{X_1}(t_1) \cdots \phi_{X_n}(t_n),$$

and that therefore the joint characteristic function of independent variables can be constructed by multiplying together characteristic functions of the single variables.

In considering more than two random variables, there is a greater variety of possible moments of the distribution. Many correlations are of interest. The *total* correlation coefficient of two of the several variables is just the correlation coefficient of their two-dimensional joint marginal distribution. A *partial* correlation coefficient of two variables is their correlation in the conditional two-dimensional distribution holding the other variables fixed. A *multiple* correlation coefficient between one variable and a set of other variables is defined to be the maximum correlation between the one and linear combinations of the others. (Cf. Reference [1], page 29 ff.)

3.2.2 Transformations and Matrix Notation. Given the outcome $(x_1, \ldots, x_n)$, one may wish to define the related quantities:

$$\begin{cases} u_1 = g_1(x_1, \ldots, x_n) \\ \vdots \qquad \vdots \\ u_n = g_n(x_1, \ldots, x_n), \end{cases}$$

for given functions $g_1, \ldots, g_n$. For inverses and integral transformations, the crucial quantity is again the *Jacobian* of the transformation:

$$\frac{\partial(u_1, \ldots, u_n)}{\partial(x_1, \ldots, x_n)} = \begin{vmatrix} \frac{\partial u_1}{\partial x_1} & \cdots & \frac{\partial u_n}{\partial x_1} \\ \vdots & & \vdots \\ \frac{\partial u_1}{\partial x_n} & \cdots & \frac{\partial u_n}{\partial x_n} \end{vmatrix}$$

If this does not vanish in a region R, there exists an inverse transformation defined on the image of R:

$$\begin{cases} x_1 = G_1(u_1, \ldots, u_n) \\ \vdots \qquad \vdots \\ x_n = G_n(u_1, \ldots, u_n), \end{cases}$$

whose Jacobian is the reciprocal of that of the forward transformation. Making the transformation from $\boldsymbol{x}$ to $\boldsymbol{u}$ in a multiple integral over R is accomplished by substituting x from the inverse transformation and transforming the volume element as follows:

$$dx_1 \cdots dx_n \quad \to \quad \left| \frac{\partial(x_1, \ldots, x_n)}{\partial(u_1, \ldots, u_n)} \right| du_1 \cdots du_n,$$

the integral in u then extending over the image of R.

If $(x_1, \cdots, x_n)$ is a possible value of the random vector $(X_1, \cdots, X_n)$, the transformation from x to u defines a random vector

$$\begin{cases} U_1 = g_1(X_1, \ldots, X_n) \\ \vdots \qquad \vdots \\ U_n = g_n(X_1, \ldots, X_n). \end{cases}$$

If S denotes a set of points $(u_1, \cdots, u_n)$ and R the set of all points $(x_1, \cdots, x_n)$ having images in S, then

$$\begin{aligned} P[(U_1, \ldots, U_n) \text{ in } S] &= P[(g_1(X_1, \ldots, X_n), \ldots, g_n(X_1, \ldots, X_n)) \text{ in } S] \\ &= P[(X_1, \ldots, X_n) \text{ in } R]. \end{aligned}$$

In the continuous case, and if it is assumed that the transformation has a nonvanishing Jacobian in R, this last probability can be expressed as an integral of the joint density function of the X's:

$$\begin{aligned} P(S) &= \int \cdots \int_R f(x_1, \ldots, x_n)\, dx_1 \cdots dx_n \\ &= \int \cdots \int_S f(G_1(u_1, \ldots, u_n), \ldots, G_n(u_1, \ldots. u_n)) \left| \frac{\partial(x_1, \ldots, x_n)}{\partial(u_1, \ldots, u_n)} \right| du_1 \cdots du_n \end{aligned}$$

The integrand of this u-integral is then the joint density function of the U's.

So far the transformed variable has been assumed to be of the same dimension as the X's, but it is possible that one may be interested in a smaller number of U's than X's:

$$\begin{cases} U_1 = g_1(X_1, \ldots, X_n) \\ \vdots \qquad \vdots \\ U_m = g_m(X_1, \ldots, X_n), \end{cases}$$

where $m \leq n$. (If m were greater than n, the U's would be "overdetermined," and if not incompatible, then not all necessary.) One could supply $n - m$ additional compatible relations and then determine the distribution of the m U's of interest as a marginal distribution of that of the n U's. However, the transformation to $(U_1, \cdots, U_m)$ and the distribution in the $\mathbf{X}$

space determine a probability distribution directly in the m-dimensional $\boldsymbol{U}$ space, in the usual way:

$$P[(U_1, \ldots, U_m) \text{ in } T] = \int_R \cdots \int f(x_1, \ldots, x_n)\, dx_1 \cdots dx_n,$$

where R is the set of $(x_1,\ldots,x_n)$ with image points in T. Taking T to be a semi-infinite rectangle and differentiating yields, as usual, the density function of $(U_1,\ldots,U_m)$.

In considering the particular important case of a linear transformation, it is convenient to use matrix notation. The vectors $(x_1,\ldots,x_n)$ and $(u_1,\ldots,u_m)$ are written as column matrices:

$$\boldsymbol{x} = \begin{pmatrix} x_1 \\ \vdots \\ x_n \end{pmatrix}, \quad \boldsymbol{u} = \begin{pmatrix} u_1 \\ \vdots \\ u_m \end{pmatrix}.$$

The linear transformation from $\boldsymbol{x}$ to $\boldsymbol{u}$ defined by the equations

$$\begin{cases} u_1 = a_{11}x_1 + \cdots + a_{1n}x_n \\ \vdots \qquad \vdots \qquad\qquad \vdots \\ u_m = a_{m1}x_1 + \cdots + a_{mn}x_n \end{cases}$$

is then written

$$\boldsymbol{u} = \boldsymbol{A}\boldsymbol{x},$$

where $\boldsymbol{A}$ is the matrix of the transformation:

$$\boldsymbol{A} = (a_{ij}) = \begin{pmatrix} a_{11} & \cdots & a_{1n} \\ \vdots & & \\ a_{m1} & \cdots & a_{mn} \end{pmatrix}.$$

(Again a matrix equality means equality element by element; matrix multiplication is defined in general much as it was for the two-by-two case. Cf. Problem 3–43.)

If $m = n$ and if the Jacobian of the transformation, which is then the determinant of the square matrix $\boldsymbol{A}$ (written det $\boldsymbol{A}$) does not vanish, the inverse transformation exists. It is given by

$$\boldsymbol{x} = \boldsymbol{A}^{-1}\boldsymbol{u},$$

with

$$\boldsymbol{A}^{-1} = \frac{1}{\det \boldsymbol{A}} \begin{pmatrix} A_{11} & \cdots & A_{n1} \\ \vdots & & \\ A_{1n} & \cdots & A_{nn} \end{pmatrix},$$

where A_{ij} is $(-1)^{i+j}$ times the determinant of order $n - 1$ obtained by striking from det $\boldsymbol{A}$ the row and column containing a_{ij}. (This reduced determinant associated with a_{ij} is its "minor," and A_{ij} is its "cofactor.") The inverse matrix $\boldsymbol{A}^{-1}$ has the property that $\boldsymbol{A}\boldsymbol{A}^{-1} = \boldsymbol{A}^{-1}\boldsymbol{A} = \boldsymbol{I}$, the "identity matrix" of order n, which has zeros in every position except along the diagonal where $i = j$, and ones along that diagonal.

Let $\boldsymbol{V}$ denote an m by n matrix whose elements are random variables V_{ij}. We define

$$E(\boldsymbol{V}) = \begin{pmatrix} E(V_{11}) & \cdots & E(V_{1n}) \\ \vdots & & \\ E(V_{m1}) & \cdots & E(V_{mn}) \end{pmatrix}$$

and observe that for any constant matrices $\boldsymbol{A}$ and $\boldsymbol{B}$ (of dimensions such that the products are defined):

$$E(\boldsymbol{A}\,\boldsymbol{V}\,\boldsymbol{B}) = \boldsymbol{A}\,E(\boldsymbol{V})\boldsymbol{B}.$$

Consider now the random vector $(X_1,\cdots,X_n)$ written as a column matrix $\boldsymbol{X}$. The column matrix of mean values is

$$\boldsymbol{\mu} = E(\boldsymbol{X}) = \begin{pmatrix} E(X_1) \\ \vdots \\ E(X_n) \end{pmatrix},$$

and the *covariance matrix* $\boldsymbol{M}$, defined to be the matrix of second moments, about the means, is

$$\boldsymbol{M} = E[(\boldsymbol{X} - \boldsymbol{\mu})(\boldsymbol{X} - \boldsymbol{\mu})'],$$

where the prime denotes transposition or interchange of rows and columns. The element in the ith row and jth column of $\boldsymbol{M}$ is m_{ij}, the covariance of X_i and X_j. Clearly M is *symmetric*: $\boldsymbol{M} = \boldsymbol{M}'$, since $m_{ij} = m_{ji}$. If $(X_1,\cdots,X_n)$ are independent, the covariance matrix is diagonal (nonzero elements occur only on the diagonal $i = j$), all covariances being zero for $i \neq j$.

A covariance matrix is *non-negative definite*. This means that it is symmetric and that for any constants $(c_1,\cdots,c_n)$ the quadratic form

$$\boldsymbol{c}'\boldsymbol{M}\boldsymbol{c} = \sum_{i=1}^{n}\sum_{j=1}^{n} c_i c_j m_{ij}$$

is non-negative. This is seen as follows:

$$\begin{aligned} \boldsymbol{c}'\boldsymbol{M}\boldsymbol{c} = \boldsymbol{c}'E[(\boldsymbol{X} - \boldsymbol{\mu})(\boldsymbol{X} - \boldsymbol{\mu})']\boldsymbol{c} &= E[\boldsymbol{c}'(\boldsymbol{X} - \boldsymbol{\mu})(\boldsymbol{X} - \boldsymbol{\mu})'\boldsymbol{c}] \\ &= E([\boldsymbol{c}'(\boldsymbol{X} - \boldsymbol{\mu})]^2) \geq 0. \end{aligned}$$

Moreover, if some c_i at least is not zero, the vanishing of $\boldsymbol{c}'\boldsymbol{M}\boldsymbol{c}$ would imply that the linear combination $\boldsymbol{c}'(\boldsymbol{X} - \boldsymbol{\mu})$ is zero with probability one and that $X_i - \mu_i$ is a linear combination of the other X's with probability one. This would mean that the distribution of $\boldsymbol{X}$ is singular; therefore if the distribution of $\boldsymbol{X}$ is *not* singular, the quadratic form $\boldsymbol{c'Mc}$ is actually positive unless $c_1 = \cdots = c_n = 0$. In this case $\boldsymbol{M}$ is said to be *positive definite.*

The joint characteristic function of $(X_1,\cdots,X_n)$ is conveniently expressed in matrix notation:

$$\phi_{\boldsymbol{X}}(\boldsymbol{t}) = E[\exp(it_1X_1 + \cdots + it_nX_n)] = E(e^{i\boldsymbol{t}'\boldsymbol{X}}),$$

where $\phi_{\boldsymbol{X}}(\boldsymbol{t})$ is short for $\phi_{X_1,\ldots,X_n}(t_1,\ldots,t_n)$.

Suppose now that $\boldsymbol{Y}$ is an m-dimensional random vector (written as a column matrix) defined by a linear transformation on $\boldsymbol{X}$:

$$\boldsymbol{Y} = \boldsymbol{AX},$$

where $m \leq n$. Then

$$\boldsymbol{\mu}_Y = E(\boldsymbol{Y}) = E(\boldsymbol{AX}) = \boldsymbol{A}E(\boldsymbol{X}) = \boldsymbol{A\mu_X},$$

and the matrix of second moments of Y is

$$\begin{aligned}\boldsymbol{M_Y} &= E[(\boldsymbol{Y} - \boldsymbol{\mu_Y})(\boldsymbol{Y} - \boldsymbol{\mu_Y})'] = E[\boldsymbol{A}(\boldsymbol{X} - \boldsymbol{\mu_X})(\boldsymbol{X} - \boldsymbol{\mu_X})'\boldsymbol{A}'] \\ &= \boldsymbol{A}\, E[(\boldsymbol{X} - \boldsymbol{\mu_X})(\boldsymbol{X} - \boldsymbol{\mu_X})']\, \boldsymbol{A}' = \boldsymbol{AM_XA}'.\end{aligned}$$

The characteristic function of $\boldsymbol{Y}$ is also easily obtained in terms of the characteristic function of $\boldsymbol{X}$:

$$\phi_{\boldsymbol{Y}}(\boldsymbol{t}) = E(e^{i\boldsymbol{t}'\boldsymbol{Y}}) = E(e^{i\boldsymbol{t}'\boldsymbol{AX}}) = E(e^{i[\boldsymbol{A}'\boldsymbol{t}]'\boldsymbol{X}}) = \phi_{\boldsymbol{X}}(\boldsymbol{A}'\boldsymbol{t}).$$

If $\boldsymbol{Y}$ is n dimensional, so that A is square, and if A is nonsingular (that is, if $\det A \neq 0$), there is an inverse transformation, $\boldsymbol{X} = A^{-1}\boldsymbol{Y}$. If $\boldsymbol{X}$ has the density function $f_{\boldsymbol{X}}(\boldsymbol{x})$, the corresponding density function for $\boldsymbol{Y}$ is

$$f_{\boldsymbol{Y}}(\boldsymbol{y}) = \frac{1}{|\det A|} f_{\boldsymbol{X}}(A^{-1}\boldsymbol{y}).$$

The assumption of nonsingularity of A simply means that the random variables $\boldsymbol{Y}$ are really n distinct random variables; that is, one is not just a linear combination of the others, in which case the distribution of $\boldsymbol{Y}$ would be singular (concentrated in the hyperplane of the linear relation).

PROBLEMS

3–40. Consider the discrete distribution for (X,Y,Z) in which the following points have equal probabilities: (0,0,0), (0,0,1), (2,0,1), (2,1,0), (1,2,1), (0,2,0).

(a) Determine the marginal distributions of X, Y, and Z.

(b) Determine the probability tables for the joint marginal distribution of (X,Y); the joint conditional distribution of (X,Y), given $Z = 0$; and the joint conditional distribution of (X,Y), given $Z = 1$.

(c) Determine the probability distribution of $X + Y + Z$. Verify that $E(X + Y + Z) = E(X) + E(Y) + E(Z)$.

(d) Compute the correlation coefficient of X and Y; the partial correlation coefficient of X and Y, given $Z = 0$; and the partial correlation coefficient of X and Y, given $Z = 1$.

3–41. Let (X, Y, Z) have a joint distribution that is uniform in the portion of the first octant bounded by the plane $x + y + z = 1$.

(a) Determine the constant value of the density function in this region.

(b) Determine the density of the marginal distribution of (X, Y) and then of X.

(c) Let $U = X$, $V = X + Y$, and $W = X + Y + Z$ and determine the joint density function of (U, V, W).

3–42. Let $(U_1, \ldots, U_n)$ have the density function

$$f_U(u) = \begin{cases} n!, & \text{for } 0 < u_1 < u_2 < \cdots < u_n < 1 \\ 0, & \text{elsewhere.} \end{cases}$$

Let $X_1 = U_1$, $X_2 = U_2 - U_1, \cdots, X_n = U_n - U_{n-1}$, and determine the joint density function of $(X_1, \cdots, X_n)$.

3–43. Given matrices $\boldsymbol{A}$ with elements a_{ij} and $\boldsymbol{B}$ with elements b_{ij}, the product $\boldsymbol{AB}$ is defined, if the number of columns of $\boldsymbol{A}$ equals the number of rows of $\boldsymbol{B}$, as a matrix in which the element of the ith row and jth column is

$$\sum_k a_{ik} b_{kj}.$$

(a) Show that $(\boldsymbol{AB})\boldsymbol{C} = \boldsymbol{A}(\boldsymbol{BC})$.

(b) If the transpose $\boldsymbol{A}'$ of $\boldsymbol{A}$ is defined as a matrix whose rows are the columns of $\boldsymbol{A}$ and whose columns are the rows of $\boldsymbol{A}$, show that $(\boldsymbol{AB})' = \boldsymbol{B}'\boldsymbol{A}'$.

(c) Show that the identity matrix $\boldsymbol{I}$ has the property that $\boldsymbol{IA} = \boldsymbol{A}$ and $\boldsymbol{BI} = \boldsymbol{B}$ (where in each case the order of $\boldsymbol{I}$ is that which makes the multiplication possible).

3–44. Let X, Y, and Z be independent normal variables with means $(0,2,0)$ and variances 4, 9, and 1, respectively.

(a) Write out the joint density function of (X, Y, Z).

(b) Write out the joint characteristic function of (X, Y, Z).

(c) Let $U = X + Y$ and $V = Y + Z$. Determine the mean vector and covariance matrix (i) directly, using properties of the expectation, variance, and covariance operations; and using (ii) the matrix formulas developed in the text.

(d) Write out the characteristic function of (U, V).

(e) Determine the joint density of (U, V).

3.2.3 The Multinomial Distribution. In treating the binomial distribution, we considered a basic Bernoulli experiment with two outcomes H and T and studied the distribution of the number of H's in a sequence of independent performances of the experiment. The situation will now be generalized to one in which the basic experiment can result in any of k ways: $A_1, \ldots, A_k$, with corresponding probabilities $p_1, \ldots, p_k$ where $p_1 + \cdots + p_k = 1$. Among n independent trials, X_i will denote the number of trials in which A_i occurs, for $i = 1, \ldots, k$. Clearly, $X_1 + X_2 + \cdots + X_k = n$, and therefore if one knows $k - 1$ of the X's he automatically knows the kth X. Thus, just as in the *bi*nomial case, with $k = 2$, in which there was only one random variable to consider, so in the *multi*nomial case, with k possible outcomes, there are only $k - 1$ random variables to consider. Call the ones that are considered $X_1, \ldots, X_{k-1}$ and then keep in mind that $X_k = n - X_1 - \cdots - X_{k-1}$.

The joint distribution of the random frequencies $X_1, \ldots, X_{k-1}$ will now be obtained in terms of its probability function

$$P(X_1 = f_1, \ldots, X_{k-1} = f_{k-1})$$

for given non-negative integers f_i such that $f_1 + \cdots + f_{k-1} \leq n$. In order that $X_1 = f_1, \ldots,$ and $X_{k-1} = f_{k-1}$, the composite experiment must result in a sequence of outcomes of which f_1 are A_1's, ..., and f_{k-1} are A_{k-1}'s (and, of course, $n - f_1 - \cdots - f_{k-1}$ are A_k's). The probability of such a sequence is

$$p_1^{f_1} p_2^{f_2} \cdots p_k^{f_k},$$

no matter what the order of the various outcomes in the sequence. Since there are

$$\frac{n!}{f_1! f_2! \cdots f_k!}$$

distinct sequences involving a given number of A_1's, of A_2's, ..., and of A_k's, and since these differently ordered sequences have identical probabilities, the desired probability is just the number of those sequences with given f's times the probability of any one:

$$P(X_1 = f_1, \ldots, X_{k-1} = f_{k-1}) = \frac{n!}{f_1! f_2! \cdots f_k!} p_1^{f_1} p_2^{f_2} \cdots p_k^{f_k}.$$

This formula holds for any non-negative integers $f_1, \ldots, f_{k-1}$ whose sum does not exceed n, with $f_k = n - f_1 - \cdots - f_{k-1}$. Equivalently, it holds for any non-negative integers $f_1, \ldots, f_k$ whose sum *equals* n.

The name "multinomial" is appropriate because this distribution is to the multinomial expansion as the binomial distribution is to the binomial expansion. That is,

$$(u_1 + \cdots + u_k)^n = \sum \frac{n!}{f_1! f_2! \cdots f_k!} u_1^{f_1} u_2^{f_2} \cdots u_k^{f_k},$$

the sum extending over all sets of k non-negative integers $f_1, \ldots, f_k$ whose sum is n. Putting $u_i = p_i$, we find that the terms in the expansion are precisely the multinomial probabilities and that the left-hand side reduces to 1, the sum of these probabilities.

The multinomial distribution can also be considered as a distribution of the k variables $X_1, \ldots, X_k$ with probability assigned only in the hyperplane

$x_1 + \cdots + x_k = n$. For $(f_1, \ldots, f_k)$ on this hyperplane, the probability is still as given above. The moment generating function of the distribution is

$$E[\exp(t_1X_1 + \cdots + t_kX_k)] = \sum \frac{n!}{f_1! \cdots f_k!} p_1^{f_1} \cdots p_k^{f_k} e^{t_1f_1} \cdots e^{t_kf_k}$$
$$= (p_1e^{t_1} + \cdots + p_ke^{t_k})^n$$
$$= 1 + np_1t_1 + \cdots + np_kt_k + \cdots.$$

Evidently $E(X_1) = np_1, \ldots$, and $E(X_k) = np_k$, which is also clear from the fact that the marginal distributions of the X's are binomial. Joint marginal distributions of sets of X's are multinomial but with fewer outcomes in the basic experiment.

Example 3–23. A die is tossed 12 times. Let X_i denote the number of tosses in which i dots turn up, for $i = 1, \ldots, 6$. Then $p_i = 1/6$, and $E(X_i) = 12/6 = 2$, for each i. A sample probability computation is

$$P(X_1 = 2, X_2 = 2, \ldots, X_6 = 2) = \frac{12!}{2!\,2! \cdots 2!} \left(\frac{1}{6}\right)^2 \left(\frac{1}{6}\right)^2 \cdots \left(\frac{1}{6}\right)^2$$
$$= \frac{1925}{549{,}872},$$

(which shows, incidentally, that the "expected" outcome is not very likely). The marginal distribution, say, of X_1 and X_2 is the trinomial distribution defined by

$$P(X_1 = f_1 \text{ and } X_2 = f_2) = \sum_{f_1+f_2 \leq 12} \frac{12!}{f_1!f_2!(12 - f_1 - f_2)!} p_1^{f_1} p_2^{f_2} p^f,$$

where $p = 1 - p_1 - p_2 = 4/6$ and $f = 12 - f_1 - f_2$.

Example 3–24. Let X have a continuous distribution with density function $f(x)$, and suppose that when the experiment involved is performed n times, data are recorded (as they must be in rounding off) by counting the number of results that fall in the "class interval" S_i, where $S_1, \cdots, S_k$ are nonoverlapping sets of possible values of X that cover all possibilities. The numbers f_i are then random variables with a multinomial distribution, where

$$p_i = P(X \text{ falls in } S_i) = \int_{S_i} f(x)\,dx.$$

3.2.4 Multivariate Normal Distributions. The random vector $\mathbf{X} = (X_1, \ldots, X_n)$, written in matrix form as a column matrix:

$$\mathbf{X} = \begin{pmatrix} X_1 \\ \vdots \\ X_p \end{pmatrix},$$

is said to have a p-variate normal distribution if it is of the form

$$\mathbf{X} = A\mathbf{Y} + \mathbf{b},$$

where A is a $p \times p$ matrix of constants, b is a column matrix of constants, and $Y_1, \cdots, Y_p$ are independent, standard normal random variables (having zero means and unit variances).

The joint distribution of the standard normal Y's has a density obtained by multiplying together the univariate densities:

$$f_Y(y_1, \ldots, y_p) = \frac{1}{(2\pi)^{p/2}} \exp[-\tfrac{1}{2}(y_1^2 + \cdots + y_p^2)]$$

$$= \frac{1}{(2\pi)^{p/2}} \exp[-\tfrac{1}{2}y'y].$$

The characteristic function of the Y's is obtained by multiplying together their univariate characteristic functions:

$$\phi_Y(s) = \prod_{k=1}^{p} \phi_{Y_k}(s_k) = \exp[-\tfrac{1}{2}(s_1^2 + \cdots + s_p^2)]$$

$$= \exp[-\tfrac{1}{2}s's].$$

The mean vector of Y is a column of zeros; and the covariance matrix has zeros off the main diagonal, since the Y's are pairwise uncorrelated, and 1's on the main diagonal, since their variances are 1:

$$M_Y = E(YY') = I.$$

The nature of the distribution of $X = AY + b$ can now be determined from the distribution of Y. The expectation of X is

$$\mu = E(X) = E(AY + b) = AE(Y) + b = b,$$

and the covariance matrix,

$$M_X = AM_YA' = AA'.$$

The characteristic function is

$$\begin{aligned}\phi_X(t) &= \exp[it'(AX + b)] = e^{it'b}\phi_{AY}(A't)\\ &= \exp[it'b - \tfrac{1}{2}(A't)'(A't)]\\ &= \exp[it'\mu - \tfrac{1}{2}t'Mt],\end{aligned}$$

in which the subscript on M has been dropped: $M = M_X$. Observe that this reduces to the univariate normal characteristic function with $p = 1$ and $M = \sigma^2$.

It is important to know that if M is a non-negative definite symmetric matrix, a distribution with characteristic function $\exp[it'\mu - \frac{1}{2}t'Mt]$ is multivariate normal. Surely, if $M = AA'$ for some matrix A, an X with this characteristic function is multivariate normal, since the distribution of $AY + \mu$ would have the same characteristic function, which uniquely determines the distribution. The fact that any non-negative definite symmetric $\boldsymbol{M}$ can be expressed in the form $\boldsymbol{AA'}$ will not be proved here (cf. F. E. Hohn, *Elementary Matrix Algebra*, New York, Macmillan, 1958). It is a consequence of a "diagonalization theorem" that will be used in Chapter 8.

It is now immediate that any marginal distribution of a multivariate normal distribution is multivariate normal. For, the characteristic function of a marginal distribution is obtained by putting 0's for the t's corresponding to the dropped variables, and the resulting expression is again of the same type, with a non-negative definite submatrix of $\boldsymbol{M}$.

If $\boldsymbol{M}$ is positive definite, a distribution with characteristic function $\exp[i\boldsymbol{t}'\boldsymbol{\mu} - \frac{1}{2}\boldsymbol{t}'\boldsymbol{M}\boldsymbol{t}]$ has a nonsingular p-variate normal distribution, the matrix $\boldsymbol{A}$ in the factorization $\boldsymbol{M} = \boldsymbol{AA'}$ being nonsingular ($\det \boldsymbol{A} \neq 0$). In this case the distribution has a density function, which can be obtained from the density of the independent standard normal Y's:

$$f_{\boldsymbol{X}}(x_1, \ldots, x_p) = \frac{1}{|\det \boldsymbol{A}|} f_{\boldsymbol{Y}}(\boldsymbol{A}^{-1}[\boldsymbol{x} - \boldsymbol{b}])$$

$$= \frac{1}{(2\pi)^{p/2}|\det \boldsymbol{A}|}[\exp -\tfrac{1}{2}(\boldsymbol{x} - \boldsymbol{\mu})'(\boldsymbol{A}^{-1})'\boldsymbol{A}^{-1}(\boldsymbol{x} - \boldsymbol{\mu})].$$

Now, since $\boldsymbol{ABB}^{-1}\boldsymbol{A}^{-1} = \boldsymbol{AIA}^{-1} = \boldsymbol{I}$, the inverse of $\boldsymbol{AB}$ is $(\boldsymbol{AB})^{-1} = \boldsymbol{B}^{-1}\boldsymbol{A}^{-1}$, and therefore

$$\boldsymbol{M}^{-1} = (\boldsymbol{AA'})^{-1} = (\boldsymbol{A'})^{-1}\boldsymbol{A}^{-1} = (\boldsymbol{A}^{-1})'\boldsymbol{A}^{-1}.$$

Also, it can be shown that $\det(\boldsymbol{AB}) = (\det \boldsymbol{A})(\det \boldsymbol{B})$, and so

$$\det \boldsymbol{M} = (\det \boldsymbol{A})(\det \boldsymbol{A'}) = (\det \boldsymbol{A})^2.$$

Consequently the density of $\boldsymbol{X}$ can be rewritten in terms of $\boldsymbol{\mu}$ and $\boldsymbol{M}$:

$$f_{\boldsymbol{X}}(\boldsymbol{x}) = \frac{1}{(2\pi)^{p/2}\sqrt{\det \boldsymbol{M}}} \exp[-\tfrac{1}{2}(\boldsymbol{x} - \boldsymbol{\mu})'\boldsymbol{M}^{-1}(\boldsymbol{x} - \boldsymbol{\mu})],$$

which again in the univariate case ($p = 1$) reduces to the univariate normal distribution of §2.5.4.

Example 3–25. Let Y_1, Y_2, and Y_3 be independent, standard normal random variables. Consider $\boldsymbol{X}$ defined by

$$\begin{cases} X_1 = 2Y_1 - Y_2 + Y_3 \\ X_2 = Y_1 - 3Y_2, \end{cases}$$

or

$$\boldsymbol{X} = \begin{pmatrix} 2 & -1 & 1 \\ 1 & -3 & 0 \end{pmatrix} \boldsymbol{Y}.$$

The covariance matrix of $\boldsymbol{X}$ is

$$\boldsymbol{M} = \begin{pmatrix} 2 & -1 & 1 \\ 1 & -3 & 0 \end{pmatrix} \begin{pmatrix} 2 & 1 \\ -1 & -3 \\ 1 & 0 \end{pmatrix} = \begin{pmatrix} 6 & 5 \\ 5 & 10 \end{pmatrix},$$

with det $\boldsymbol{M} = 35$ and

$$\boldsymbol{M}^{-1} = \frac{1}{35}\begin{pmatrix} 10 & -5 \\ -5 & 6 \end{pmatrix}.$$

With these one can write out the characteristic function of $\boldsymbol{X}$:

$$\exp[-\tfrac{1}{2}(6t_1^2 + 10t_1t_2 + 10t_2^2)];$$

and the density function:

$$\frac{1}{2\pi\sqrt{35}} \exp[-\tfrac{1}{70}(10x_1^2 - 10x_1x_2 + 6x_2^2)].$$

Given $\boldsymbol{X}$ with a multivariate normal distribution, let $\boldsymbol{Z}$ be a linear function of $\boldsymbol{X}$,

$$\boldsymbol{Z} = \boldsymbol{CX} + \boldsymbol{d},$$

with no restriction on the number of components of $\boldsymbol{Z}$. The characteristic function of $\boldsymbol{Z}$ is

$$\begin{aligned} \phi_{\boldsymbol{Z}}(\boldsymbol{u}) &= e^{i\boldsymbol{u}'\boldsymbol{d}}\,\phi_{\boldsymbol{X}}(\boldsymbol{C}'\boldsymbol{u}) \\ &= \exp[i\boldsymbol{u}'(\boldsymbol{C\mu} + \boldsymbol{d}) - \tfrac{1}{2}\boldsymbol{u}'\boldsymbol{CMC}'\boldsymbol{u}] \end{aligned}$$

It is concluded from the form of this characteristic function that $\boldsymbol{Z}$ has a multivariate normal distribution with mean $\boldsymbol{C\mu} + \boldsymbol{d}$ and covariance matrix $\boldsymbol{CMC}'$. Thus any set of linear combinations of normal X's is normal; in particular, any single linear combination of normal variables is normal.

Example 3–26. Given the normal $\boldsymbol{X}$ of Example 3–25, let $\boldsymbol{Z}$ be obtained from $\boldsymbol{X}$ as follows:

$$\boldsymbol{Z} = \begin{pmatrix} 1 & -1 \\ 2 & 1 \\ 1 & 2 \end{pmatrix} \boldsymbol{X}.$$

The distribution of $\boldsymbol{Z}$ must be singular, since there are more Z's than X's; indeed, $Z_3 = Z_2 - Z_1$, so the distribution of $\boldsymbol{Z}$ is concentrated in the plane $z_1 - z_2 + z_3 = 0$. The covariance matrix of $\boldsymbol{Z}$ is

$$\boldsymbol{M_Z} = \begin{pmatrix} 1 & -1 \\ 2 & 1 \\ 1 & 2 \end{pmatrix} \begin{pmatrix} 6 & 5 \\ 5 & 10 \end{pmatrix} \begin{pmatrix} 1 & 2 & 1 \\ -1 & 1 & 2 \end{pmatrix} = \begin{pmatrix} 6 & -3 & -9 \\ -3 & 54 & 57 \\ -9 & 57 & 66 \end{pmatrix},$$

which, of course, is singular.

PROBLEMS

3–45. One black, three white, and two red balls are placed in a container. One ball is selected at random and replaced, and then a second ball is selected at random. Let X and Y denote, respectively, the number of red and white balls that turn up. Construct a probability table for (X, Y) and determine from it the marginal distributions of X and Y. (Notice that these are binomial distributions.)

3–46. Four independent observations are to be made on a random variable with density $f(x) = 1 - |x|$, $-1 < x < 1$. Suppose that the interval from -1 to 1 is divided into four class intervals of equal length. What is the probability that one observation with fall in the left-most class interval, one in the next, two in the next, and none in the right-most class interval?

3–47. Let $\boldsymbol{X}$ have a multivariate normal distribution with mean and covariance matrices

$$\boldsymbol{\mu} = \begin{pmatrix} 3 \\ 3 \\ 0 \\ 0 \end{pmatrix}, \quad \boldsymbol{M} = \begin{pmatrix} 2 & 0 & 2 & 0 \\ 0 & 1 & 1 & 0 \\ 2 & 1 & 5 & 1 \\ 0 & 0 & 1 & 1 \end{pmatrix}.$$

(a) Show that $\boldsymbol{M}$ is nonsingular.
(b) Compute the total correlation between X_1 and X_3.
(c) Let $\boldsymbol{Y} = \boldsymbol{C}\boldsymbol{X} + \boldsymbol{d}$, with

$$\boldsymbol{C} = \begin{pmatrix} 1 & 1 & 1 & -1 \\ 1 & -1 & 1 & 1 \\ 1 & 0 & 1 & 0 \end{pmatrix}, \quad \boldsymbol{d} = \begin{pmatrix} 2 \\ 0 \\ -1 \end{pmatrix}$$

Compute the mean and covariance matrices of $\boldsymbol{Y}$.
(d) Determine the characteristic function and density function of Y_1 and Y_2 in (c).
(e) Determine the mean and variance of Y_3 directly, using $E(\cdot)$ computations.

3–48. Use the result about a linear transformation of a multivariate normal distribution to show that any subset of $(X_1, \cdots, X_n)$ with a multivariate normal distribution is also multivariate normal.

4/Sums of Random Variables

Sums of random variables were treated occasionally in earlier chapters as particular functions of several random variables. This chapter is devoted to a more systematic study of sums of random variables, and especially of sums of independent random variables. Sums of random variables seem to be met at every turn in statistical problems, either because a variable of interest is inherently an additive combination of ingredients, or because many quantities computed from data for purposes of inference involve summation of random variables.

4.1 The Distribution of a Sum

Inasmuch as the sum of random variables is again a random variable, it is in order to inquire as to the probability distribution of the sum. Consider the sum of the n random variables $(X_1, \cdots, X_n)$ whose joint distribution has a density function $f(x_1,\cdots,x_n)$. The distribution function of the sum

$$Y = X_1 + X_2 + \cdots + X_n$$

can be computed in terms of the joint density function:

$$F_Y(y) = P(X_1 + \cdots + X_n \le y) = \int \cdots \int_R f(x_1, \ldots, x_n)\, dx_1 \cdots dx_n,$$

where R is the region in the space of points $(x_1,\ldots,x_n)$ consisting of those points the sum of whose coordinates does not exceed y.

Although it is easy to write down the distribution function of a sum of random variables as a multiple integral over a region in the space of the joint distribution of the summands, it is not always possible to express the results in the form of an explicit, well-known function. But if worse comes to worst, one can carry out a numerical integration for each of a collection of y values and so obtain a useful tabulation of the distribution function values.

Example 4–1. Let X and Y be independent and normally distributed each with mean zero and variance 1. Their joint density function is then

$$\frac{1}{2\pi} \exp[-\tfrac{1}{2}(x^2 + y^2)].$$

The distribution function of the sum $Z = X + Y$ is a double integral:

$$F_Z(z) = P(Z \le z) = \int_R\int \frac{1}{2\pi} \exp[-\tfrac{1}{2}(x^2 + y^2)]\, dA,$$

where R is the region of the xy plane in which $x + y \le z$, as shown in Figure 4–1. The double integral over R can then be expressed as an iterated integral and the

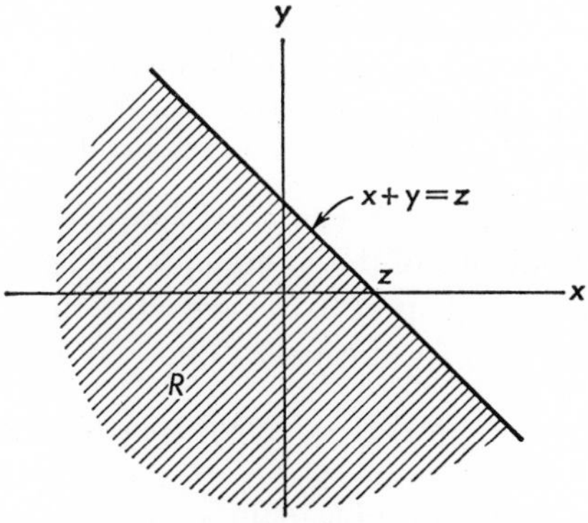

Figure 4–1

density function is obtained by differentiation:

$$f_Z(z) = \frac{1}{2\pi}\frac{d}{dz}\int_{-\infty}^{\infty}\int_{-\infty}^{z-x} \exp[-\tfrac{1}{2}(x^2 + y^2)]\, dy\, dx$$

$$= \frac{1}{2\pi}\int_{-\infty}^{\infty} \exp\{-\tfrac{1}{2}(x^2 + [z - x]^2)\}\, dx$$

$$= \frac{1}{2\pi}\exp(-\tfrac{1}{4}z^2)\int_{-\infty}^{\infty} \exp[-(x^2 - zx + \tfrac{1}{4}z^2)]\, dx$$

$$= \frac{1}{\sqrt{2\pi}\sqrt{2}}\exp(-\tfrac{1}{4}z^2).$$

The result is recognized as the density function of a normal distribution with mean zero and variance 2.

Example 4–2. Let (X, Y) have the discrete distribution defined by the probabilities in the accompanying table. The distribution is sufficiently simple that one can read

Y \ X	1	2	3
1	0	$\frac{1}{6}$	$\frac{1}{6}$
2	$\frac{1}{6}$	0	$\frac{1}{6}$
3	$\frac{1}{6}$	$\frac{1}{6}$	0

from the table the possible values of the sum $X + Y$ and the corresponding probabilities. These are as follows:

z	2	3	4	5	6
$p(z)$	0	$\frac{1}{3}$	$\frac{1}{3}$	$\frac{1}{3}$	0

This distribution of (X, Y) was encountered in Example 3–1 as the joint distribution of the number on the first ball drawn and the number on the second ball drawn, when two balls are drawn without replacement from three balls numbered 1, 2, and 3. The sum $X + Y$ is the sum of the numbers on the two balls drawn.

Moments of the distribution of a sum are frequently pertinent and can be expressed in terms of moments of the summands. The first moment is particularly simple, for, as seen in Chapter 2, the expectation of a sum of two random variables is the sum of the expectations. Thus, by induction,

$$E(X_1 + \cdots + X_n) = E(X_1) + \cdots + E(X_n).$$

Expression of higher moments of a sum in terms of marginal and mixed moments is not so simple, and only the variance is taken up here. It is observed first that for any quantities $U_1, \cdots, U_n$,

$$\left(\sum_i U_i\right)^2 = \sum_i U_i \sum_j U_j = \sum_i \sum_j U_i U_j.$$

Using this, and again the fact that the expectation of a sum is the sum of the expectations (even though the sum be a double sum), we find

$$\begin{aligned}
\operatorname{var}\left(\sum_i X_i\right) &= E\left\{\sum_i X_i - E\left(\sum_i X_i\right)\right\}^2 = E\left\{\sum_i [X_i - E(X_i)]\right\}^2 \\
&= E\left\{\sum_i \sum_j [X_i - E(X_i)][X_j - E(X_j)]\right\} \\
&= \sum_i \sum_j E\{[X_i - E(X_i)][X_j - E(X_j)]\} \\
&= \sum_i \sum_j \operatorname{cov}(X_i, X_j).
\end{aligned}$$

It is understood, of course, that for the terms in the sum in which $i = j$, one can write $\operatorname{cov}(X_i, X_i) = \operatorname{var} X_i$. The result can thus be written this way:

$$\operatorname{var}\left(\sum_i X_i\right) = \sum_i \operatorname{var} X_i + \sum_{i \neq j} \operatorname{cov}(X_i, X_j).$$

The variance of a sum can be more or less than the sum of the variances, depending on the magnitudes and signs of the covariances of pairs of summands.

It is important to notice that if each pair of X's in the sum $X_1 + \cdots + X_n$ is *uncorrelated*, all the covariance terms vanish, leaving:

$$\operatorname{var}\left(\sum_i X_i\right) = \sum_i \operatorname{var} X_i.$$

4.2 Distribution of a Sum of Independent Variables

When the terms in a sum of random variables are *independent*, a great deal more can be said about the distribution of the sum than can be said in general. We discuss here the expression of the density of a sum as a "convolution" of the densities of the summands, the simplification of the variance, the impact of independence on the characteristic function of a sum, and the use of the characteristic function in obtaining the distribution of a sum.

4.2.1 The Distribution Function. Consider first two independent random variables X and Y, and assume their distributions to be of the continuous type. Their joint density function is then defined and is the product:

$$f(x,y) = f_X(x)f_Y(y).$$

The distribution function of the sum $Z = X + Y$ is now obtained following the procedure used in Example 4–1 for a special case:

$$\begin{aligned} P(X + Y \leq z) &= \iint\limits_{x+y\leq z} f_X(x)f_Y(y)\,dx\,dy \\ &= \int_{-\infty}^{\infty}\int_{-\infty}^{z-y} f_X(x)f_Y(y)\,dx\,dy. \end{aligned}$$

Differentiating with respect to z yields the density function:

$$f_Z(z) = \int_{-\infty}^{\infty} f_Y(y)f_X(z - y)\,dy,$$

a combination of f_X and f_Y called their *convolution*. Observe that this can be written equally well (putting $z - y = u$) as

$$f_Z(z) = \int_{-\infty}^{\infty} f_Y(z - u)f_X(u)\,du.$$

Thus the binary operation of convolving two functions is commutative:

$$f_X * f_Y = f_Y * f_X,$$

where the asterisk denotes the convolution operation. It can also be shown to be associative:

$$f_X * (f_Y * f_Z) = (f_X * f_Y) * f_Z = f_X * f_Y * f_Z,$$

and this combination, incidentally, is the density function of the sum of the three independent random variables X, Y, and Z. The density function of a sum of n independent random variables is expressible similarly as an n-fold convolution of the densities of the summands.

Example 4–3. Suppose that X and Y have independent distributions each uniform on [0,1]. That is,

$$f_X(\lambda) = f_Y(\lambda) = \begin{cases} 1, & 0 < \lambda < 1, \\ 0, & \text{elsewhere.} \end{cases}$$

But then

$$f_X(z - y) = \begin{cases} 1, & \text{if } 0 < z - y < 1, \quad \text{or } z - 1 < y < z, \\ 0, & \text{elsewhere,} \end{cases}$$

and so, if $0 < z < 1$,

$$f_{X+Y}(z) = \int_{-\infty}^{\infty} f_Y(y) f_X(z - y)\, dy = \int_0^z dy = z.$$

If $1 < z < 2$,

$$f_{X+Y}(z) = \int_{z-1}^{1} dy = 2 - z.$$

For $z < 0$ or $z > 2$, the density is zero. The graph of this density function of the sum of two independent uniform variates is that shown in Figure 4–2.

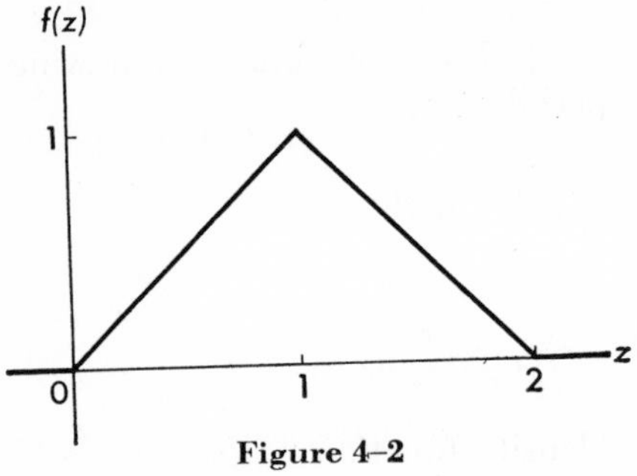

Figure 4–2

4.2.2 The Variance. Since any two independent variables are automatically uncorrelated, it follows that, as in the uncorrelated case, if $X_1, \ldots, X_n$ are independent:

$$\operatorname{var}\left\{\sum_i X_i\right\} = \operatorname{var} X_i + \cdots + \operatorname{var} X_n.$$

Taking square roots, one finds the standard deviation of a sum of independent random variables to be a "root-sum-square" combination of the standard deviations of the summands:

$$\sigma_{\Sigma X_i} = \sqrt{\sum \sigma_{X_i}{}^2}.$$

Example 4–4. When resistors are placed in "series," the resistance of the combination is the sum of the individual resistances. Suppose that two 400-ohm and one 200-ohm resistors are placed in series and that they are "5 per cent" resistors. Let us assume that a "5 per cent" resistor is one of a population of resistors whose resistances have a probability distribution about the nominal resistance with a standard deviation that is 5 per cent of the nominal resistance. Then the standard deviations of the given resistances are 20, 20, and 10 ohms, respectively. The standard deviation of the resistance of the series combination is

$$\sqrt{20^2 + 20^2 + 10^2} = 30 \text{ ohms},$$

which is 3 per cent of the nominal series resistance of 1000 ohms. The series combination (considered as a random one of possible series combinations made up at random from the populations of 400-ohm and 200-ohm resistors) has a precision that is better than that of the components.

[It must be admitted that the "5 per cent" label on a resistor is probably not to be interpreted as one standard deviation. This might even vary with the individual manufacturer; but if the measure of variability quoted is proportional to the standard deviation, the above calculation of percentage would remain valid. At any rate, it is usually not appropriate to add the absolute values of the tolerance figures given (to obtain 50 ohms or 5 per cent in the example cited), since the probability is small that the errors would combine without some cancellation of positive and negative errors.]

PROBLEMS

4–1. Determine the distribution of the sum in Example 4–3 directly, interpreting the double integral giving the distribution function as an area.

4–2. Use the convolution formula to obtain the density function of the sum of two independent, negative exponential random variables, each with mean value $1/\lambda$.

4–3. Thirteen cards are drawn at random (without replacement, as in dealing) from a standard bridge deck. Let $X_1, \cdots, X_{13}$ denote the numbers of points assigned to the cards drawn (as in Problem 2–9: 4 for Ace, 3 for King, 2 for Queen, 1 for Jack, and 0 for anything else).

(a) Compute the expected total number of points.

(b) Determine the variance of the total number of points. [*Hint*: First compute var X_i to be 290/169 and $\text{cov}(X_i, X_j)$ to be $-290/(169 \times 51)$, and then use these in the general formula for the variance of a sum.]

4–4. Gears A, B, and C have basic widths 0.5 inch, 0.3 inch, and 0.7 inch, with standard deviations of 0.001 inch, 0.004 inch, and 0.002 inch, respectively. If these are assembled side by side on a single shaft, what is the basic width of the assembly and the standard deviation of this total width?

4–5. The position error (in nautical miles) in a certain guidance system after a given time of operation is given by

$$\delta = 5\delta_a + 20\delta_g,$$

where δ_a and δ_g are independent random errors in an accelerometer and in a gyro (measured in ft/sec² and deg/hr, respectively.) Determine the standard deviation of position error corresponding to standard deviations of 0.1 ft/sec² and 0.05 deg/hr in δ_a and δ_g, respectively.

4–6. Show that $\text{cov}(X, X + Y) = \text{var } X + \text{cov}(X, Y)$. More generally, show that

$$\text{cov}\left(\sum_i a_i X_i, \sum_j b_j Y_j\right) = \sum_i \sum_j a_i b_j \,\text{cov}(X_i, Y_j).$$

4–7. Let the two adjacent sides of a parallelogram have lengths σ_X and σ_Y and the angle between them have a cosine equal to ρ_{XY}, where (X, Y) have a given bivariate distribution. Show that the length of the diagonal of the parallelogram is the standard deviation of the sum $X + Y$. Show also that there are linear combinations of X and Y (that is, combinations of the form $aX + bY$) which are not correlated with X.

4–8. Given the following formulas for conditional probabilities:

$$P(Z \text{ in } A \text{ and } Y \text{ in } B) = \int_B P(Z \text{ in } A \mid Y = y) f_Y(y)\, dy$$

and

$$P(g(X, Y) \text{ in } C \mid Y = y) = P(g(X, y) \text{ in } C \mid Y = y);$$

set $Z = X + Y$, $A = \{Z \leq z\}$, and B equal to the whole space of y values to obtain the formula for the density function of $X + Y$, in the case of independent X and Y.

4.2.3 The Characteristic and Moment Generating Functions. The characteristic function of the sum of independent summands possesses an important factorization property. Stated for two independent random variables, it is as follows:

$$\phi_{X+Y}(t) = E[e^{it(X+Y)}] = E(e^{itX})\, E(e^{itY}) = \phi_X(t)\, \phi_Y(t).$$

In words, the characteristic function of a sum of two independent random variables is the product of their characteristic functions. By induction, then, the characteristic function of any finite sum of independent random variables is the product of their characteristic functions:

$$\phi_{\Sigma X_i}(t) = \prod_{j=1}^{n} \phi_{X_j}(t),$$

where Π denotes a product over the indicated subscript set. Thus, knowing the characteristic functions of the terms in a sum of independent variables, one can easily obtain the characteristic function of the sum. This may turn out to be something that is recognizable as the characteristic function of a familiar distribution—but then again it may not. In any case the inversion formula (1), page 65, can be used to obtain the distribution function of the sum from its characteristic function.

The factorization property holds also for the moment generating function and for the factorial moment generating function of a sum of independent random variables when these variables possess such generating functions.

Example 4–5. Let $X_1, \cdots, X_n$ be independent random variables, each with the Bernoulli distribution: $P(X_i = 1) = p$, $P(X_i = 0) = q = 1 - p$. For each X_i, the moment generating function is

$$\psi(t) = E(e^{tX_i}) = pe^t + q.$$

Therefore the moment generating function of the sum $S = X_1 + \cdots + X_n$ is

$$\psi_S(t) = [\psi_X(t)]^n = (pe^t + q)^n.$$

(Here, as will be done frequently in what follows, the symbol X is used when the X_i's are identically distributed to refer to their common characteristics.) Since we already know that the sum S is binomially distributed, we have derived anew the moment generating function of a binomial distribution.

Example 4–6. Let $X_1, \cdots, X_n$ be independent, and let each have the negative exponential distribution defined by the density function

$$f(x) = \lambda e^{-\lambda x}, \qquad x > 0,$$

and characteristic function

$$\phi(t) = \lambda \int_0^\infty e^{itx} e^{-\lambda x}\, dx = \frac{\lambda}{\lambda - it}.$$

The characteristic function of the sum $S = X_1 + \cdots + X_n$ is the nth power:

$$\phi_S(t) = [\phi(t)]^n = \left(\frac{\lambda}{\lambda - it}\right)^n.$$

This does not happen to be a characteristic function already encountered; however, it can be shown that the density

$$\lambda^n x^{n-1} \frac{e^{-\lambda x}}{(n-1)!}, \qquad x > 0,$$

does have $\phi_S(t)$ as its characteristic function and so is the density function of the sum S. The distributions defined by this density function (and indexed by λ) belong to the family of what are called *gamma distributions.* These will appear again in Chapter 8.

Example 4–7. Consider a sequence of independent, Bernoulli trials. Let the outcomes at each trial be thought of as "success" or "failure," and let p and q, respectively, denote the corresponding probabilities. The number of failures prior to the first success was seen in §2.4.4 to have a geometric distribution with probability function $f(k) = pq^k$ and factorial moment generating function $p/(1 - qt)$. Now let X_1 denote the number of failures prior to the first success, X_2 the number of failures between the first and second successes, and so on, so that

$$S = X_1 + X_2 + \cdots + X_r$$

is the total number of failures before the rth success. It is a sum of independent geometrically distributed random variables. Hence, its factorial moment generating function is

$$\begin{aligned}\eta_S(t) &= \prod_{i=1}^r \eta_{X_i}(t) = \left(\frac{p}{1 - qt}\right)^r = p^r(1 - qt)^{-r} \\ &= p^r \sum_{k=0}^\infty (-qt)^k \binom{-r}{k} \\ &= \sum_{k=0}^\infty p^r(-q)^k \binom{-r}{k} t^k.\end{aligned}$$

The probability of k failures prior to the rth success can be read from this as the coefficient of t^k:

$$P(S = k) = p^r(-q)^k \binom{-r}{k}.$$

A distribution with this probability function is said to be of the *negative binomial* type.

This formula can be deduced more directly by observing that the rth success occurs on the $(r + k)$th trial if and only if $r - 1$ successes and k failures occur in the first $r + k - 1$ trials and they are followed by a success. That is,

$$P(S = k) = \binom{r + k - 1}{k} p^{r-1}q^k p,$$

which can be shown equal to the expression obtained above (cf. Problem 4–11).

Just as the negative exponential is the continuous analogue of the geometric distribution, this negative binomial distribution of the sum of several spacings between successes finds its continuous counterpart in the gamma distributions of the preceding example.

PROBLEMS

4–9. Determine the moment generating function of the sum of two independent random variables each uniform on $[0,1]$, and compare the result with the moment generating function of the "triangular" distribution obtained in Example 4–3.

4–10. Use factorial moment generating functions to show that the sum of independent negative binomial variables with a common parameter p has again the negative binomial distribution. Interpret this result in terms of success runs.

4–11. Demonstrate the equality of the two formulas for a negative binomial probability, recalling that $\binom{-r}{k}$ means $(-r)_k/k!$. Also obtain the mean and variance of a negative binomial distribution.

4–12. Show that a sum of independent binomial variables with a common parameter p is binomial.

4–13. Show that a sum of independent normal variables is normal.

4–14. Show that a sum of independent Poisson variables is Poisson.

4–15. Show that the distribution function of S in Example 4–6 is given by

$$1 - \sum_{k=0}^{n-1} e^{-\lambda x} \frac{(\lambda x)^k}{k!}.$$

[*Hint:* Show that the derivative of this expression is the density obtained in Example 4–6 and that this expression has the correct value at $x = \infty$. Explain the appearance in this expression of Poisson probabilities.]

4–16. Let $X_1, \cdots, X_n$ have independent, identical Poisson distributions. Compute $P(X_1 = 0 \mid X_1 + \cdots + X_n = k)$ in terms of n and k, and then show that the expectation of this quantity with respect to the distribution of $(X_1 + \cdots + X_n)$ is $P(X_1 = 0)$.

4.3 Limit Theorems

The statistical theory of "large samples" makes use of certain results concerning the limiting behavior of sequences of random variables and probability distributions. The rigorous development of such "limit theorems" is usually not elementary, and the mathematical background assumed here precludes a complete presentation of useful results. (For more complete discussions cf. References [4], [7], [13], and B. Gnedenko and A. Kolmogorov, *Limit Distributions for Sums of Independent Random Variables*, Addison-Wesley, Cambridge, Mass., 1954.)

4.3.1 Types of Limits. Consider an infinite sequence of random variables $Y_1, Y_2, \cdots$ defined on a probability space Ω. (This space may be taken to be the space of infinite sequences, in which case the Y's are the coordinate functions.) Let the corresponding distribution functions be $F_1(y), F_2(y), \cdots$. The sequence $\{Y_n\}$ is said to approach the limiting random variable Y with distribution function $F(y)$:

1. *In distribution*, if at each point where $F(y)$ is continuous, one has
$$\lim_{n\to\infty} F_n(y) = F(y).$$
2. *In probability*, if for each $\epsilon > 0$,
$$\lim_{n\to\infty} P(|Y_n - Y| \geq \epsilon) = 0.$$
3. *With probability one*, if
$$P[\lim_{n\to\infty} Y_n = Y] = 1.$$
4. *In the mean*, if
$$\lim_{n\to\infty} E[(Y_n - Y)^2] = 0.$$

Convergence with probability one is sometimes called *strong* convergence; convergence in probability, *weak* convergence.

That convergence in probability is a consequence of convergence in the mean can be seen by using the basic inequality of §2.3.1. With $h(x) = x^2$, $b = \epsilon^2$, $X = |Y_n - Y|$, and A the set of x such that $x \geq \epsilon$, the inequality becomes

$$P(|Y_n - Y| > \epsilon) \leq \frac{1}{\epsilon^2} E(|Y_n - Y|^2).$$

The right-hand side approaches zero as $n \to \infty$, for convergence in the mean, and therefore the left-hand side also approaches zero.

In the special case in which Y is a constant k, the relation

$$E(|Y_n - k|^2) = \text{var } Y_n + [k - E(Y_n)]^2$$

shows that if var Y_n tends to zero and $E(Y_n)$ to k, the sequence $\{Y_n\}$ tends to k in the mean—and therefore in probability. In the next section will be found use for the fact that convergence in probability to a constant is equivalent to convergence in distribution, the limiting distribution being the singular one which lumps all probability at the value $x = k$:

$$F^*(x) = \begin{cases} 1, & \text{if } x \geq k, \\ 0, & \text{if } x < k. \end{cases}$$

To see this, observe first that for $\epsilon > 0$,

$$P(|Y_n - k| \geq \epsilon) = [1 - F_n(k + \epsilon)] + F_n(k - \epsilon) + P(Y_n = k + \epsilon),$$

and

$$P(|Y_n - k| \geq 2\epsilon) \leq [1 - F_n(k + \epsilon)] + F_n(k - \epsilon) - P(Y_n = k - \epsilon).$$

The first of these relations shows that if $Y_n \to k$ in probability, then both $F_n(k + \epsilon) \to 1$ and $F_n(k - \epsilon) \to 0$. The converse follows from the second relation.

Other interrelations exist among these types of limits, but we shall not pursue them further except to state that strong convergence does imply weak convergence, as the names might suggest. (Cf. Reference [13], page 248.)

4.3.2 Laws of Large Numbers. Consider a container with 100 beads, some black and some white, a fraction p of the total being black. A bead is drawn at random repeatedly and replaced after each drawing, and the color of the bead drawn is noted. Most everyone would perhaps agree that if the selections of a bead are really "random," the proportion of black beads among those selected should be close to the actual proportion of black beads in the container, especially if the number of selections is very large. Experience tends to bear out this intuitive feeling—or perhaps the intuitive feeling results from the experience. One expects, and finds in practice, that if k black beads are observed in n selections, k/n is close to p for large n.

If a probability model for this situation is to be useful, it must have a property such as the one described. The theorem that the probability model we have been developing *does* have such a property is called a *law of large numbers*. In a way, the validity of a law of large numbers is a "clincher" in the argument for using probability theory as the basis of statistics.

A *law of large numbers* states, then, that if in a sequence of independent Bernoulli trials, k successes are observed among n trials, it must then follow that in some sense

$$\lim_{n \to \infty} \frac{k}{n} = p,$$

where p is the probability of "success" in a given trial. If this limit is a strong limit, the relation is called the *strong law of large numbers;* if the limit is a weak limit, or limit in probability, the relation is called the *weak law of large numbers.*

The weak law of large numbers is a special case of *Khintchine's theorem:* If $X_1, X_2, \cdots$ are identically distributed with expected value μ and if any finite number of them are independent, then $(X_1 + \cdots + X_n)/n$ tends to μ in probability.

To prove Khintchine's theorem, we begin with the characteristic function of the common distribution of the X_i's, expressed according to (4) of §2.3.3:

$$\phi(t) = 1 + i\mu t + o(t).$$

This has the derivative $\phi'(0) = i\mu$ and is then also continuous at $t = 0$. Since $\phi(0) = 1$, $\phi(t)$ is positive for sufficiently small t, and for such t we define

$$\zeta(t) = \log \phi(t).$$

Then

$$\zeta'(0) = \lim_{n\to\infty} \frac{\zeta(t/n) - \zeta(0)}{(t/n) - 0} = \frac{\phi'(0)}{\phi(0)} = i\mu.$$

The quantity $(X_1 + \cdots + X_n)/n$ has a characteristic function $\phi^*(t)$ whose logarithm is

$$\log \phi^*(t) = \log\left[\phi\left(\frac{t}{n}\right)\right]^n = n \log \phi\left(\frac{t}{n}\right)$$

$$= n\zeta\left(\frac{t}{n}\right) = t\frac{\zeta(t/n)}{t/n} \to i\mu t,$$

as $n \to \infty$. But then (the logarithm function being continuous)

$$\phi^*(t) \to e^{i\mu t},$$

which is the characteristic function of the singular distribution at μ. Therefore, according to property (3) page 66, of the characteristic function, $(X_1 + \cdots + X_n)/n$ tends to μ in distribution and therefore in probability, as claimed.

4.3.3 Central Limit Theorems. Laws of large numbers assert that if a sum of independent, identically distributed random variables $S_n = X_1 + \cdots + X_n$ is divided by n, the number of summands, the result tends to be constant for large n: $S_n/n \to \mu$ (in probability), where μ is the mean of the common distribution. This does *not* mean, however, that the sum S_n tends to be a constant multiple of n. On the contrary, the variability in S_n *increases* as n increases (it is $n\sigma^2$, where σ^2 is the variance of the common distribution). Thus, as n increases, the center of the distribution of S_n moves off to infinity, *and* the spread becomes greater and greater.

It is desirable to know whether anything can be said about the *shape* of the distribution of the sum S_n, and it is a very remarkable thing that there is a "universal" limiting shape, one that is approached no matter what the common distribution of the summands, subject to reasonable restrictions. To examine this limiting shape, it is necessary to modify S_n to keep its mean and variance finite. This is done with a linear transformation, assuming that such translating and stretching does not alter what one would think of as the basic shape of the distribution.

By centering S_n at its expectation and considering instead the random variable $S_n - n\mu$, one obtains a quantity whose expectation remains at 0 as n is allowed to become infinite. The scale change used must be adequate to keep the variance from becoming infinite, yet not so violent as to reduce it to zero. (This is what happens with S_n/n; the scale change in the division by n not only keeps the mean finite but also reduces the variance to zero as n becomes infinite, so that the distribution of the quotient becomes singular and has no "shape.") It has already been seen (Problem 2–50) that the "standardizing" transformation of subtracting the mean from a random variable and dividing by its standard deviation yields a random variable with mean zero and variance 1. So, here let

$$Z_n = \frac{S_n - n\mu}{\sqrt{n}\,\sigma}.$$

For each n this has mean zero and variance 1, and it is the distribution of this quantity that is examined as n becomes infinite.

It is assumed that the variance σ^2 of the common distribution of the terms making up S_n exists; the characteristic function of the distribution of $X_i - \mu$ is then expressible in the form

$$\phi_{X_i-\mu}(t) = 1 - \sigma^2\frac{t^2}{2!} + o(t^2).$$

Then, if

$$Y_i = \frac{X_i - \mu}{\sqrt{n}\,\sigma},$$

so that $Z_n = Y_1 + \cdots + Y_n$, the characteristic function of Y_i is

$$\phi_{Y_i}(t) = \phi_{X_i-\mu}\left(\frac{t}{\sigma\sqrt{n}}\right) = 1 - \frac{t^2}{2n} + o\left(\frac{t^2}{n}\right).$$

But then the characteristic function of Z_n must be the nth power:

$$\phi_{Z_n}(t) = \left[1 - \frac{t^2}{2n} + o\left(\frac{t^2}{n}\right)\right]^n = \left(1 - \frac{t^2}{2n}\right)^n + o(1).$$

By definition, $o(1) \to 0$; and in the first term, setting $h = -t^2/2n$:

$$\begin{aligned}\lim_{n\to\infty}\left(1 - \frac{t^2}{2n}\right)^n &= \lim_{h\to 0}(1+h)^{-t^2/2h}\\ &= \left\{\lim_{h\to 0}(1+h)^{1/h}\right\}^{-t^2/2} = \exp\left(-\frac{t^2}{2}\right),\end{aligned}$$

which is the characteristic function of a standard normal distribution. The uniqueness and continuity theorems for characteristic functions (§2.3.3) then imply that the limiting distribution of Z_n is standard normal. This result is called a *central limit theorem*, and in this form it will be referred to as *the* central limit theorem. A formal statement is as follows:

Central Limit Theorem. Let $X_1, X_2, \cdots$ be a sequence of identically distributed random variables, any finite number of which are independent. Let the mean and variance be μ and σ^2, with $\sigma^2 < \infty$. Denote by S_n the sum $X_1 + \cdots + X_n$. Then, for each z,

$$\lim_{n\to\infty} P\left[\frac{S_n - n\mu}{\sigma\sqrt{n}} < z\right] = \frac{1}{\sqrt{2\pi}}\int_{-\infty}^{z} \exp(-\tfrac{1}{2}u^2)\, du.$$

This result is often described by saying that S_n is asymptotically normally distributed with parameters $n\mu$ and $n\sigma^2$. According to the definition of a limit, the theorem says that the following approximation can be made as close as desired:

$$P(X_1 + \cdots + X_n \leq y) \doteq N\left(\frac{y - n\mu}{\sigma\sqrt{n}}\right),$$

for large n, where $N(z)$ denotes the standard normal distribution function.

Naturally it is of practical importance to know the accuracy of the approximation suggested here. However, although something is known about the "order" of the approximation (cf. Reference [13], page 288), a useful numerical bound on the approximation error cannot be given because the error depends so much on the nature of the distribution of the summands. If the summands are normal, of course, the sum of even a finite number of them is normal. But if they depart from normality—in being more lumpy, or more skewed, for example—a finite sum is only approximately normal, the accuracy depending on the degree of lumpiness or skewness or whatever it is about the summands' distribution that is not normal. Some of the examples and problems that will be encountered will help give some idea as to the success of such approximations.

The form of central limit theorem given above is not the most general in that the same conclusion of asymptotic normality of a sum is valid under weaker conditions. It is not necessary that the terms in the sum be identically distributed, provided their third moments satisfy a certain mild condititition, for instance. (Cf. Reference [4], pages 213 ff.) There are also circumstances under which the assumption of independence of the terms can be relaxed (cf. Reference [7], page 215).

4.3.4 Applications of the Central Limit Theorem. The central limit theorem has many applications in the study of the limiting distributions of "sample statistics" to be treated in later chapters. However, there are also many direct applications, as in the following examples.

Example 4–8. People using a certain elevator are considered to be drawn randomly from a large population of people with mean 175 pounds and standard deviation 20 pounds. What is the probability that 16 persons would have a combined weight exceeding the load limit of 3000 pounds?

Assuming the total weight W of 16 persons to be approximately normally distributed with mean $16 \times 175 = 2800$ lb and variance $16 \times 400 = 80^2$ lb^2, we find

$$P(W > 3000 \text{ lb}) = 1 - P(W < 3000 \text{ lb})$$
$$= 1 - F_W(3000) \doteq 1 - N\left(\frac{3000 - 2800}{80}\right) = 0.0062.$$

The central limit theorem is useful in providing a means of approximate computation of binomial probabilities when direct computation is tedious. This application hinges upon the fact that a binomially distributed random variable has the distribution of a sum of independent, identical Bernoulli variables. That is, if $X_i = 0$ with probability $1 - p$ and $X_i = 1$ with probability p, and if $X_1, \cdots, X_n$ are independent, then their sum has the binomial distribution (n,p) ,with mean np and variance $np(1 - p)$. According to the central limit theorem, then, the distribution of the sum S_n, and hence the binomial distribution, is asymptotically normal for large n. More precisely, for fixed p,

$$\lim_{n\to\infty} P\left(\frac{S_n - np}{\sqrt{np(1-p)}} \le z\right) = N(z).$$

Hence,

$$P(S_n \le x) = P\left(\frac{S_n - np}{\sqrt{np(1-p)}} \le \frac{x - np}{\sqrt{np(1-p)}}\right) \doteq N\left(\frac{x - np}{\sqrt{np(1-p)}}\right).$$

Example 4–9. Consider a binomial distribution with $n = 8$ and $p = 1/2$. The actual distribution function is

$$P(X \le x) = \sum_{k \le x} \binom{8}{k}\left(\frac{1}{2}\right)^k\left(\frac{1}{2}\right)^{n-k},$$

and the normal approximation is

$$P(X \le x) \doteq N\left(\frac{x - 4}{\sqrt{2}}\right).$$

The graphs of these two functions are shown in Figure 4–3.

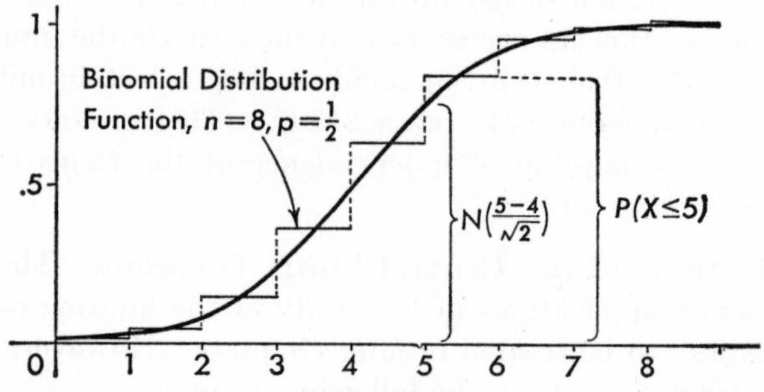

Figure 4–3

It is seen in Figure 4–3 that the normal approximation to the binomial is good when x is about halfway between integers; but it is *at* the integers that the value of $F(x)$ is needed. A better approximation to the value $F(k)$ is obtained by taking the ordinate on the continuous curve one-half unit to the right of k:

$$F(k) = P(X \leq k) \doteq N\left(\frac{k + \frac{1}{2} - np}{\sqrt{np(1-p)}}\right).$$

With this "continuity correction," the normal approximation can be quite good even for rather small values of n, as in the next example.

Example 4–10. Consider a binomial distribution with $n = 4$ and $p = 1/2$:

$$P(X \leq k) \doteq N\left(\frac{k + \frac{1}{2} - 2}{\sqrt{1}}\right).$$

These approximate values and the values computed from the actual distribution function are given in the following table.

	k	0	1	2	3	4
$F_X(k)$		0.0625	0.3125	0.6875	0.9375	1.0000
Normal Approx.	With cont. corr.	0.0668	0.3085	0.6915	0.9332	0.9938
	Without cont. corr.	0.0228	0.1587	0.5000	0.8413	0.9972

When p is near 0.5, the binomial distribution is rather symmetric, and the normal approximation is useful even for quite small n, as seen above. However, values of p near 0 or 1 result in a somewhat skewed distribution, and a larger value of n is required for an acceptable approximation. In such a case, of course, an alternative approximation is available with the Poisson distribution.

Example 4–11. For $n = 20$ and $p = 0.8$, a direct computation of binomial probabilities yields $P(X \geq 16) = 0.6296$. The normal approximation in this case (with continuity correction) gives 0.6103. The Poisson approximation (taking $nq = 4$ as the parameter in the approximating Poisson distribution of $20 - X$) gives 0.6289, which is considerably more successful.

Example 4–12. In the table below are given the exact binomial probabilities, the normal approximation, and the Poisson approximation for certain values of k in the case $n = 8$, $p = 1/8$.

k	Binomial	Normal	Poisson
0	0.3516	0.300	0.368
1	0.7443	0.704	0.736
2	0.9407	0.946	0.920
3	0.9961	0.996	0.981
4	1.0000	1.000	0.996

PROBLEMS

4–17. Let X_1, X_2, and X_3 be independent and each be normally distributed with mean 10 and variance 4. Compute $P(X_1 + X_2 + X_3 > 27)$.

4–18. Booklets are packaged in bundles of 100 by weighing them. Suppose that the weight of an individual booklet is considered to be a random variable with mean 1 ounce and standard deviation 0.05 ounce. If a bundle is counted as containing 100 when it weighs 100 ounces to the nearest ounce, determine the probability that a bundle that actually contains 100 booklets is rejected as containing more than 100 booklets.

4–19. A coin is tossed 100 times. Determine approximate probabilities that (a) less than 50 Heads turn up, (b) exactly 50 Heads turn up, (c) more than 40 but less than 60 Heads turn up.

4–20. Determine approximately the probability that in at least 28 of 72 tosses of a die the outcome is a *one* or a *two*.

4–21. Let X denote the number of Heads in 1600 tosses of a coin and let Y denote the number of sixes in 1620 tosses of a die. Compute $P(X + Y \leq 1000)$.

4–22. In adding n real numbers, each is rounded off to the nearest integer. Assuming that the round-off error for each is uniformly distributed on $(-0.5, 0.5)$, determine the probability that the error in the sum is no greater than $\sqrt{n}/2$ in magnitude, for large n.

4–23. Use the result of Problem 4–14 to show that the asymptotic distribution of a Poisson random variable with expectation nm, as $n \to \infty$ with m fixed, is normal.

4–24. Deduce the conclusion of Khintchine's theorem—that $(X_1 + \cdots + X_n)/n$ converges in probability to $E(X)$, the common mean of the X_i's—under the assumption of existence of var X_i, by showing that $(X_1 + \cdots + X_n)/n$ converges in the mean to $E(X)$.

4–25. Determine the asymptotic distribution of a sum of independent, negative exponential, random variables, each with mean $1/\lambda$.

4–26. Apply Khintchine's theorem to show that if $X_1, X_2, \ldots$ are independently and identically distributed with $E(X^k) < \infty$, then $(X_1{}^k + \cdots + X_n{}^k)/n$ converges in probability to $E(X^k)$.

5/*Statistical Problems and Procedures*

A common conception of statistics is that it is a subject which deals with the gathering and interpretation of data. This conception is not exactly incorrect, but it needs amplification and clarification.

One is often called upon to make a decision or to take some action in the face of uncertainty as to the way things are—the "state of nature." An experiment involving this state of nature in a deterministic way could resolve the uncertainty; but frequently the only experiments available are experiments of chance, and the state of nature is described by a probability distribution for the experiments.

When the correct probability model for a given chance experiment is not completely known, there are two alternatives. One can proceed in complete ignorance of the true model, or he can try to discover something about the model by performing the chance experiment and, hopefully then, be in a better position to judge what is a correct action. If the result of one performance of the experiment is helpful, several performances would be more helpful—at least this is the general feeling. Of course there are usually costs involved in the performance of an experiment, and these might be such that it would be cheaper to act without performing the experiment than it would be to learn about the true model by experimenting.

Although many problems call for the selection of some action from a set of available actions, sometimes the problem is simply to indicate what information concerning the state of nature is contained in the data. The information might not be used by the statistician in a specific decision process but would be made public for use in a variety of situations. In such instances the problem can be included in the framework of "making decisions" if the making of a certain inferential statement about the population is interpreted as the decision.

To illustrate: The decision might be between accepting or rejecting a lot of drugs on the basis of tests on a sample from the lot. It might be to announce the value of a certain physical constant or a range of values within which the constant is almost sure to lie. It might be to rank the effectiveness of several agricultural treatments based on an experiment in which all treatments are used. It might be to predict the degree of success of a college student, based on his score in a preliminary test and based on the known records of many students in the past. And so on.

Viewed broadly, statistical problems and procedures include those of designing the experiment which is to yield pertinent data—determining what experiment to perform and how much data to gather; of gathering data in such a way that the results are representative of the experiment one thinks he is performing; and of drawing inferences or taking action on the basis of the data. Of these three broad aspects of a statistical problem, the third is the one that has the most highly developed mathematical theory and with which this book is mainly concerned.

What we are about to study, then, is a theory aimed at providing ways for making sensible decisions under uncertainty. It will be seen that the theory does not always yield a unique "best" rule of behavior, yet it turns out to be sufficiently adequate to afford some degree of confidence in using the procedures or "tests" that are proposed.

It is convenient to think of the set of all actions available to the statistician as a "space" $\mathcal{A}$ whose individual "points" a are the various individual actions. His decision problem is to select one of these actions. The most intensively studied problems are those in which the space of actions consists of two points and those in which the space of actions is infinite. The former, two-action problems, are often called *hypothesis-testing* problems. The latter are usually *estimation* problems, the space of actions corresponding to the space of values of some parameter of a probability model.

The general decision problem is considered in this chapter, although many of the examples presented will be estimation problems or hypothesis-testing problems. In Chapters 6 and 7 the notions, language, and procedures peculiar to those two important kinds of problems will be considered separately.

5.1 Utility, Loss, and Regret.

One could not expect to discuss rationally a problem of making decisions without taking into account the *consequences* of those decisions. One of the major practical difficulties in applying a theory for making decisions lies in evaluating these consequences on a quantitive scale. Yet, unless this can be done, at least crudely, a decision procedure can scarcely be assured a rational, theoretical basis.

The space of possible "states of nature" will be denoted by Θ. By a particular state of nature θ in Θ is meant a particular probability model for the random phenomenon in question—the phenomenon that has introduced uncertainty and made the correct decision less than obvious. By the "actual" or "true" state of nature is meant the "correct" probability model—a model that faithfully describes the random phenomenon. Although in many instances θ will denote an actual real parameter of a family of probability distributions, for the present it is to be considered simply as a label for a particular probability model.

It will be assumed that there is given a function which tells one the loss incurred corresponding to each combination of action and state of nature. That is, a function $\ell(\theta,a)$ is given which measures the loss incurred if action a is taken when nature is in state θ. This function is called the *loss function.* If there is actually a *gain* for some combination of action and state, this is counted as a negative loss.

Loss is not necessarily monetary. It can be as vague as loss of prestige, comfort, or good will. But to be useful, loss must be measured on at least an ordered, if not a numerical, scale. The term *utility* has come to be used to denote a kind of measure of gain (or negative loss) which appears to be appropriate for decision problems. Specifically, *utility* denotes a bounded measure on prospects with which one is faced, a measure that satisfies these properties: (1) Utility expresses *preference* in the sense that if one prospect is preferable to another, the utility of the one is no less than that of the other. (2) Utility for random prospects is computed as is an expected value from the utilities of the possible prospects and their probabilities; that is, if P denotes the prospect of facing prospect P_1 with probability p_1 and prospect P_2 with probability p_2, the utility of P is the average of the utilities of P_1 and P_2 weighted with the probabilities p_1 and p_2. It may not be easy for one to determine whether he has a utility function satisfying these properties, and it is usually even more difficult to determine what this function is. The *existence* of a utility function can be shown to follow from certain simple, reasonable axioms concerning preference patterns. (Cf. Reference [2], pages 104–111.)

Loss is often measured in terms of money, but it is doubtful whether utility for money is a *linear* function of the *amount* of money except over a limited range.

Utility is clearly a personal matter, but it is not uncommon that two people have similar utility functions. If they do, a reasonable theory of decisions based on utility as a measure of gain should lead them to similar behavior rules in a given problem. On the other hand, if they have quite different utility functions, they might well be led to opposite behaviors, and still both be considered rational.

It will be assumed that loss functions to be used will measure utility—except that it will sometimes be mathematically convenient to use a loss function that is not bounded (whereas utility has been assumed to be bounded). In such instances the unboundedness will not play a crucial role or lead to a behavior significantly different from what is obtained by using a bounded modification of loss.

It is felt by some that actions should be based on what is called *regret* instead of on *loss*. The regret function $r(\theta,a)$ is defined as the result of subtracting from the loss $\ell(\theta,a)$ the minimum loss for the given θ:

$$r(\theta,a) = \ell(\theta,a) - \min_a \ell(\theta,a).$$

That is, for each state of nature, one determines the smallest loss he could get by with if that state of nature were known to be the true state; this is a contribution to loss that even a *good* decision cannot avoid, and so, to obtain a quantity more appropriate to the decision process, it is subtracted from the loss. The difference $r(\theta,a)$ represents the loss that could have been avoided had the state of nature been known—hence the term *regret*.

A regret function has a minimum value of zero for each θ. Conversely, a loss function $\ell(\theta,a)$ that has a minimum of zero for each θ is equal to the corresponding $r(\theta,a)$; such a loss function is already a regret function, with no modification necessary.

Example 5–1. When there are only two actions available and only two possible states of nature, the loss function is completely described by the four entries in a table such as the following:

Loss Table

		States of Nature θ_1	θ_2
Actions:	a_1	10	10
	a_2	15	0

The table of corresponding regrets is obtained by subtracting from each entry in a column the minimum in that column. The result is as follows:

Regret Table

		States of Nature θ_1	θ_2
Actions:	a_1	0	10
	a_2	5	0

The correct action for state θ_1 (according to either table) is a_1, since the loss is smaller for that action. This minimum loss for θ_1 cannot be avoided when nature is in state θ_1; it is not the fault of the decision. On the other hand, the loss of 15 for action a_2 can be reduced to 10 by taking action a_1 instead—if the state is θ_1. The difference of 5 would be "regretted."

5.2 The No-Data Decision Problem

In the absence of data to assist in the making of a decision, the problem presented is simply that of selecting an action from the set $\mathcal{A}$ of available actions so as to minimize in some sense the loss or regret. Whether loss or regret should be used as a basis for decisions is not a matter of general agreement. Many common statistical procedures are explained in terms of a loss function that is in fact a regret function.

When the state of nature is known, choosing an action is a simple matter of choosing it to minimize $\ell(\theta,a)$ or $r(\theta,a)$ for the known state θ. The difficulty lies in the fact that the state of nature is usually *not* known—or at any rate, not completely known. But then one is faced with the realization that what might be a best action for one state of nature might be disastrous for another; not knowing the state of nature, he does not know the action that is best for the way things actually are.

Choosing an action without knowing the state of nature is something like a game, and as such might be thought amenable to treatment using the notions of game theory. However, in that theory the opponent is considered to be an intelligent person trying his best to win—one who may even know game theory. In a statistical decision problem the "opponent" (if there be one) is "nature," and whether this opponent is really trying to defeat the statistician is open to question. Even so, it appears to be instructive to view decision problems as games, and the language and concepts of game theory crop up in statistical decision theory. For instance, a choice of action is sometimes called a *strategy;* similarly, a state of nature can be thought of as a strategy of the opponent, nature.

A more satisfying game theory is achieved if "mixed" strategies are allowed. A *mixed strategy* is a procedure that consists of using a random device to make the actual choice of action. Selecting a mixed strategy amounts to selecting a particular random device. The originally available actions are special cases of the new mixed strategies, and as such are called *pure strategies.*

If the action to be taken is determined by a random device, the loss incurred is random, and it is consistent with a property of utility to use the *expected loss* (or expected regret, when using regret) as the basis for selecting strategies. A mixed strategy is a probability distribution $P^{\mathcal{A}}$ on the action space $\mathcal{A}$, and it is with respect to this distribution that the expectation is computed to obtain the expected loss:

$$L(\theta,P^{\mathcal{A}}) = E[\ell(\theta,a)] = \int_{\mathcal{A}} \ell(\theta,a)\, dP^{\mathcal{A}}.$$

Example 5–2. Consider a problem in which there are two states of nature and three possible actions. For instance, the states of nature might be "rain" and "no rain," and the actions "stay at home," "go out without an umbrella," and "go out with an umbrella." Suppose that the losses are as given in the following table:

		States of Nature	
		θ_1(rain)	θ_2(no rain)
Actions:	a_1(stay home)	4	4
	a_2(go, no umb.)	5	0
	a_3(go with umb.)	2	5

A mixed strategy is here a vector of probabilities $\boldsymbol{p} = (p_1,p_2,p_3)$, where $p_i \geq 0$ for each i and $p_1 + p_2 + p_3 = 1$. Here p_1 is assigned to action a_1, p_2 to action a_2, and p_3 to a_3. The strategy (1,0,0) is then the pure strategy a_1, (0,1,0) is a_2, and (0,0,1) is a_3. For a given $\boldsymbol{p}$, the expected loss is as follows:

$$L(\theta,\boldsymbol{p}) = \begin{cases} 4p_1 + 5p_2 + 2p_3, & \text{if } \theta = \theta_1 \\ 4p_1 + 5p_3, & \text{if } \theta = \theta_2. \end{cases}$$

A graphical interpretation is helpful. Let each strategy $\boldsymbol{p}$ be associated with the pair of numbers (L_1,L_2), where $L_i = L(\theta_i,\boldsymbol{p})$, and let this pair be plotted as a point in a rectangular coordinate system. The three actions a_1, a_2, and a_3 (that is, the pure strategies) are thus associated with the three points (4,4), (5,0), and (2,5), whose coordinates are found directly in the loss table. A mixed strategy (p_1,p_2,p_3) is associated with the center of gravity of a mass system consisting of a mass p_1 at (4,4), a mass p_2 at (5,0), and a mass p_3 at (2,5). The set of all mixed strategies is then the set of all possible centers of gravity of a system of masses at the three pure strategies; it is the convex set "generated" by the pure strategies. (Cf. Problem 5–7.) The pure and mixed strategies, identified with losses under θ_1 and θ_2, are shown plotted in Figure 5–1.

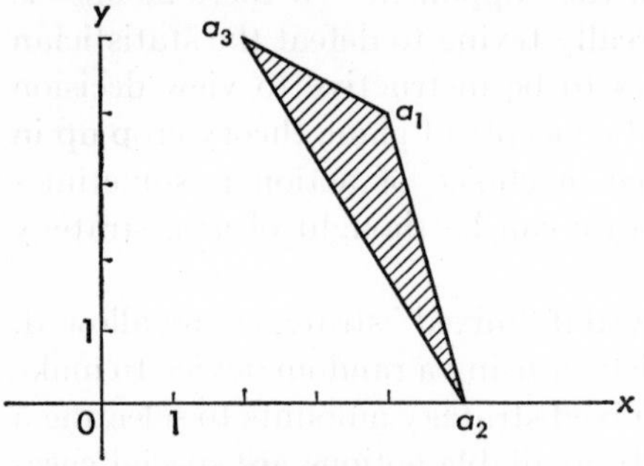

Figure 5–1

PROBLEMS

5–1. A man needs \$6.00 to buy a ticket to a certain ball game, but he has only \$3.00. He wants to see the game badly. Are the numbers of dollars good representatives of his utility? Devise a graph that would better indicate his utility as a function of how much money he has at the time. In terms of this utility scale, determine his utility in tossing a coin for his \$3.00, double or nothing. Is his utility improved in playing this game—that is, should he play it?

5–2. You are given the opportunity to play the following game: A coin is tossed, and if the first heads appears on the kth toss, you win 2^k dollars. How much would *you* pay to play this game? Is the expected value of the game in money the same as in your utility? (Cf. Problem 2–40, page 59.)

5–3. Determine the regret table corresponding to the loss table shown.

	θ_1	θ_2	θ_3
a_1	2	−3	−1
a_2	4	0	5
a_3	1	1	−2
a_4	0	2	−2

5–4. Describe a mixed strategy for Problem 5–3, and write out the corresponding expected loss function. Interpret the pure and mixed strategies geometrically.

5–5. Suppose that the loss in taking k as an estimate of the mean μ in a normal population with unit variance is $(\mu - k)^2$. Determine the corresponding regret function. Describe a mixed strategy and give a formula for the expected loss function.

5–6. If P and Q are points, let kP be the point whose coordinates are each k times those of P, and let $P + Q$ be the point whose coordinates are the sums of the corresponding coordinates of P and Q. (That is, P and Q are treated as vectors.) The center of gravity of a mass m_1 at P_1, m_2 at P_2, ... is given by $\bar{P} = \sum m_i P_i / \sum m_i$. Determine the center of gravity of a system of masses situated as follows: 2 grams at (1,2,−3), 4 grams at (0,2,0), 3 grams at (1,−4,3), and 1 gram at (2,5,−1).

5–7. A linear combination of the form $\sum c_i P_i$, where $0 \leq c_i \leq 1$ and $\sum c_i = 1$, is called a *convex* combination of the points $P_1, P_2, \ldots$.

(a) Show that a convex combination is a center of gravity for an appropriate set of masses and that any center of gravity is a convex combination.

(b) A set is called *convex* if it contains the entire line segment joining any pair of its points. The line segment joining two points is the set of convex combinations of those two points. Show that the set of convex combinations of n points is convex (that is, that the set of possible centers of gravity, or the set "generated" by the n points, is convex).

5.2.1 The Minimax Principle. In even the simplest of problems (as in Example 5–1) the desire to select an action to minimize loss is not a sufficient guide, since what yields a minimum loss for one state does not usually do so for another state. It is not surprising then to find no single method or principle for selecting actions that is acceptable to everyone as the "best" method or principle. The two principles to be considered in this and in the next section propose two ways of assigning a single number to each action, the action selected being the one with the smallest number assigned to it.

The minimax principle suggests that one should prepare for the worst in whatever action he takes, and that the proper action is the one for which the maximum loss is smallest. That is, each action a is measured according to the maximum of the loss $\ell(\theta,a)$ for that a, and then is arranged with other actions according to this measure.

Example 5–3. Consider again the loss table of Example 5–2; a column has been added, listing the maximum loss for each action:

	θ_1	θ_2	max $\ell(\theta,a)$
a_1	4	4	4
a_2	5	0	5
a_3	2	5	5

If action a_1 is selected, the maximum loss is 4, incurred for either state of nature. This maximum is smaller than the maximum of 5 encountered for a_2 or a_3, and so a_1 is the minimax action.

The minimax principle can also be applied to the regret function. The regret table corresponding to the above loss table is the following, in which a column of maximum regrets for the various actions is given:

	θ_1	θ_2	max $r(\theta,a)$
a_1	2	4	4
a_2	3	0	3
a_3	0	5	5

The minimum of the maximum regrets is 3, achieved for action a_2. The minimax regret action is not the same as the minimax loss action in this example.

A graphical representation is enlightening. As in Example 5–2 the actions are represented by the points (L_1,L_2), with $L_i = \ell(\theta_i,a)$. Now, for any point (x,y) above the line $x = y$, the second coordinate (y) is the maximum one; for a point below the line $x = y$, the first coordinate (x) is maximum. To choose between two actions *both above* $x = y$, we take the one with the smaller y—the lowest one, or the one first met by a horizontal line moving upward. To choose between two actions *both below* $x = y$, we take the one first met by a vertical line moving to the right. For points some of which lie above, some on, and some below the line $x = y$, we take (for the minimax action) the one first hit in moving together a horizontal line up *and* a vertical line to the right—the point first met by a wedge moving with its vertex on $x = y$, as shown in Figure 5–2.

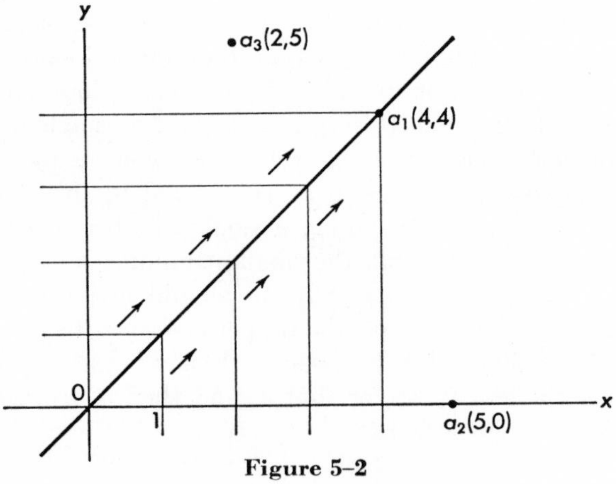

Figure 5–2

In selecting a strategy from among mixed strategies the minimax principle is applied to the expected loss. That is, a mixed strategy or probability distribution P^a on the action space $\mathcal{A}$ is selected so as to minimize the maximum over θ of the loss averaged with respect to P^a. The following example illustrates this in a simple case.

Example 5–4. For the loss table in Examples 5–2 and 5–3 there was computed in Example 5–2 the following expected losses, $L_i = E[\ell(\theta_i,a)]$:

$$\begin{cases} L_1 = 4p_1 + 5p_2 + 2p_3 \\ L_2 = 4p_1 \qquad\quad + 5p_3, \end{cases}$$

corresponding to the mixed strategy (p_1,p_2,p_3). The minimax mixed strategy can be determined graphically just as in the case of the pure strategies (Example 5–3), except that the actions considered are all mixtures of a_1, a_2, and a_3. As seen in Figure 5–3, the first point of this set of mixtures hit by a wedge moving out along $x = y$ is (25/8, 25/8). This point is the center of gravity of weights 0 at a_1, 3/8 at a_2, and 5/8 at a_3. The minimax mixed strategy is therefore (0, 3/8, 5/8).

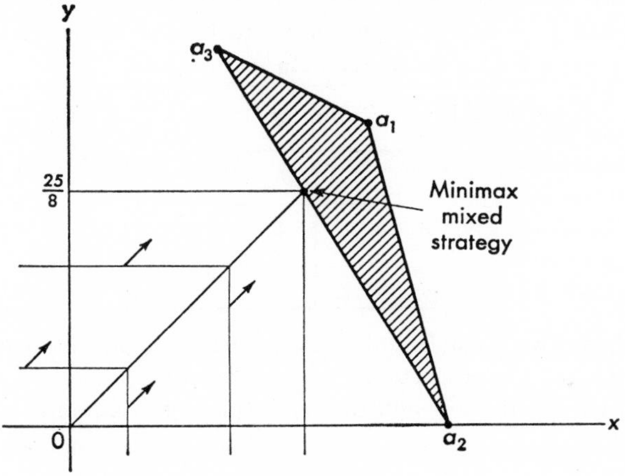

Figure 5–3

The analytical determination of minimax mixed strategies is a matter that will not be investigated here in general, or even in the relatively simple example just treated. Such an investigation would be in order if the minimax principle were a major tool in determining good statistical procedures. However, although the principle provides a means of selecting a procedure, it is felt by many to be overly pessimistic, guarding against all possibilities no matter how remote. A means of incorporating feelings about "remoteness" of possible states is taken up in the next section.

5.2.2 Bayes Solutions. Whereas the minimax principle leads to the same result no matter who applies it, Bayes procedures are based on information, experiences, and hunches of the individual. Their motivation is that, although the state of nature may not be known, it is unusual when one does not have *some* information about the state of nature, which could and should be used to assist in a decision.

Such "a priori" information concerning nature is used to set up a weighting for the states of nature called a *prior* distribution (or an *a priori* distribution). It is set up to correspond to the relative importance of the various states in the context in which the decision is to be made. It is sometimes thought of as a probability distribution, as though the state of nature were random, and as such it can be considered as a mixed strategy for Nature.

The *Bayes principle* assigns to each possible action a measure of the consequences of that action, the Bayes solution then being to take the action with the minimum Bayes measure. This measure is taken to be the average of the losses (for a given action) with respect to the prior distribution. (Notice that this is a second interpretation of "expected loss"; in the earlier use of the term the average was taken with respect to a distribution on the actions. Here it is with respect to a distribution on the states.)

Observe that since the final result is an action that minimizes expected loss, the weighting chosen does not have to be normalized so that the total weight is 1, or even finite, to use the Bayes method.

Example 5–5. Again consider the "rain" or "no rain" loss table of Example 5–2:

	θ_1	θ_2
a_1	4	4
a_2	5	0
a_3	2	5

A weighting of the two possible states can be described by the proportion w of the weight assigned to θ_1, the proportion $1 - w$ automatically going to θ_2. Each w then determines a prior distribution, and the corresponding expected losses are as follows:

For a_1: $4w + 4(1 - w) = 4$,
For a_2: $5w + 0(1 - w) = 5w$,
For a_3: $2w + 5(1 - w) = 5 - 3w$.

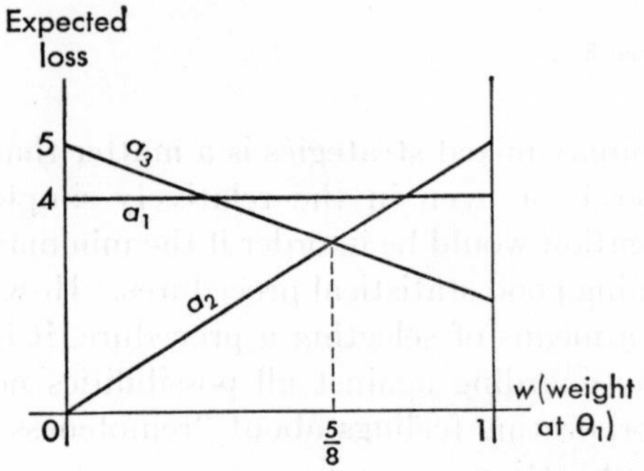

Figure 5–4

Which of these is smallest depends on w. When $w = 0.2$, the smallest is for a_2, and so on. The whole picture can be considered at once if the functions of w for each action are plotted on a single set of axes, as in Figure 5–4. From this figure it is seen that if $w < 5/8$, the minimum expected loss comes from using a_2, and that if $w > 5/8$, the minimum comes from using a_3. If $w = 5/8$, either a_2 or a_3 would be used, both having the same expected loss.

The same conclusions are obtained from a different graphical approach, namely, that used in earlier examples, in which the actions are plotted as (L_1, L_2), with $L_i = \ell(\theta_i, a)$. The expected loss for each action is $wL_1 + (1 - w)L_2$, for a prior distribution with weight w on θ_1. This happens to be proportional to the distance from the origin to that line of the family $wx + (1 - w)y = k$ which passes through (L_1, L_2). Therefore the action having losses (L_1, L_2) such that the corresponding line of the family through (L_1, L_2) is closest to the origin is the Bayes solution for that w. As suggested in Figure 5–5, then, the action first met by a line moving upward with slope $-w/(1 - w)$ is the Bayes action. It need not be unique.

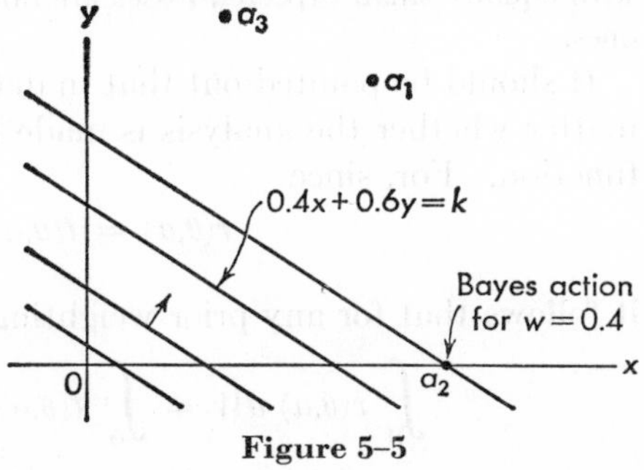

Figure 5–5

If mixed strategies are allowed, the Bayes principle can be applied to the expected loss—the average with respect to the distribution on the actions which defines a mixed strategy.

Example 5–6. For a given prior distribution $(w, 1 - w)$ on the states θ_1 and θ_2 in the loss table of Example 5–6, the expected value of the expected loss, using a mixed strategy (p_1, p_2, p_3), is just the weighted average of the losses $(4p_1 + 5p_2 + 2p_3)$ and $(4p_1 + 5p_3)$ which were computed in Example 5–2. This average is

$$w(4p_1 + 5p_2 + 2p_3) + (1 - w)(4p_1 + 5p_3),$$

the same as though the expectations had been taken in the other order:

$$p_1[4w + 4(1 - w)] + p_2[5w + 0(1 - w)] + p_3[2w + 5(1 - w)].$$

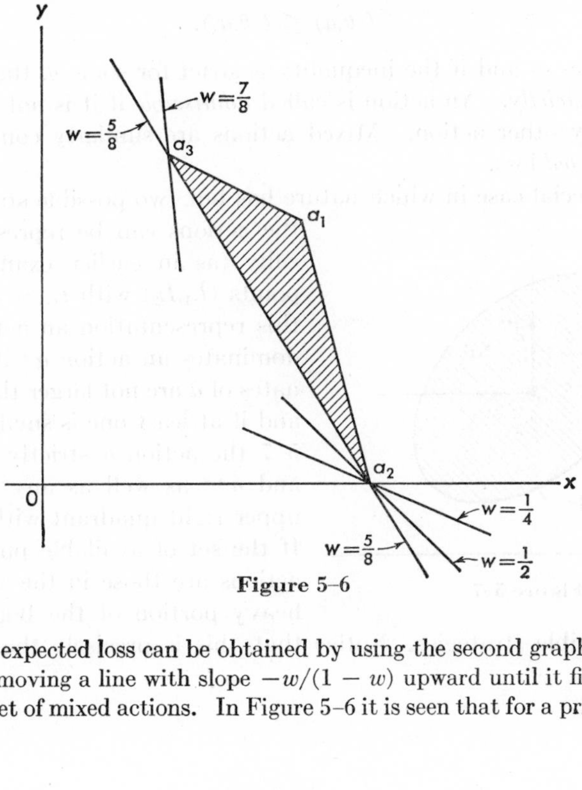

Figure 5–6

The minimum expected loss can be obtained by using the second graphical method of Example 5–5, moving a line with slope $-w/(1 - w)$ upward until it first hits a point of the convex set of mixed actions. In Figure 5–6 it is seen that for a prior distribution

$w < 5/8$, the Bayes action is the (pure) action a_2, and for $w > 5/8$, the (pure) action a_3. For $w = 5/8$, any mixture of a_2 and a_3 could be used. Notice that including the possibility of mixed actions has added nothing to the solution; the same solutions with equally small expected losses are obtained by using only pure actions as mixed ones.

It should be pointed out that in determining Bayes procedures, it does not matter whether the analysis is made by using the loss function or the regret function. For, since

$$r(\theta,a) = \ell(\theta,a) - \min_a \ell(\theta,a),$$

it follows that for any prior weighting W on Θ,

$$\int_\Theta r(\theta,a)\,dW = \int_\Theta \ell(\theta,a)\,dW - \int_\Theta \min_a \ell(\theta,a)\,dW,$$

Since the second term on the right is independent of a, any action a that minimizes the expected regret also minimizes the expected loss, and conversely. (In two-state problems represented graphically as in Example 5–5, a plot based on regret simply translates the whole picture without affecting which action is first hit by a line moving upward with given slope.)

5.2.3 Dominance and Admissibility. An action a is said to *dominate* the action a_1 if, for all states θ,

$$\ell(\theta,a) \leq \ell(\theta,a_1).$$

If a dominates a_1 and if the inequality is strict for some θ, than a is said to dominate a_1 *strictly*. An action is called *admissible* if it is not strictly dominated by any other action. Mixed actions are similarly compared on the basis of *expected* loss.

For the special case in which nature has but two possible states, θ_1 and θ_2, the actions can be represented graphically (as in earlier examples) by the points (L_1,L_2) with $L_i = E[\ell(\theta_i,a)]$. In this representation an action a strictly dominates an action a^* if both coordinates of a are not larger than those of a^* and if at least one is smaller. In Figure 5–7 the action a strictly dominates a^* and a^{**} as well as any action in the upper right quadrant with a as vertex. If the set of available pure and mixed actions are those in the shaded set, the heavy portion of the boundary is the set of admissible strategies. Notice that this is precisely the set of Bayes strategies.

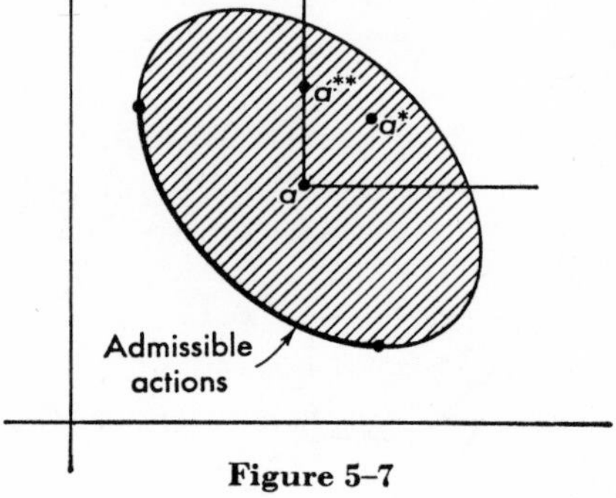

Figure 5–7

Example 5–7. Consider a no-data problem with two states of nature and four actions, the losses being those in the following table:

	Actions			
	a_1	a_2	a_3	a_4
States: θ_1	4	5	2	3
θ_2	4	0	5	5

Action a_4 is strictly dominated by action a_3 and so is inadmissible; for, the loss in taking a_4 is always at least as large as the loss in taking a_3, and it is actually larger for state θ_1. There is no dominance relation among a_1, a_2, and a_3, but if *mixed* actions are allowed, some mixtures of a_2 and a_3 dominate a_1 strictly. For example, the mixed action (0, 0.5, 0.5, 0) does. In Figure 5–8 the heavy line indicates the mixtures of a_2 and a_3 which dominate a_1. In the set of mixed actions, only mixtures of a_2 and a_3 are admissible.

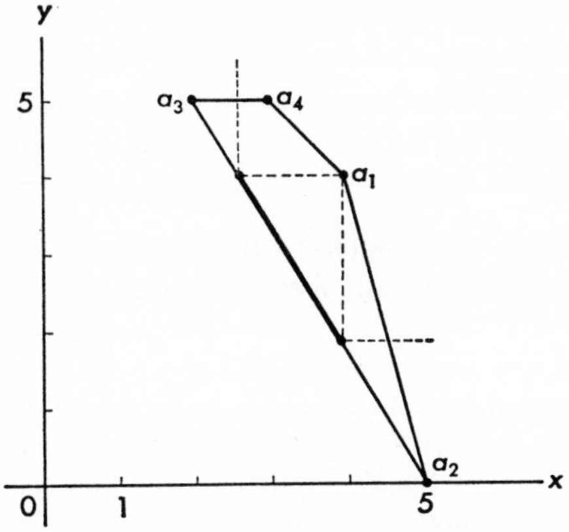

Figure 5–8

A class of strategies is called a *complete class* if any strategy not in the class is strictly dominated by some strategy in the class. Such a class contains all admissible strategies, since if a strategy is not in the class, it is strictly dominated by one which is, and is therefore inadmissible. A *minimal complete class* is a complete class that does not contain a complete proper subclass. If the class of admissible strategies is complete, it is the minimal complete class; and if a minimal complete class exists, it is identical with the class of admissible strategies.

Admissibility appears to be a good property, since it would seem pointless to consider one procedure if another had no larger losses and actually a smaller loss for some states. However, an "inadmissible" procedure that is only a little bit inadmissible might still be very useful. In Figure 5–7, for instance, there are clearly actions that are arbitrarily close to being admissible. In view of the fact that loss functions are usually far from precise, one might find it hard to argue that a slight amount of inadmissibility should condemn a procedure.

For a discussion of conditions under which the class of Bayes strategies is complete, and other relevant matters (such as ϵ-admissibility), refer to References [2] (Chapt. 5) and [19].

PROBLEMS

5–8. Investigate the minimax strategies (pure and mixed, using loss and then regret) for the following loss table:

	θ_1	θ_2
a_1	10	10
a_2	15	0

5–9. Given the loss table shown, determine the minimax loss (pure) action and also the minimax regret (pure) action.

	θ_1	θ_2	θ_3
a_1	2	-3	-1
a_2	4	0	5
a_3	1	1	-1
a_4	0	2	-2

5–10. Determine the Bayes actions for the loss table of Problem 5–8, using a prior distribution $(w, 1 - w)$ for (θ_1,θ_2).

5–11. Given the prior distribution (1/6, 1/3, 1/2) for $(\theta_1,\theta_2,\theta_3)$ in Problem 5–9, determine the corresponding Bayes action.

5–12. Use the graphical technique of Figure 5–5 in Example 5–5 to investigate the Bayes solutions based on regret for that example.

5–13. A lot of five articles is to be accepted or rejected (with no data). Suppose that the loss is taken to be twice the number of defectives for lots that are passed and equal to the number of good articles in lots that are rejected. (a) Determine the minimax mixed strategy. (b) Determine also the Bayes pure strategy corresponding to a prior probability for k defectives in the lot which is binomial with parameter $p = 1/5$.

5–14. Look for dominance relations in the loss table of Problem 5–9 and show that a_2 and a_3 are not admissible in the class of mixed actions.

5–15. Use the first two columns of the loss table of Problem 5–9 for a problem with two states and four actions and determine geometrically the set of admissible mixed actions.

5–16. Show that if a strictly dominates a_1, neither a minimax solution nor a Bayes solution requires a_1.

5.3 Sampling

The process of gathering data or of obtaining results from several performances of an experiment of chance is called *sampling.* The results themselves are called *observations*, and the collection of observations is called a *sample.*

Although the result of an experiment of chance may be more general, we shall speak mainly of the case in which the result of each performance of the experiment is a single random variable.

5.3.1 Random Sampling. Some of the terminology of sampling stems from the following situations that are frequently encountered in statistics:

1. Objects are drawn one at a time from an actual, finite collection of objects called a *population*, and a particular characteristic of interest is determined for each object drawn. After each observation, and before the next drawing, the object just drawn is replaced and the population of objects is thoroughly mixed.
2. Objects are drawn from an actual, finite population as in (1) except that the objects are *not* replaced.

The population of objects is frequently a collection of people, and the observed characteristic may be such a thing as weight, eye color, political preference, etc., or a combination of these. The basic probability space—the experiment of chance—is this collection of people or objects, although probability would naturally be transferred to the space of "values" of the characteristic of interest, and this space can be conceived of as the basic probability space.

When objects are drawn in such a way that at each drawing all remaining objects are equally likely to be chosen, the sampling is called *random*, a usage that conforms to the layman's notion of "selecting at random." It is to make each drawing random that the population should be mixed when objects drawn are replaced. With this understanding that each selection is random, the sampling in (1) is called *random sampling with replacement;* and in (2), *random sampling without replacement.*

In a sense, random sampling without replacement is better than random sampling with replacement, for in the former case objects that have been drawn are not put back into the pool of available objects to confound things. To take an extreme case, suppose there are only two objects in the population; when one is drawn, selection of a second object would furnish complete information about the original population *if* the first were not replaced. Drawing without replacement is also sometimes more convenient in that the mixing required with replacement of objects is not always easy to achieve. On the other hand, as will be seen in a moment, the mathematically simpler process is sampling *with* replacement. Of course, if a population is enormous with respect to the size of the sample to be drawn, it is practically immaterial whether the objects drawn are or are not replaced; sampling without replacement merges into sampling with replacement as the population size becomes infinite. The theory of one could then be used with the practice of the other.

Suppose that when an object is drawn, the characteristic measured or otherwise ascertained is X. This is a random quantity whose distribution is determined by the proportions of the various values of X among the objects in the population and the agreement that the objects are equally likely. It is this distribution of X that will be called the *population distribution.*

Example 5-8. In a group of 100 freshmen, 73 are 18, 22 are 17, 4 are 19, and 1 is 16 years old. Selecting one freshman from the group at random is represented by assigning probability 0.01 to each freshman. The population random variable X that is of interest is the age of a freshman drawn, and this variable has the following probability table:

Age	16	17	18	19
Probability	0.01	0.22	0.73	0.04

The following notation will be used consistently: X_1 denotes the characteristic X of the first object drawn; X_2 denotes the characteristic X of the second object drawn; and so on. A random sample is then written in the form $(X_1, X_2, \ldots, X_n)$, listing the values of the observed characteristic as they are obtained, where n is the size of the sample.

It is clear that in either (1) or (2), the quantity X_1 is a random variable with the population distribution—the distribution of X. It is also clear that in (1), *all* observations $X_1, \ldots, X_n$ have this population distribution as a common distribution because prior to each drawing the population of objects is restored to its original condition. It is not quite so clear, but true, that also in (2) the observations share a common distribution. This statement refers to the marginal distributions of the observations—to the distribution of X_7, for instance, unconditioned by information as to the values of any previous or subsequent X's.

Example 5-9. A bowl contains four beads numbered from 1 to 4. Two are drawn at random, one at a time. Let X_1 denote the number on the first bead drawn and X_2 the number on the second bead drawn. There are 12 possible samples:

$$\begin{array}{cccccc} (1,2), & (1,3), & (1,4), & (2,3), & (2,4), & (3,4) \\ (2,1), & (3,1), & (4,1), & (3,2), & (4,2), & (4,3), \end{array}$$

As discussed in Example 1-35, each of these 12 outcomes has probability 1/12. From this, one can compute the distributions of X_1 and X_2. For instance,

$$P(X_1 = 1) = P[(1,2), (1,3), \text{ or } (1,4)] = 1/4.$$

Similarly,

$$P(X_2 = 1) = P[(2,1), (3,1), \text{ or } (4,1)] = 1/4.$$

In like fashion it is found that for X_1, each of the possible values 1, 2, 3, and 4 has probability 1/4, and that X_2 has exactly the same distribution—the population distribution.

Thus the basic difference between sampling of types (1) and (2) is not in the marginal distributions of the individual observations, for in both cases these observations are identically distributed. The difference is that in (1) the result of any one observation is not affected by the results of any other observations. The observations are *independent* random phenomena. In case (2) the observations are *not* independent.

There is another kind of commonly occurring situation, mechanically different from (1) and (2), in which the results are mathematically of the same type as (1), random sampling with replacement:

3. Observations are obtained as the result of repeated, independent performances of an experiment, under conditions that are identical with respect to those factors which can be controlled.

Here there may be no tangible "population" from which an object is to be selected, but one may imagine an infinite population of possible results. The performance of the experiment selects one of these results, and performing the experiment again selects a result from the same collection of possible results as was available in the first performance. That is, repeating the experiment under "identical" conditions means that the first result is "replaced" and is again one of the candidates to be "drawn" the next time. In both (1) and (3), then, the observations are identically distributed and independent. The term *random sampling* without further qualification will denote such a process:

Definition. A *random sample* from a population random variable X is a set of independent, identically distributed, random variables $X_1, \cdots, X_n$, each with the distribution of X.

A random sample (with replacement) is simpler to treat mathematically than is a sample obtained without replacement. This is a result of the independence in a random sample, which implies that the joint density function of the sample observations is a product of their marginal distribution densities:

$$\begin{aligned} f_{X_1,\ldots,X_n}(u_1, \ldots, u_n) &= f_{X_1}(u_1)\cdots f_{X_n}(u_n) \\ &= \prod_{i=1}^{n} f_X(u_i), \end{aligned}$$

where X denotes the population random variable, whose distribution is shared by each of the observations.

Example 5–10. The life of a certain type of electron tube in a given application has a negative exponential distribution with mean life of 10 hours. The life of each tube operated in this way then has the density

$$f_X(u) = 0.1e^{-0.1u}, \qquad u > 0.$$

The joint density function of the lives $X_1, \ldots, X_n$ of n such tubes operated independently is

$$f(u_1, \ldots, u_n) = (0.1)^n \prod_{i=1}^{n} e^{-0.1u_i} = (0.1)^n \exp[-0.1\sum_{i=1}^{n} u_i].$$

Whether an actual sampling process is faithfully described by a mathematical model for sampling is usually a moot question, one that will not be considered here. In the last analysis it is really unanswerable, and about all one can do is to make every effort to see that the process used in collecting data conforms as nearly as can be determined to a definite mathematical model, otherwise the grounds for inference are wobbly indeed. How to make such efforts will not be considered in this book; in the case of scientific experiments their consideration would require knowledge of the field of application, and in the case of sampling from actual populations, the subject is so extensive as to be beyond our scope. (Cf. Reference [10].)

5.3.2 Statistics. In assimilating the information contained in a sample, in describing and comparing samples, and in making decisions on the basis of the results of a sample, it is convenient to be able to use, rather than the complete list of observations as they were obtained, some more readily comprehended measures computed from the sample. It will be seen subsequently that there are principles that lead naturally to certain measures as being appropriate to certain problems. Here we present some of the sample measures or characteristics that actually do find many useful applications. This we do to have in our "vocabulary" some of the simpler, common sample characteristics for purposes of illustration. For the present these can be thought of as being constructed by using intuition, and historically this is perhaps not too inaccurate. Actually, more than just furnishing illustrations, intuitively derived sample measures and procedures based on them frequently turn out to work pretty well. They can and should at least be compared with others developed more systematically.

The term *statistic* is applied to a descriptive measure computed from the observations in a sample. The value of a given measure then depends on the values of the observations; hence the following:

Definition. A *statistic* is a function of the observations in a sample.

(In particular, computation of a statistic does not require knowledge of any unknown population characteristics.)

Actually, the term *statistic* applies either to what a mathematician thinks of as the "function"—the *relationship* between independent and dependent variables—or to the random variable defined by the functional relation. If $(x_1,\ldots,x_n)$ is a possible sample point (a possible list of observations in a sample), the functional relationship

$$y = t(x_1,\ldots,x_n)$$

provides a transformation or mapping from the space of all sample points to the space of values of the function. This mapping induces a probability distribution in the latter space and thereby defines a random variable:

$$Y = t(X_1, \ldots, X_n).$$

Computation of a statistic from a set of observations constitutes a reduction of the data to a single number, or to a vector of numbers, if the function defining the statistic is vector-valued. In the process of such reduction certain information about the population may be lost, but ideally the measure computed would be chosen so that the information lost is not pertinent to the particular problem at hand, so that the measure is still sufficient to handle the problem. This notion of "sufficiency" of a statistic for a given problem will be made more precise in §5.5.

Frequently, in an attempt to create order out of the chaos of a mass of data, the observations are put in *numerical* order. The result is a permutation of the original observations and will be denoted by $(X_{(1)}, \cdots, X_{(n)})$. That is, $X_{(1)}$ is the smallest observation, $X_{(2)}$ is the next smallest, and so on. The vector of these ordered observations is sometimes referred to as the *order statistic*. Various other quantities based on order are also thought of as order statistics; for example, any component $X_{(i)}$, the ith smallest observation, or $[X_{(1)} + X_{(n)}]/2$, the average of the smallest and largest observations.

The *range* of a sample is defined as the difference between the largest and smallest observations:

$$R = X_{(n)} - X_{(1)}.$$

The *median* of a sample is defined as the midvalue (if there are an odd number of observations) or as the average of the two middle values (if there are an even number of observations), in the list of *ordered* observations. That is,

$$\text{Median} = \begin{cases} X_{([n+1]/2)}, & \text{for } n \text{ odd}, \\ \frac{1}{2}[X_{(n/2)} + X_{(n/2+1)}], & \text{for } n \text{ even}. \end{cases}$$

Both the range and the median involve a reduction of the order statistic, the range being appropriate in certain problems of dispersion and the median in certain problems of location.

Example 5–11. Consider the following observations:

31, 28, 27, 32, 36, 33, 29, 35, 24, 33.

The smallest is $x_{(1)} = 24$, the largest is $x_{(10)} = 36$, and the order statistic is

(24, 27, 28, 29, 31, 32, 33, 33, 35, 36),

or, to indicate the permutation of the original order of observation;

$$(x_9, x_3, x_2, x_7, x_1, x_4, x_6, x_{10}, x_8, x_5).$$

The range is the difference $36 - 24 = 12$, and the median is the average of the fifth smallest and sixth smallest observations:

$$\tfrac{1}{2}(31 + 32) = 31.5.$$

Corresponding to a given sample, we define a *sample distribution function* (which is not to be interpreted as the model for any chance experiment): Let a "mass" of amount $1/n$ be place at each observed value. The distribution function of this mass distribution is

$$F_n(x) = \frac{1}{n} \times (\text{number of observations not exceeding } x).$$

This is the sample distribution function. It is intended to mimic the population distribution function, and it will be seen to provide a natural estimate of the population distribution function. The sample distribution function can be computed from the order statistic, and conversely.

The sample distribution function is mathematically just like a probability distribution function for a discrete distribution and shares the mathematical properties of such a function. For instance, $F_n(x)$ has moments, at least the first two of which turn out to be rather useful. The first moment about zero is called the *sample mean:*

$$\bar{X} = \frac{1}{n} \sum_{i=1}^{n} X_i,$$

with the usual property that the first moment about this value is zero:

$$\frac{1}{n} \sum_{i=1}^{n} (X_i - \bar{X}) = 0.$$

The second moment of the sample distribution function about the sample mean is called the *sample variance:*

$$s_x^2 = \frac{1}{n} \sum_{i=1}^{n} (X_i - \bar{X})^2 = \frac{1}{n} \sum_{i=1}^{n} X_i^2 - \bar{X}^2.$$

The positive square root of the sample variance is called the *sample standard deviation:*

$$s_x = \sqrt{s_x^2}.$$

It is useful to observe and easy to show that under the important particular kind of transformation of data called *linear*, the sample mean undergoes exactly the same transformation, and the sample variance is multiplied by the square of the scale factor. That is, if $Y_i = aX_i + b$, then $\bar{Y} = a\bar{X} + b$ and $s_y^2 = a^2 s_x^2$. These relations can be seen directly, but they follow from the fact that a sample distribution can be considered mathematically as a probability distribution. We have already seen that they hold for probability distributions.

In large samples it is often convenient to gather or present the data in the form of a *frequency table.* In such a table, the original measurements or observations are grouped: The *distinct* values in the sample are listed in order with a number called *frequency*, giving the number of times the corresponding value occurs in the data. The data will usually have such multiplicities of values because of the round-off required in recording a measurement.

The data might also be regrouped by what is effectively a coarser rounding-off of the original data. To regroup, one selects a collection of nonoverlapping (and usually equal-sized) *class intervals* which cover the range of values in the data. The observations in each class interval are represented by, say, the midpoint of that interval; a frequency is assigned to that midpoint value according to the number of the original observations that fall in the interval. The regrouped data are patently different data from the original data but may serve to give a more digestible delineation of the sample's coarser features, if the regrouping is not carried to the extreme.

Given below is the type of array usually used to exhibit the data in grouped (or regrouped) form, and to compute the sample moments. The frequency of the class interval represented by x_i is denoted by f_i.

x_i	f_i	$f_i x_i$	$f_i x_i^2$
x_1	f_1	$f_1 x_1$	$f_1 x_1^2$
$\vdots$	$\vdots$	$\vdots$	$\vdots$
x_k	f_k	$f_k x_k$	$f_k x_k^2$
Sums	n	$\Sigma f_i x_i$	$\Sigma f_i x_i^2$

In this tabulation, $x_1, \cdots, x_k$ represent the distinct values among the n observations, and the summations extend from $i = 1$ to $i = k$. The sum of the frequencies is necessarily the sample size n.

Computations of the sample mean and variance proceed as follows: For the mean,

$$\bar{X} = \frac{1}{n}\text{(sum of the observations)} = \frac{1}{n}\sum_{i=1}^{k} f_i x_i,$$

and for the variance,

$$s_x^2 = \frac{1}{n}\sum_{i=1}^{k} f_i x_i^2 - (\bar{X})^2.$$

(If the frequencies in these computations are those resulting from regrouping the original data into wider class intervals, the computed mean and variance are not quite the mean and variance of the original data. Sometimes "Sheppard's corrections" are applied, which for the above moments amount to leaving the mean as it is and subtracting from the computed variance $h^2/12$, where h is the class interval width. Cf. Reference [3], page 361 ff. and Reference [18], page 80 ff.)

Computation is often simpler if the data are transformed so that the new origin is near the mean and the new unit is the class interval width, as in the following example.

Example 5–12. In the following tabulation, x_i denotes dial tension in grams and f_i the corresponding frequencies among 200 observations. The quantities y_i are given by

$$y_i = \frac{x_i - 9.0}{0.5} \quad \text{or} \quad x_i = 9.0 + 0.5y_i.$$

x_i	y_i	f_i	f_iy_i	$f_iy_i^2$
6.5	−5	3	−15	75
7.0	−4	2	−8	32
7.5	−3	30	−90	270
8.0	−2	42	−84	168
8.5	−1	36	−36	36
9.0	0	28	0	0
9.5	1	28	28	28
10.0	2	15	30	60
10.5	3	8	24	72
11.0	4	3	12	48
11.5	5	1	5	25
12.0	6	1	6	36
12.5	7	1	7	49
13.0	8	0	0	0
13.5	9	1	9	81
14.0	10	1	10	100
Totals		200	−102	1080

$$\bar{Y} = -\frac{102}{200} = -0.51$$

$$\bar{X} = 9.0 + 0.5\bar{y}$$
$$= 9.0 - 0.255 = 8.745$$

$$s_y^2 = \frac{1080}{200} - (-0.51)^2$$
$$= 5.4 - 0.26 = 5.14$$

$$s_x^2 = (0.5)^2 s_y^2$$
$$= 1.285.$$

The various quantities associated with a sample distribution—the sample median, sample range, sample mean, sample variance, and so on—are often useful in particular in studying related parameters of the distribution of probability in the population from which the sample was taken. It should be kept in mind, though, that statistics are random variables; they vary from sample to sample according to the observations one happens to obtain. Population parameters are constants but are frequently unknown.

PROBLEMS

5–17. A bowl contains three white and seven black beads. A bead is drawn from the bowl four times. Let X_i be 0 or 1 according as the ith bead drawn is white or black. Determine the joint probability function of the observations X_1, X_2, X_3, and X_4 if (a) each bead drawn is replaced before the next drawing; (b) the beads are not replaced.

5–18. Write out the joint density or probability function of the observations $X_1, \ldots, X_n$ in a random sample from a (a) uniform distribution on $[a,b]$; (b) normal distribution (μ,σ^2); (c) Bernoulli distribution (p); (d) Poisson distribution with expectation m; (e) geometric distribution with parameter p.

5–19. Compute the median, mean, range, and standard deviation of the following observations: $-3, 2, 5, 0, -4$.

5–20. Given that $x_1^2 + \cdots + x_{10}^2 = 160$ and that $s_x^2 = 12$, determine two possible values of $\bar{x}$, with $n = 10$.

5–21. Given the following 30 test scores: 51, 52, 52, 58, 59, 59, 61, 62, 63, 69, 72, 74, 76, 80, 80, 80, 81, 81, 82, 83, 83, 84, 86, 87, 87, 88, 88, 89, 90, 94.

(a) Determine the mean and standard deviation and plot the sample distribution function.

(b) Round off the above scores to the nearest multiple of 5 and compute the mean and standard deviation of the rounded-off data.

5–22. The mean and standard deviation of the numbers $x_1, \ldots, x_n$ are 5 and 2, respectively. Determine the average of their squares and the mean and standard deviation of $y_1, \ldots, y_n$, where $y_i = 3x_i + 4$.

5–23. (a) Show that

$$\frac{1}{n}\sum_{i=1}^{n} x_i^2 - \bar{x}^2 = \frac{1}{n}\sum_{i=1}^{n}(x_i - \bar{x})^2.$$

(b) Show that if $y_i = ax_i + b$, then $\bar{y} = a\bar{x} + b$ and $s_y = |a| s_x$.

(c) Show that the second moment of a set of observations is smallest when taken about their mean.

5.3.3 Distributions of Statistics. As a random variable a statistic has a probability distribution, a distribution induced by the population distribution. If (as has been hinted) a statistic is to provide information concerning the population, it is essential to know what there is about the distribution of a statistic that has to do with the population distribution.

The statistic $\bar{X}$, to consider a very important example, has a distribution whose characteristic function is readily expressed in terms of the characteristic function of the population (assuming a random sample):

$$\begin{aligned}\phi_{\bar{X}}(t) = E(e^{it\bar{X}}) &= E[e^{it(X_1+\cdots+X_n)/n}] \\ &= E[e^{itX_1/n}]\cdots E[e^{itX_n/n}] \\ &= \left[\phi_X\left(\frac{t}{n}\right)\right]^n.\end{aligned}$$

From this, or from the linearity of the expectation operation (even when the observations are *not* independent), it follows that

$$E(\bar{X}) = E(X),$$

which says that the "center" of the distribution of $\bar{X}$ is the population mean. Further, since the observations in a random sample, are uncorrelated:

$$\operatorname{var} \bar{X} = \operatorname{var}\left(\sum \frac{X_i}{n}\right) = \frac{\sigma^2}{n}.$$

where σ^2 is the population variance. The *asymptotic* distribution of the mean of a random sample is (according to the central limit theorem) normal with mean μ and variance σ^2/n. That is, the limiting distribution of

$$\frac{\bar{X} - \mu}{\sigma/\sqrt{n}},$$

as n becomes infinite, is the standard normal—independent of the population distribution as long as the latter has second moments. Another limit theorem, Khintchine's theorem, says that $\bar{X}$ tends in probability to $E(X)$.

The sample variance s_x^2 is by no means so easy to treat as is the sample mean. The expected value of s_x^2 is readily computed:

$$E(s_x^2) = E\left\{\frac{1}{n}\sum(X_i - \mu)^2 - (\bar{X} - \mu)^2\right\}$$

$$= \sigma^2 - \operatorname{var} \bar{X} = \sigma^2\left(1 - \frac{1}{n}\right).$$

The variance of s_x^2 is considerably more complicated:

$$\operatorname{var} s_x^2 = \frac{\mu_4 - \mu_2^2}{n} - \frac{2(\mu_4 - 2\mu_2^2)}{n^2} + \frac{\mu_4 - 3\mu_2^2}{n^3},$$

where μ_k denotes the kth population moment about the population mean. It will be convenient to have a reduction of this expression for the particular case of a normal population, in which case $\mu_4 = 3\mu_2^2$:

$$\operatorname{var} s_x^2 = \frac{2\sigma^4(n-1)}{n^2} \qquad \text{(random sample from normal population).}$$

Higher-order sample central moments can be treated with ever increasing complexity of detail. (Cf. Reference [4], page 348.)

Sample moments about 0 are simpler to analyze, since for a random sample each $\sum X_i^k/n$ is a sum of independent random variables. The mean is clearly $E(X^k)$, and the variance is easily expressible (Problem 5–26) in terms of $E(X^{2k})$ if the latter exists. Further, the limiting distribution is normal (by the central limit theorem) and the limit in probability is $E(X^k)$ (by Khintchine's theorem).

By using the fact that sample central moments are expressible as polynomial functions of sample moments about zero, one can show that the sample central moments are asymptotically normal and tend in probability to the corresponding population moments. (Cf. Reference [4], page 365).

The sample distribution function is known to converge to the population distribution function with probability one, uniformly in x. We content ourselves here with showing that the sample distribution function approaches the population distribution function at each x in quadratic mean (or "in the mean"), and therefore in probability. This follows from the fact that $nF_n(x)$

is just the number of observations not exceeding x and is therefore binomial (n,p), where

$$p = P(X \leq x) = F(x).$$

For, then

$$E[nF_n(x)] = nF(x) \quad \text{and} \quad \text{var}\,[nF_n(x)] = nF(x)[1 - F(x)],$$

and consequently,

$$E[F_n(x)] = F(x) \quad \text{and} \quad \text{var}\,F_n(x) = \frac{F(x)[1 - F(x)]}{n}.$$

Since the expectation is right and the variance tends to zero, the assertion is established.

PROBLEMS

5–24. Determine the density function of the mean of a random sample from a negative exponential population, using the result of Example 4–6, page 141.

5–25. Two independent random samples are taken from a normal population with mean 150 and variance 28.6. The sample sizes are 10 and 25, and the corresponding sample means are $\bar{X}_1$ and $\bar{X}_2$. Determine

$$\text{(a) } E(\bar{X}_1 - \bar{X}_2), \quad \text{(b) var } (\bar{X}_1 - \bar{X}_2), \quad \text{(c) } P(|\bar{X}_1 - \bar{X}_2| > 4).$$

[*Hint:* The sample means and hence their difference are all normal.]

5–26. (a) Express the variance of the kth sample moment about zero in terms of $E(X^{2k})$ and $E(X^k)$.

(b) Determine the relationship between the third moment about zero and the third moment about the mean, for a population and for a sample, and observe that the same polynomial is involved. (Why must this be the case?)

5–27. A population consists of four chips numbered 1, 2, 3, 4. A random sample without replacement of size two is drawn: (X_1,X_2), where X_i is the number on the chip in the ith drawing. (Cf. Example 5–9).

(a) Determine the joint probability distribution of the statistics $X_{(1)}$ and $X_{(2)}$, where $X_{(1)}$ is the smaller and $X_{(2)}$ the larger of the two observations.

(b) Determine the probability distribution of $R = X_{(2)} - X_{(1)}$.

(c) Compute the expected value of the average of $X_{(1)}$ and $X_{(2)}$.

5–28. What is the asymptotic distribution of $\sum(X_i - E(X))^2/n$?

5–29. Consider a random sample of size n without replacement from a finite population of size N. Given (cf. Reference [21], page 83)

$$\text{var}\,\bar{X} = \frac{\sigma^2}{n}\frac{N - n}{N - 1},$$

show that

$$E(s_x^2) = \frac{n - 1}{n}\frac{N}{N - 1}\sigma^2,$$

where σ^2 is the population variance.

5–30. Derive an expression in terms of the population distribution function $F(x)$ for the distribution function of $X_{(n)}$, the largest observation.

5.4 Using Data in Decisions

Looking at data resulting from performing the experiment whose model is under study can be thought of as a form of "spying" on our "opponent," Nature. Such spying usually costs something, so that the amount of spying permitted or desired is not necessarily infinite. How much should be done depends on the extent to which spying increases one's information about nature; if he is spying in the wrong way—doing the wrong experiment—a large amount of it may be futile. Before a balance of cost of experimentation and gain of information can be made, it is necessary to see what information is to be gained in experimenting, and for a given amount of experimenting, how to get the most out of the data. For the present, then, the size of the sample used will be considered fixed and often given.

The general discussion will be given in terms of "data" Z, where Z may be the value of a single observation on a univariate distribution or on a multivariate distribution; or it may be a vector of the values in a sample, or the value of some statistic computed from the sample. In any case there is a corresponding distribution of Z.

5.4.1 The Risk Function. A decision rule or strategy that is to lead to a decision based on the data Z must take into account that Z can have many values. A rule for choosing an action is not then complete until it prescribes an action a for each conceivable value z of Z. Such a rule is called a *statistical decision function:*

$$a = d(z).$$

This is a mapping from the space of possible data points to the space of actions. The statistician's task is then the selection of a suitable decision rule, or decision function, $d(z)$.

The action taken is random, since the data to which the decision rule is applied are random. Hence, the loss is random: $\ell(\theta,d(Z))$. It is customary and again consistent with rules for utility to base the analysis on the *expected value* of this loss:

$$R(\theta,d) = E_\theta[\ell(\theta,d(Z))].$$

Notice that this is the third use so far of the term *expected loss*. In one use, it denoted an average with respect to a randomized action; in the second use, it denoted an average with respect to a prior distribution (or randomized strategy for Nature); and in the present usage, the average is computed with respect to the distribution of the data Z. This distribution of Z depends on θ, so the dependence of the function $R(\theta,d)$ on θ enters through the θ in $\ell(\theta,a)$ and also through the θ in the distribution of Z. The expected loss $R(\theta,d)$ is called the *risk function*.

Some use the term *risk function* to denote the expectation of the *regret* function. If the loss function used is already a regret function, as will be the case in many of the important statistical applications to be discussed, there is no difference in usage. It is interesting that the expected regret is the same as what would be obtained by applying the "regret-izing" process to the risk function:

$$E_\theta[r(\theta,d(Z))] = R(\theta,d) - \min_d R(\theta,d).$$

(This is an exercise in inequalities and minima.)

The data have thus been used to change the problem of the statistician from one of selecting an action in view of a certain loss function, to one of selecting a decision function d in view of a certain risk function. Interpreting an "action" as a *decision function* and "loss" as *risk*, the problem is now like the original no-data problem, and the concepts developed for no-data problems can be carried over to the present situation. The difficulty of no unique best approach also carries over, of course.

Example 5–13. Consider the rain problem of Example 5–2, with loss function as follows:

	θ_1(rain)	θ_2(no rain)
(Stay home) a_1	4	4
(Go, no umb.) a_2	5	0
(Go with umb.) a_3	2	5

A single observation of a rain indicator (or a weather report) will make up the "datum" Z. If this datum is to be useful, there must be known the way in which the distribution of the datum depends on the state of nature. For this problem we assume the following, in which z_1 indicates an observation (or prediction) of "rain," and z_2, of "no rain":

	θ_1(rain)	θ_2(no rain)
z_1 (rain)	0.8	0.1
z_2 (no rain)	0.2	0.9

That is, it is known from past experience that when it is going to rain, the probability is 0.8 that the indicator will show "rain," and 0.2 that it will show "no rain."

Since there are finitely many possible actions and possible values of Z, the number of decision functions is finite. Indeed, it is $3^2 = 9$, since there are three actions and two values of Z (a decision function assigns an action to each value of Z). These nine decision functions are listed as follows:

	d_1	d_2	d_3	d_4	d_5	d_6	d_7	d_8	d_9
If outcome is z_1, take action	a_1	a_2	a_3	a_1	a_2	a_1	a_3	a_2	a_3
If outcome is z_2, take action	a_1	a_2	a_3	a_2	a_1	a_3	a_1	a_3	a_2

The computation of the risk function $R(\theta,d)$ proceeds as follows: For $\theta = \theta_1$ and $d = d_5$,

$$\begin{aligned} R(\theta_1,d_5) &= E_{\theta_1}[\ell(\theta_1,d_5(Z))] \\ &= \ell(\theta_1,d_5(z_1))p_{\theta_1}(z_1) + \ell(\theta_1,d_5(z_2))p_{\theta_1}(z_2) \\ &= \ell(\theta_1,a_2) \times 0.8 + \ell(\theta_1,a_1) \times 0.2 = 5 \times 0.8 + 4 \times 0.2 = 4.8. \end{aligned}$$

In similar fashion one can compute $R(\theta,d)$ for each combination of decision function d and state θ. The results are tabulated:

	θ_1	θ_2
d_1	4	4
d_2	5	0
d_3	2	5
d_4	4.2	0.4
d_5	4.8	3.6
d_6	3.6	4.9
d_7	2.4	4.1
d_8	4.4	4.5
d_9	2.6	0.5

This array can now be attacked as though it gave the loss function in a no-data problem. For instance, d_1, d_5, d_6, and d_8, are *inadmissible*, even in the set of pure strategies, and can be eliminated from the competition. Similarly, d_4 and d_7 are *dominated* by mixtures of other strategies, but there is still no clear choice among d_2, d_3, and d_9.

Example 5–14. The problem is to estimate the value of the parameter θ in a negative exponential density with mean θ. That is, it is assumed that nature is in one of the states described by this family of distributions. The actions here are the various possible choices of an estimated value of θ, so the action space is the same as the state space. For purposes of this example, assume that the loss function is quadratic and has a zero minimum for each action:

$$\ell(\theta_0,a) = (a - \theta_0)^2,$$

the loss incurred by choosing a as the estimate when the state is θ_0.

A decision procedure is to be based on the result of n performances of the negative exponential experiment, a sample of size n from the population. As illustrations of the computation of risks, consider the following (arbitrarily selected) decision procedures:

$$d_1(\mathbf{X}) = \bar{X}, \qquad d_2(\mathbf{X}) = \bar{X} + 1, \qquad d_3(\mathbf{X}) = X_n.$$

The risk functions for these procedures are as follows:

$$\begin{aligned} R(\theta,d_1) &= E_\theta(\bar{X} - \theta)^2 = \text{var } \bar{X} = \frac{\theta^2}{n}, \\ R(\theta,d_2) &= E_\theta(\bar{X} + 1 - \theta)^2 = \text{var } \bar{X} + 1 = \frac{\theta^2}{n} + 1 \\ R(\theta,d_3) &= E_\theta(X_n - \theta)^2 = \text{var } X = \theta^2. \end{aligned}$$

These are plotted as functions of θ in Figure 5–9. It is clear from the figure that d_1 dominates both d_2 and d_3 strictly but that d_2 and d_3 are not comparable with each other. All three risk functions are unbounded because the loss function given is unbounded.

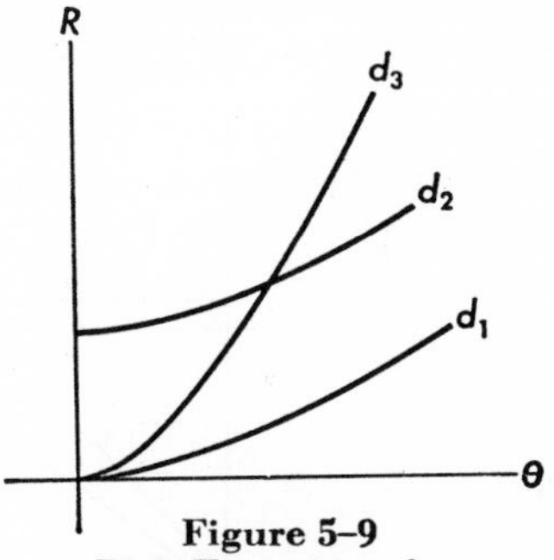

Figure 5–9
Risk Functions for Example 5–14

Example 5–15. Flash bulbs come in "lots" of ten, and one is taken from each lot and tested (a process that ruins it). The remaining nine are either to be sold at fifteen cents each, with a double-your-money-back guarantee, or to be junked at a cost of ten cents for the lot. One of two actions is to be selected: sell the lot or junk it. The state of nature is described by the number k of defective bulbs among the ten.

Since the experiment has only two outcomes, assigning one of the two actions to each outcome can be done in four distinct ways; these are the possible decision functions:

d_1: Sell the lot if the test bulb is good; junk if defective.
d_2: Junk the lot if the test bulb is good; sell if defective.
d_3: Sell the lot if the test bulb is good; sell if defective.
d_4: Junk the lot if the test bulb is good; junk if defective.

Consider first $d_1(X)$, where X denotes the outcome of the test. The loss is

$$\ell(k,d_1(X)) = \begin{cases} -1.35 + (0.30)k, & \text{if } X = \text{good}, \\ 0.10, & \text{if } X = \text{defective}, \end{cases}$$

and the risk function is then

$$\begin{aligned} R(k,d_1) &= E_k[\ell(k,d_1(X)] \\ &= (-1.35 + 0.3k)(10/k) + 0.10(1 - 10/k) \\ &= -0.01(3k^2 - 44.5k + 135). \end{aligned}$$

For $d_2(X)$,

$$\ell(k,d_2(X)) = \begin{cases} 0.10, & \text{if } X = \text{good}, \\ -1.35 + 0.30(k-1), & \text{if } X = \text{defective}, \end{cases}$$

and

$$R(k,d_2) = 0.01(3k^2 - 17.5k + 10).$$

Similarly,

$$\begin{aligned} R(k,d_3) &= -0.09(15 - 3k), \\ R(k,d_4) &= 0.10. \end{aligned}$$

These four risk functions are plotted (as though k were continuous, for ease in following the graphs) in Figure 5–10. For some states the best decision function is d_3; for others it is d_2; and for still others it is d_4. And d_1, which is never best, is not far from being best at all states.

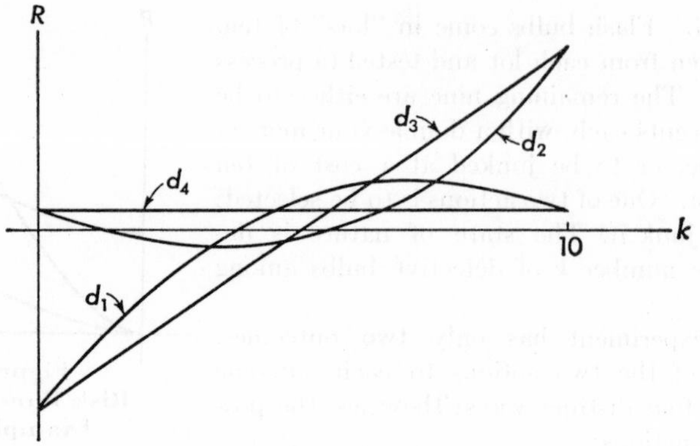

Figure 5–10
Risk Functions for Example 5–15

A minimax decision function is selected from the available decision functions on the basis of the risk function, just as a minimax action was selected on the basis of the loss function in a no-data problem. That is, the decision function that makes

$$\max_{\theta} R(\theta,d)$$

smallest is the minimax decision function. As mentioned before, such an approach is rather pessimistic—guarding against situations that are "unlikely" to arise.

Example 5–16. Referring to Figure 5–10 in the flash-bulb problem of Example 5-15, it is apparent that d_4 has the risk function with the lowest maximum point. The minimax decision function is that which rejects all lots. It would be an unusual manufacturer who would manufacture flash bulbs and then junk everything he made for fear of the large loss he might incur if the proportion of defectives in the lots were quite high. The manufacturing process would be developed, rather, so that a lot with more than, say, half defective would "practically" never occur. Thus, in a realistic situation, the maximum risk would be considered over small values of k, where the smallest maximum would be achieved by using d_3. Actually, this focusing of the attention on certain practically possible states is perhaps better handled using Bayes principle.

PROBLEMS

5–31. A coin is known to be biased, with probability of heads either 1/4 or 3/4. After two tosses of the coin, one is required to choose between 1/4 and 3/4. Given the loss function $\ell(p,a) = (p - a)^2$, where p is the actual probability of heads and a is the statistician's choice, determine the possible decision functions and the risk function for each.

5–32. In the problem of estimating the mean μ in a normal population with unit variance, determine the risk function for the procedure that takes the mean of a sample of size n as the estimate of μ, first using the loss function $(\mu - a)^2$ and then using $|\mu - a|$. Observe the dependence of risk on n in each case.

5–33. Referring to Example 5–14, consider the class of decision functions of the form $d_A(X) = A\bar{X}$, where A is a positive constant. Determine the value of A such that the risk function corresponding to d_A is (uniformly) smallest, and determine that smallest risk function.

5–34. Determine the minimax decision function for Problem 5–31.

5–35. In estimating the parameter p of a Bernoulli population, consider only decision functions that take as the estimated value the quantity $(k/n) + b$, where k is the number of "successes" among the n independent trials and b is a constant. Select b according to the minimax risk principle, taking the loss function to be $(p - a)^2$, where a is the estimate.

5–36. In the flash-bulb problem, Example 5–15, determine the decision function that minimizes the maximum risk, not over all k but over $k \leq 5$.

5–37. Discuss the modification of Example 5–14 in which there is incorporated in the risk function a term representing the cost of sampling, proportional to the size of the sample (assuming that such a cost can be measured on the same utility scale as that of the assumed loss function).

5.4.2 Bayes Solutions. In selecting a decision function for a problem with data, the principle of Bayes is applied to the risk function. For a given prior weighting M on the space of states of nature, we define for each d the *Bayes risk* corresponding to M:

$$B(d) = \int_{\Theta} R(\theta,d)\, dM.$$

The Bayes decision procedure is that which minimizes this quantity. If θ is a real parameter with values on I, the weighting M defines a "distribution function" $G(\theta)$, with

$$B(d) = \int_{I} R(\theta,d)\, dG(\theta),$$

and further reductions if G has a "density" or is discrete.

It is not really essential that M denote a probability-type measure, with total probability 1, or even that it be a finite measure. Given any measure M, the quantity $B(d)$ is a linear function of the risk function and assigns to each decision function d a single number in terms of which the decision functions are judged. If $B(d)$ is really to be an *average* risk, measured on the same scale as the risk itself, the total weighting should be 1.

Example 5–17. In the flash-bulb problem of Example 5–15, consider a weighting on k (the number of defectives in a lot) which is uniform for $k = 0$, 1, and 2. Assigning a unit weight to each of these values, we have

$$B(d_1) = -0.01\sum_{k=0}^{2}(3k^2 - 44.5k + 135) = -2.865,$$

$$B(d_2) = 0.01\sum_{k=0}^{2}(3k^2 - 17.5k + 10) = -0.075,$$

$$B(d_3) = -0.09\sum_{k=0}^{2}(15 - 3k) = -3.24,$$

$$B(d_4) = \sum_{k=0}^{2}(0.10) = 0.30.$$

The minimum of these is obtained by using d_3, which is the Bayes procedure for the assumed prior weighting: Sell the lot, regardless of the outcome of the test. The same minimizing procedure is obtained by using a weighting 1/3 for each of $k = 0, 1, 2$; the only difference would be that the $B(d)$ in each case would be divided by 3, the result being then comparable to values of the original risk function.

Although the language of "prior distribution" for θ is customary, it is not necessary in using a Bayes procedure to believe that the state of nature is random. Indeed, one of the basic assumptions in estimating a parameter of a distribution is that there is a fixed value of the parameter which can be estimated. On the other hand, not knowing the actual state of nature, one must take into account somehow the various possible states of nature. A distribution on the states of nature weights the possible states according to one's pleasure—or more accurately, according to one's past experience or other information. There may be situations, of course, in which it is not unreasonable to think of the state of nature as random in that the state came to pass by a random process and, though now fixed, is still unknown (as in the toss of a coin: after the coin has fallen the result is not really random, but not knowing the outcome, one is forced to behave as though it were random).

Example 5–18. Referring once more to the flash-bulb problem of Example 5–15, one could think of the "population parameter" k as the number of defectives in a sample of ten bulbs from a production line that is "in control," putting out flash bulbs with a constant probability p_0 of a defective. The appropriate prior distribution would then be binomial, with parameters $(10, p_0)$. The expected risks for the four decision functions considered are then as follows:

$$\begin{aligned} B(d_1) &= -0.05(54p_0^2 - 83p_0 + 27), \\ B(d_2) &= 0.05(54p_0^2 - 29p_0 + 2), \\ B(d_3) &= -1.35(1 - 2p_0), \\ B(d_4) &= 0.10. \end{aligned}$$

For a given p_0 (that is, a given prior distribution), the Bayes solution is to choose the d with the smallest $B(d)$. Examining the above as functions of p_0, one finds that the

Bayes solution would be d_3 over a broad range of small values of p_0. Thus d_3 would appear to be appropriate even though p_0 is unknown and possibly changing from lot to lot—if it can be assumed small.

Not only does the Bayes principle permit one to insert his personality into the decision problem, it *forces* him to do so in a very explicit way. This may be considered a drawback of the principle—that someone has to choose the weighting function or prior distribution. It might also be considered a good point, since the statistician's role is so explicit; for, with *any* procedure or principle for selecting procedures, the statistician's whims play a role, but not usually in a way that is so clearly exposed.

5.4.3 Posterior Distributions. If one is going to picture θ as a random variable, he may as well go a step further and consider that its distribution may be altered by information furnished in the experimentation, that is, by the value of the statistic Z. We therefore consider the *conditional* distribution of θ, given that $Z = z$. This is called the *posterior* (or *a posteriori*) distribution of θ corresponding to the given prior distribution and the data $Z = z$. Assuming continuous distributions, we find the density of the posterior distribution as follows:

$$h(\theta \mid z) = \frac{g(\theta)f(z \mid \theta)}{f(z)},$$

where $g(\theta)$ is the prior density, $f(z \mid \theta)$ is a way of writing $f(z;\theta)$ which reflects the present point of view, and $f(z)$ is the *absolute density* of Z, defined by

$$f(z) = \int f(z \mid \theta)g(\theta)\, d\theta = E_g[f(z \mid \theta)].$$

If θ is discrete, the integrals are replaced by sums:

$$f(z) = \sum f(z \mid \theta_i)g(\theta_i),$$

and

$$h(\theta_i \mid z) = \frac{f(z \mid \theta_i)g(\theta_i)}{f(z)},$$

where the f is either a density or a probability function.

Example 5–19. For the rain problem (Example 5–13) assume a prior distribution of 0.7 for θ_1 (rain) and 0.3 for θ_2 (no rain). That is, past experience shows that it tends to be rainy on the day in question. The absolute probability of the observation z_1 (rain indicated) is

$$\begin{aligned} f(z_1) &= \sum f(z_1 \mid \theta_i)g(\theta_i) \\ &= 0.8 \times 0.7 + 0.1 \times 0.3 = 0.59, \end{aligned}$$

and the posterior probabilities for θ_1 and θ_2, given an indication of rain, are the ratios of the terms in this sum to the sum:

$$h(\theta_1 | z_1) = \frac{0.56}{0.59} \qquad h(\theta_2 | z_1) = \frac{0.03}{0.59}.$$

The indication of rain modifies the odds from 7 to 3 in favor of rain to 56 to 3 in favor of rain.

Similarly, for the observation z_2 (no rain indicated) the absolute probability is

$$f(z_2) = 0.2 \times 0.7 + 0.9 \times 0.3 = 0.41,$$

and the posterior probabilities, given an indication of no rain, are

$$h(\theta_1 | z_2) = \frac{14}{41} \qquad h(\theta_2 | z_2) = \frac{27}{41}.$$

With this data the odds are altered to 14 to 27 against rain. Observe that the amount of alteration depends on the way in which the data are influenced by the state of nature. For instance, if the state θ_1 defined the distribution of Z to be $f(z_1 | \theta_1) = 1$ and $f(z_2 | \theta_1) = 0$, the posterior distribution of θ, given z_2, is an assignment of probability 1 to the state θ_2. In words: If, when it is going to rain, the rain indicator indicates this unfailingly, an indication of "no rain" calls for putting all one's money on the state "no rain," no matter what the prior distribution.

Example 5–20. Consider the estimation of p in the Bernoulli probability function $p^x(1-p)^{1-x}$, $x = 0$ or 1, using the statistic k, the number of "successes" in n independent trials. Given p, the probability function for k is binomial:

$$f(k | p) = \binom{n}{k} p^k (1-p)^{n-k}, \qquad k = 0, 1, \ldots, n.$$

Assuming a uniform prior distribution for p on [0,1], we find the following absolute probability function for k:

$$f(k) = \binom{n}{k} \int_0^1 p^k (1-p)^{n-k}\, dp = \frac{1}{n+1},$$

for $k = 0, 1, \cdots, n$. (The integration is performed, using the following formula to be derived in Chapter 8:

$$\int_0^1 x^r (1-x)^s\, dx = \frac{r!\, s!}{(r+s+1)!},$$

where r and s are non-negative integers.) The posterior density of p, given k, is then the integrand of $f(k)$ divided by $f(k)$:

$$h(p | k) = \frac{1 \cdot f(k | p)}{f(k)} = \binom{n}{k} (n+1) p^k (1-p)^{n-k}.$$

For instance, if the n trials all result in "success," then $k = n$ and the distribution function for p is

$$H(p | k = n) = p^{n+1}, \qquad 0 \le p \le 1.$$

For large n, a sequence of n successes would put most of the weight near $p = 1$ in the posterior distribution.

It is of interest to observe that if the posterior distribution is used as a prior distribution for a second experiment, the resulting new posterior distribution based on the outcome of the second experiment is the same as the posterior distribution that would have been obtained based on the *combined* data from the two experiments and the initial prior distribution. For, let the outcomes of the experiments be (X, Y), with joint density

$$f(x,y \mid \theta) = f(x \mid \theta) f(y \mid x,\theta).$$

The posterior density of θ, given $X = x$ and assuming a prior density $g(\theta)$, is

$$h(\theta \mid x) = \frac{g(\theta) f(x \mid \theta)}{\int g(\theta) f(x \mid \theta)\, d\theta},$$

and using this as a prior distribution together with the result $Y = y$, one obtains the posterior distribution:

$$\begin{aligned} k(\theta \mid x,y) &= \frac{h(\theta \mid x) f(y \mid x,\theta)}{\int h(\theta \mid x) f(y \mid x,\theta)\, d\theta} \\ &= \frac{g(\theta) f(x \mid \theta) f(y \mid x,\theta)}{\int g(\theta) f(x \mid \theta) f(y \mid x,\theta)\, d\theta} = \frac{g(\theta) f(x,y \mid \theta)}{\int g(\theta) f(x,y \mid \theta)\, d\theta}, \end{aligned}$$

which is what would have been obtained by using the combined result $X = x$ and $Y = y$ together with the prior distribution given by $g(\theta)$. This property of posterior distributions is illustrated in Problem 5–41.

The posterior distribution can be used as a tool in computing Bayes strategies. The method is to compute the posterior expected loss:

$$E_h[\ell(\theta,a)] = \int \ell(\theta,a) h(\theta \mid z)\, d\theta$$

and then to select the action a (for the given z) that minimizes this quantity. The dependence of the chosen a on the given z provides a decision function $a = d^*(z)$, which is precisely the Bayes decision function for the given prior distribution.

To establish this claim, we manipulate the expression for the Bayes risk corresponding to a decision function $d(z)$:

$$\begin{aligned} B(d) = E_g[R(\theta,d)] &= \int R(\theta,d) g(\theta)\, d\theta \\ &= \int\int \ell(\theta,d(z)) f(z \mid \theta) g(\theta)\, dz\, d\theta \\ &= \int f(z) \left\{ \int \ell(\theta,d(z)) h(\theta \mid z)\, d\theta \right\} dz \\ &= \int f(z) E_h[\ell(\theta,d(z))]\, dz. \end{aligned}$$

From the last representation of $B(d)$ it is apparent that $B(d)$ is minimized by a function $d(z)$ whose value a for each z is selected to minimize the expected posterior loss, $E_h[\ell(\theta,a)]$.

The method, then, is equivalent to the following: Determine the posterior distribution, given $Z = z$, and use it as a prior distribution for θ in a no-data problem with the original loss function. The Bayes solution for this no-data problem is the desired Bayes action for the given problem.

The significance of this method of determining $d(z)$ is that it is only necessary to compute the value of $d(z)$ for the z actually obtained as the result of experimentation. Computing $d(z)$ as a Bayes strategy or decision function from the basic definition involves a determination of the whole function—the value of $d(z)$ for each foreseeable z. Mathematically, a problem in the calculus of variations (minimizing over a set of possible functions) is replaced by a problem in the calculus (minimizing over a set of numbers). It may prove helpful to consider the schematic diagrams for computation of Bayes strategies according to the two methods, as shown in Figures 5–11 and 5–12.

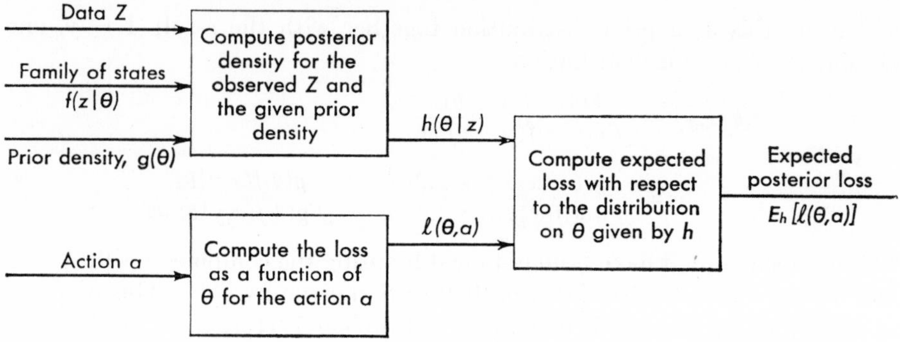

Bayes action for data Z is the a which yields a minimum expected posterior loss

Figure 5–11

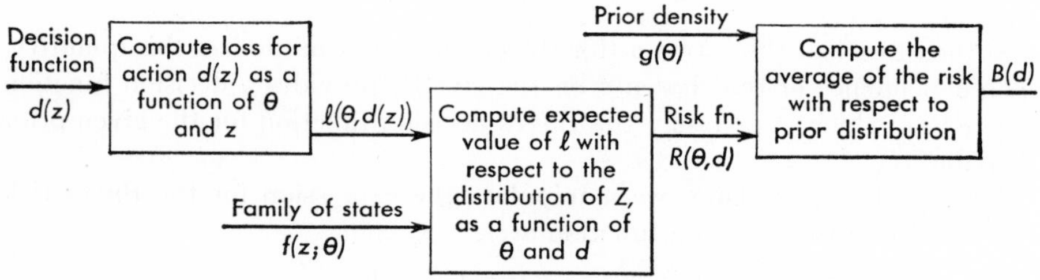

Bayes decision function is the $d(z)$ which yields the minimum $B(d)$

Figure 5–12

Example 5–21. We illustrate the computation of Bayes strategies according to the two methods above for the rain problem, Example 5–13. It was seen there that all strategies except d_2 (go without umbrella, no matter what the data), d_3(go with umbrella, no matter what the data), and d_9 (go with, if indicator shows rain; go without, if it shows no rain) are inadmissible, and that the risk table for these three is as follows:

	θ_1(rain)	θ_2(no rain)
d_2	5	0
d_3	2	5
d_9	2.6	0.5

Assuming prior probabilities of 0.7 for rain and 0.3 for no rain (as in Example 5–19), we find expected risks of $5 \times 0.7 + 0 \times 0.3 = 3.5$, $2 \times 0.7 + 5 \times 0.3 = 2.9$, and $2.6 \times 0.7 + 0.5 \times 0.3 = 1.97$. The last is smallest, and so d_9 is the Bayes decision rule (for the assumed prior distribution!).

To proceed with the alternate computation, assume first that the indicator shows rain (z_1 is observed). In Example 5–19 it was found that the corresponding posterior weights are 56/59 for θ_1 and 3/59 for θ_2. Using these weights in the original loss table, we find expected posterior losses of $(4 \times 56 + 4 \times 3)/59$, $(5 \times 56 + 0 \times 3)/59$, and $(2 \times 56 + 5 \times 3)/59$, for actions a_1, a_2, and a_3, respectively. The smallest of these is the last, and so when the indicator shows rain, the Bayes action is a_3, which agrees with part of decision rule d_9. It is seen similarly that when the indicator shows no rain, the Bayes action is a_2 (go without umbrella), the other part of d_9.

Example 5–22. In Example 5–20 there was computed the posterior distribution for the parameter p in a Bernoulli family, assuming a uniform prior distribution on [0,1]. The result, given k "successes" in n trials, is

$$h(p \mid k) = \binom{n}{k} (n + 1)p^k(1 - p)^{n-k}.$$

Given the quadratic loss function $(p - a)^2$ for an estimate a when the actual value is p, the posterior expected loss is

$$E_h[\ell(p,a)] = E_h[(p - a)^2].$$

This is a second moment, and the smallest such second moment is that taken about the *mean* of the distribution; that is, about $E_h(p)$. This mean is therefore the Bayes action:

$$E_h(p) = \int_0^1 p \binom{n}{k} (n + 1)p^k(1 - p)^{n-k}\, dp$$
$$= \frac{k + 1}{n + 2},$$

computed by using again the integration formula given in Example 5–20. In particular, for instance, the Bayes estimates of p corresponding to $k = 0, 1, \cdots, 8$ successes in eight trials are, respectively, 1/10, 2/10, $\cdots$, 9/10.

A *restricted Bayes procedure* is one that minimizes the Bayes risk among the class of procedures whose risk functions do not exceed some constant C, where C is greater than the minimum-maximum risk. The idea is that in using such a procedure, one guards to some extent against a catastrophic loss that might be caused by a poor or imprecise prior distribution used in an ordinary Bayes process. The more certain is the prior distribution, the larger the C that would be used. (Cf. J. L. Hodges, Jr., and E. L. Lehmann, "The Use of Previous Experience in Reaching Statistical Decisions," *Ann. Math. Stat.*, 23(1952), pages 396–407).

A point of contact between the minimax and Bayes notions should be mentioned. It happens that a minimax mixed strategy can be thought of generally as a Bayes strategy corresponding to a prior distribution on the states of nature which is "least favorable" in the sense of giving the largest minimum Bayes risk. This will not be pursued here, but attention is called to this phenomenon in Example 5–4 and 5–16. (Cf. Reference [2] or [19] for a complete discussion of this point.)

PROBLEMS

5–38. Determine the Bayes decision function for Problem 5–31 corresponding to a prior distribution that weights the two possible values of p equally.

5–39. Compute the posterior distribution of p for Problem 5–38, given that the outcomes of both tosses are Heads. Determine the corresponding posterior expected loss and the action that minimizes it. Compare this with the action determined by the Bayes decision function obtained in Problem 5–38.

5–40. Verify the expressions for Bayes risk given in Examples 5–17 and 5–18.

5–41. Consider a uniform prior distribution on the parameter p in a Bernoulli family. Using the posterior distribution determined in Example 5–20, based on k successes in the first n trials, as a prior distribution for m additional trials, compare the posterior distribution based on j successes in these m trials with the posterior distribution based on $j + k$ successes in $n + m$ trials (using a uniform distribution on p in the latter computation).

5–42. Show that the prior weighting $1/(pq)$ for $0 < p < 1$ and $p + q = 1$ yields the Bayes estimate k/n for the p in a Bernoulli distribution, based on k successes in n independent trials, using a quadratic loss. (This weighting does not define a probability distribution because its integral over [0,1] is not convergent.)

5–43. Compute the minimum Bayes risk for Example 5–22 in two ways: (1) as the minimum expected value of the risk function, using the Bayes decision function to obtain this minimum; (2) as the average with respect to the absolute distribution of k of the posterior expected loss, again using the estimate that minimizes this posterior expected loss.

5.4.4 Maximum Likelihood Procedures. Suppose first that the population of interest is discrete, so that it is meaningful to speak of the probability that $\mathbf{X} = \mathbf{x}$, where $\mathbf{X}$ denotes a sample $(X_1, \ldots, X_n)$ and $\mathbf{x}$ a possible realization $(x_1, \ldots, x_n)$. This probability that $\mathbf{X} = \mathbf{x}$ depends on $\mathbf{x}$, of course, but it also depends on the state of nature θ which governs. As a function of θ for given $\mathbf{x}$, it is called the likelihood function:

$$L(\theta) = P_\theta(\mathbf{X} = \mathbf{x}).$$

The principle of *maximum likelihood* requires first that a value $\theta = \hat{\theta}$ be found which furnishes the "best explanation" of a given result that is observed. That is, holding x fixed, we allow θ to wander over the various possible states of nature and select one, $\hat{\theta}$, which maximizes the probability $L(\theta)$ of obtaining the result actually observed. Then, having found a state $\hat{\theta}$ that best explains the observed result x, we take the action that would be best if $\hat{\theta}$ really were the true state. This best action for a given state of nature is naturally determined by the loss function (or, equivalently, by the regret function) as that action which minimizes the loss (or regret).

Because the best explanation of a given x depends on that x, held fixed during the maximization of $L(\theta)$, the minimizing θ depends on x. It defines a function of the observations—a statistic. The rule of taking the action that minimizes $\ell(\theta,a)$ is then a decision function, an assignment of an action to each possible outcome of the sampling experiment.

Example 5–23. Consider once again the flash-bulb problem: Flash bulbs come in lots of ten, and one is selected from the lot for testing (cf. Example 5–15). Let k denote the number of defective bulbs in a lot of ten, let $p = k/10$, and let X denote the outcome of the test (X = good or X = defective). The likelihood function is

$$L(p) = P_p(X = x) = \begin{cases} 1 - p, & \text{if } x = \text{good}, \\ p, & \text{if } x = \text{defective}. \end{cases}$$

The maximizing value of p for a given x is then

$$\hat{p} = \begin{cases} 0, & \text{if } x = \text{good}, \\ 1, & \text{if } x = \text{defective}. \end{cases}$$

From the loss function given in Example 5–15 are found the following:

$$\ell(0, \text{sell}) = -1.35, \qquad \ell(1, \text{sell}) = 1.35,$$
$$\ell(0, \text{junk}) = 0.10, \qquad \ell(1, \text{junk}) = 0.10.$$

If p is really 0, the minimum loss is achieved by selling; if p is really 1, the minimum loss is achieved by junking. Hence, the maximum likelihood decision function is to sell the lot if the bulb tested is good and to junk the lot if the bulb tested is bad.

In the case of a continuous population, maximizing the probability that $X = x$ accomplishes nothing, since each such probability is zero. Instead, one maximizes the "probability element" for given dx; that is, a value of θ is chosen which maximizes the density function of X at the point x. The maximizing value of θ is again the state assumed to be correct in choosing an action to minimize the loss.

The joint density function of the sample observations at x is called (as a function of θ) the *likelihood function:*

$$L(\theta) = f(x;\theta) = f(x_1,\ldots,x_n;\theta).$$

In the case of a random sample, with identically distributed, independent observations, this becomes

$$L(\theta) = \prod_{i=1}^{n} f(x_i;\theta),$$

where $f(x;\theta)$ is the population density function.

Example 5–24. We treat from the point of view of maximum likelihood the estimation problem considered in Example 5–14, in which it was desired to estimate θ in the negative exponential density $(1/\theta)\exp(-x/\theta)$, $x > 0$, on the basis of a random sample of size n. For a given sample $\mathbf{x}$, the likelihood function is

$$L(\theta) = \prod_{i=1}^{n} \frac{1}{\theta}\exp\left(\frac{-X_i}{\theta}\right) = \frac{1}{\theta^n}\exp\left(\frac{-n\bar{X}}{\theta}\right).$$

This function has a maximum at $\theta = \bar{X}$. If, then, the loss function has the natural property of being smallest when $a = \theta$, the right choice of action would be to take $\bar{X}$ (now assumed to be the true state) as the estimate of θ. Hence, for such loss functions, the sample mean is the maximum likelihood estimate of θ.

We point out that the quantity $\hat{\theta}$ that maximizes $L(\theta)$ and which is used as the true state in determining the right action can be thought of as the number that maximizes the density of the posterior distribution of θ, assuming a uniform prior distribution.

For,

$$h(\theta\,|\,x) = \frac{f(x;\theta)g(\theta)}{f(x)},$$

where $g(\theta)$ is the prior density and $f(\mathbf{x})$ the absolute density of $\mathbf{X}$. Clearly, if $g(\theta)$ is constant, the maximum of $L(\theta) = f(\mathbf{x};\theta)$ is attained for the value of θ that maximizes $h(\theta\,|\,\mathbf{x})$. (The maximum of a density function, when it has a single maximum, is called the *mode* of the distribution; it may or may not coincide with the mean or the median of the distribution.)

It is to be observed that the quantity θ (which indexes the states of nature), although frequently a real parameter, can be a vector-valued parameter—$(\theta_1 \ldots, \theta_k)$—or it could be non-numerical.

PROBLEMS

5–44. Write out likelihood functions for a random sample of size n from each of the following populations: (a) normal (μ,σ^2); (b) Poisson (m); (c) Bernoulli (p); (d) uniform on $[0,k]$, where k is the parameter.

5–45. Let M denote the number of defectives in a lot of five articles, and let the possible actions be a_1, accept the lot, and a_2, reject the lot. Let the loss function be M for action a_1 and $2(5 - M)$ for a_2. Determine the maximum likelihood action for the results of tests on samples of size two from the lot.

5–46. Referring to Example 5–24, determine the posterior distribution of θ, given $X = x$ and a uniform prior distribution. Compute the mode of this distribution to verify the result $\hat{\theta} = \bar{x}$ and also compute the mean of this distribution, which minimizes the Bayes risk, using the quadratic loss $(\theta - a)^2$. The latter is the Bayes solution. [You will need the formula (to be obtained in Chapter 8)

$$\int_0^\infty u^t e^{-u}\, du = t!,$$

for any non-negative integer t.]

5.5 Sufficient Statistics

The notion of sufficiency was discussed rather imprecisely earlier in this chapter when considering the reduction of the data in a sample to more manageable measures—a reduction hopefully not so drastic as to throw away information in the sample pertinent to the problem at hand. Although the notion will now be made more precise, a rigorous treatment of sufficiency in the general case requires a rigorous treatment of conditional probability as a basis. Not having this, we can only reason intuitively and state results (except in the discrete case, in which it is possible to be quite precise and rigorous with the background assumed).

Before taking up the general definition, we consider the following example, a discrete case that illustrates the main idea without the complications of general notation.

Example 5–25. Consider the family of Bernoulli distributions indexed as usual by the probability p of "success" in a single trial:

$$P(X = x) = p^x(1 - p)^{1-x}, \qquad x = 0 \text{ (failure)}, 1 \text{ (success)}.$$

There are eight distinct samples of size three, and the probability function of (X_1,X_2,X_3) is

$$P(\mathbf{X} = \mathbf{x}) = P(X_1 = x_1, X_2 = x_2, X_3 = x_3) = p^k(1 - p)^{3-k},$$

where $x_1 + x_2 + x_3 = k$, the number of 1's among the values (x_1,x_2,x_3). Let the statistic T denote the number of successes among three trials: $T = X_1 + X_2 + X_3$, with probability function

$$P(T = k) = P(k \text{ successes in 3 trials}) = \binom{3}{k} p^k(1 - p)^{3-k}.$$

The *conditional* probability of obtaining (x_1,x_2,x_3), given that $T = k$, is the quotient

$$p(\mathbf{x} \mid T = k) = P(\mathbf{X} = \mathbf{x} \mid T = k) = \frac{P(\mathbf{X} = \mathbf{x} \text{ and } T = k)}{P(T = k)}.$$

The numerator is zero unless $x_1 + x_2 + x_3 = k$, in which case the condition $T = k$ is redundant; hence,

$$p(x \mid T = k) = \begin{cases} 0, & \text{if } x_1 + x_2 + x_3 \neq k, \\ \dfrac{p^k(1-p)^{3-k}}{\dbinom{3}{k} p^k(1-p)^{3-k}} = \dfrac{1}{\dbinom{3}{k}}, & \text{if } x_1 + x_2 + x_3 = k. \end{cases}$$

These probabilities for the various samples and conditions are itemized in the following tabulation:

Sample	T	Prob.	Prob. given $T = 0$	Prob. given $T = 1$	Prob. given $T = 2$	Prob. given $T = 3$
(0,0,0)	0	$(1-p)^3$	1	0	0	0
(0,0,1)	1	$p(1-p)^2$	0	$\frac{1}{3}$	0	0
(0,1,0)	1	$p(1-p)^2$	0	$\frac{1}{3}$	0	0
(1,0,0)	1	$p(1-p)^2$	0	$\frac{1}{3}$	0	0
(0,1,1)	2	$p^2(1-p)$	0	0	$\frac{1}{3}$	0
(1,0,1)	2	$p^2(1-p)$	0	0	$\frac{1}{3}$	0
(1,1,0)	2	$p^2(1-p)$	0	0	$\frac{1}{3}$	0
(1,1,1)	3	p^3	0	0	0	1

Notice in particular that the distribution of (X_1, X_2, X_3), given any particular value of T, *does not involve the parameter p*.

One can imagine that a sample point, say (1,1,0), is obtained in this way: First a game is played which gives the value of T, namely, $T = 2$. Then, among the three samples for which the sample sum is 2, the particular result (1,1,0) comes from playing a second game—tossing a three-sided object with equal probabilities. This second game does not depend on p, and it would seem quite pointless to play the second game whose outcome depends in no way on the parameter of interest. That is, whatever there is in a particular sample which has to do with p is contained in the sample sum, and it does no good to learn further which particular sample with that sum is the one that actually resulted.

The statistic T is said to be *sufficient* for the family of Bernoulli distributions because knowing T is just as good as knowing the actual sample insofar as knowledge of p is concerned. But notice that the same would be true of $T/3$, or of T^2, or of any other function of T whose values for distinct T values are distinct. Indeed, sufficiency is basically a property of the partitioning of the space of possible samples into these four sets:

$$\{(0,0,0)\}$$
$$\{(0,0,1),\ (0,1,0),\ (1,0,0)\}$$
$$\{(0,1,1),\ (1,0,1),\ (1,1,0)\}$$
$$\{(1,1,1)\}$$

On any one of these sets of sample points, T is constant—a different constant each—and so T serves to identify the sets. Similarly, $T/3$ would also serve to identify them, etc. The point is that no matter how these partition sets are coded, the conditional distribution of X, given that the result is in a particular partition set, does not depend on p, and one is no better off knowing exactly which sample point occurred than he is knowing which partition set occurred.

Consider a family of states of nature, or the equivalent family of distributions of the sample point $\mathbf{X}$. The statistic $T = t(\mathbf{X})$ is said to be *sufficient* for the family if the conditional distribution of $\mathbf{X}$, given the value of T, is the same for all members of the family. If the family is indexed by a (real or vector) parameter θ, the conditional distribution of $\mathbf{X}$, given the value of T, is to be independent of θ.

The statement that $T = t(\mathbf{X})$ has a certain value, say, $T = k$, is interpreted geometrically to mean that the sample point $\mathbf{X}$ lies on the hypersurface $t(x_1,\ldots,x_n) = k$, which is the set of *all* points for which $t(\mathbf{x}) = k$. If T is sufficient for a family of distributions, the conditional distribution of probability on such hypersurfaces induced by one member of the family is the same as that induced by any other. Knowledge of $\mathbf{X}$ beyond just the value of $t(\mathbf{X})$ does not then help in chasing down the particular member of the family that is the true state of nature. The hypersurfaces on which $t(\mathbf{x}) = k$ for various values of k are the sets of a partition of the whole sample space defined by the statistic T. It is this partition that is really the thing which is sufficient, and any function $g(\mathbf{x})$ that has distinct values on distinct partition sets is also a sufficient statistic. The most that a sample can say regarding the underlying state of nature is contained in the statement that the sample point is on some one of the partition sets, and no pertinent information is discarded in the reduction $T = t(\mathbf{x})$—or in $g(\mathbf{x})$, if distinct values of g correspond to distinct values of t.

The statistic T in this definition of sufficiency can be a vector. It might be, for instance, the order statistic $(X_{(1)}, \ldots, X_{(n)})$, or even the original sample point itself: $(X_1, \ldots, X_n)$. With this understanding, it is clear that the sample itself is trivially a sufficient statistic for any family of distributions. The partitioning of the sample space is into sets, each consisting of just the one point $\mathbf{x}$.

The significance of a sufficient statistic T in statistical problems is that by restricting the attention to procedures based on T, no information is overlooked. For, as was argued in the illustrative example, the original experiment of chance which determines a sample point $\mathbf{x}$ can be thought of as first an experiment that determines the value of T followed by one that does not depend on which member of the family of distributions is the one that governs. That is, to determine the sample and hence any other statistic, one can first play the game to find T and then play the second game, which is the same for all states of nature considered. This implies that *any decision procedure can be viewed as a randomized (mixed) decision procedure based on the sufficient statistic T.*

5.5.1 The Factorization Criterion. To determine whether a given statistic is sufficient, it is usually easier, rather than to determine the conditional distribution given the value of the statistic, to use the following criterion:

In order that the statistic $T = t(\mathbf{X})$ be sufficient for the family $f(\mathbf{x};\theta)$, it is necessary and sufficient that the sample joint density function factor:

$$f(\mathbf{x};\theta) = g[t(\mathbf{x}),\theta]h(\mathbf{x}),$$

where g depends on the observations only through the value of $t(\mathbf{x})$, and h does not involve the parameter θ.

In this statement we have omitted certain regularity conditions that must be imposed for the continuous case (cf. Reference [12], page 19, and the references given there). However, in the discrete case [in which $f(\mathbf{x};\theta)$ is interpreted as a probability function], the argument runs as follows: If a factorization is assumed,

$$P_\theta(\mathbf{X} = \mathbf{x}) = g[t(\mathbf{x}),\theta]h(\mathbf{x}),$$

then for any given t_0,

$$P(T = t_0) = \sum_{t(\mathbf{x})=t_0} P_\theta(\mathbf{X} = \mathbf{x}) = \sum_{t(\mathbf{x})=t_0} g[t(\mathbf{x}),\theta]h(\mathbf{x})$$
$$= g[t_0,\theta] \sum_{t(\mathbf{x})=t_0} h(\mathbf{x}).$$

The conditional distribution of $\mathbf{X}$, given $T = t_0$, is then

$$P(\mathbf{X} = \mathbf{x} \mid T = t_0) = \frac{P(\mathbf{X} = \mathbf{x} \text{ and } T = t_0)}{P(T = t_0)} = \begin{cases} 0, & \text{if } t(\mathbf{x}) \neq t_0, \\ \dfrac{P(\mathbf{X} = \mathbf{x})}{P(T = t_0)}, & \text{if } t(\mathbf{x}) = t_0, \end{cases}$$

where, if $t(\mathbf{x}) = t_0$,

$$\frac{P(\mathbf{X} = \mathbf{x})}{P(T = t_0)} = \frac{g[t_0,\theta]h(\mathbf{x})}{g[t_0,\theta] \sum_{t(\mathbf{x})=t_0} h(\mathbf{x})},$$

which is independent of θ. Hence, T is sufficient.

Conversely, if the conditional probability that $\mathbf{X} = \mathbf{x}$, given $T = t_0$, is independent of θ:

$$P(\mathbf{X} = \mathbf{x} \mid T = t_0) = c(\mathbf{x},t_0),$$

then for a given $\mathbf{x}$, with t_0 defined to be $t(\mathbf{x})$,

$$P(\mathbf{X} = \mathbf{x}) = P(\mathbf{X} = \mathbf{x} \text{ and } t(\mathbf{X}) = t_0)$$
$$= c(\mathbf{x}, t_0)\, P(t(\mathbf{X}) = t(\mathbf{x})),$$

the first factor on the right being independent of θ and the second depending on $\mathbf{x}$ only through the values of $t(\mathbf{x})$.

Although we shall forego the pleasure of a precise statement and proof of the factorization criterion in the general case, it does apply in the cases in which we shall use it.

Actually, the factorization criterion is most often used in this way: A joint density function $f(\mathbf{x};\theta)$ is inspected to determine whether there is any factorization of the type required—in terms of some function of $\mathbf{x}$. If there is, that function of $\mathbf{x}$ defines a sufficient statistic.

Example 5-26. Consider a normal population with parameters (μ,σ^2). The joint density function of the observations in a random sample $\mathbf{X}$ is

$$f(\mathbf{x};\theta) = \prod_{i=1}^{n} f(x_i;\mu,\sigma^2)$$

$$= \frac{1}{(\sqrt{2\pi}\sigma)^n} \exp\left\{-\sum_{i=1}^{n} \frac{(x_i-\mu)^2}{2\sigma^2}\right\}.$$

Now, since

$$\sum_{i=1}^{n}(x_i-\mu)^2 = n[s_x^2 + (\bar{x}-\mu)^2],$$

$f(\mathbf{x};\theta)$ itself depends on the observations only through the values of $(\bar{x}, s_x^2)$. The factorization criterion is satisfied (using $h \equiv 1$, which is surely independent of θ), and therefore $(\bar{X}, s_x^2)$ is sufficient for (μ, σ^2).

It is not usually easy to use the factorization criterion to show that a statistic T is *not* sufficient, since this would mean showing that $f(\mathbf{x};\theta)$ cannot be factored in the right way. But if we can't seem to factor $f(\mathbf{x};\theta)$, it might be just that we are not clever enough. To show that T is not sufficient, it is usually easier to show that the conditional distribution of $\mathbf{X}$, given $T = t$, *does* depend on θ.

PROBLEMS

5–47. Show that the number of successes in n independent trials of a Bernoulli experiment is sufficient for the probability p of Heads. (Do this two ways: using the definition and using the factorization criterion.)

5–48. Show that in the geometric distribution, with $p(k) = p(1-p)^{k-1}$, for $k = 1, 2, \ldots$, the total number of trials of the underlying Bernoulli experiment necessary to get n Heads is sufficient.

5–49. Determine a sufficient statistic based on a random sample of size n for the family of negative exponential densities.

5–50. Determine a sufficient statistic based on a random sample of size n for the family of Poisson distributions.

5–51. Let X be normal with unit variance, and consider a sample of size three. Determine the conditional distribution of the sample, given the mean of the first two observations. Is this mean sufficient?
[*Hint:* If $U = g(X_1,X_2,X_3)$, the conditional density is

$$f(x_1,x_2,x_3 \mid U = u) = \frac{f(x_1,x_2,x_3)}{f_U(u)}, \text{ if } g(x_1,x_2,x_3) = u,$$

and is zero otherwise.]

5–52. Show that in random sampling without replacement from a population of N objects, M of one type and $N - M$ of another type, the conditional probability of a sample of size n (given the number of objects of the first type in the sample) is $1/\binom{n}{k}$ and that therefore the number of objects of one type (or of the other type) in a sample is sufficient. Also show this sufficiency, by using the factorization criterion.

5.5.2 Minimal Sufficient Statistics. Before defining the notion of minimality, let us review and amplify the relation between *partition* and *statistic*. A partition is simply a division of the sample space into mutually exclusive subsets or groups of points, the union of which subsets is the whole sample space. A statistic $T = t(\mathbf{X})$ defines a partition as follows: Each possible value t_0 of T determines a set of sample points, namely, the set of points $\mathbf{x}$ for which $t(\mathbf{x}) = t_0$. These sets of sample points corresponding to the possible values of T are mutually exclusive, and each $\mathbf{x}$ lies in one of them so that their union is the whole sample space; they make up a partition.

Conversely, a partition can lead to a variety of statistics, each of which would induce (in the manner just described) that partition. All that is required is that the sets of the partition be coded with distinct labels. For, if the set E is one of the sets of the partition, and it is assigned the code name $H(E)$, then for any $\mathbf{x}$ in E, $t(\mathbf{x}) = H(E)$ defines a statistic. Clearly, the sets of the partition are the sets on which $t(\mathbf{x})$ is constant.

Any set that has probability zero can be ignored in these considerations, since such sets and the values of $t(\mathbf{x})$ on them would not affect the probability distribution of $t(\mathbf{X})$.

The sample $(X_1, \cdots, X_n)$ is itself an n-dimensional statistic that corresponds to a partitioning of the sample space into its individual points. The order statistic $(X_{(1)}, \cdots, X_{(n)})$ is constant over a set of points with the property that any one point has coordinates that are a permutation of those of any other point in the set. These symmetric sets of points are the partition sets defined by the order statistic. This partition is said to be a *reduction* of the partition defined by the sample itself, in that each of its sets are made up of partition sets of the latter. Similarly, the partition consisting of sets in each of which $X_1 + \cdots + X_n$ is constant would be a further reduction, since a set in which the sum is constant is made up of partition sets of the order statistic.

Example 5–27. Consider a sample (X_1,X_2,X_3) from a distribution on positive values. Sets of points in which $x_1 + x_2 + x_3$ is constant are portions of planes in the first octant. In Figure 5–13 is shown the plane $x_1 + x_2 + x_3 = 6$; the coordinates of each point on this plane add up to 6. Shown also is one of the sets of the partition defined by the order statistic, namely, the set defined by (1,2,3). This set consists of (1,2,3) and the five other points whose coordinates are permutations of (1,2,3). Each such set will lie on one of the planes $x_1 + x_2 + x_3 = k$, since the sum of the coordinates is not affected by a permutation of coordinates.

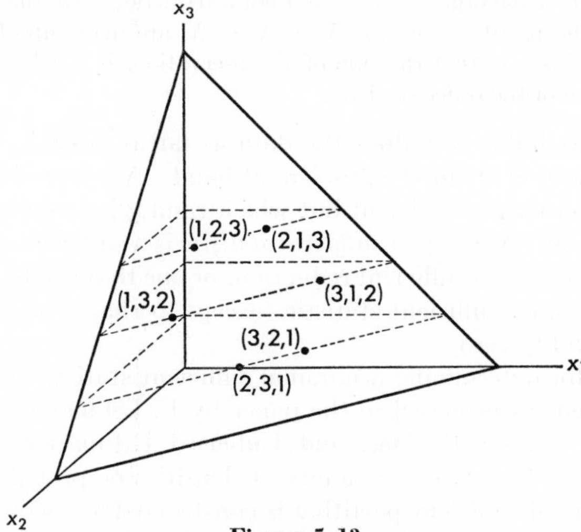

Figure 5–13

If one partition is a reduction of another, any statistic defined on the one is a function of any statistic defined on the other, and conversely, if the statistic S is a function of T, the partition defined by S is a reduction of the partition defined by T.

Example 5–28. Referring to Example 5–27, consider the statistic (Y,Z) where $Y = X_1 + X_2$ and $Z = X_3$. This is constant on a horizontal line, as shown in Figure 5–14.

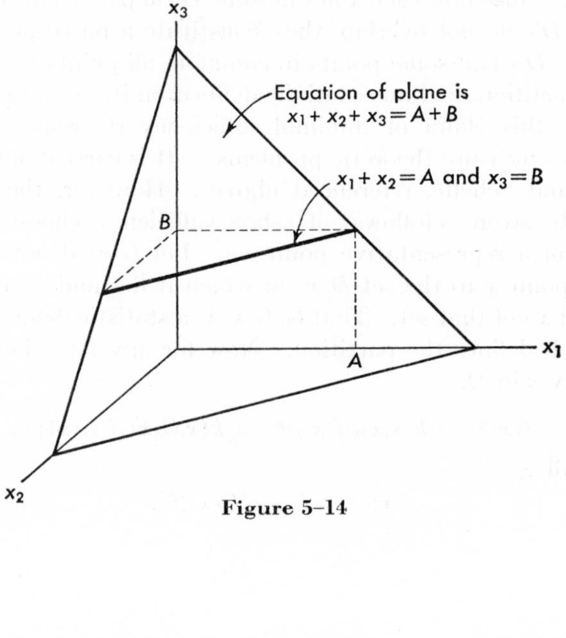

Figure 5–14

Such a partition set is not made up of partition sets corresponding to the order statistic, and the quantity (Y,Z) cannot be computed from a knowledge of the order statistic—it is not a function of the order statistic and not a reduction. On the other hand, the planes that are the partition sets for $X_1 + X_2 + X_3$ are made up of the horizontal lines defined by (Y,Z), so that the sum of all observations is a reduction of (Y,Z) as well as a reduction of the order statistic.

It would be desirable to reduce the data as far as possible without losing pertinent information about the problem at hand. A *minimal sufficient partition* is a partition that is sufficient but which cannot be reduced further to a sufficient partition. A *minimal sufficient statistic* is a sufficient statistic whose partition does not have a sufficient reduction, or one that can be expressed as a function of any other sufficient statistic (except, perhaps, on a set of sample points of probability zero).

A technique for determining a minimal sufficient statistic or partition will now be presented (as proposed in the paper by E. Lehmann and H. Scheffé, "Completeness, Similar Regions, and Unbiased Estimation," *Sankhya*, 10 (1950), pages 327 ff.). Given a family of densities or probability functions $\{f(x;\theta)\}$, a minimal sufficient partition is constructed as follows:

Let $f(\mathbf{x};\theta)$ denote the joint density (or probability function) of the observations $\mathbf{X}$. For each point $\mathbf{x}$ in the sample space, define an associated set $D(\mathbf{x})$ as the set of all $\mathbf{y}$ such that

$$f(\mathbf{y};\theta) = k(\mathbf{y},\mathbf{x})f(\mathbf{x};\theta),$$

where $k(\mathbf{y},\mathbf{x})$ is not zero and is independent of θ. Clearly, $\mathbf{x}$ lies in $D(\mathbf{x})$; and if y is in $D(\mathbf{x})$, then $\mathbf{x}$ is in $D(\mathbf{y})$, so that $D(\mathbf{x})$ and $D(\mathbf{y})$ are in this case the same set of points. All points for which $f(\mathbf{x};\theta) = 0$ for all θ lie in the same D; call this D_0. Since now each $\mathbf{x}$ lies in some D [in particular, it lies in $D(\mathbf{x})$], and since the D's do not overlap, they constitute a partition of the sample space. (If two D's had some points in common, all points would be in common.) This partition, and any statistic defined on it, are minimal sufficient.

Establishing this claim of minimal sufficiency rigorously is not trivial, since it involves measure theoretic problems. (It is carried out in the article of Lehmann and Scheffé, referenced above). However, the basic idea of the proof can be given as follows: To show sufficiency, choose for each set D of the partition a representative point $\mathbf{x}_D$. Let $G(\mathbf{x})$ denote the mapping from a given point $\mathbf{x}$ to the set $D(\mathbf{x})$ in which it lies and then to the representative point $\mathbf{x}_D$ of that set. That is, $G(\mathbf{x})$ is a statistic defined on the partition, and which defines the partition. Now for any partition set D except D_0, and for any $\mathbf{x}$ in D,

$$f(\mathbf{x};\theta) = k(\mathbf{x},\mathbf{x}_D)f(\mathbf{x}_D;\theta) = k(\mathbf{x},G(\mathbf{x}))f(G(\mathbf{x});\theta).$$

But then for all $\mathbf{x}$,

$$f(\mathbf{x};\theta) = h(\mathbf{x})g[G(\mathbf{x}),\theta],$$

where

$$h(\boldsymbol{x}) = \begin{cases} 0, & \text{if } \boldsymbol{x} \text{ is in } D_0 \\ k(\boldsymbol{x},G(\boldsymbol{x})), & \text{otherwise,} \end{cases}$$

and

$$g[G(\boldsymbol{x}),\theta] = f(G(\boldsymbol{x});\theta).$$

The function $h(\boldsymbol{x})$ does not involve θ, and the function $g[G(\boldsymbol{x}),\theta]$ depends on $\boldsymbol{x}$ only through the values of the statistic $G(\boldsymbol{x})$. Thus $G(\boldsymbol{x})$ is sufficient, as is therefore the given partition, which it defines.

To see the minimality of the sufficient statistic $G(\boldsymbol{x})$ and the corresponding partition, consider any other sufficient statistic $t(\boldsymbol{X})$ with corresponding partition sets E. The minimality follows when it is shown that each set E is contained in some D of the constructed partition (except possibly for points in a set of probability zero). Let $\boldsymbol{x}$ and $\boldsymbol{y}$ be points in E so that $t(\boldsymbol{x}) = t(\boldsymbol{y})$. Since $t(\boldsymbol{X})$ is sufficient,

$$f(\boldsymbol{x};\theta) = r(\boldsymbol{x})s[t(\boldsymbol{x}),\theta] = r(\boldsymbol{x})s[t(\boldsymbol{y}),\theta],$$

and

$$f(\boldsymbol{y};\theta) = r(\boldsymbol{y})s[t(\boldsymbol{y}),\theta].$$

If $r(\boldsymbol{x}) \neq 0$,

$$f(\boldsymbol{y};\theta) = r(\boldsymbol{y})\frac{f(\boldsymbol{x};\theta)}{r(\boldsymbol{x})} = k(\boldsymbol{y},\boldsymbol{x})f(\boldsymbol{x};\theta),$$

where

$$k(\boldsymbol{y},\boldsymbol{x}) = \frac{r(\boldsymbol{y})}{r(\boldsymbol{x})}$$

is not zero if $r(\boldsymbol{y})$ is not zero. Hence, if $r(\boldsymbol{y}) \neq 0$, $\boldsymbol{x}$ and $\boldsymbol{y}$ belong to the same D. Thus, all E is contained in D, except possibly for those points $\boldsymbol{x}$ such that $r(\boldsymbol{x}) = 0$; but for such points, $f(\boldsymbol{x};\theta) = 0$ for all θ, and the totality of all such points has probability zero.

Example 5–29. Consider the Bernoulli family with probability function

$$f(x;p) = p^x(1-p)^{1-x}, \qquad x = 0, 1.$$

For a sample $\boldsymbol{X}$ of independent observations, the joint probability function is

$$f(\boldsymbol{x};p) = p^{\Sigma x_i}(1-p)^{n-\Sigma x_i}.$$

Writing out also $f(\boldsymbol{y};p)$ is similar fashion and taking the quotient, we obtain

$$\frac{f(\boldsymbol{x};p)}{f(\boldsymbol{y};p)} = \left\{\frac{p}{1-p}\right\}^{\Sigma x_i - \Sigma y_i},$$

which is independent of p if and only if $\sum x_i = \sum y_i$. Thus, points whose coordinates have the same sum lie in the same set of the minimal sufficient partition. The sum $X_1 + \cdots + X_n$ is therefore a minimal sufficient statistic.

Example 5–30. Consider the normal family

$$f(x;\mu,\sigma^2) = \frac{1}{\sqrt{2\pi}\sigma} \exp\left[\frac{-(x-\mu)^2}{2\sigma^2}\right].$$

Letting $f(\mathbf{x};\mu,\sigma^2)$ denote the joint density function of independent observations, we find the pertinent quotient to be

$$\frac{f(\mathbf{x};\mu,\sigma^2)}{f(\mathbf{y};\mu,\sigma^2)} = \exp\left\{-\frac{1}{2\sigma^2}\left[\sum x_i^2 - \sum y_i^2 - 2\mu\left(\sum x_i - \sum y_i\right)\right]\right\}$$

This is independent of the parameters (μ,σ^2) if and only if both $\sum x_i^2 = \sum y_i^2$ and $\sum x_i = \sum y_i$. Therefore, $(\sum X_i^2, \sum X_i)$ is a minimal sufficient statistic for the normal family.

In each of the above examples there turns out to be a minimal sufficient statistic of the same dimension as the parameter indexing the family of states. This is not always the case; in the case of a Cauchy family, for instance, the minimal sufficient statistic is the order statistic, and any further reduction sacrifices sufficiency.

5.5.3 The Exponential Family. Many of the distributions encountered so far are special cases of the *exponential family* of distributions. This family consists of those distributions with densities or probability functions expressible in the following form:

$$f(x;\theta) = B(\theta)\exp[Q(\theta)R(x)]h(x).$$

The Bernoulli, binomial, Poisson, geometric, and gamma distributions, for instance, are all of this kind.

A minimal sufficient statistic for the family is found by using the technique given in §5.5.2. The joint density function (or probability function) for a random sample $\mathbf{X}$ is

$$f(\mathbf{x};\theta) = B^n(\theta)\exp[Q(\theta)\sum R(x_i)]\prod h(x_i).$$

From this is obtained

$$\frac{f(\mathbf{x};\theta)}{f(\mathbf{y};\theta)} = \exp[Q(\theta)\{\sum R(x_i) - \sum R(y_i)\}]\prod\frac{h(x_i)}{h(y_i)}.$$

This is independent of θ if and only if $\sum R(x_i) = \sum R(y_i)$, and therefore $t(\mathbf{X}) = \sum R(X_i)$ is minimal sufficient.

The statistic $t(\mathbf{X})$ has itself a distribution that belongs to the exponential family. Rather than show this in the continuous case, which would require transformation of a multiple integral, we write out the verification in the discrete case. The probability function for $t(\mathbf{X})$ is

$$\begin{aligned} p(t;\theta) &= P\left(\sum R(X_i) = t\right) \\ &= \sum_{\Sigma R(x_i)=t} B^n(\theta) \exp\left[Q(\theta) \sum R(x_i)\right] \prod h(x_i) \\ &= b(\theta) \exp[tQ(\theta)] H(t), \end{aligned}$$

where $b(\theta) = B^n(\theta)$ and

$$H(t) = \sum_{\Sigma R(x_i)=t} \prod h(x_i).$$

Clearly, then, $p(t;\theta)$ belongs to the exponential family.

Example 5–31. The geometric family, with probability function $p(1-p)^x$ for $x = 0, 1, \cdots$ is contained in the exponential family, since

$$p(1-p)^x = p \exp[x \log(1-p)].$$

The number of trials before the first Heads in a sequence of independent Bernoulli trials has this distribution. If $(X_1,\ldots,X_n)$ is a random sample from this distribution, the minimal sufficient statistic $X_1 + \cdots + X_n$ is the number of Tails thrown before n Heads appear. It has the negative binomial distribution, which, then, is also one of the exponential family.

For the case of a multidimensional parameter $\boldsymbol{\theta} = (\theta_1,\ldots,\theta_k)$, the name "exponential family" is used to describe the family of distributions with densities (or probability functions) of the form

$$f(x;\boldsymbol{\theta}) = B(\boldsymbol{\theta}) \exp[Q_1(\boldsymbol{\theta})R_1(x) + \cdots + Q_k(\boldsymbol{\theta})R_k(x)]\, h(x).$$

Given a random sample X, the k-dimensional statistic

$$\left(\Sigma R_1(X_i), \ldots, \Sigma R_k(X_i)\right)$$

(sums extending from $i = 1$ to $i = n$, the sample size) is a minimal sufficient statistic for the family. The normal and multinomial distributions belong to this family.

It is interesting (cf. [12], page 51) that under certain regularity assumptions, and if the set on which $f(x;\boldsymbol{\theta})$ is positive does not depend on $\boldsymbol{\theta}$, then if there exists a k-dimensional sufficient statistic on a random sample of size n from $f(x;\boldsymbol{\theta})$ with $n > k$, the distribution $f(x;\boldsymbol{\theta})$ must belong to the exponential family. In this sense the exponential family consists of those distributions for which there is a sufficient statistic of the same dimension as that of the parameter.

A multivariate density $f(\mathbf{x};\theta)$ is said to belong to the exponential family if it is of the form

$$f(\mathbf{x};\boldsymbol{\theta}) = B(\boldsymbol{\theta}) \exp[Q_1(\boldsymbol{\theta})S_1(\mathbf{x}) + \cdots + Q_k(\boldsymbol{\theta})S_k(\mathbf{x})]h(\mathbf{x}).$$

The joint distribution of a random sample from a member of the univariate exponential family is of this type, with the $S_j(\mathbf{x})$ given by the sum $\sum R_j(x_i)$ for fixed j, where the $R_j(x)$ denotes the corresponding factor in the univariate density.

PROBLEMS

5–53. List the 16 samples of 4 from a Bernoulli distribution and determine the partition defined by the statistic $\sum X_i$. Determine also the partition defined by the statistic $(X_1 + X_2, X_3 + X_4)$, and show that the sample sum is a reduction of this. Show sufficiency in each case.

5–54. An urn contains five beads marked 1, 2, 3, 4, 5. Three are drawn, one at a time without replacement. The 60 sample points are partitioned into 10 sets according to the 10 distinct possible order statistics. List these 10, and determine the further partition defined by (S,L), where S is the smallest observation and L the largest in a sample. Show in terms of partitions that $R = L - S$ is yet a further partition.

5–55. Apply the construction technique directly to obtain a minimal sufficient partition for the family $\theta \exp(-\theta x)$, $x > 0$, in terms of a random sample of size n.

5–56. Show that the negative exponential, Poisson, and normal distributions belong to the exponential family.

5–57. Consider the Rayleigh distribution defined by the density

$$f(x) = \left(\frac{x}{\theta}\right)^2 \exp\left(\frac{-x^2}{2\theta^2}\right), \qquad x > 0.$$

Determine a minimal sufficient statistic for this family, and describe the corresponding partition sets. Show also that these distributions belong to the exponential family.

5–58. Show (directly) that for a sample of size n from a population with k distinct outcomes and corresponding probabilities $p_1,\ldots,p_k$ the minimal sufficient statistic is $(f_1,\ldots,f_k)$, where f_j is the frequency of occurrence of the jth outcome among the n trials. What is the distribution of this statistic?

5.6 Some Properties of Procedures

A variety of properties of statistical procedures have been formulated over the years, among which are *admissibility*, *efficiency*, *consistency*, *invariance*, and *unbiasedness*. These have usually been proposed as good properties, and it is evident that the names used were chosen to perpetuate this notion. Most of these properties seem desirable, but none of them guarantees a uniformly small risk function. They are discussed here not so much to provide criteria for good procedures as to provide an acquaintance with the ideas involved and with the significance and limitations of each.

Some of these properties will be studied in more detail in the subsequent two chapters, having rather different forms in the two types of statistical problems to be considered there. However, a general definition shows that the concepts can be unified in the decision framework and that they apply in problems that are not estimation or testing problems.

The notion of *admissibility* was defined in §5.2.3 for the no-data problem. In general the definition is the same, except that it is applied to the risk function. That is, d dominates d_1 if

$$R(\theta,d_1) \geq R(\theta,d), \quad \text{for all } \theta.$$

A procedure would be called *inadmissible* if it were strictly dominated by some other procedure. However, whether this is bad or not depends on the degree to which it is dominated, as discussed in §5.2.3.

If two procedures d and d' are both based on samples of a given size, and if d dominates d' strictly, d can be thought of as more *efficient* than d', since in general it would take more observations using d' to equalize the risks. The relative efficiency of d' with respect to d might be defined as the ratio of the risk of d to that of d' for a given sample size, or as the ratio of sample sizes needed to make the risks equal, if this be possible. These ratios need not agree and would usually depend on the state θ. The notion of efficiency is most commonly applied to the case of estimation with a quadratic loss function, in which the usual situation is that the ratios do agree and do not depend on θ. Further, the risk then often has a lower bound or minimum achievable risk (in restricted classes of procedures) that can be used as the basis of an "absolute" efficiency measure. This will be discussed in Chapter 6.

A procedure d is said to be *consistent* if the expected regret tends to zero as the sample size becomes infinite. This implies that the "procedure" include instructions as to how to apply it to samples of different sizes; or equally well one can think of consistency as applying to a sequence of procedures, one for each sample size. Presumably, if the expected regret tends to zero, it will be small for "large" samples; this is of little comfort if a large sample is expensive. Indeed, one is always forced to work with finite samples. Nevertheless, consistent procedures frequently turn out to have good properties even for small samples. Consistency will be interpreted in Chapters 6 and 7 for the particular cases of estimation and testing.

The notion of *invariance* is best treated in a setting of groups of transformations, and we shall consider this as beyond our scope, not discussing the way in which invariance can be exploited in deriving procedures. It is a property whose desirability is generally agreed on when it is pertinent. (See References [7] and [12] for treatments of invariance.) Put rather vaguely, the requirement of invariances says that when a problem is invariant under certain transformations, or has certain symmetries, good procedures should also be invariant, or have those symmetries.

Example 5–32. Consider the problem of estimating the parameter θ in the negative exponential density $\theta \exp(-\theta x)$, $x > 0$, $\theta > 0$, using a random sample from this distribution, with loss function

$$\ell(\theta,a) = \frac{(a - \theta)^2}{\theta^2}.$$

The action a is the making of the inference that the parameter value is a, and a decision function is a mapping from the sample point x to a corresponding estimate: $a = d(x)$. The negative exponential distribution is the model for the spacing between events in a Poisson process, and the parameter θ is the mean number of events per unit time; the reciprocal $1/\theta$ is the mean time between events. If x is measured in minutes, θ is measured in reciprocal minutes.

Suppose now that x is in minutes but that measurements are made in seconds. The number of seconds in a given time interval is 60 times the number of minutes; if x' is the number of seconds, $x' = 60x$. The density of x' is

$$\tfrac{1}{60}\theta e^{-\theta x/60} = \theta' e^{-\theta' x'},$$

where $\theta' = \theta/60$. The correct action a', if θ' is the true state, is 1/60 of the correct action a for state θ. The loss function given can be expressed in terms of a' and θ':

$$\frac{(a - \theta)^2}{\theta^2} = \frac{(a/60 - \theta/60)^2}{(\theta/60)^2} = \frac{(a' - \theta')^2}{(\theta')^2}.$$

The transformed problem is this: Given measurements $x_1', \cdots, x_n'$, construct an estimate a' of θ' for the density $\theta' \exp(-\theta' x')$, with loss function $(a' - \theta')^2/(\theta')^2$. But this is precisely the original mathematical problem with new labels. The problem is therefore invariant under the transformation $x' = 60x$ (or under any scale change: $x' = kx$). Since the new problem is the same as the original one, a decision function d that is good for the original one should be good for the new—applied to the transformed datum point $\mathbf{x}'$. That is, $d(\mathbf{x}')$ should be used in the new problem. Now,

$$d(\mathbf{x}') = d(x_1', \ldots, x_n') = d(60x_1, \ldots, 60x_n),$$

and because this is an estimate of θ' in reciprocal seconds, the corresponding estimate of θ in reciprocal minutes is $60d(60\mathbf{x})$. The invariance principle says that this should agree with $d(\mathbf{x})$, since it is a solution of the original problem:

$$d(\mathbf{x}) = 60d(60\mathbf{x}).$$

A decision function with this property is called *invariant under the transformation.* Notice that $d(\mathbf{x}) = 1/\bar{x}$ has this property.

More generally, a "group" of transformations $\mathbf{x}' = T\mathbf{x}$ on the sample space ($T\mathbf{x}$ means the result of operating with transformation T on each $\mathbf{x}$) induces corresponding transformations $\theta' = T^*\theta$ in the space of states of nature. If the family of distributions under study in a problem is unchanged under this transformation of parameter, and if there is a "suitable" transformation T^{**}

of the action space such that the loss function is invariant, the problem is called *invariant under T*. For such problems, an invariant procedure **d** is one that satisfies the condition

$$d(T\mathbf{x}) = T^{**}d(\mathbf{x})$$

for all $\mathbf{x}$ and each T being considered. (Cf. Reference [12], page 11, for details.)

A procedure based on the statistic Z is said to be *unbiased* if for all states of nature θ and θ',

$$E_\theta[\ell(\theta',d(Z))] \geq E_\theta[\ell(\theta,d(Z))],$$

where again the subscript on E denotes the state to be used in computing the expectation. This can be interpreted to sound very plausible: Thinking of $\ell(\theta,a)$ as related to how close the action a comes to the action which should correspond to θ, the relation states that the decision procedure **d** comes closer on the average to the correct decision than to an incorrect one. Yet, despite the appealing sound of this statement, fulfillment of the condition of unbiasedness by no means guarantees a good procedure. In fact, unbiasedness has little to do with the value of a procedure.

For instance, if a sample of 1000 is to be used, a procedure based on only the first observation in the sample can be unbiased even through it ignores the remaining 999 observations. Indeed, it can and does happen that by restricting his attention to unbiased procedures, one eliminates procedures that are better in terms of risk than those he keeps.

Example 5–33. In Problem 5–33 it was seen that for the problem of estimating the mean μ of a negative exponential distribution with quadratic regret, the decision function $d(\bar{X}) = n\bar{X}/(n+1)$ has the risk

$$R(\mu,d) = \frac{\mu^2}{n+1}.$$

This is uniformly smaller than the risk μ^2/n found in Example 5–14 for the procedure $d^*(\bar{X}) = \bar{X}$. Yet (Problem 5–59) d is biased and d^* is unbiased.

5.7 Monotone Problems and Procedures

Among statistical problems concerned with families of distributions indexed by a single real-valued parameter, many are of a type that will be called *monotone*. These are problems involving a family with a "monotone likelihood ratio" and a "monotone regret function."

A regret function associates with each possible action a certain region of parameter values corresponding to states of nature for which the action is the correct one. On this region of parameter values, the regret function for that action is smaller than the regrets for the other actions.

The regret function $r(\theta,a)$ defines a set of functions of θ, one for each action a, and can be represented graphically by these functions of θ, all plotted on a set of r versus θ coordinate axes. A regret function will be said to be *monotone* when the following conditions are fulfilled:

1. The regions of optimality for the various actions are nonoverlapping intervals (finite, infinite, or degenerate) which fill out the parameter axis.
2. For each action the corresponding regret curve does not decrease as it moves away from a region of zero regret.
3. For any pair of actions a_1 and a_2, the difference $r(\theta,a_1) - r(\theta,a_2)$ changes sign at most once.

Figure 5–15 gives three examples of a monotone regret function. In Figure 5–15(a) is shown a quadratic regret $(\theta - a)^2$ for the estimation problem, although curves are drawn for only three values of a. For each action a, there is just one parameter value ($\theta = a$) for which a is the correct action, and these points of zero regret fill out the θ axis; it is also clear that the other two conditions are fulfilled. Figures 5–15(b) and (c) show monotone regret functions for the two and three-action cases, respectively.

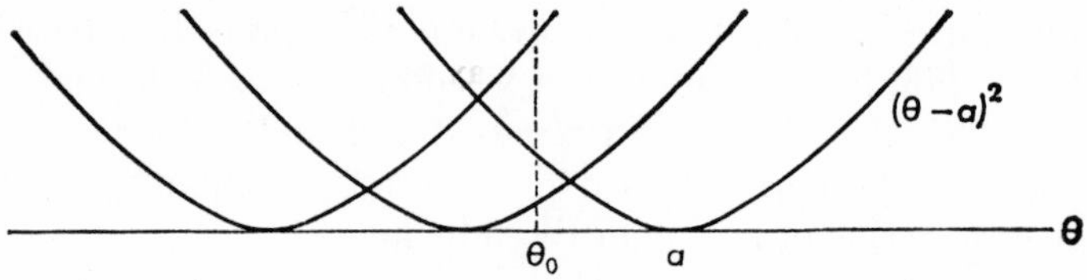

Figure 5–15A

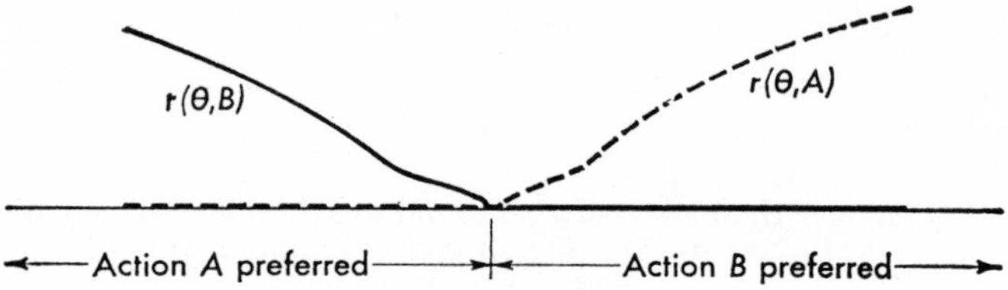

Figure 5–15–B

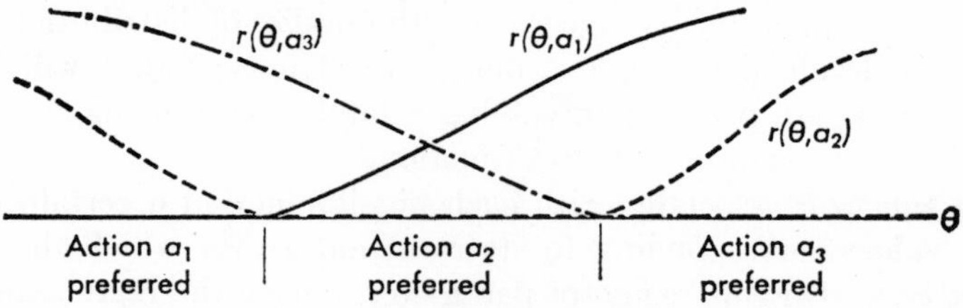

Figure 5–15C

In Figure 5–16 are shown regret functions that are *not* monotone. In (a), the first two conditions are fulfilled but (3) is not, since $r(\theta,a_1) - r(\theta,a_2)$ changes sign twice. In (b), both conditions (1) and (3) are violated.

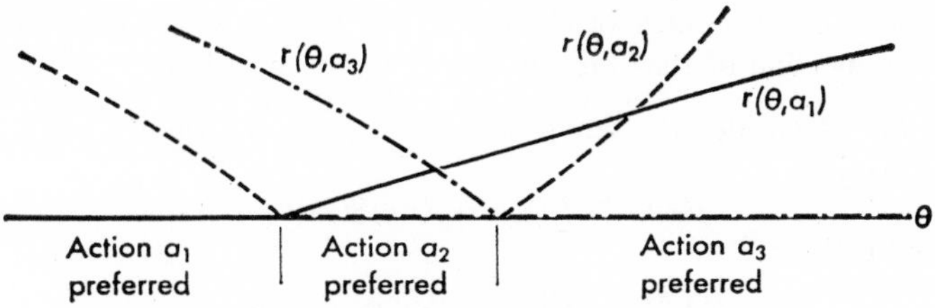

Figure 5–16A

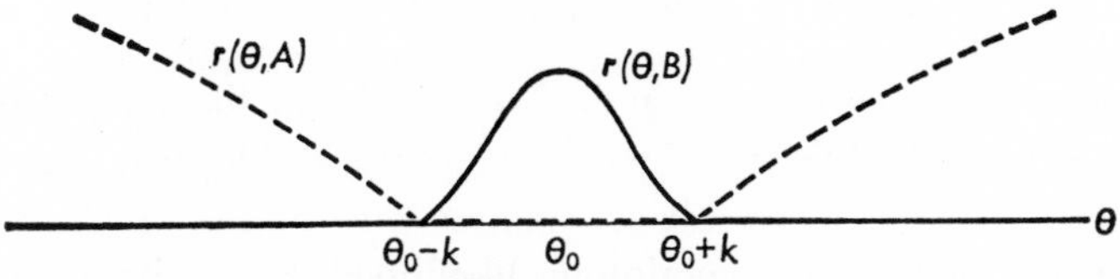

Figure 5–16B

Example 5–34. Lots of a certain product (say, eggs) are to be classified into three grades according to the average lot quality θ. That is, if $\theta > \theta_2$, the lot is grade A. If $\theta_1 < \theta < \theta_2$, it is grade B; and if $\theta < \theta_1$, it is grade C. The classification is to be done on the basis of a sample from each lot. Suppose that the penalties for misclassifications are those given in the following regret table:

		Lot Quality (State of Nature, θ) $\theta < \theta_1$	$\theta_1 < \theta < \theta_2$	$\theta > \theta_2$
Actions (grade assigned)	A	$2k$	k	0
	B	k	0	k
	C	0	k	$2k$

This regret function satisfies (1), (2), and (3) and so is monotone.

The family of distributions with density (or probability function) $f(x;\theta)$, where θ is a real parameter, is said to have a *monotone likelihood ratio* if the distributions defined by distinct θ's are distinct and if there is a function $t(x)$ such that the likelihood ratio

$$\frac{f(x;\theta)}{f(x;\theta')}, \qquad \theta > \theta',$$

is a nondecreasing function of $t(x)$. In particular, when x is one-dimensional, $f(x;\theta)$ can be the density or probability function of a single random variable; when x is n-dimensional, $f(x;\theta)$ can denote the joint density function of a sample $\mathbf{X}$.

Example 5–35. The inequality established in Problem 2–79 (page 76) shows that the hypergeometric family of distributions has a monotone likelihood ratio, the $t(X)$ being just the observation X. That is, in random sampling without replacement from a population of objects, so many of one kind and the remainder of another kind, the statistic defined as the number of objects of one kind in the sample is directly related to the proportion of that kind of object in the population.

Example 5–36. Consider the one-parameter exponential family, with density (or probability function)

$$f(x;\theta) = B(\theta) \exp[Q(\theta)S(x)]h(x).$$

The likelihood ratio is

$$\frac{f(x;\theta)}{f(x;\theta')} = \frac{B(\theta) \exp[Q(\theta)S(x)]h(x)}{B(\theta') \exp[Q(\theta')S(x)]h(x)}$$

$$= C(\theta,\theta') \exp\{[Q(\theta) - Q(\theta')]S(x)\}.$$

If $Q(\theta)$ is monotone nondecreasing in θ, then for $\theta > \theta'$, this likelihood ratio is a monotone nondecreasing function of $S(x)$, and so the given family has a monotone likelihood ratio.

The property of having a monotone likelihood ratio with respect to $t(x)$ reflects a preservation of order between the value of the parameter and the value of $t(X)$. For instance, in the hypergeometric example cited, a large number of defectives in the population corresponds to a large number of defectives in the sample, so that observing the latter one infers the former. That there is such a correspondence and that such inferences are right are ways of describing the known results concerning monotone likelihood ratio families. Even without the monotone likelihood ratio property, as in the case of the one-parameter Cauchy family, $[\pi(1 + [x - \xi]^2)]^{-1}$, it can sometimes be said that if the parameter is small, small values of X are most likely. But what is needed in statistical inference is the reverse kind of statement—that if X is small, one should behave as though the parameter were small.

The known results concerning monotone problems are to the effect that one should use monotone procedures based on the $t(x)$ in terms of which the family of distributions has a monotone likelihood ratio. A monotone procedure for an estimation problem is one that takes as an estimate of θ a monotone increasing function of $t(x)$. For an n-action problem, a monotone procedure is one defined by $n - 1$ critical values $t_1 \leq t_2 \leq \cdots \leq t_{n-1}$ and $n - 1$ corresponding probabilities $\xi_1, \ldots, \xi_{n-1}$ such that action i is taken when $t(X)$ falls in the interval (t_{i-1},t_i), where $t_0 = -\infty$ and $t_n = \infty$, and actions i and $i + 1$ are taken with probabilities ξ_i and $1 - \xi_i$ if $t(X) = t_i$. (Actions $1, \ldots, n$ are labeled such that the corresponding θ intervals are consecutive.) Such procedures are known to constitute a class having the property that for any given procedure not in the class, there is one in the class at least as good in terms of risk—one that dominates it but not necessarily strictly. It is also known that under certain mild conditions, monotone procedures for the two-action problem are admissible, and that in many important n-action problems, monotone procedures are also admissible. These results are discussed in an article by S. Karlin and H. Rubin, "The Theory of Decision Procedures for Distributions with Monotone Likelihood Ratios," *Annals Math. Stat.*, 27(1956), pages 272–299. Reference should also be made to the somewhat more accessible paper by Karlin and Rubin in *Jour. Amer. Stat. Assn.*, 51(1956), pages 637–643.

5.8 Sample Size and Cost of Sampling

In the discussion thus far it has been assumed that the choice of experiment and the number of times it is to be performed are given and are not part of the decision process. In practice, of course, these must be decided upon.

Since the risk associated with a given procedure usually involves the size of the sample used, one might expect to be able to select the sample size so as to keep the risk within a certain amount or, with a knowledge of the cost of sampling, to balance a reduction in risk against the expense of additional sampling. However, since the risk usually also depends on the state of nature, which is unknown, this proposed analysis of risk and sample cost is not so simple. But as the sampling proceeds, information is gradually accumulated about the population, information which could then be used to determine approximately how much more sampling to do. For example, if 20 Heads appear among the first 20 tosses of a coin, the evidence points strongly towards $p = 1$ and suggests that the sampling may as well stop. Such considerations give rise to the notion of multiple or sequential decision procedures, in which at certain stages one decides either to take some one of the available actions, if the accumulated evidence at that stage is sufficiently strong, or to continue sampling. Sequential procedures for a certain simple type of two-action problem will be treated in Chapter 7.

More generally still, one could include at each stage of a sequential process a decision as to what one of various available experiments to perform next. Finding optimum designs in such general settings is usually very difficult, and has been done in few instances. These will not be considered.

The cost of sampling is a contribution to loss which would be removed in working with regret. One could then either work with loss, or as suggested above, weigh sampling costs against reduction of expected regret. Perhaps the simplest model for the cost of sampling would regard it as a linear function of sample size—a fixed amount for "setup" costs plus an amount proportional to the sample size.

In working with Bayes or minimax procedures, one has a functional of the risk or expected regret to minimize; the minimum achievable value could then be used as a measure of goodness of the procedure. Further, this minimum would depend on n independently of the state of nature and so be usable in measuring the effect of additional sampling.

Example 5–37. In Example 5–22 the Bayes procedure for estimating the p in a Bernoulli distribution with quadratic loss $(p - a)^2$ and uniform prior distribution on p was found to be $d(k) = (k + 1)/(n + 2)$, where k is the number of successes in n independent trials. The risk, using this procedure, is

$$R\left(p, \frac{k+1}{n+2}\right) = E_p\left[\ell\left(p, \frac{k+1}{n+2}\right)\right] = E_p\left[\left(\frac{k+1}{n+2} - p\right)^2\right]$$

$$= \frac{1}{(n+2)^2} E_p[(k - np + [1 - 2p])^2]$$

$$= \frac{npq + (1 - 2p)^2}{(n+2)^2}.$$

The Bayes risk is now obtained by averaging this risk with respect to the uniform density for p on $[0,1]$:

$$B(d) = \frac{1}{(n+2)^2} \int_0^1 [np(1 - p) + (1 - 2p)^2]\, dp = \frac{1}{6(n+2)}.$$

Since d is the Bayes solution, $B(d)$ is the *minimum* Bayes risk. (This could also have been obtained by averaging the posterior expected loss with respect to the absolute distribution of k.)

If the cost of sampling is $An + B$, and if it is measured on the same utility scale as is the loss function, the total risk for a sample of size n is

$$An + B + \frac{1}{6(n+2)},$$

which has a minimum in n at $n = 1/\sqrt{6A} - 2$. Sampling beyond this number of observations would not be worth while, since the cost of additional sampling would be more than the reduction in minimum Bayes risk which it would achieve.

PROBLEMS

5–59. Using the definition of an unbiased procedure, show that the procedures d^* and d in Example 5–33 are, respectively, unbiased and biased (assuming a quadratic regret), as claimed.

5–60. Determine the invariance condition for the problem of estimating μ for the family

$$f(x;\mu) = \frac{1}{\sigma} h\left(\frac{x - \mu}{\sigma}\right),$$

where σ is given, using the loss function $(a - \mu)^2/\sigma^2$.

5–61. Show that the regret function $r(\theta,a) = |\theta - a|^\alpha$ is monotone, for $\alpha > 0$.

5–62. Show that for the family $[\pi(1 + [x - \theta]^2)]^{-1}$, the likelihood ratio (for a single observation) is not a monotone function of x. (Reason geometrically, interpreting $1 + y^2$ in terms of the Pythagorean theorem.)

6 / *Estimation*

The problem of estimation will now be treated in greater detail. Although such problems have been introduced in Chapter 5 as special decision problems, it may be noticed that the development that follows is not always completely in the spirit of satistical decision theory. Historically, the unifying notions of decision theory came after the estimation problem had already been intensively studied.

The estimation problems to be considered are those called *parametric*. It is known or assumed in these problems that the distribution of probability in an experiment of chance is one of a family of distributions indexed by one or more real parameters. The problem is that of determining estimates for the unknown parameters of the model on the basis of observations on the experiment. The framework of decision theory is thought of as including the estimation problem by considering the "action" to be taken as the announcement of the estimated value. The action space is then coincident with the parameter space.

Thus it is desired to estimate the parameter vector $(\theta_1,\ldots,\theta_k)$ in the density function (or probability function, in a discrete case)

$$f(x;\theta_1,\ldots,\theta_k)$$

on the basis of the observations $X_1, \ldots, X_n$. A "decision function" in this problem is a function associating with each possible sample point $(x_1,\ldots,x_n)$ an estimate $(T_1,\ldots,T_k)$, T_j being the estimate for θ_j. This function defines a statistic

$$(T_1,\ldots,T_k) = t(X_1,\ldots,X_n)$$

called an *estimator* of $(\theta_1,\ldots,\theta_k)$. In the common case of a single parameter, an estimator is a real-valued function $T = t(X_1,\ldots,X_n)$.

Much of the traditional practice in estimation problems involves implicitly a *quadratic* loss function of the form (in the case of a single parameter)

$$\ell(\theta,a) = A(\theta)(\theta - a)^2,$$

where $A(\theta)$ is a specified weighting factor, frequently assumed for simplicity to be a constant. This quadratic loss function has a zero minimum in a for each state θ, and so the regret is the same as the loss. The risk function then is the expected loss or regret:

$$R(\theta,T) = A(\theta)\, E_\theta[(\theta - T)^2].$$

Strictly speaking, a quadratic loss cannot be utility, with the earlier agreement that utility is bounded. It can happen with a quadratic loss that the maximum risk is infinite for all estimates, which would mean that all estimates are minimax. For minimax considerations, then, the loss must be modified; but for other purposes the unboundedness of a quadratic loss does not seem to be troublesome.

A partial justification of quadratic loss lies in these considerations: First, for properties that depend on the character of the loss in the neighborhood of its minimum, other reasonably smooth and not too flat loss functions can be approximated there by a quadratic function. Further, in the important case of normally distributed unbiased estimates, a quadratic loss serves as well as any other loss function that has the property of increasing as $|\theta - a|$ increases. For, consider a loss function $L(\theta - a)$, such that $L(x)$ is nonincreasing for $x < 0$ and nondecreasing for $x > 0$. The corresponding risk for a normal, unbiased T is

$$R_L(\theta, T) = E_\theta[L(\theta - T)] = \int_{-\infty}^{\infty} L(t)\, dF_T(t)$$

$$= \int_0^1 L(F_T^{-1}(u))\, du,$$

where $F_T(t)$ is the normal distribution function with mean zero and the same variance as T. Now, the risk based on a quadratic loss is proportional to the variance of T, and so an estimate T dominates an estimate T' if var $T \leq$ var T', both assumed unbiased. But this condition on the variances is equivalent to

$$R_L(\theta, T) = \int_0^1 L(F_T^{-1}(u))\, du \leq \int_0^1 L(F_{T'}^{-1}(u))\, du = R_L(\theta, T'),$$

which means that comparison of risks based on L would be equivalent to comparison based on the quadratic loss.

A third argument for quadratic loss is that mathematical manipulations are much more tractible than with other loss functions; but this argument carries weight only in the presence of other arguments. Even so, if there are questionable aspects of quadratic loss functions, these would not necessarily invalidate procedures derived on the basis of quadratic loss.

6.1 Some Properties of Estimators

Of the properties of procedures treated in Chapter 5, three are discussed further here: bias, consistency, and efficiency. This is not to imply that these are the most desirable or significant properties; they are, however, properties that are traditionally referred to in discussions of estimation, and it is well to learn the language and to consider what the properties do or do not mean.

6.1.1 Bias. A procedure for an estimation problem is a statistic. A statistic T, then, is unbiased according to the definition of Chapter 5 if

$$E_\theta[\ell(\theta_1,T)] \geq E_\theta[\ell(\theta,T)], \quad \text{for all } \theta,\ \theta_1.$$

Using the quadratic loss $A(T - \theta)^2$ for an estimator T of θ, this condition for unbiasedness becomes

$$E_\theta[(T - \theta_1)^2] \geq E_\theta[(T - \theta)^2], \quad \text{for all } \theta,\ \theta_1.$$

This condition is certainly satisfied when $E(T) = \theta$, since the right member is then the variance of T, which is the smallest second moment of T. Conversely, if the condition is satisfied, then

$$[E_\theta(T) - \theta_1]^2 \geq [E_\theta(T) - \theta]^2, \quad \text{all } \theta_1;$$

and therefore since this is true for $\theta_1 = E_\theta(T)$, the right member must be zero, which implies that $E_\theta(T) = \theta$. That is, under the assumption of a quadratic loss function, the property of unbiasedness becomes equivalent to the property that the distribution of the estimator T be centered at the parameter θ in the sense of expectation.

Using the loss function $|T - \theta|$, one would find that the condition of unbiasedness is equivalent to the condition that the distribution of the estimator T be centered at θ in the sense of the median; that is, that the median of T be θ. An estimator with this property is sometimes called *median unbiased.* (Cf. Reference [12], page 22.)

The condition that $E(T) = \theta$ is often taken as the defining condition for an unbiased estimator, and what has just been shown is that this is consistent with the general definition of Chapter 5 in the case of a quadratic loss function. The difference

$$b = E(T) - \theta = E(T - \theta)$$

is referred to as the *bias* in T as an estimate of θ. The estimator T is then unbiased if $b = 0$, and conversely. Observe that the (quadratic) risk can be expressed in terms of the bias as follows:

$$E_\theta[(T - \theta)^2] = \text{var } T + b^2.$$

Example 6–1. Because

$$E\left(\frac{1}{n}\sum X_i^k\right) = E(X^k),$$

it follows that the sample kth moment about zero is an unbiased estimate of the population kth moment about zero.

Example 6–2. In §5.3.3, the expected value of the sample variance was computed, with the result

$$E\left[\frac{1}{n}\sum(X_i - \bar{X})^2\right] = \sigma^2\left(1 - \frac{1}{n}\right).$$

The sample variance is therefore biased as an estimate of the population variance. The amount of the bias is $-\sigma^2/n$, which is negligible for large samples.

If an estimator has a bias proportional to the parameter estimated, multiplication by a constant yields an unbiased estimator. For, if $E(T) = k\theta$, then $E(T/k) = \theta$.

Example 6–3. Consider the statistic

$$\tilde{s}_x^2 = \frac{1}{n-1}\sum_{i=1}^{n}(X_i - \bar{X})^2.$$

This is just $n/(n-1)$ times what we have termed the sample variance, and its expectation is therefore

$$E(\tilde{s}_x^2) = \frac{n}{n-1}E(s_x^2) = \sigma^2.$$

The statistic $\tilde{s}_x^2$ is then unbiased as an estimate of σ^2.

Despite the un-American connotations of the word "bias," a biased estimator is not necessarily to be rejected as inferior. Indeed, there are slightly biased estimates that are very good in other respects, and certainly there are unbiased estimates which no one in his right mind would use (cf. Problem 6–1). The point is that arranging things so that the center of gravity of the distribution of an estimator is at θ is of little help in obtaining an estimated value that is close to θ.

6.1.2 Consistency. A sequence of procedures was called *consistent* in Chapter 5 if the expected regret approaches zero for each state, as the sample size becomes infinite. With the assumption of a quadratic risk function, consistency of $\{T_n\}$ means that $T_n \to \theta$ in quadratic mean:

$$\lim_{n\to\infty} E[(T_n - \theta)^2] = 0.$$

Denoting the bias in T_n by $b(T_n)$, this condition can be written

$$\lim_{n\to\infty} [\text{var } T_n + b^2(T_n)] = 0.$$

This holds if and only if both the variance and the bias of T_n tend to zero as n becomes infinite.

It was seen in §4.3.1 that convergence in quadratic mean to a constant implies convergence in probability to that constant. Thus, if $\{T_n\}$ is consistent in the above sense, it is also true that T_n tends to θ in probability:

$$\lim_{n\to\infty} P(|T_n - \theta| \geq \epsilon) = 0, \quad \text{for any } \epsilon > 0.$$

This convergence in probability of T_n to θ is the condition that traditionally defines consistency of $\{T_n\}$. Since existence of second moments is not required, it is more widely applicable. (Of course, if T_n does not have second moments, quadratic loss should not be used.) If it becomes necessary to distinguish between consistency in the sense of convergence in probability and consistency in the sense of convergence in quadratic mean we can write "consistent (in prob.)" for the former and "consistent (in q. m.)" for the latter.

Example 6–4. The fact that sample moments tend in probability to corresponding population moments was discussed in §5.3.3. The sample moments are therefore consistent (in prob.) estimates of the corresponding population moments.

Example 6–5. Consider the estimate $\tilde{s}_x^2$ of σ^2, which was seen in Example 6–3 to be unbiased. Since this differs from the consistent estimate s_x^2 by a factor that tends to 1, it, too, is consistent.

If a statistic T_n has a variance that tends to zero while its expectation converges to k, a number different from θ, then T_n converges in probability—but to the wrong value, k. Consequently, even though the significance of bias has been minimized, an estimator that has a bias which does not disappear as n becomes infinite would have to be modified to remove the bias in order to obtain an estimator which is consistent (in q. m.).

Example 6–6. Consider the one-parameter family of Cauchy distributions defined by the density

$$f(x;\theta) = \frac{1/\pi}{1 + (x - \theta)^2}.$$

This is symmetrical about θ, but $\bar{X}$ is not a consistent estimate of θ. For, the characteristic function of the sample mean is

$$\exp\left[-n\left|\frac{t}{n}\right| + n\left(\frac{it\theta}{n}\right)\right] = \exp[-|t| + it\theta],$$

which is the characteristic function of the population itself (according to Problem 2–60). That is, the distribution of the sample mean is the same as that of the population, no matter how large the sample. The sample mean cannot converge in probability to any constant, let alone θ.

PROBLEMS

6–1. Show that in a random sample of size n, the first observation obtained, X_1, is an unbiased estimate of the population mean. Show also that the average of any two sample observations is an unbiased estimate of the population mean.

6–2. Determine the bias of $\sum(X_i - \mu)^2/n$ as an estimate of σ^2, in a problem in which $\mu = E(X)$ is given.

6–3. Determine the condition under which $\sum a_i X_i$ is an unbiased estimate of $E(X)$.

6–4. Show that if T is an unbiased estimate of θ, $aT + b$ is an unbiased estimate of $a\theta + b$. Is T^2 an unbiased estimate of θ^2?

6–5. Show that the estimates in Problem 6–1 are not consistent.

6–6. Show that the estimate of Problem 6–2 is consistent.

6–7. Show that the square of the sample mean is asymptotically unbiased as an estimate of the square of the population mean.

6.1.3 Efficiency. A procedure d was said in Chapter 5 to be more efficient than a procedure d' based on a sample of the same size if

$$R(\theta,d) \leq R(\theta,d_1),$$

with strict inequality for some θ. Using a quadratic loss, this condition would say that an estimator T of θ is more efficient than T' if

$$E[(T - \theta)^2] \leq E[(T' - \theta)^2],$$

with strict inequality for some θ. The relative efficiency of T' with respect to T is the ratio

$$e(T',T) = \frac{E[(T - \theta)^2]}{E[(T' - \theta)^2]}.$$

This would generally depend on θ, but it turns out frequently to be independent of θ. In the case of unbiased estimators the ratio is just the ratio of their variances, and the most efficient such estimator would be the one with minimum variance.

Example 6–7. The linear combination of observations $\sum a_i X_i$ is an unbiased estimate of $E(X)$ if $\sum a_i = 1$. The particular combination that is most efficient is the one which minimizes

$$\text{var}(\textstyle\sum a_i X_i) = \sum a_i^2 \text{ var } X_i = (\text{var } X) \sum a_i^2,$$

or the one that minimizes $\sum a_i^2$ subject to $\sum a_i = 1$.

For such restricted minimization problems it will be convenient to have the tool of the method of Lagrange's multipliers. It is shown in advanced calculus that the minimum of $g(y)$ subject to $h(y) = K$ is found by locating the minimum of the function $g(y) - \lambda h(y)$. This will not be proved here; but it is easily seen that if y satisfies $h(y) = K$ and minimizes $g(y) - \lambda h(y)$ for some λ, then for any other y' such that $h(y') = K$,

$$g(y) - \lambda h(y) \leq g(y') - \lambda h(y'),$$

or, since $h(y) = h(y')$,

$$g(y) \leq g(y').$$

Thus y is the desired minimizing quantity.

Applying this method in the case at hand, we minimize the quantity $\sum a_i^2 - \lambda \sum a_i$. The derivative of this with respect to a_j must vanish:

$$2a_j - \lambda = 0, \qquad j = 1, \ldots, n.$$

The minimizing a's are therefore all equal, and equal to $1/n$. The sample mean is thus the most efficient unbiased linear combination of the observations in a random sample.

An absolute measure of efficiency of an estimate would require that its mean square deviation from the parameter being estimated be compared with a lower bound or absolute minimum of such mean square deviations, if one that is not zero exists. The "information inequality" is aimed at providing such a lower bound.

The level of presentation here precludes a rigorous derivation of the information inequality, but the following manipulations for the continuous case indicate the line of reasoning used to establish the inequality. (Cf. Reference [4], §32.3.)

The statistic $T = t(\mathbf{X})$ based on a sample $\mathbf{X}$ from $f(x;\theta)$ is considered as an estimator for the parameter θ (one-dimensional). Let the joint density function of the sample observations be

$$f(x_1, \ldots, x_n;\theta) = f(\mathbf{x};\theta).$$

Let V denote the following random variable:

$$V = \frac{\partial}{\partial\theta} \log f(\mathbf{X}:\theta).$$

The expected value of V is zero:

$$E(V) = \int \frac{1}{f(\mathbf{x};\theta)} \left(\frac{\partial}{\partial\theta} f(\mathbf{x};\theta)\right) f(\mathbf{x};\theta)\, d\mathbf{x} = \frac{d}{d\theta} \int f(\mathbf{x};\theta)\, d\mathbf{x} = 0.$$

The variance of V is therefore its expected square, and the covariance of the random variables V and T is their expected product:

$$\begin{aligned}
\operatorname{cov}(V,T) = E(VT) &= E\left[T \frac{\partial}{\partial\theta} \log f(\mathbf{x};\theta)\right] \\
&= \int t(\mathbf{x}) \frac{1}{f(\mathbf{x};\theta)} \left(\frac{\partial}{\partial\theta} f(\mathbf{x};\theta)\right) f(\mathbf{x};\theta)\, d\mathbf{x} \\
&= \frac{d}{d\theta} E(T) = \frac{d}{d\theta} [\theta + b_T(\theta)] = 1 + b'_T(\theta),
\end{aligned}$$

where $b_T(\theta)$ is the bias in T.

The information inequality now results from the fact that a correlation is numerically bounded by 1 (that is, from Schwarz' inequality):

$$\text{var } T \geq \frac{[\text{cov}(V,T)]^2}{\text{var } V} = \frac{[1 + b'_T(\theta)]^2}{I(\theta)},$$

where

$$I(\theta) = \text{var } V = E\left\{\left[\frac{\partial}{\partial\theta}\log f(\mathbf{X};\theta)\right]^2\right\}.$$

The quantity $I(\theta)$ is called the *information* in the sample. (The information inequality is also known as the Cramer-Rao inequality, or the Fréchet inequality.)

The validity of the above derivation depends on fulfillment of conditions that permit interchange of integration and differentiation operations, on the existence and integrability of the various partial derivatives, on the differentiability of $b_T(\theta)$, and on the nonvanishing of $I(\theta)$. In the case of a discrete random variable with finitely many values, the $f(\mathbf{x};\theta)$ is a probability, the expectations are finite sums, and the interchange of differentiation and summation is permitted.

If $\mathbf{X}$ and $\mathbf{Y}$ are independent samples from $f(x;\theta)$, the information in the combined sample is the sum of the information in $\mathbf{X}$ and that in $\mathbf{Y}$. To see this, it is convenient to have another expression for $I(\theta)$. Writing prime to denote differentiation with respect to θ:

$$\frac{\partial V}{\partial\theta} = \frac{ff'' - (f')^2}{f^2} = \frac{f''}{f} - V^2.$$

But since

$$E\left(\frac{f''}{f}\right) = \frac{d^2}{d\theta^2}\int f(\mathbf{x};\theta)\,d\mathbf{x} = 0,$$

it follows that

$$I(\theta) = E(V^2) = -E\left(\frac{\partial}{\partial\theta}V\right).$$

If now $f_1(\mathbf{x};\theta)$ and $f_2(\mathbf{y};\theta)$ are densities for $\mathbf{X}$ and $\mathbf{Y}$, the joint density of $(\mathbf{X},\mathbf{Y})$ is the product $f_1(\mathbf{x};\theta)\, f_2(\mathbf{y};\theta)$. And then

$$I_{\mathbf{X},\mathbf{Y}}(\theta) = -E\left(\frac{\partial}{\partial\theta}V_{\mathbf{X},\mathbf{Y}}\right) = -E\left(\frac{\partial^2}{\partial\theta^2}[\log f_1 + \log f_2]\right)$$
$$= -\left[E\left(\frac{\partial}{\partial\theta}V_{\mathbf{X}}\right) + E\left(\frac{\partial}{\partial\theta}V_{\mathbf{Y}}\right)\right] = I_{\mathbf{X}}(\theta) + I_{\mathbf{Y}}(\theta).$$

If $\mathbf{X}$ is a random sample from $f(x;\theta)$, the information in the sample is the sum of the informations for the individual observations, or n times the information in a single observation:

$$I(\theta) = nE\left\{\left[\frac{\partial}{\partial\theta}\log f(X;\theta)\right]^2\right\}.$$

In the class of unbiased estimators, the lower bound in the information inequality is $1/I(\theta)$, independent of which estimator is considered. The *efficiency* of an unbiased estimate T is therefore defined as

$$e(T) = \frac{1/I(\theta)}{\text{var } T}.$$

An estimator of efficiency 1 is said to be *efficient.*

Example 6–8. Consider a normal population with given mean μ and unknown variance v. The population density has the logarithm

$$\log f(x;v) = \frac{-(\log 2\pi)}{2} - \frac{(\log v)}{2} - \frac{(x-\mu)^2}{2v}.$$

This is differentiated with respect to v:

$$\frac{\partial}{\partial v} \log f(x;v) = \frac{-1}{2v} + \frac{(x-\mu)^2}{2v^2}$$

to obtain

$$E\left\{\left[\frac{\partial}{\partial v} \log f(X;v)\right]^2\right\} = \frac{1}{4v^4}\left[E(X-\mu)^4 - 2vE(X-\mu)^2 + v^2\right]$$

$$= \frac{1}{4v^4}(3v^2 - 2v^2 + v^2) = \frac{1}{2v^2}.$$

For a random sample of size n, then, $I(\theta) = n/2v^2$.

The estimate

$$v^* = \sum \frac{(X_i - \mu)^2}{n}$$

is unbiased and has variance

$$\text{var } v^* = \sum \frac{\text{var }[(X_i-\mu)^2]}{n^2}$$

$$= \frac{[E(X-\mu)^4 - (E[X-\mu]^2)^2]}{n} = \frac{2v^2}{n}.$$

Since this is equal to $1/I(\theta)$, the efficiency of v^* is 1.

Example 6–9. Consider the estimation of μ in a normal population with unit variance. The information $I(\mu)$ based on a random sample of size n is readily shown to be n. The estimate $T \equiv 0$, on the other hand, has a risk equal to μ^2, which is less than $1/I(\mu) = 1/n$ for any μ between $1/\sqrt{n}$ and $-1/\sqrt{n}$. The "lower bound" would appear to be violated—except that the estimate $T \equiv 0$ is biased for any $\mu \neq 0$. The information inequality is just $0 \geq 0$, since var $T = 0$ and $1 + b'_T(\mu) = 0$.

An examination of the situation in which the lower bound in the information inequality is achieved proves interesting. The inequality is an equality if the correlation between V and T is $+1$ or -1. If this is the case, then either T is identically constant or V is a linear function of T with probability one, and conversely. The coefficients in the linear relationship between V and T can be functions of θ:

$$V = A'(\theta)T + B'(\theta),$$

where again the prime denotes differentiation with respect to θ. Integrating with respect to θ, one obtains

$$\log f(\mathbf{X};\theta) = A(\theta)T + B(\theta) + K(\mathbf{X}),$$

where the "constant" of integration $K(\mathbf{X})$ does not depend on θ but might depend on $\mathbf{X}$. Equivalently:

$$\begin{aligned} f(\mathbf{X};\theta) &= \exp[A(\theta)T + B(\theta) + K(\mathbf{X})] \\ &= C(\theta)\exp[A(\theta)T]\,h(\mathbf{X}), \end{aligned}$$

which shows that $f(x;\theta)$ is in the exponential family and that T is sufficient. Conversely, if $f(x;\theta)$ is in the exponential family, the statistic T that occurs in the exponent is such that the lower bound in the information inequality is achieved. Among the class of estimators with the same bias, T has minimum variance and hence minimum risk (with a quadratic loss). If this T is unbiased, it is efficient.

By *asymptotic efficiency* is meant the limit of the efficiency as the sample size becomes infinite. In order for this limit to be a finite positive number, it is necessary that the variance of the estimator behaves asymptotically as $1/n$. The limiting or asymptotic efficiency is then

$$\lim_{n\to\infty} e(T) = \lim_{n\to\infty} \frac{1/I(\theta)}{\text{var } T} = \frac{1}{c^2E([(\partial/\partial\theta)\log f(X;\theta)]^2)},$$

where

$$c^2 = \lim_{n\to\infty} n \text{ var } T.$$

When the asymptotic efficiency is 1, the estimator is said to be asymptotically efficient.

Asymptotic efficiency is sometimes defined even when the efficiency for finite samples is not defined for one reason or another. (The estimator may be biased or may not have moments.) If T is asymptotically normal with mean θ and variance c^2/n, the asymptotic efficiency of T is defined to be an expression given as the limit of $e(T)$ above. Whether this is meaningful in a given situation depends on the loss function; this question will not be investigated here.

PROBLEMS

6–8. Determine the efficiency of the estimates in Problem 6–1 relative to the sample mean.

6–9. Show that the sample mean is efficient in estimating the mean of a normal population with given variance.

6–10. Show that the sample mean is efficient as an estimate of p in a Bernoulli population.

6–11. Show that the sample mean is efficient in estimating the mean of a negative exponential distribution.

6–12. Determine the lower bound of unbiased estimates of the location parameter θ in the Cauchy family with density $[\pi(1 + [x - \theta]^2)]^{-1}$.

6.2 Determination of Estimators

As discussed in Chapter 5, there is usually no single best decision procedure—and therefore in estimation problems, no single best estimate of a parameter. It pays, then, to consider estimates derived from various considerations: Bayes estimates, maximum likelihood estimates, minimax estimates, intuitively proposed estimates.

The minimax principle is not feasible in the case of a quadratic loss. Some work has been done in obtaining minimax estimates for bounded modifications of a quadratic loss, but these will not be considered here. Bayes estimates are numerous—one for each assumed prior distribution in the set of states of nature. As discussed previously, the principle of Bayes gives a class of admissible estimates, but their admissibility does not guarantee their suitability; some other condition (preferably a knowledge of the most suitable prior distribution) is needed to select one from the class. In the case of quadratic regret the Bayes estimate is the mean of the posterior distribution.

In this section we treat mainly the method of maximum likelihood, as applied to the estimation problem, and mention briefly certain other methods of determining estimators which have not been introduced in the preceding chapter.

6.2.1 The Method of Moments. The oldest method of determining estimates (devised by K. Pearson in about 1894) is the method of moments. If there are k parameters to be estimated, the method consists of expressing the first k population moments in terms of these k parameters, equating them to the corresponding sample moments and taking the solutions of the resulting equations as estimates of the parameters. The method usually leads to relatively simple estimates.

The estimates obtained in this way are clearly functions of the sample moments. Since the sample moments are consistent estimates of population moments, the parameter estimates will generally be consistent.

Although the asymptotic efficiency of estimates obtained by the method of moments is often less than 1, such estimates may conveniently be used as first approximations from which more efficient estimates may be obtained by other means.

Example 6–10. The estimate of μ^2 in any population having a mean would be the square of the sample mean, $\bar{X}^2$, according to the method of moments. This is biased but consistent. Efficiency could not be discussed without further assumptions as to the nature of the population.

Example 6–11. The estimate of the parameter m in the Poisson family would be, according to the method of moments, the sample mean. For, m is the population mean, and although m is also the population variance, the lowest order population moment is used.

6.2.2 Maximum Likelihood Estimates. According to the maximum likelihood principle given in §5.4.4, a state $\hat{\theta}$ is found which "best explains" a given sample $\mathbf{X}$ in the sense that the likelihood function

$$L(\theta) = f(\mathbf{X};\theta)$$

is maximized for that value $\hat{\theta}$. The action taken is, then, the one that would be best if $\hat{\theta}$ were known to be the actual state.

In the case of estimation any reasonable regret function has the property that $r(\theta,\theta) = 0$, which means that the most appropriate action to take if $\hat{\theta}$ is the actual state is to announce $\hat{\theta}$ as the state. In particular, the quadratic regret $A(\theta)(\theta - a)^2$ has this property. A *maximum likelihood estimate*, therefore, is a value of θ that maximizes the likelihood function. If θ is multidimensional, so is $\hat{\theta}$, and the components are said to be joint maximum likelihood estimates of the corresponding components of θ.

Example 6–12. Consider a system that will either operate or fail in a certain mission, and let p denote the probability of successful operation. Eight trials are conducted, with these results: S, F, S, S, S, F, S, S. The probability of observing this sequence, assuming independence of the trials, is

$$L(p) = p^6(1 - p)^2.$$

This is positive for $0 < p < 1$ and zero at $p = 1$ and at $p = 0$, so the maximum occurs in the interior of the interval $[0,1]$ at a point where $L'(p)$ vanishes. Now,

$$L'(p) = p^5(1 - p)(6 - 8p),$$

and this is clearly zero at $p = 3/4$, which is the relative frequency of successes among the eight trials. This is the maximum likelihood estimate of p. If it were the actual value of p, the probability of six successes would be $(6/8)^6(2/8)^2$, and this is larger than the probability of six successes using any other value of p.

When the population is continuous, the likelihood function is not a probability but at each point is approximately proportional to the probability of a tiny region including the point. At any rate, whether or not the intuition is satisfied by so doing, this likelihood function is maximized even in the continuous case, according to the maximum likelihood principle.

If the sample is a random sample, the likelihood function is a product of the population densities for each value in the sample:

$$L(\theta) = \prod_{i=1}^{n} f(X_i,\theta).$$

Consequently, manipulation is frequently simpler if the *logarithm* of the likelihood function is maximized:

$$\log L(\theta) = \sum_{i=1}^{n} \log f(X_i;\theta).$$

Since the logarithm function is monotone increasing, $L(\theta)$ and its logarithm are maximized by the same value θ. If $L(\theta)$ is a differentiable function [as is, then, also $\log L(\theta)$], and if its maximum is attained at a point $\hat{\theta}$ which is interior to the range of values of θ, it follows that

$$\left[\frac{\partial}{\partial\theta} \log L(\theta)\right]_{\theta=\hat{\theta}} = 0.$$

This is called the *likelihood equation*. If $\theta = (\theta_1,\ldots,\theta_k)$, the condition for a maximum is really k equations:

$$\begin{cases} \dfrac{\partial}{\partial\theta_1} \log L(\theta_1,\ldots,\theta_k) = 0 \\ \quad\vdots \qquad\qquad\qquad\qquad \vdots \\ \dfrac{\partial}{\partial\theta_k} \log L(\theta_1,\ldots,\theta_k) = 0. \end{cases}$$

A solution $(\theta_1,\ldots,\theta_k)$ of this system, assuming it corresponds to a maximum of L, is a maximum likelihood estimate of $(\theta_1,\ldots,\theta_k)$.

One might wonder whether an estimate obtained as the solution of the likelihood equation actually maximizes the likelihood function when the vanishing of $L'(\theta)$ does not by itself guarantee this. When there is any doubt on this point, it should be investigated. The usual situation is that the likelihood function (being a product of probabilities or densities) is bounded above and continuous in θ, and that the likelihood equation has only one solution, which then must maximize $L(\theta)$.

Example 6–13. Consider a normal population, first with *known* mean μ and unknown variance v. The logarithm of the likelihood function is

$$\log L(v) = -\frac{n}{2}\log(2\pi v) - \frac{1}{2v}\sum(X_i - \mu)^2,$$

and its derivative is

$$-\frac{n}{2v} + \frac{1}{2v^2}\sum(X_i - \mu)^2.$$

This vanishes when v is given the value

$$\hat{v} = \frac{1}{n}\sum(X_i - \mu)^2,$$

which is the maximum likelihood estimate of v when μ is known.

Suppose next that *both* μ and v are *unknown*; the likelihood function is now a function of these two parameters, but in fact it is given by the same expression as $L(v)$ above:

$$\log L(\mu,v) = -\frac{n}{2}\log(2\pi v) - \frac{1}{2v}\sum(X_i - \mu)^2.$$

The likelihood equations are obtained by setting equal to zero the partial derivatives of log L with respect to μ and v:

$$\begin{cases} \dfrac{1}{\hat{v}} \sum (X_i - \hat{\mu}) = 0, \\ -\dfrac{n}{2\hat{v}} + \dfrac{1}{2\hat{v}^2} \sum (X_i - \hat{\mu})^2 = 0. \end{cases}$$

From the first equation it is seen that $\hat{\mu} = \bar{X}$, and substitution of this into the second equation yields $\hat{v} = s_x^2$. That is, $\bar{X}$ and s_x^2 are joint maximum likelihood estimates of μ and v. Recall that these estimates have been found to be sufficient for the normal family.

Example 6–14. Consider the basic experiment of a multinomial distribution, one that can result in any of k ways: $A_1, \ldots, A_k$. The parameters of the distribution are the corresponding probabilities $p_1, \ldots, p_k$, where $\sum p_i = 1$. Suppose that among n independent observations on this experiment there are f_i outcomes of type A_i, $i = 1, \ldots, k$. The probability of such a result is the required likelihood function

$$L(p_1, \ldots, p_k) = p_1^{f_1} \cdots p_k^{f_k},$$

with logarithm

$$\mathcal{L} = \log L(p_1, \ldots, p_k) = \sum_{i=1}^{k} f_i \log p_i.$$

In maximizing this, the probability vector $(p_1, \ldots, p_k)$ is restricted by the condition that $\sum p_i = 1$. Using the Lagrange method, we maximize $\mathcal{L} - \lambda \sum p_i$, differentiating this with respect to each p_j:

$$\frac{\partial}{\partial p_j} [\mathcal{L} - \lambda \sum p_i] = \frac{f_j}{p_j} - \lambda.$$

These derivatives vanish for $j = 1, \ldots, k$ only if f_j/p_j is the same (equal to λ) for all j. That is, the maximum likelihood estimates must be proportional to the frequencies f_j. With the condition that $\sum p_j = 1$, this means that $\hat{p}_j = f_j/n$, the relative frequency of outcomes of type A_j.

Having found a maximum likelihood estimate for θ, one might inquire about a maximum likelihood estimate for ξ, where $\xi = g(\theta)$. It is assumed that the function g is continuous and has a continuous inverse $\theta = g^{-1}(\xi)$ over the range of parameter values of interest. Under these conditions we can show the maximum likelihood estimate for ξ is $\hat{\xi} = g(\hat{\theta})$, where $\hat{\theta}$ is the maximum likelihood estimate of θ.

Suppose that the joint density function of the observations is $f(\mathbf{x};\theta)$, and let

$$\tilde{f}(\mathbf{x};\xi) = f(\mathbf{x};g^{-1}(\xi)),$$

so that

$$\tilde{f}(\mathbf{x};g(\theta)) = f(\mathbf{x};g^{-1}(g(\theta))) = f(\mathbf{x};\theta).$$

The likelihood function for ξ is

$$\tilde{L}(\xi) = \tilde{f}(\boldsymbol{x};\xi) = f(\boldsymbol{x};g^{-1}(\xi)) = L(g^{-1}(\xi)).$$

Now, if $\hat{\theta}$ maximizes $L(\theta)$, then for θ in the neighborhood of $\hat{\theta}$,

$$L(\theta) \leq L(\hat{\theta}).$$

But if ξ is in the neighborhood of $g(\hat{\theta})$, continuity implies that $g^{-1}(\xi)$ is in the neighborhood of $\hat{\theta}$, so that

$$\tilde{L}(\xi) = L(g^{-1}(\xi)) \leq L(\hat{\theta}) = \tilde{L}(g(\hat{\theta})).$$

This implies that $g(\hat{\theta})$ maximizes $\tilde{L}(\xi)$ and is the maximum likelihood estimate of ξ.

Example 6–15. Consider a normal population with mean 0 and unknown variance v. The maximum likelihood estimate of v is $\sum X_i^2/n$, and therefore the maximum likelihood estimate of the population standard deviation is $(\sum X_i^2/n)^{1/2}$. (This is not the sample standard deviation.)

One property of the method of maximum likelihood is that if there is a statistic T sufficient for the family $f(x;\theta)$, any solution of the likelihood equation is a function of T. For, the likelihood function factors, according to the factorization criterion for sufficiency:

$$L(\theta) = f(\boldsymbol{X};\theta) = g[T,\theta]h(\boldsymbol{X}).$$

But then

$$\log L(\theta) = \log g[T,\theta] + \log h(\boldsymbol{X}),$$

and

$$\frac{\partial}{\partial\theta}\log L(\theta) = \frac{\partial}{\partial\theta}\log g[T,\theta].$$

Any quantity $\hat{\theta}$ that makes this zero depends on the observations only through the value of T.

Another property is that if there is an unbiased, efficient estimator T, the maximum likelihood method will produce it. This is seen as follows: The information inequality for T is an equality (if T is efficient), so that

$$V = \frac{\partial}{\partial\theta}\log f(\boldsymbol{X}:\theta) = A'(\theta)T + B'(\theta).$$

This has (as shown in §6.1.3) mean zero for all θ:

$$E(V) = A'(\theta)E(T) + B'(\theta) = A'(\theta)\theta + B'(\theta) \equiv 0.$$

The derivative of the logarithm of the likelihood function is

$$\frac{\partial}{\partial\theta}\log f(\mathbf{X};\theta) = A'(\theta)T + B'(\theta),$$

and this is zero for $\theta = \hat{\theta}$, a maximum likelihood estimate:

$$-\frac{B'(\hat{\theta})}{A'(\hat{\theta})} = T.$$

But since for *all* θ, $-B'(\theta)/A'(\theta) = \theta$, the left member is $\hat{\theta}$. That is, the statistic T is the maximum likelihood estimate $\hat{\theta}$.

A third property, which will not be derived here, is that a maximum likelihood estimate is asymptotically normally distributed with variance $1/I(\theta)$ under certain conditions of regularlity. That is, it is asymptotically efficient. (Cf. Reference [4], page 500.)

Example 6–16. Consider the density function that is uniform on the interval $[0,b]$, where b is unknown, and is therefore a parameter of the distribution:

$$f(x,b) = \begin{cases} 1/b, & \text{for } 0 \le x \le b, \\ 0, & \text{elsewhere.} \end{cases}$$

Given a set of observations in a random sample $\mathbf{X}$, we have $f(X_i;b) = 1/b$ if $X_i < b$; but if any $X_i > b$, the corresponding density function is zero, as is then the likelihood function:

$$L(b) = \prod_{i=1}^{n} f(X_i;b) = \begin{cases} 1/b^n, & \text{if } b > \text{all } X_i, \\ 0, & \text{otherwise.} \end{cases}$$

The graph of this function of b for given $\mathbf{X}$ is shown in Figures 6–1.

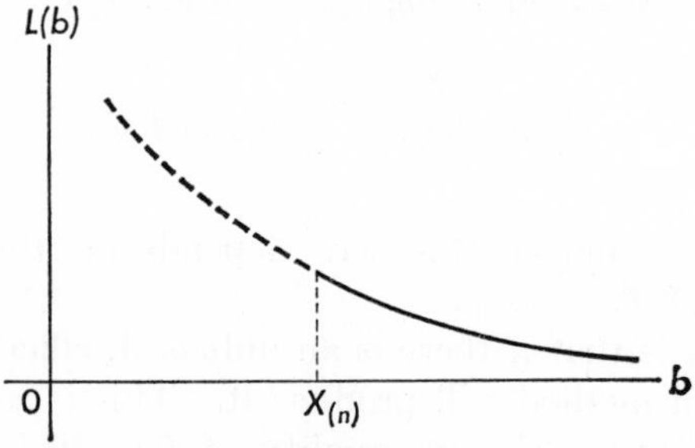

Figure 6–1

The maximum is clearly achieved for $\hat{b}$ equal to the largest observation in the sample. But the derivative of $L(b)$ does not vanish at this maximum. In this example the conditions for the standard theorems on maximum likelihood are not satisfied, the density function being discontinuous at a point whose location depends on the parameter being estimated.

PROBLEMS

6–13. Repeat the computation of Example 6–12 for k successes in n trials.

6–14. Determine the maximum likelihood estimate of the parameter in a Poisson distribution.

6–15. Determine the maximum likelihood estimate of θ in the negative exponential density $\theta \exp(-\theta x)$, $x > 0$. Determine also the maximum likelihood estimates of the mean and variance.

6–16. A lot contains ten articles, and a sample of four is drawn without replacement from the lot. Given that one of the four articles drawn is defective, what number of defectives in the lot would give the largest probability of this result?

6–17. Determine the maximum likelihood estimate of the parameter b in the density function

$$f(x;b) = \begin{cases} \exp(-|x - b|), & \text{for } x > b, \\ 0, & \text{for } x < b. \end{cases}$$

6.2.3 Using a Sufficient Statistic. As in general a decision procedure can be replaced by one based on a sufficient statistic, so in estimating a parameter an estimator can be replaced by a function of a sufficient statistic without deterioration of the risk. In particular, given an unbiased estimate U of the parameter $h(\theta)$, an unbiased estimate based on the sufficient statistic T can be constructed whose variance is not greater than that of U. In some instances the method yields an unbiased estimate of *minimum* variance.

Given the statistic U, then, consider the function

$$g(t) = E(U \mid T = t).$$

If T is sufficient, the conditional distribution of X and therefore that of the statistic U are independent of the state θ. The function $g(t)$ really depends, then, only on t, as the notation implies. It defines a statistic

$$V = g(T),$$

whose mean is the same as that of U:

$$E(V) = E[E(U \mid T = t)] = E(U).$$

Consequently, if U is an unbiased estimate of $h(\theta)$, so is V.

The variance of U can be expressed as follows:

$$\begin{aligned} \text{var } U &= E[(U - E(V))^2] \\ &= \text{var } V + E[(U - V)^2] + 2E[(U - V)(V - E(V))]. \end{aligned}$$

The assertion that var $U \geq$ var V will be established as soon as it is shown that the cross-product term vanishes. So, consider

$$E[(U - V)(V - E(V))] = \int_{-\infty}^{\infty} E[(U - V)(V - E(V)) \mid T = t] \, dF_T(t),$$

where $F_T(t)$ is the distribution function of T. Now,

$$E(V - U|T = t) = E(V|T = t) - E(U|T = t)$$
$$= g(t) - g(t) = 0,$$

and

$$E[(U - V)(V - E(V))|T = t] = E[(U - V)(g(t) - h(\theta))|T = t]$$
$$= [g(t) - h(\theta)]E(U - V|T = t) = 0.$$

Thus the above integral vanishes, and var $U \geq$ var V. The variance of V is actually smaller if U does not depend on the data through the value of T only, and so one can do better using V then using U.

If there is any hope of doing still better (in terms of risk) than by using V, it would have to be with another function of T, say, $k(T)$. If $E[k(T)] = h(\theta) = E[g(T)]$ for all θ, then it can be shown in many instances that $k(t) = g(t)$ wherever T has nonzero density for all θ; $k(T)$ would then be equivalent to $g(T)$. A family of states where this is true is said to be "complete." (Cf. Reference [9], pages 104–110.)

Example 6–17. Consider a random sample $(X_1,\ldots,X_n)$ from a normal population with mean μ and known variance v. Let U denote the statistic X_1, which is unbiased as an estimate of μ, and let T denote the sufficient statistic $\sum X_i$. Since U and T are linear combinations of normal variables, they have a joint normal distribution; the mean vector is $(\mu,n\mu)$ and the covariance matrix is

$$M = \begin{pmatrix} v & v \\ v & nv^2 \end{pmatrix}.$$

Using these, one can write out the joint density $f(u,t)$ and the marginal density $f_T(t)$ and with these compute the conditional density

$$f_{U|T=t}(u) = \frac{f(u,t)}{f_T(t)} = \frac{1}{\sqrt{2\pi v(n-1)/n}} \exp\left\{-\frac{(u - t/n)^2}{2v(n-1)/n}\right\}$$

The expected value of the conditional distribution of U, given $T = t$, is then $t/n = g(t)$. The statistic $g(T) = T/n = \sum X_i/n = \bar{X}$ is the desired statistic based on T, whose risk is better than that of any estimate not based on T.

6.2.4 B.A.N. Estimates. Although maximum likelihood estimates are known to be consistent, asymptotically efficient, and asymptotically normal, there are usually other estimates that have these properties and which would then appear to serve just as well for large samples. (They might even be better for small samples). Such estimates are called *best asymptotically normal*, or BAN, and can be obtained in various ways.

One class of BAN estimates consists of certain "minimum chi-square" estimates, defined as follows: Consider a sample $\mathbf{X}_1, \ldots, \mathbf{X}_n$ from a vector-valued population $\boldsymbol{X}$ with mean vector $\boldsymbol{\mu}(\theta)$ and covariance matrix $\boldsymbol{M}(\theta)$, θ being the parameter to be estimated (it could be multidimensional). The quadratic expression

$$\chi^2 = \frac{1}{n}(\bar{\boldsymbol{X}} - \boldsymbol{\mu}(\theta))'[\boldsymbol{M}(\theta)]^{-1}(\bar{\boldsymbol{X}} - \boldsymbol{\mu}(\theta))$$

(where the prime means transpose) is minimized as a function of θ for given $\boldsymbol{X}_1, \ldots, \boldsymbol{X}_n$. The minimizing value $\theta(\boldsymbol{X}_1,\ldots,\boldsymbol{X}_n)$ is called the *minimum chi-square estimate* of θ. It is known to be BAN when $\boldsymbol{X}$ has a distribution belonging to the exponential family. Various modifications of the minimum chi-square method also yield BAN estimates.

Example 6–18. Let X have the negative exponential distribution with mean $1/\theta$ and variance $1/\theta^2$. Given a random sample $X_1, \ldots, X_n$, we have

$$\chi^2 = \frac{1}{n}\left(\bar{X} - \frac{1}{\theta}\right)\theta^2\left(\bar{X} - \frac{1}{\theta}\right) = \frac{1}{n}(\theta\bar{X} - 1)^2.$$

This is minimized for $\theta = 1/\bar{X}$, which is then the minimum chi-square estimate of θ.

In minimizing χ^2 or in maximizing the likelihood function, one may be confronted with equations that are not readily solvable, say,

$$G'(\theta) = 0,$$

where G denotes either the likelihood or χ^2. Newton's method of solving such an equation approximately is to make a guess θ_0 and then obtain an improved guess by solving the linear approximation

$$G'(\theta) \doteq G'(\theta_0) + G''(\theta_0)(\theta - \theta_0) = 0,$$

to obtain

$$\theta_1 = \theta_0 - \frac{G'(\theta_0)}{G''(\theta_0)}.$$

It turns out that if θ_0 is taken to be any consistent estimate of θ such that $\sqrt{n}(\theta_0 - \theta)$ is asymptotically normal when θ is the true state, then the first approximation θ_1 is BAN. (These matters are discussed more fully in an article by T. S. Ferguson, "A Method of Generating Best Asymptotically Normal Estimates...," *Ann. Math. Stat.* 29, (1959), pages 1046–1062.)

6.3 Interval Estimates

In presenting an estimate of a population parameter (giving the value of $\bar{X}$, for example, as an estimate of the population mean), no indication of the reliability of the estimate is found in the bare announcement of the estimated value. Giving the size of the sample used along with the estimate would be helpful but would assume that everyone who is to interpret the result is equipped to interpret sample size in terms of the "accuracy" of the estimate. Such is not ordinarily the case, and a more direct indication is desirable.

One device for indicating the accuracy of an estimate is to give what has been called the *standard error of the estimate.* Ideally this would be the square root of the expected square deviation of the estimate about the parameter being estimated (at any rate, this would appear to be appropriate under the assumption of a quadratic loss). For an unbiased estimate, this would simply be the standard deviation of the estimator, But, unfortunately, this standard deviation sometimes depends on unknown population parameters; in this case it is the practice to replace such unknown parameters by sample estimates and still to name the result the "standard error of the estimate," assuming a large sample.

Example 6–19. The mean $\bar{X}$ of a random sample of size n has expectation μ and variance σ^2/n. The quantity $\sigma/\sqrt{n}$ is called the *standard error of estimate* when σ is known; if σ is not known, it is replaced by s_x, the assumption being that in a large sample, s_x will not differ appreciably from σ.

The notion of "standard error" came into use perhaps because estimators used often had a normal distribution (at least asymptotically), and the standard deviation of this normal distribution then adequately described the distribution. What was wanted, no doubt, was a range of values within which the population parameter is in some sense almost sure to lie.

Example 6–20. Consider a sample of n from a normal population with unit variance. The interval from $\bar{X} - 2/\sqrt{n}$ to $\bar{X} - 2/\sqrt{n}$ is four standard deviations wide and ought to trap the actual population mean within it, one feels. What *can* be said is that the random interval from $\bar{X} - 2/\sqrt{n}$ to $\bar{X} + 2/\sqrt{n}$ has the property that

$$P\left(-\frac{2}{\sqrt{n}} < \bar{X} - \mu < +\frac{2}{\sqrt{n}}\right) = P\left(\bar{X} - \frac{2}{\sqrt{n}} < \mu < \bar{X} + \frac{2}{\sqrt{n}}\right) \doteq 0.95.$$

That is, an interval computed in this way will happen to cover the actual population mean 95 per cent of the time. Such a random interval is called a (95 per cent) *confidence interval* for the population mean.

In general a confidence interval for a parameter θ is constructed from a statistic T whose distribution depends on θ, in the following way: Determine two numbers depending on θ, $t_1(\theta)$, and $t_2(\theta)$, such that for a given *confidence coefficient* η,

$$P(t_1(\theta) < T < t_2(\theta)) = \eta.$$

Then invert the inequalities here: solve for θ, to obtain an equivalent inequality of the form $g(T) < \theta < h(T)$. This has the same probability η, and the statistics $g(T)$ and $h(T)$ are called *confidence limits* for θ. These limits are random (they vary from sample to sample); some of the time they do include the actual value of θ, and some of the time they don't.

Unfortunately, giving a confidence interval in an actual problem with actual numbers sounds like something different from what is really meant. Stating that a 90 per cent confidence interval for θ is (9.1,9.6), for instance, would suggest that θ is a random variable that, with probability 0.90, lies between 9.1 and 9.6. In the analysis leading to a confidence interval, however, it is assumed that θ is a *constant* that, although not known, remains fixed throughout the sampling process. Nevertheless, a user of statistics (who is not a statistician) is likely to interpret a confidence interval statement as giving a probability for the "random variable" θ; in other words, as coming from a posterior distribution for θ. That in certain instances this point of view has some basis is seen in the following example.

Example 6–21. If the mean of a random sample of size 100 from a normal population with unit variance is $\bar{X} = 20$, the 95 per cent confidence interval for μ, as obtained in Example 6–20, is defined by the limits $20 \pm 2/\sqrt{100}$, or 19.8 and 20.2.

Assuming a uniform prior weighting for μ, the absolute distribution of $\bar{X}$ has the density function

$$f_{\bar{X}}(y) = \sqrt{\frac{n}{2\pi}} \int_{-\infty}^{\infty} \exp\left[\frac{-n\,(y-\mu)^2}{2}\right] d\mu = 1,$$

and the posterior distribution for μ is then defined by the density

$$h(\mu \mid \bar{X} = y) = \frac{f_{\bar{X}}(y;\,\mu)g(\mu)}{f_{\bar{X}}(y)} = \sqrt{\frac{n}{2\pi}} \exp\left[-\frac{1}{2}n(y-\mu)^2\right]$$

and then (with $y = 20$)

$$P_h(19.8 < \mu < 20.2) = \sqrt{\frac{n}{2\pi}} \int_{19.8}^{20.2} \exp\left[\frac{-n\,(20-\mu)^2}{2}\right] d\mu = 0.95,$$

so the confidence interval has the interpretation of a 95 per cent probability interval for μ in the posterior distribution, assuming a uniform prior weighting. For other prior weightings this is not necessarily true.

PROBLEMS

6–18. Referring to the computation of a confidence interval for μ in a normal population in Example 6–21, do similar computations with these modifications: (a) samples of size 25 and 400; (b) variance of 4, with $n = 100$; (c) confidence coefficients of 0.90 and 0.99, with $n = 100$ and $\sigma^2 = 1$.

6–19. It is known from long experience that the reliability of a certain chemical measurement is indicated by a standard deviation $\sigma = .005$ gm/ml. Determine a sample size n such that a 99 per cent confidence interval for μ has a width of 0.001 gm/ml. (Is it necessary to assume that the measurements are normal in order that the normal table be used?)

6–20. A sample of 60 observations from a Poisson population with parameter m has a mean of 2.1. Construct a 90 per cent confidence interval for m, assuming that the sample size is large enough for a normal approximation.

7 / Testing Hypotheses

An important class of statistical decision problems consists of those in which there are just two possible actions. It is assumed that if only the actual state of nature were known, it would be clear as to which of the two actions would be preferred. The problem is statistical when observations related to the state of nature can be made which, although not giving complete information as to the state, provide some information toward making a reasonable decision between the two possible actions.

Problems that are basically of this nature have been treated from a variety of viewpoints prior to the introduction of decision theory, and a language peculiar to these problems has been developed. The possible states of nature are said to be *hypotheses* about nature, each state being called a *simple hypothesis*. Any collection of more than one simple hypothesis is called a *composite* hypothesis; a composite hypothesis is said to be true if some one of the simple hypotheses that make it up is the true state of nature.

Example 7–1. The statement that X is normally distributed is a composite statistical hypothesis, since the property of normality does not completely define the distribution of X, the state of nature. This hypothesis includes such simple hypotheses as this one: X is normal with mean 2 and variance 9.

The hypothesis that X has mean 2 and variance 9 is in general composite, since the mean and variance do not alone define a distribution.

The set of possible states of nature or simple hypotheses that might be true in a given problem is partitioned naturally into two sets, one called H_0, for which action A is preferred, and one called H_1, for which action B is preferred. Because one of these is often a hypothesis of no change from the "status quo" or of no difference in the results of two treatments, it (usually H_0) is sometimes referred to as "the null hypothesis," or "the hypothesis being tested." The other (H_1) is then referred to as the "alternative hypothesis."

The decision problem is to choose between behaving as though H_0 were true (taking action A) and behaving as though H_1 were true (taking action B), on the basis of observations on nature. A decision function in such a problem is a rule that prescribes one or the other of these actions for each possible observation vector $(x_1,\ldots,x_n)$. The rule is also called a *test of* H_0 *against* H_1.

A rule or test or decision function divides the sample space into two parts, one part consisting of those points $\mathbf{x}$ for which the test selects action A (that is, accepting H_0 and rejecting H_1), and the other consisting of those $\mathbf{x}$ for which the test selects action B (that is, rejecting H_0 and accepting H_1). The part of the sample space corresponding to action B under the test is called the *critical region* of the test. If a sample $\mathbf{X}$ falls in the critical region of a test, action B is taken (H_0 is rejected in favor of H_1); if $\mathbf{X}$ does not fall in the critical region, action A is taken (H_0 is accepted over H_1). Thus specification of the critical region of a test defines the test, and conversely.

Often decision procedures are used that depend on the sample $\mathbf{X}$ only through the value of some statistic T. The decision function is then of the form $d(T)$, where $T = t(\mathbf{X})$. The statistic T is then referred to as the test statistic. Since each sample point $\mathbf{x}$ is assigned a value of T, the partition of the sample space corresponding to a given test induces a partition of the range of values of T, one part consisting of those values for which $d(T)$ calls for accepting H_0 and the other consisting of those values for which $d(T)$ calls for rejecting H_0. The latter set of T values is again called the critical region of the test. Thus the term *critical region* is used either for the set of sample points $\mathbf{x}$ or for the set of values of $T = t(\mathbf{X})$ which call for rejection of H_0.

Example 7–2. Given some H_0 and H_1 concerning a family of states of nature, consider the following statistical test: Accept H_0 if the mean of a sample of size two does not exceed 1. The value of the test statistic $\bar{X}$ can be any number on the range of values of the population variable X; let this be $-\infty < x < \infty$. The critical region of the proposed test is the interval $(1,\infty)$ of values of $\bar{X}$. In the space of possible sample points (x_1,x_2), the critical region consists of those points the sum of whose coordinates exceeds 2, as shown in Figure 7–1.

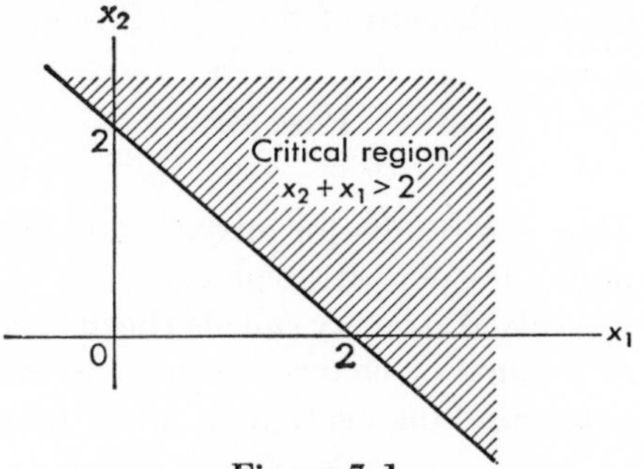

Figure 7–1

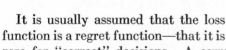

It is usually assumed that the loss function is a regret function—that it is zero for "correct" decisions. A correct decision is the choice of action A when H_0 is true or the choice of action B when H_1 is true. Taking action B when H_0 is true is wrong; it is called a *type* I *error*, and the penalty is, say, $a(\theta) \geq 0$, where θ denotes the state of nature. Taking action A when H_1 is true is also wrong; it is called a *type* II *error*, and the penalty is, say, $b(\theta) \geq 0$.

The loss function is then as follows:

$$\ell(\theta,A) = \begin{cases} 0, & \text{if } \theta \text{ is in } H_0, \\ b(\theta), & \text{if } \theta \text{ is in } H_1, \end{cases}$$

$$\ell(\theta,B) = \begin{cases} a(\theta), & \text{if } \theta \text{ is in } H_0, \\ 0, & \text{if } \theta \text{ is in } H_1 \end{cases}$$

The risk function for a test defined by the critical region C is then

$$R(\theta,C) = \begin{cases} a(\theta)P_\theta(\mathbf{X} \text{ falls in } C), & \text{if } \theta \text{ is in } H_0, \\ b(\theta)P_\theta(\mathbf{X} \text{ falls in } \bar{C}), & \text{if } \theta \text{ is in } H_1. \end{cases}$$

A mixed strategy or *randomized* decision procedure can be thought of either as an auxiliary game of chance that selects one of the available decision functions (or one of the available critical regions) or as a game of chance assigned to each outcome $\mathbf{x}$ of the experiment used for decision. These formulations are equivalent, but it is convenient to use the latter. The game of chance assigned to each $\mathbf{x}$ depends on the $\mathbf{x}$, of course, and is a simple game with two outcomes: action A or action B (accept H_0 or accept H_1). The game is specified by a probability ϕ for action B, and because this probability is in general different at different points, a randomized decision procedure is a function $\phi(\mathbf{x})$ such that $0 \leq \phi(\mathbf{x}) \leq 1$ for each $\mathbf{x}$. A randomized procedure is then carried out in this way: The statistical experiment (obtaining of observations on nature) is performed, with outcome $\mathbf{X}$; a biased coin is then tossed with probability $\phi(\mathbf{X})$ of Heads, and H_0 is rejected if Heads appears.

A pure strategy or decision function is a special case of a mixed strategy, obtained by using $\phi(\mathbf{x}) = 1$ for the critical region of the test and $\phi(\mathbf{x}) = 0$ for the complement of the critical region:

$$\text{Pure strategy:} \quad \phi(\mathbf{x}) = \begin{cases} 1, & \text{if } \mathbf{x} \text{ falls in } C, \\ 0, & \text{if } \mathbf{x} \text{ falls in } \bar{C}. \end{cases}$$

Thus any results for mixed strategies would include as special cases the same results for pure strategies.

A mixed strategy can also be defined in terms of a decision statistic $T = t(\mathbf{X})$ as a game of chance assigned to each outcome t of T, again with the two outcomes "take action A" and "take action B" and probabilities

$$\begin{cases} \phi(t) = P(\text{take action } B \text{ when } T = t), \\ 1 - \phi(t) = P(\text{take action } A \text{ when } T = t). \end{cases}$$

7.1 Simple H_0 and H_1

The simplest two-action problem is one in which H_0 and H_1 are each composed of a single, simple hypothesis. In this case the losses $a(\theta)$ and $b(\theta)$

are given by constants $a \geq 0$ and $b \geq 0$. For each test of simple H_0 against simple H_1, the following error "sizes" are defined:

$$\begin{cases} \text{Size of the type I error:} & \alpha = P_{H_0}(\text{reject } H_0) \\ \text{Size of the type II error:} & \beta = P_{H_1}(\text{accept } H_0), \end{cases}$$

where, for instance, the event "reject H_0" means the event that **X** falls in the critical region C. In terms of these error sizes, the risk function can be expressed as follows:

$$R(\theta,C) = \begin{cases} a\alpha, & \text{if } \theta \text{ is } H_0, \\ b\beta, & \text{if } \theta \text{ is } H_1. \end{cases}$$

So, for any given losses a and b, a knowledge of α and β is equivalent to a knowledge of the risk function, and the attention is ordinarily focused on the error sizes α and β.

Example 7–3. Consider the following simple hypotheses:

$$H_0\text{: } X \text{ is normal } (0,4), \qquad H_1\text{: } X \text{ is normal } (1,4).$$

Since $\bar{X}$ is sufficient for the normal family with given variance, it makes sense to consider $\bar{X}$ as the test statistic. Recalling, too, that the normal family with fixed variance is a monotone likelihood ratio family, we consider the monotone procedure given by the critical region $\bar{X} > K$, for some constant K. The error sizes for this test are as follows (written for a sample size $n = 25$):

$$\alpha = P_{\mu=0}(\bar{X} > K) = 1 - N\left(\frac{K - 0}{2/\sqrt{25}}\right),$$

$$\beta = P_{\mu=1}(\bar{X} < K) = N\left(\frac{K - 1}{2/\sqrt{25}}\right).$$

If $K = 0.4$, for instance, these are $\alpha = 0.1587$ and $\beta = 0.0668$. They are indicated graphically in Figure 7–2 as areas under the appropriate density function for $\bar{X}$. It is clear from an examination of this figure that adjusting K to decrease α would increase β, and conversely. It is also clear that since increasing the sample size would narrow the distributions of $\bar{X}$ under H_0 and H_1, doing so would decrease both error sizes.

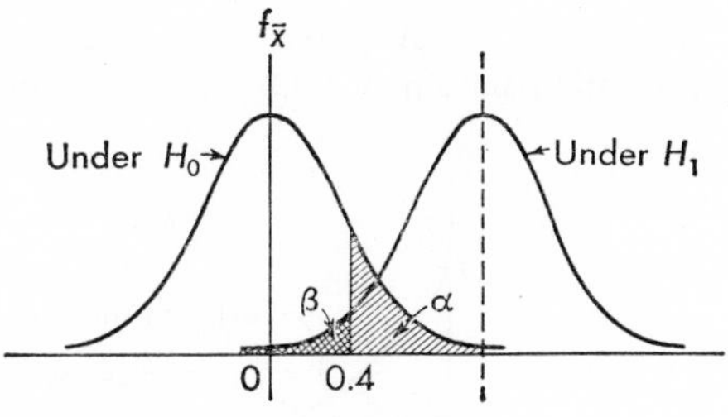

Figure 7–2

These things can be seen also in a plot of β versus α for a given test $\bar{X} > K$. Solving the equation giving α for K and substituting the result in the other equation, one obtains

$$\beta = N\left[N^{-1}(1 - \alpha) - \frac{\sqrt{n}}{2}\right],$$

where N^{-1} is the inverse of the standard normal distribution function N. Such curves are plotted for $n = 25$ and for $n = 4$ in Figure 7–3. Also plotted in this figure is the curve for the test $\bar{X} < K$, which shows the disastrous result of such an unintuitive procedure.

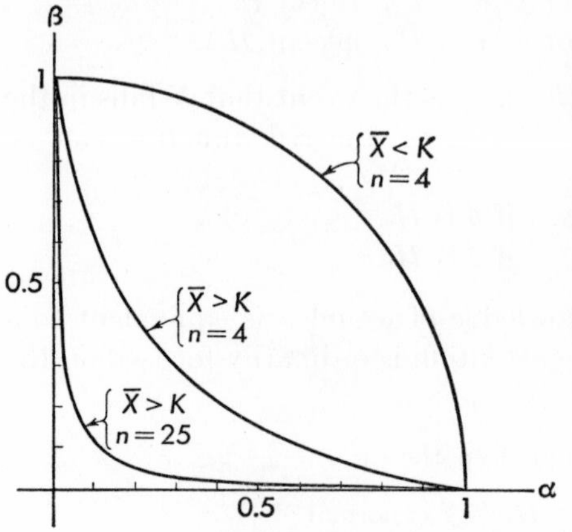

Figure 7–3

The selection of a "correct" procedure has not been made more obvious with the introduction of α and β than it is in the general decision problem. The difficulties persist. The graphical analysis of Example 5–2 (page 155) may again prove instructive. Corresponding to each procedure or test d, define

$$L_0 = R(\theta_0,d) = a\alpha,$$

and

$$L_1 = R(\theta_1,d) = b\beta,$$

and consider the representation of the test d as the point (L_0,L_1), or $(a\alpha,b\beta)$. This is like the plot of Figure 7–3 except that the losses are introduced as scale factors. Having thus represented the risk function, the minimax and Bayes procedures can be applied graphically as in Examples 5–3 and 5–4: The minimax procedure is that corresponding to the point first hit by a wedge moving out along $L_0 = L_1$, and a Bayes procedure is one corresponding to the point first hit in moving a line parallel to a given direction (defined by the prior distribution) away from the origin. Another procedure that might be considered is one which corresponds to the point closest to the origin—which minimizes $L_0^2 + L_1^2$.

Example 7–4. Consider the problem of Example 7–3, that of choosing between $\mu = 0$ and $\mu = 1$ in a normal population with given variance 4. The plot of (L_0,L_1) for tests of the form $\bar{X} > K$ is shown in Figure 7–4 for losses $b = 1$ and $a = 3$. On this graph are indicated also the minimax test, the Bayes test corresponding to a prior distribution (0.2,0.8) on (θ_0,θ_1), and the test that minimizes $L_0^2 + L_1^2$.

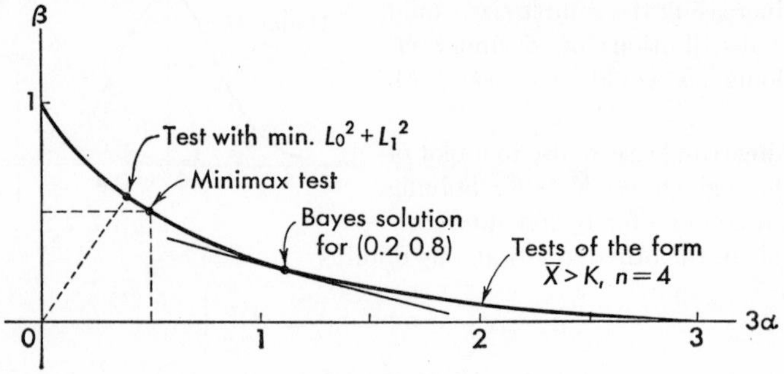

Figure 7–4

The type I and type II error sizes can also be computed for a randomized test of simple H_0 against simple H_1. A randomized test is defined by a probability $\phi(x)$ of taking action B, given the condition that $\mathbf{X} = \mathbf{x}$. The absolute probability of taking action B or rejecting H_0 is then the integral of the conditional probability with respect to the distribution of $\mathbf{X}$:

$$\begin{cases} \alpha = E_{H_0}[\phi(\mathbf{X})], \\ \beta = E_{H_1}[1 - \phi(\mathbf{X})] = 1 - E_{H_1}[\phi(\mathbf{X})]. \end{cases}$$

For a pure strategy defined by a critical region C, these reduce to $P_{H_0}(C)$ and $1 - P_{H_1}(C)$, respectively.

PROBLEMS

7–1. Determine in each case whether the hypothesis given is simple or composite:
(a) A pair of dice is "straight."
(b) A pair of dice is "crooked."
(c) $E(X) = 3$.
(d) X is negative exponential with mean 3.
(e) X is uniformly distributed.
(f) A coin is biased.
(g) The distribution function of X is $1 - e^{-x}$, $x > 0$.
(h) The distribution function of X is not $1 - e^{-x}$, $x > 0$.

7–2. A bag contains five beads, some white and the others not white. Consider testing

$$\begin{cases} H_0\text{: At most one bead is white} \\ H_1\text{: At least two beads are white} \end{cases}$$

on the basis of a sample of two drawn without replacement from the bag.
(a) List all possible tests based on the sample of two—sensible or not.
(b) Determine the probability of a type I error for each simple hypothesis in H_0 and the probability of a type II error for each simple hypothesis in H_1, for the test that rejects H_0 if and only if any white beads are drawn.
(c) Is there a test with smaller type II error sizes than the test in (b)?

7–3. Referring to Example 7–3, determine α and β for the test with critical region $\bar{X} < -0.5$, $n = 25$, and interpret graphically as in Figure 7–2.

7–4. Referring to Example 7–3 and considering tests of the form $\bar{X} > K$, determine:
(a) n and K so that $\alpha = \beta = 0.01$.
(b) n and K so that $\alpha = 0.01$ and $\beta = 0.10$.
(c) K and β for $n = 4$ and $\alpha = 0.05$.

7–5. Referring to Example 7–4, suppose that $n = 4$ and that the losses are $a = 2$ and $b = 1$. Determine the minimax test among those of the form $\bar{X} > K$.

7–6. Referring to Problem 7–5, among the tests of the form $\bar{X} > K$ determine the Bayes procedure corresponding to weights 0.2 and 0.8 for H_0 and H_1, respectively.

7.1.1 A Most Powerful Test. If two tests of simple H_0 against simple H_1 have the same α, the one with the smaller β dominates the other and is the preferred test of the two. It is said to be more *powerful*.

Definition. A test is said to be *most powerful* if among the class of tests whose α's are not greater, none has a β which is smaller.

The quantity $1 - \beta$ is referred to as *power* (the "power" of a test to detect the alternative hypothesis); it is the probability of taking action B when action B should be taken (H_1 is true). Even though a given test is most powerful, there may be tests with greater power achieved by sacrificing the size of the type I error.

The notion of "greatest power for given α" stems from situations in which one type of error is far more serious than the other; by proper labeling of hypotheses, this can be made the type I error. In such cases the risk can be controlled by controlling the size of the type I error, and so α is fixed at some acceptable level (called the *significance level* of the test), selecting the test that does as well as possible with respect to β.

When H_0 and H_1 are both simple, a most powerful test can always be constructed. The following reasoning suggests the way to construct this test: Let the sample observations have joint density $f_0(\mathbf{x})$ under H_0 and $f_1(\mathbf{x})$ under H_1. These functions attach numbers or measures to each point in the space of observation vectors $\mathbf{x}$. We imagine that f_0 assigns to each $\mathbf{x}$ a certain "cost" and that f_1 assigns a "return." Choosing a critical region C so as to have a certain size α amounts to putting into C enough points $\mathbf{x}$ so that the total "cost" of C is α:

$$\alpha = \int_C f_0(\mathbf{x})\, d\mathbf{x} = \text{total "cost" of } C.$$

Then, among those regions having the same total cost, we look for one that has the smallest β or largest $1 - \beta$:

$$1 - \beta = \int_C f_1(\mathbf{x})\, d\mathbf{x} = \text{total "return" from } C.$$

It is now clear that the way to make this selection is to construct C by putting into it those points $\mathbf{x}$ having the largest "return" per unit "cost": $f_1(\mathbf{x})/f_0(\mathbf{x})$. That is, points $\mathbf{x}$ are lined up according to the value of this ratio, and the points with the largest such values are put into C. The best critical region would then appear to be defined by

$$\frac{f_0(\mathbf{x})}{f_1(\mathbf{x})} < \text{constant},$$

where the "constant" is chosen to make the size of C equal to α.

Neyman-Pearson Lemma. In testing simple H_0 against simple H_1, using samples of a given size n, the test defined by the critical region containing those points $\mathbf{x}$ for which

$$\frac{f_0(x_1, \cdots, x_n)}{f_1(x_1, \cdots, x_n)} < K$$

is most powerful, where $f_0(x)$ and $f_1(x)$ denote the joint density (or probability) functions of the sample X under H_0 and H_1, respectively.

Although the discussion above was intended to make this seem correct, a more precise argument will now be given, one that shows the given critical region not only most powerful among critical regions of the same or smaller size but also among the set of mixed strategies having the same or smaller α's. Thus consider an arbitrary mixed strategy defined by $\phi(x)$, with

$$\alpha(\phi) = E_{H_0}[\phi(x)]$$

no larger than the α of the pure strategy defined by C:

$$\alpha(C) = E_{H_0}[\phi_C(x)],$$

where

$$\phi_C(x) = \begin{cases} 1, & \text{if } x \text{ is in } C, \\ 0, & \text{if } x \text{ is in } \overline{C}. \end{cases}$$

The difference in β's for $\phi(x)$ and $\phi_C(x)$ is

$$\begin{aligned} \beta(\phi) - \beta(C) &= E_{H_1}[1 - \phi(X)] - E_{H_1}[1 - \phi_C(X)] \\ &= E_{H_1}[\phi_C(X) - \phi(X)] \\ &= \int_C [\phi_C(x) - \phi(x)]f_1(x)\,dx + \int_{\overline{C}} [\phi_C(x) - \phi(x)]f_1(x)\,dx. \end{aligned}$$

Now, on C,

$$[\phi_C(x) - \phi(x)] = 1 - \phi(x) \geq 0,$$

and on $\overline{C}$,

$$[\phi_C(x) - \phi(x)] = -\phi(x) \leq 0.$$

Also, according to the definition of C, $f_1(x) \geq K'f_0(x)$, while on $\overline{C}$, $f_1(x) \leq K'f_0(x)$. Therefore,

$$\int_C [\phi_C(x) - \phi(x)]f_1(x)\,dx \geq K'\int_C [\phi_C(x) - \phi(x)]f_0(x)\,dx$$

and

$$\int_{\overline{C}} [\phi_C(x) - \phi(x)]f_1(x)\,dx \geq K'\int_{\overline{C}} [\phi_C(x) - \phi(x)]f_0(x)\,dx.$$

Finally, then,

$$\beta(\phi) - \beta(C) \geq K'E_{H_0}[\phi_C(X) - \phi(X)] = K'[\alpha(C) - \alpha(\phi)] \geq 0.$$

Example 7–5. Let X be normally distributed with variance 4 and consider testing H_0: $\mu = 0$ against H_1: $\mu = 1$, as in Examples 7–3 and 7–4, using a sample of size n. The joint density of X is, under H_0,

$$f_0(x) = \frac{1}{(8\pi)^{n/2}} \exp\left[-\frac{1}{8}\sum x_i^2\right],$$

and under H_1,

$$f_1(x) = \frac{1}{(8\pi)^{n/2}} \exp\left[-\frac{1}{8}\sum (x_i - 1)^2\right].$$

The crucial ratio is then

$$\frac{f_0(x)}{f_1(x)} = \exp\left[-\Sigma\frac{x_i^2}{8} + \frac{1}{8}\Sigma(x_i-1)^2\right]$$

$$= \exp\left[-\Sigma\frac{(2x_i - 1)}{8}\right].$$

This does not exceed K′, provided

$$\bar{x} > \frac{1}{2} - \frac{4 \log K'}{n} = K.$$

Therefore a critical region of the type $\bar{X} > K$ is best among those having a given α. The value of K' would be determined by that α. For example, if $\alpha = 0.1$ and $n = 25$,

$$0.1 = P_{\mu=0}(\bar{X} > K) = 1 - N\left(\frac{K - 0}{2/\sqrt{25}}\right),$$

so that

$$\frac{5K}{2} = 1.28 \quad \text{or} \quad K = 0.512.$$

As in this last example, the method used to determine a best critical region in the space of possible sample points frequently introduces a natural test statistic that is easier to work with than **X** itself. The critical region is then defined in terms of this statistic.

The computation of Example 7–5 is just as easily carried out when **X** has a distribution in the general exponential family with one parameter θ:

$$f(\mathbf{x};\theta) = B(\theta)\, e^{Q(\theta)S(\mathbf{x})}h(\mathbf{x});$$

with $H_0\colon \theta = \theta_0$ and $H_1\colon \theta = \theta_1$, provided $Q(\theta)$ is a monotone function of θ. The most powerful test is as follows:

$Q(\theta)$ monotone increasing: accept larger of (θ_0,θ_1) when $S(\mathbf{X}) > K$,
$Q(\theta)$ monotone decreasing: accept larger of (θ_0,θ_1) when $S(\mathbf{X}) < K$.

7.1.2 Randomization for Given Size. In setting up a most powerful test using the Neyman-Pearson Lemma, it can turn out (particularly in discrete cases) that it is not possible to find a critical region of the proper type that has *exactly* a specified size α. That is, in putting points into the critical region according to the value of the likelihood ratio $f_0(\mathbf{x})/f_1(\mathbf{x})$, it can happen that, with the addition of a single point, the size of the critical region jumps from below α to something above α.

If it is insisted that a critical region have a size precisely α, this can be accomplished with a randomized procedure in which the randomization occurs only at the boundary of the critical region. In such a procedure the only actual "coin tossing" takes place if $\mathbf{X}$ happens to fall at this boundary. The test function $\phi(x)$ is of the following form:

$$\phi(x) = \begin{cases} 0, & \text{if } f_0(x)/f_1(x) > K, \\ p, & \text{if } f_0(x)/f_1(x) = K, \\ 1, & \text{if } f_0(x)/f_1(x) < K. \end{cases}$$

Thus, if f_0/f_1 turns out to be equal to K, a coin is tossed having probability p of Heads, and H_0 is rejected if the coin falls Heads. The probability p is adjusted to make the α of the test equal to the value specified.

Example 7–6. Consider the problem of testing between $\lambda_0 = 0.1$ and $\lambda_1 = 0.2$ in a Poisson distribution for the number of events in an interval of 1 minute. The most powerful tests have critical regions of the form $\sum X_i > K$, where X_i is the number of events in the ith minute in a series of 1 minute intervals. Using ten such intervals (that is, a sample of size ten), one finds the type I error sizes to be as follows:

Test	$\Sigma X_i > 0$	$\Sigma X_i > 1$	$\Sigma X_i > 2$	$\Sigma X_i > 3$
α	0.6321	0.2642	0.0803	0.0190

None of these gives exactly, say, 0.05. If a most powerful test with $\alpha = 0.05$ is desired, it must be a randomized test. Consider then the randomized test that rejects λ_0 if $\sum X_i > 3$, accepts λ_0 if $\sum X_i < 3$, and rejects λ_0 with probability p if $\sum X_i = 3$. The α for this test is

$$\begin{aligned} P_{\lambda_0}(\text{reject } \lambda_0) &= P(\text{rej. } \lambda_0 | \textstyle\sum X_i > 3) P_{\lambda_0}(\sum X_i > 3) \\ &\quad + P(\text{rej. } \lambda_0 | \textstyle\sum X_i = 3) P_{\lambda_0}(\sum X_i = 3) \\ &\quad + P(\text{rej. } \lambda_0 | \textstyle\sum X_i < 3) P_{\lambda_0}(\sum X_i < 3) \\ &= 1 \times 0.0190 + p \times 0.0613 + 0 \times 0.9197. \end{aligned}$$

This can be made equal to 0.05 by taking $p = 0.506$.

7.1.3 Bayes and Maximum Likelihood Tests. The "likelihood ratio" procedure of §7.1.1, guaranteed by the Neyman-Pearson Lemma to be most powerful for simple H_0 and H_1, can be shown to be a modified maximum likelihood procedure. According to the maximum likelihood principle given in §5.4.4, the action to take is that which would be appropriate if the state of nature were the θ that maximizes the likelihood function $f(\mathbf{X};\theta)$. In the present context, with only two states, the principle would call for rejecting H_0 if $f(\mathbf{X};H_0) < f(\mathbf{X};H_1)$, or in the above notation, if

$$\frac{f_0(\mathbf{X})}{f_1(\mathbf{X})} < 1.$$

The reverse inequality would call for accepting H_0.

Example 7–7. In testing between $\mu = 0$ and $\mu = 1$ in a normal population with $\sigma^2 = 4$, the critical region defined by $f_0(\boldsymbol{x}) < f_1(\boldsymbol{x})$ is (using the calculations of Example 7–5) equivalent to

$$\exp[-\tfrac{1}{8}\sum(2X_i - 1)] < 1,$$

or

$$\bar{X} > \tfrac{1}{2}.$$

The corresponding error sizes are equal: $\alpha = \beta$.

As seen in Example 7–7. the maximum likelihood procedure clearly does not take into account the different regrets that might be associated with the two types of error. A *modified maximum likelihood* procedure calls for acting as though the state of nature were the θ that maximizes $w(\theta)L(\theta) = w(\theta)f(\mathbf{X};\theta)$, where $w(\theta)$ is a weighting function indicating a gain in utility for a correct decision when θ is the state relative to zero gain for an incorrect decision. In the case at hand, H_1 is accepted (H_0 rejected) if the sample $\mathbf{X}$ is such that

$$w(H_0)f_0(\mathbf{X}) < w(H_1)f_1(\mathbf{X}),$$

or

$$\frac{f_0(\mathbf{X})}{f_1(\mathbf{X})} < \frac{w(H_1)}{w(H_0)} = \text{constant}.$$

This is a most powerful test.

It is also of interest to know that in the simple two-state case being considered, a Bayes solution is most powerful. To see this, consider prior probabilities g_0 for H_0 and g_1 for H_1 and the corresponding posterior probability function:

$$h(\theta|\mathbf{X} = \boldsymbol{x}) = \begin{cases} \dfrac{g_0f_0(\boldsymbol{x})}{g_0f_0(\boldsymbol{x}) + g_1f_1(\boldsymbol{x})}, & \text{if } \theta = H_0, \\ \dfrac{g_1f_1(\boldsymbol{x})}{g_0f_0(\boldsymbol{x}) + g_1f_1(\boldsymbol{x})}, & \text{if } \theta = H_1. \end{cases}$$

The posterior expected losses are

$$E_h[\ell(\theta,A)] = \frac{bg_1f_1(\boldsymbol{x})}{f(\boldsymbol{x})},$$

$$E_h[\ell(\theta,B)] = \frac{ag_0f_0(\boldsymbol{x})}{f(\boldsymbol{x})},$$

where $f(\boldsymbol{x}) = g_0f_0(\boldsymbol{x}) + g_1f_1(\boldsymbol{x})$. The Bayes procedure is then to take action A or B according to which of these posterior expected losses is the smaller, taking action B (rejecting H_0) if

$$ag_0f_0(\boldsymbol{x}) < bg_1f_1(\boldsymbol{x}),$$

or

$$\frac{f_0(\boldsymbol{x})}{f_1(\boldsymbol{x})} < \frac{bg_1}{ag_0} = \text{constant}.$$

PROBLEMS

7–7. Let m denote the parameter of a Poisson distribution, and suppose it is desired to test $H_0: m = m_0$ against $H_1: m = m_1$, where $m_1 > m_0$. Determine the nature of the best test based on a sample $(X_1, \ldots, X_n)$, and the α and β for the test with critical region $\sum X_i > 4$, when $n = 3$, $m_0 = 1$, $m_1 = 2$.

7–8. Assuming that the sample size turns out to be large enough for a normal approximation, determine approximately the sample size and critical boundary corresponding to $\alpha = \beta = 0.01$ for the best test in Problem 7–7.

7–9. Determine the best type of critical region for testing θ_0 against θ_1, where $\theta_1 > \theta_0$, in the negative exponential density: $\theta \exp(-\theta x)$, $x > 0$.

7–10. Consider testing $\sigma = \sigma_0$ against $\sigma = \sigma_1$ in a normal population with given mean μ. Obtain the most powerful test, given $\sigma_1 > \sigma_0$, and determine the sample size and critical boundary corresponding to $\alpha = \beta = 0.01$ and $\sigma_0 = 2$, $\sigma_1 = 3$.

7–11. Obtain the most powerful test for θ_0 against θ based on a random sample from $f(x, \theta) = B(\theta) \exp [Q(\theta) R(x)] h(x)$.

7.2 Composite Hypotheses

Since risk depends upon the state θ, it is not uniquely defined for H_0 if H_0 is composite, and not uniquely defined for H_1 if H_1 is composite.

The simplest form of loss function for the case of composite H_0 or H_1 (or both) is that in which the losses are constant on H_0 and constant on H_1:

$$\ell(\theta,A) = \begin{cases} 0, & \text{for } \theta \text{ in } H_0, \\ b, & \text{for } \theta \text{ in } H_1, \end{cases}$$

$$\ell(\theta,B) = \begin{cases} a, & \text{for } \theta \text{ in } H_0, \\ 0, & \text{for } \theta \text{ in } H_1. \end{cases}$$

It must be admitted that this loss function is usually not very realistic, but nevertheless it is the one that will be used in the discussion to follow. In practice, losses are not easy to determine with great precision, and it therefore seems reasonable to develop the theory of testing in terms of a loss function that is as simple as possible. The theory could not be so well developed if a more general loss were used, and it is questionable that such theory would be any more appropriate in view of the difficulties in measuring loss.

In terms of the simple loss function given above, then, the risk function for a statistical test with critical region C becomes

$$R(\theta,C) = \begin{cases} aP_\theta(C), & \text{for } \theta \text{ in } H_0, \\ b[1 - P_\theta(C)], & \text{for } \theta \text{ in } H_1. \end{cases}$$

For a randomized test $\phi(x)$, the risk is

$$R(\theta,\phi) = \begin{cases} aE_\theta[\phi(\mathbf{X})], & \text{for } \theta \text{ in } H_0, \\ b\{1 - E_\theta[\phi(\mathbf{X})]\}, & \text{for } \theta \text{ in } H_1. \end{cases}$$

7.2.1 The Power Function. The risk function is now seen to be determined by the probability of taking action B (rejecting H_0) as a function of the state θ. This is called the *power function* of the test:

$$\pi(\theta) = \begin{cases} P_\theta(\mathbf{X} \text{ falls in } C), & \text{for pure strategy with critical region } C, \\ E_\theta[\phi(\mathbf{X})], & \text{for mixed strategy } \phi(\mathbf{X}) \end{cases}$$

The second formula includes the first as a special case.

It should be noted that for a problem with simple H_0 and simple H_1, the power function has just two values, $\alpha = \pi(H_0)$, and $1 - \beta = \pi(H_1)$. The latter quantity was called power in §7.1.

The function $1 - \pi(\theta)$ is called the *operating characteristic* of the test, but knowing $1 - \pi(\theta)$ is clearly equivalent to knowing $\pi(\theta)$. Which of these complementary functions is used is a matter of taste. In some applications it is the operating characteristic function that is tabulated, but in theoretical work the language of power is perhaps more common. The term *power* (as before) refers to the ability of a test to detect that H_0 is false when such is the case.

Example 7–8. Consider a Bernoulli experiment—success with probability p and failures with probability $1 - p$, and the following composite hypotheses:

$$\begin{cases} H_0: & 0 \le p \le 0.5, \\ H_1: & 0.5 < p \le 1. \end{cases}$$

Consider the particular test based on three observations that rejects H_0 if three successes occur. The power function for this test is as follows:

$$\pi(p) = P_p(3 \text{ successes in 3 trials}) = p^3.$$

For the test that rejects H_0 when either two or three successes occur in three trials, the power function is

$$\pi(p) = P_p(2 \text{ or 3 successes in 3 trials}) = 3p^2(1 - p) + p^3.$$

These two power functions are plotted on the same axes in Figure 7–5.

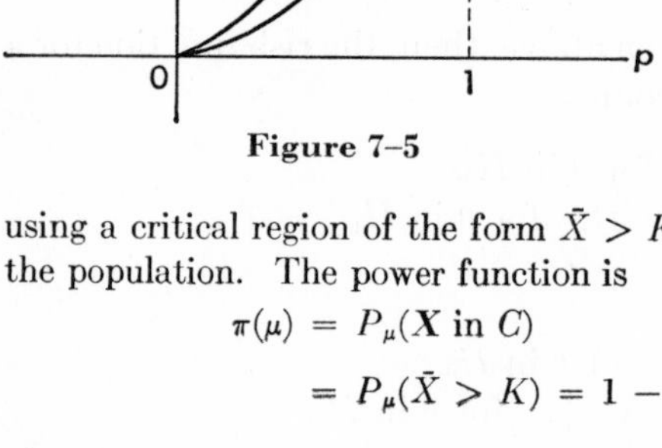

Figure 7–5

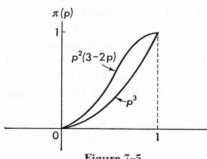

Notice that the division of $[0,1]$ into H_0 and H_1 does not enter the computation of $\pi(p)$, but of course it will enter in deciding whether a power function is acceptable or not. The power function for the second test is higher than that for the first test, not only on H_1 (which is desirable) but also on H_0 (which is not so desirable).

Example 7–9. Consider a normal population with variance 9; it is desired to test

$$H_0: \mu \le 1 \quad \text{against} \quad H_1: \mu > 1,$$

using a critical region of the form $\bar{X} > K$, based on a random sample of size n from the population. The power function is

$$\begin{aligned} \pi(\mu) &= P_\mu(\mathbf{X} \text{ in } C) \\ &= P_\mu(\bar{X} > K) = 1 - N\left(\frac{K - \mu}{3/\sqrt{n}}\right) = N\left(\frac{\mu - K}{3/\sqrt{n}}\right). \end{aligned}$$

This function of μ looks like a cumulative normal distribution; it is shown in Figure 7–6 for $K = 1$, $n = 36$, and for $K = 1$, $n = 144$. Both functions are high on H_1 and not so high on H_0. The center of symmetry of the graphs is at $\mu = 1$, and it is clear from the computations above that a change in the boundary of the critical region from $K = 1$ to, say, $K = 2$ would shift the curve laterally so that the center of symmetry would be $\mu = 2$.

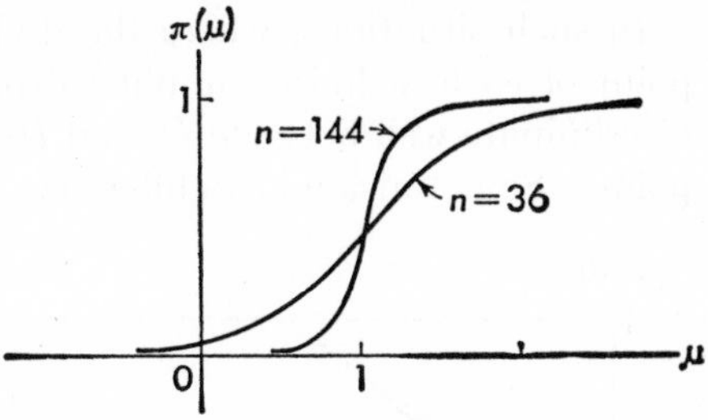

Figure 7–6

An ideal test, of course, is one that always calls for action A when action A should be taken and always calls for action B when action B should be taken. This will happen with probability 1 if the power function is 1 on H_1 and 0 on H_0, as shown in Figure 7–7. With this power function, the risk function is identically zero for all θ. The power functions considered in Examples 7–8 and 7–9 are certainly not ideal, yet the two curves shown in Figure 7–6 for different sample sizes suggest that the power function in that case could be made arbitrarily close to the ideal one by taking a sufficiently large sample.

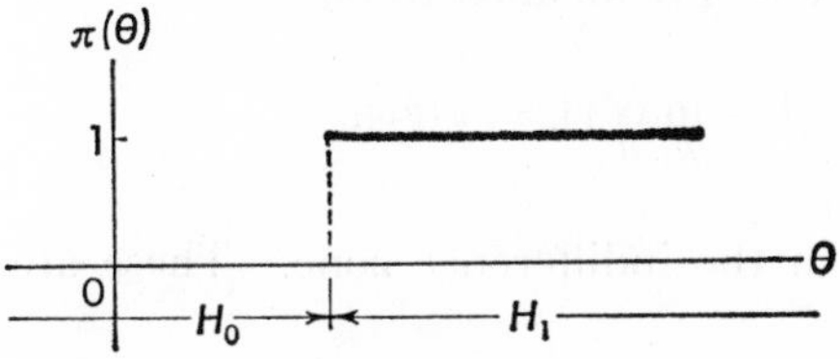

Figure 7–7

Although the probability of rejecting H_0 when H_0 is true is not uniquely defined (depending as it does on the state θ), one might define a "size" for type I errors as the maximum (or supremum, if the maximum does not exist) of such probabilities:

$$\alpha = \max_{\theta \text{ in } H_0} P_\theta(\text{reject } H_0) = \max_{\theta \text{ in } H_0} \pi(\theta).$$

This is sometimes called the *significance level* of the test. The size for type II errors could similarly be taken to be

$$\beta = \max_{\theta \text{ in } H_1} [1 - \pi(\theta)].$$

In problems in which θ is a real parameter or a vector of real parameters and where $\pi(\theta)$ does not jump at the boundary between the region H_0 and the region H_1, the sizes defined in this way will add up to 1. They could not *both* be made small, no matter how closely the power function approximates the ideal function for θ not on the boundary. A typical situation might be that in Figure 7–8.

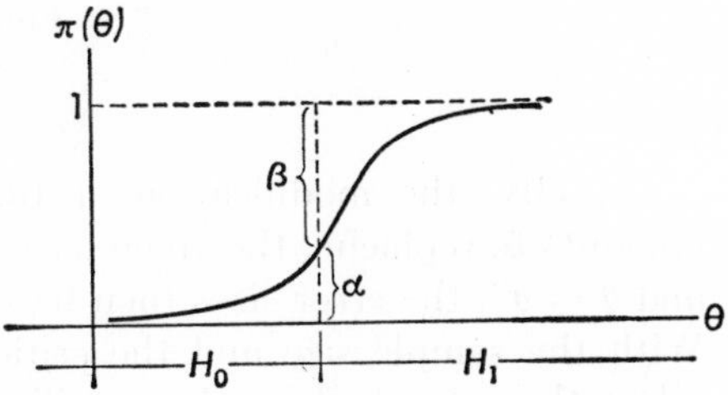

Figure 7–8

That is, increasing the sample size, which might steepen the power curve, as in Example 7–9, could not reduce both α and β to acceptably small levels.

In such situations, where the division between H_0 and H_1 is a boundary point of each, a finite sampling experiment could not really be expected to discriminate well between H_0 and H_1 if the actual state is near that boundary point. Sometimes an "indifference zone" or "no man's land" including the boundary is defined, say, from θ' to θ'', in which one is indifferent to the action taken. This amounts to a revision of the loss function to be zero in this indifference zone for both actions, and the ideal power function (to produce zero risk) is unrestricted there, as in Figure 7–9.

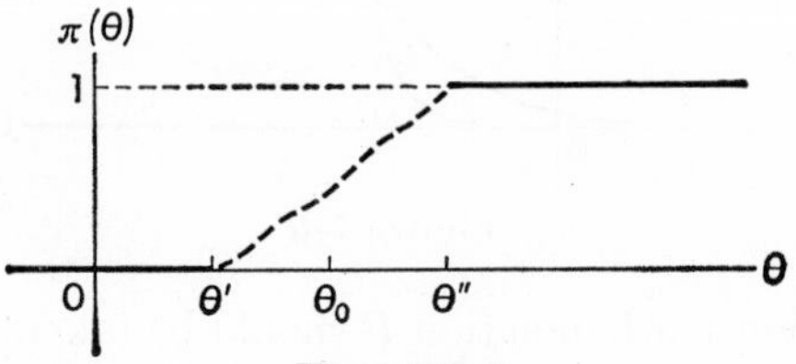

Figure 7–9

With such a modification the error sizes could be defined to be

$$\alpha = \max_{H_0 - I} \pi(\theta) \qquad \text{and} \qquad \beta = \max_{H_1 - I} [1 - \pi(\theta)],$$

where I denotes the set of values of θ in the indifference zone. These are shown in Figure 7–10.

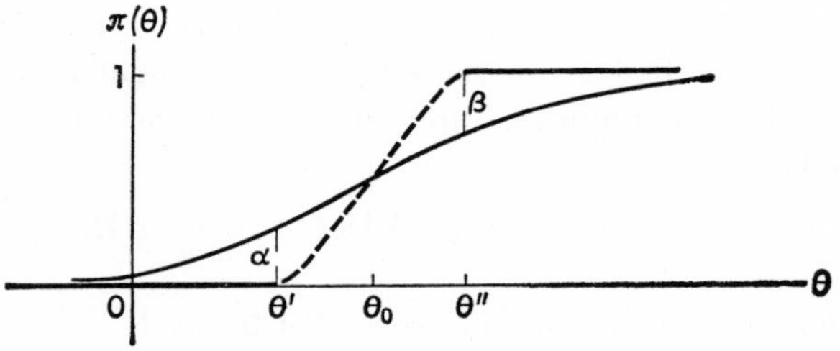

Figure 7–10

Actually, the modification of the original testing problem in this way amounts to replacing the given hypotheses with the simple hypotheses $\theta = \theta'$ and $\theta = \theta''$, the error sizes then being those defined for this simpler problem. With the sample size and the critical boundary at one's disposal, one can select them to produce the specified α and β. However, having used this method as a practical means of constructing a test, one should realize that the test cannot be characterized by the two numbers α and β; the whole power function should be examined to see what protection is afforded at other values of θ.

Example 7–10. Let X be normal with variance 9. It is decided that the probability of rejecting $\mu \leq 1$ when $\mu = 0.8$ should not exceed 0.05, and that the probability of accepting $\mu \leq 1$ when $\mu = 1.2$ should not exceed 0.10. If the test used is $\bar{X} > K$, then

$$0.05 = P_{\mu=0.8}(\bar{X} > K) = 1 - N\left(\frac{K - 0.8}{3/\sqrt{n}}\right),$$

and

$$0.10 = P_{\mu=1.2}(\bar{X} < K) = N\left(\frac{K - 1.2}{3/\sqrt{n}}\right),$$

These are readily solved with the aid of Table I (Appendix), giving the values of the standard normal distribution function $N(z)$, to obtain $n = 481$ and $K = 1.025$.

When the notion of sufficiency was introduced in Chapter 5, it was observed that any procedure could be viewed as a randomized procedure based on a sufficient statistic. This can be seen explicitly for the case of testing hypotheses, as follows: Let $\phi(\mathbf{X})$ define a test, and let T denote a sufficient statistic. Then the conditional expectation $E[\phi(\mathbf{X}) \mid T = t]$ is independent of the state of nature and so defines a function $h(t)$. The randomized test based on T defined by $h(T)$,

$$P(\text{reject } H_0 \mid T = t) = h(t),$$

has the power function

$$\pi_h(\theta) = E_\theta[h(T)] = E[E(\phi(\mathbf{X}) \mid T)] = E[\phi(\mathbf{X})] = \pi_\phi(\theta).$$

The test based on T has the same power function as the test $\phi(X)$ and therefore the same risk function. The tests are then equivalent.

7.2.2 Test Properties in Terms of Power. Assuming losses that are constant over H_0 and constant over H_1, we have found the risk function to be expressible in terms of the power function:

$$R(\theta,\phi) = \begin{cases} a\pi(\theta), & \text{for } \theta \text{ in } H_0, \\ b[1 - \pi(\theta)], & \text{for } \theta \text{ in } H_1, \end{cases}$$

where a and b are the losses and $\pi(\theta)$ is the power function of the test $\phi(\mathbf{X})$. In view of this, properties of statistical procedures defined in terms of risk can be interpreted in terms of the power function $\pi(\theta)$.

A procedure was called *consistent* if, as the sample size tends to infinity, the expected regret tends to zero. This will occur if the power function tends to 0 for θ in H_0 and tends to 1 for θ in H_1; in other words, if it tends to the ideal power function at each θ.

A procedure d was said to *dominate* a procedure d' if $R(\theta,d) \le R(\theta,d')$ for all θ. In terms of power, then, a test ϕ will dominate ϕ' if

$$\begin{cases} \pi_\phi(\theta) \le \pi_{\phi'}(\theta), & \text{for } \theta \text{ on } H_0, \\ \pi_\phi(\theta) \ge \pi_{\phi'}(\theta), & \text{for } \theta \text{ on } H_1. \end{cases}$$

Figure 7–11 shows power curves for tests ϕ and ϕ' such that ϕ dominates ϕ'.

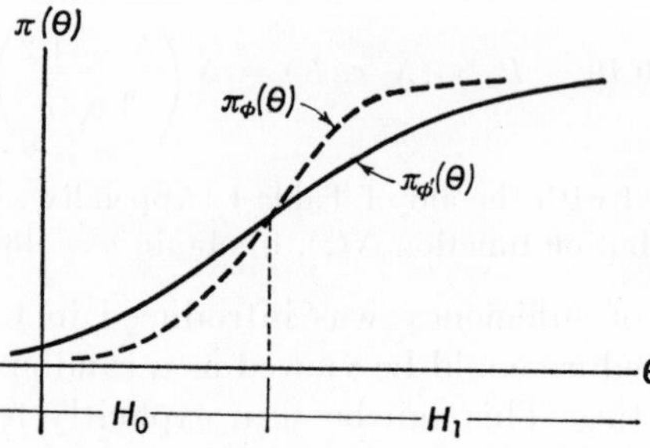

Figure 7–11

A procedure d was called *unbiased* if for all θ and θ',

$$E_\theta[\ell(\theta',d(\mathbf{X}))] \ge E_\theta[\ell(\theta,d(\mathbf{X}))].$$

In the present context this would imply that if θ is in H_0, and θ' is in H_0,

$$E_\theta[\ell(\theta',d(\mathbf{X}))] = a\pi(\theta) \ge E_\theta[\ell(\theta,d(\mathbf{X}))] = a\pi(\theta).$$

For θ in H_0 and θ' in H_1, it implies that

$$E_\theta[\ell(\theta',d(\mathbf{X}))] = b[1 - \pi(\theta)] \ge E_\theta[\ell(\theta,d(\mathbf{X}))] = a\pi(\theta).$$

The first of these conditions is not a restriction, and so for θ in H_0,

$$b[1 - \pi(\theta)] \ge a\pi(\theta).$$

Similarly, for θ in H_1, unbiasedness requires that

$$a\pi(\theta) \ge b[1 - \pi(\theta)].$$

That is, it must be that

$$\pi(\theta) \le \frac{b}{a+b}, \quad \text{for } \theta \text{ in } H_0,$$

$$\pi(\theta) \ge \frac{b}{a+b}, \quad \text{for } \theta \text{ in } H_1.$$

The power function must therefore be smaller for any θ in H_0 than for any θ in H_1. This last condition is usually taken as the definition of an unbiased test; if it is fulfilled, then there are losses a and b such that $b/(a+b)$ is an upper bound for $\pi(\theta)$ on H_0 and a lower bound for $\pi(\theta)$ on H_1, in which case the general definition of an unbiased procedure is fulfilled.

PROBLEMS

7–12. Determine and sketch the power function of the test that calls for action B when no successes or three successes occur in three independent trials of a Bernoulli experiment. For what choice of H_0 and H_1 would this test be unbiased?

7–13. Consider a test with critical region $\bar{X} > K$, where $\bar{X}$ is the mean of a random sample from a normal population with standard deviation 10. Select K and the sample size n so that the probability of the critical region is 0.05 when $\mu = 100$ and 0.98 when $\mu = 110$. Sketch the power function of the test. For what H_0 and H_1 is the test suited?

7–14. A lot contains ten articles. To choose between accepting and rejecting the lot, a sample of four is drawn (without replacement). If more than one defective is found, the lot is rejected, but otherwise it is accepted. Determine the operating characteristic function of the test.

7–15. A test concerning the variance of a normal population has the critical region $s_x^2 > K$, where s_x^2 is the variance of a random sample of size 100. Use the asymptotic normality of the sample variance to determine K and the power function given that the power is 0.98 at $\sigma^2 = 0.05$.

7–16. Show that the test $\bar{X} > 1$ in Example 7–9 is consistent.

7.2.3 Uniformly Most Powerful Tests. In the case of simple H_0 and H_1, a test was called most powerful among the class of tests having no larger α's if it had maximum power for H_1. When H_1 is composite, the power for H_1 depends on which state of H_1 is true; consequently a test that is most powerful for certain states of H_1 may not be so for others. A test that is most powerful for each simple hypothesis in H_1 (for a given α) is called *uniformly most powerful* for simple H_0 against composite H_1.

Example 7–11. In testing $\mu = \mu_0$ against $\mu > \mu_0$ in a normal population with given variance, it was seen in Example 7–7 that against any single μ which exceeds μ_0, the test $\bar{X} > K$ is most powerful, K being determined so that the level of the test is α:

$$P_{\mu_0}(\bar{X} > K) = \alpha.$$

But then for each $\mu > \mu_0$,

$$P_{\mu}(\bar{X} > K) \geq P_{\mu}(C^*),$$

where C^* is any other test of level not exceeding α. Hence, $\bar{X} > K$ is uniformly most powerful against the composite $\mu > \mu_0$.

Next suppose that H_0 and H_1 are both composite. Let the critical region C have size

$$\alpha = \sup_{H_0} \pi_C(\theta).$$

The test defined by C is said to be *uniformly most powerful* with respect to the class of tests $\phi(X)$ with no larger levels:

$$\sup_{H_0} \pi_\phi(\theta) \leq \alpha,$$

provided

$$\pi_\phi(\theta) \leq \pi_C(\theta), \text{ for all } \theta \text{ in } H_1.$$

A uniformly most powerful test can sometimes be found by locating a θ_0 such that for the simple hypothesis $\theta = \theta_0$, a region C is uniformly most powerful on H_1, and such that the power function of C at any other θ in H_0 is less than or equal to the power at θ_0.

Example 7–12. As in Example 7–11, consider testing $\mu \leq \mu_0$ against $\mu > \mu_0$ in a normal population with given variance. The power function of the test $\bar{X} > K$ is

$$\pi(\mu) = P(\bar{X} > K) = N\left(\frac{\mu - K}{\sigma/\sqrt{n}}\right) \leq N\left(\frac{\mu_0 - K}{\sigma/\sqrt{n}}\right) = \alpha,$$

for any $\mu \leq \mu_0$. Then, since $\bar{X} > K$ is uniformly most powerful among all tests whose type I error at μ_0 does not exceed α, it is automatically uniformly most powerful among the smaller class of tests whose power is no larger than

$$\sup_{H_0} \pi(\mu) = \pi(\mu_0) = \alpha$$

at *every* μ in H_0.

A uniformly most powerful test is necessarily an unbiased test. For, given a uniformly most powerful test of level α, the randomized test defined by $\phi(\mathbf{X}) \equiv \alpha$ for all $\mathbf{X}$ has level α and has power α at each θ in H_1. The UMP test must therefore have power at least α at each θ in H_1, and so is unbiased.

A uniformly most powerful test need not always exist. Perhaps the most common situation of this kind is that of testing $\theta_1 \leq \theta \leq \theta_2$ against the alternative: $\theta > \theta_2$ or $\theta < \theta_1$. Such problems are discussed in §7.2.5.

7.2.4 Monotone Problems. When the possible states are indexed by a single real parameter, one can speak of monotone problems, as defined in §5.7. In order to have a monotone regret function for the hypothesis testing problem, the states in H_0 must lie all to one side of those in H_1. The losses $a(\theta)$ and $b(\theta)$ must be monotone functions, nondecreasing as θ moves away from H_1 and H_0, respectively. In particular, the regret function is monotone for constant losses a and b.

Suppose that the family $f(x;\theta)$ has a monotone likelihood ratio; that is, that there is a statistic $T = t(\mathbf{X})$ such that for $\theta > \theta'$, $f(\mathbf{X};\theta)/f(\mathbf{X};\theta')$ is a monotone increasing function of T. This means that the critical region

$$C: \quad \frac{f(\mathbf{X};\theta)}{f(\mathbf{X};\theta_0)} > \text{constant},$$

which is most powerful for θ_0 against any single $\theta > \theta_0$, is equivalent to the T region

$$C: \quad T > \text{constant}.$$

Now, because C is most powerful for any θ' against any particular $\theta'' > \theta'$, it is at least as powerful as the test $\phi(\mathbf{X}) \equiv \pi_C(\theta')$:

$$\pi_C(\theta'') \geq \pi_\phi(\theta'') = \pi_C(\theta').$$

That is, the power function of C is monotone nondecreasing. But then, as before, $T >$ constant is not only UMP for θ_0 versus $\theta > \theta_0$, it is also UMP for $\theta \leq \theta_0$ versus $\theta > \theta_0$.

In particular, if $\mathbf{X}$ has a distribution in the exponential family, with density

$$f(x;\theta) = B(\theta)\exp[Q(\theta)S(x)]h(x),$$

and if $Q(\theta)$ is monotone increasing, then the test $S(\mathbf{X}) >$ constant is UMP for $\theta \leq \theta_0$ against $\theta > \theta_0$. (Obvious modifications of the directions of the inequalities apply if Q is monotone decreasing, or for H_0 given by $\theta \geq \theta_0$.)

Example 7–13. It is desired to test $\tau \leq 2$ against $\tau > 2$, where τ is the mean life of a system whose time to failure has the negative exponential distribution, with density $(1/\tau)\exp(-x/\tau)$, $x > 0$. The joint density of a random sample $\mathbf{X}$ is

$$f(x;\tau) = \frac{1}{\tau^n}\exp\left[-\frac{1}{\tau}\sum x_i\right], \qquad x_i > 0.$$

Since $-1/\tau$ is a monotone increasing function of τ, the critical region $\sum X_i >$ constant is UMP for $\tau \leq 2$ against $\tau > 2$.

7.2.5 Two-Sided Alternatives. A common problem that is *not* monotone, and for which a uniformly most powerful test may fail to exist, is that defined by

$$\begin{cases} H_0: & \theta_1 \leq \theta \leq \theta_2 \\ H_1: & \theta < \theta_1 \quad \text{or} \quad \theta > \theta_2. \end{cases}$$

Example 7–14. Let X have a Bernoulli distribution with unknown p, and let $S = X_1 + \cdots + X_5$ denote the number of successes in five independent trials. To test $p = 0.5$ against $p \neq 0.5$, it would seem reasonable to reject $p = 0.5$ for values of S

that are either too small or too large. The test with critical region $S = 0, 1, 4,$ or 5 has the power function

$$\begin{aligned}\pi(p) &= P_p[S = 0, 1, 4, \text{ or } 5]\\ &= 1 - \binom{5}{2} p^2(1-p)^3 - \binom{5}{3} p^3(1-p)^2\\ &= \tfrac{3}{8} + 5(p-0.5)^2 - 10(p-0.5)^4.\end{aligned}$$

This is shown in Figure 7–12. It is symmetrical about $p = 0.5$ and has a minimum at that value of p. Since H_0 is a simple hypothesis, α is uniquely defined as $\pi(0.5) = 3/8$.

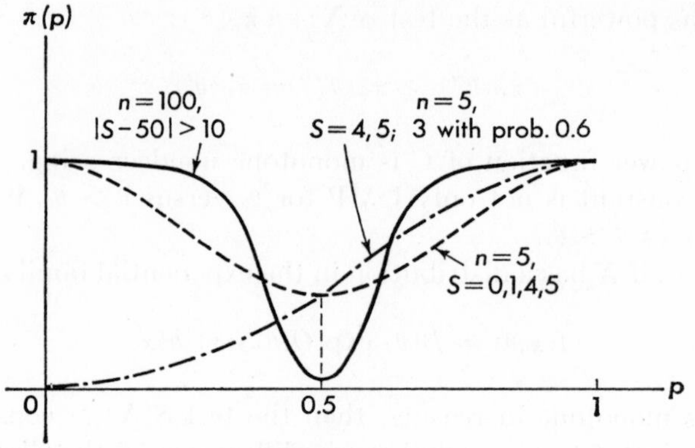

Figure 7–12

To see the effect of an increase in sample size, consider also the test under which H_0 is rejected if more than 60 or fewer than 40 successes occur in 100 independent trials. With this sample size, the sample sum S is approximately normal:

$$\begin{aligned}\pi(p) &= P_p(|S - 50| > 10)\\ &\doteq 1 - N\left(\frac{60.5 - 100p}{\sqrt{100pq}}\right) + N\left(\frac{39.5 - 100p}{\sqrt{100pq}}\right).\end{aligned}$$

The graph of this power function is also shown in Figure 7–12. The value of α is $\pi(0.5) = 0.036$.

The possibility that a uniformly most powerful test may not exist in the case of a simple H_0 and a two-sided alternative can be seen as follows: A UMP test is unbiased, and its power function therefore has a minimum at $H_0: \theta = \theta_0$. On the other hand, a most powerful test of θ_0 against θ_1 where $\theta_1 > \theta_0$ would have a power function that in general would be increasing as θ passes through θ_0. For some θ's just to the right of θ_0, it would exceed the power function with a minimum at θ_0. This excess power on one side of θ_0 is paid for in considerably less power on the other. The following example illustrates this point.

Example 7–15. Referring to Example 7–14, consider also the randomized test that calls for rejection of $p = 0.5$ when $S = 4$ or 5, and for rejection of $p = 0.5$ with probability 0.6 when $S = 3$, the statistic S again denoting the number of successes in three trials. The power function here is

$$\begin{aligned}\pi(p) &= 5p^4(1-p) + p^5 + (0.6)\,10p^3(1-p)^2 \\ &= p^3(p-2)(2p-3).\end{aligned}$$

The graph of this power function is shown in Figure 7–12 along with the power function corresponding to the rejection region $S = 0, 1, 4$, or 5. The randomization here was fixed up so that these two tests have the same α, but this one-sided test is more powerful than the symmetric one for $p > 0.5$. This extra power is achieved by sacrificing power on $p < 0.5$. At any rate, it is clear that the symmetric test is *not* UMP, although it is unbiased.

7.2.6 Likelihood Ratio Tests. In the case of simple H_0 and H_1 a likelihood ratio test (or modified maximum likelihood procedure) is most powerful. In the more general case of composite hypotheses, the maximum likelihood method does not guarantee a good test. (Indeed, examples have been constructed of maximum likelihood tests that are worse than acting in ignorance of the data.) Nevertheless, in many standard problems the method does give tests that have good characteristics, and it pays to consider the method.

As discussed in §7.1.3, the generalized maximum likelihood method consists in choosing the θ that maximizes the weighted likelihood function $w(\theta)L(\theta)$ and taking the action that would be correct if the maximizing θ were the true state of nature. This procedure applied to the testing of hypotheses is equivalent to determining the θ in H_0 that maximizes $w(\theta)L(\theta)$, determining the θ in H_1 that maximizes $w(\theta)L(\theta)$, and then acting as though that θ were true which gives the greater maximum. It is now assumed that the gain $w(\theta)$ is w_0 (a constant) for all θ in H_0 and w_1 (another constant) for all θ in H_1. With this assumption a critical region is defined to be the set of $\mathbf{X}$ such that

$$\sup_{\theta \text{ in } H_0} w_0 L(\theta) < \sup_{\theta \text{ in } H_1} w_1 L(\theta),$$

or

$$\lambda^* \equiv \frac{\sup_{H_0} L(\theta)}{\sup_{H_1} L(\theta)} < \text{constant}.$$

(The "sup" or smallest upper bound is used here because it will exist when the "max" does not; whereas if the maximum exists, it is equal to the "sup.")

The numerator in λ^* is thought of as the best "explanation" in H_0 of the observed result, and the denominator as the best explanation in H_1. If the ratio is large, a better explanation is found in H_0 than in H_1, and action A is taken; if the ratio is small, a better explanation is found in H_1, and action B is taken. Fixing the "constant" (deciding how large is "large") is again a matter of weighing the importance of the two types of errors.

In many instances it is convenient to alter the method slightly. Instead of λ^* one considers

$$\lambda = \frac{\sup_{H_0} L(\theta)}{\sup_{H_0+H_1} L(\theta)} < \text{constant}.$$

Observe that if $\lambda^* < 1$, then $\lambda = \lambda^*$, but if $\lambda^* \geq 1$, then $\lambda = 1$. The rejection region defined by $\lambda < K$ is exactly the same as that defined by $\lambda^* < K$, provided $K \leq 1$. In the problems in which we shall use the method, least upper bound over $H_0 + H_1$ will be the same as the least upper bound over H_1, so that $\lambda = \lambda^*$.

For random samples it is again convenient to work with the logarithm of the likelihood function and to use $-\log \lambda$, for which the critical region becomes $-\log \lambda >$ constant.

If a test is to be based on the statistic λ (or on $-\log \lambda$), it is necessary to know the distribution of λ. This is ordinarily very complicated, and it is useful to know that the asymptotic distribution of $-2 \log \lambda$ is asymptotically of the chi-square type (Table II, Appendix), to be discussed in detail in Chapter 8. The parameter of this chi-square distribution is the difference in the dimension of $H_0 + H_1$ and the dimension of H_0. (Cf. Reference [12], §7.1.3.)

Often the likelihood ratio test can be shown equivalent to a test involving a more natural or convenient statistic, whose distribution is known or readily derived. This is illstrated in the following example.

Example 7–16. Consider testing H_0: $\mu = \mu_0$ against H_1: $\mu \neq \mu_0$ in a normal population with given variance v. The likelihood function is

$$L(\mu) = (2\pi v)^{-n/2} \exp\left[\frac{-1}{2v}\sum(X_i - \mu)^2\right].$$

This is a maximum over all μ for $\hat{\mu} = \bar{X}$, the maximum likelihood estimate of μ, and so the denominator of λ is $L(\bar{X})$. The numerator is just $L(\mu_0)$, since H_0 consists of the single point μ_0. The ratio λ is then $L(\mu_0)/L(\bar{X})$, and

$$\begin{aligned}\log \lambda &= \log L(\mu_0) - \log L(\bar{X}) \\ &= -\frac{1}{2v}\{\Sigma(X_i - \mu_0)^2 - \Sigma(X_i - \bar{X})^2\} \\ &= -\frac{n}{2v}[\bar{X} - \mu_0{}^2].\end{aligned}$$

The critical region log $\lambda <$ constant is therefore equivalent to

$$|\bar{X} - \mu_0| > \text{constant},$$

which is intuitively very appealing. (Incidentally, under H_0, $-2 \log \lambda$ is not only *asymptotically* of the chi-square type, it *is* the square of a standard normal variable. This will be seen in Chapter 8 to be exactly of the chi-square type with one "degree of freedom.")

PROBLEMS

7–17. Consider a normal population with mean 0 and unknown variance v. For H_0: $v \leq 1$ against H_1: $v > 1$ determine a uniformly most powerful test based on a random sample of 25 observations, such that $\alpha = 0.05$. (Show that the population belongs to the exponential family, so that the UMP test can be deduced from that for the exponential family.)

7–18. Referring to Example 7–14, determine a test based on 100 observations with the same α as in that example but which is UMP against $p > 0.5$. Compare the power function of this test with that of the two-sided test in Example 7–14.

7–19. Construct the likelihood ratio test for $\theta = \theta_0$ against $\theta \neq \theta_0$ in the density $\theta \exp(-\theta x)$, $x > 0$, obtaining as the critical region: $\bar{X} \exp(-\theta_0 \bar{X}) <$ constant. Sketch the graph of this function of $\bar{X}$ and indicate the corresponding critical region in terms of $\bar{X}$. Is this symmetrical about the population mean corresponding to θ_0? (In practice, one would probably take symmetrical tails for the rejection region, even though the right and left boundaries would correspond to different values of λ, using the likelihood ratio notion only to justify the selection of a two-tailed critical region.)

7–20. Consider testing $p = 0.5$ against $p \neq 0.5$, using three independent observations on a Bernoulli variable. Construct the probability distribution of the statistic λ under H_0.

7–21. Discuss the likelihood ratio test for $v = v_0$ against $v \neq v_0$ in a normal population with given mean and variance v.

7.3 Sequential Tests

In testing a simple hypothesis against a simple alternative, the most powerful test was found to be given by a critical region of the form

$$\lambda_n = \frac{f_0(X_1, \ldots, X_n)}{f_1(X_1, \ldots, X_n)} < K,$$

where $f_0(x)$ and $f_1(x)$ are the joint density functions of the observations (or probability functions in the discrete case) corresponding to H_0 and H_1, respectively. Given any two of the four quantities α, β, n, and K, the other two are determined by the relations

$$\alpha = P_{H_0}(\lambda_n < K), \qquad \beta = P_{H_1}(\lambda_n \geq K).$$

In carrying out such a test, one picks, say, α and β, and determines from them values of n and K. He then gathers the data, using that n as the size of the sample, computes λ_n, and accepts or rejects H_0 according as $\lambda_n \geq K$ or $\lambda_n < K$. No provision is made to fulfill the natural desire to obtain more data when the nature of the sample is not sufficiently suggestive either of H_0 or of H_1 as to be really convincing. Nor, on the other hand, is there opportunity to cut the sampling short if a conclusion becomes obvious early in the process of obtaining the sample. Of course nothing really *prevents* one from doing these things—gathering more or less data than dictated by the choice of α and β according to how things go—but it must be recognized that doing them alters the test and makes the given error sizes meaningless.

A procedure of "double sampling" would be somewhat more satisfying. For such a plan there is chosen a preliminary sample size m with corresponding constants C and D, and a second sample size $n - m$ with corresponding constant K. The procedure is then to draw a sample of size m, compute λ_m, and

$$\begin{cases} \text{Accept } H_0, & \text{if } \lambda_m \geq D, \\ \text{Reject } H_0, & \text{if } \lambda_m \leq C, \\ \text{Draw a sample of size } n - m, & \text{if } C < \lambda_m < D. \end{cases}$$

If the second sample is called for, it is drawn, λ_n computed, and

$$\begin{cases} H_0 \text{ accepted}, & \text{if } \lambda_n \geq K, \\ H_0 \text{ rejected}, & \text{if } \lambda_n < K. \end{cases}$$

Such double sampling plans will not be examined here; charts and tables associated with such plans in the case of "acceptance sampling" (passing or rejecting lots on the basis of the number of defectives in samples) are available in *Sampling Inspection Tables*, by Dodge and Romig (Wiley).

The idea can clearly be extended to plans with more than two stages at each of which a decision is made to reject, to accept, or (except at the last stage) to continue sampling. Intuition leads one to suspect that with such multiple sampling schemes, he might be able to get away with less sampling than would be needed, using a test based on a fixed sample size. And such is usually the case.

Sequential sampling carries the idea a step further and calls for a computation and decision as each observation is obtained. In multiple sampling or in sequential sampling, the size of the sample ultimately required is not fixed; indeed, since it depends on the results of observation, it is a random variable. As such it has an expected value (finite or infinite), called the *average sample number* or ASN. This ASN, of course, depends on the hypothesis which is assumed to be correct in computing it. Generally the ASN turns out to be less than the size of sample required in a test of comparable sensitivity based on a test of fixed sample size.

For a treatment of sequential procedures in the framework of decision theory, reference is made to [2], Chapters 3, 9, and 10. There will be considered here only the Wald sequential likelihood ratio procedure and its operating characteristic, the study of its optimality and of optimal tests in general being beyond our scope. (Cf. Reference [2], §10.3 and §10.9.)

7.3.1 The Sequential Likelihood Ratio Test. A. Wald (in Reference [20]) first presented and systematically studied the following sequential test of a simple hypothesis $H_0: f_0(x)$ against a simple alternative $H_1: f_1(x)$. Numbers A and B are selected, with $A < B$, and after each in a sequence of independent observations the value of the likelihood ratio λ_n is computed:

$$\lambda_n = \frac{f_0(X_1, \ldots, X_n)}{f_1(X_1, \ldots, X_n)}.$$

The procedure is then defined by the following rule:

$$\begin{cases} \text{If } \lambda_n \leq A, \text{ reject } H_0; \\ \text{If } A < \lambda_n < B, \text{ obtain another observation;} \\ \text{If } \lambda_n \geq B, \text{ accept } H_0. \end{cases}$$

The samples to be considered will usually be random samples, in which case

$$\lambda_n = \prod_{i=1}^{n} \frac{f_0(X_i)}{f_1(X_i)}.$$

Since this likelihood ratio is a product, the logarithm is easier to work with, as in the case of the standard likelihood ratio test for fixed sample size. The inequality for continuing sampling can be written

$$\log A < \log \lambda_n < \log B,$$

inasmuch as the logarithm function is an increasing function. The test can be followed graphically as in Figure 7–13. The points $(n, \log \lambda_n)$ are plotted there for a typical sequence of observations, the points being connected by straight lines for ease in following the progress of the test. A decision is reached when the path crosses either the upper or the lower boundary, as indicated.

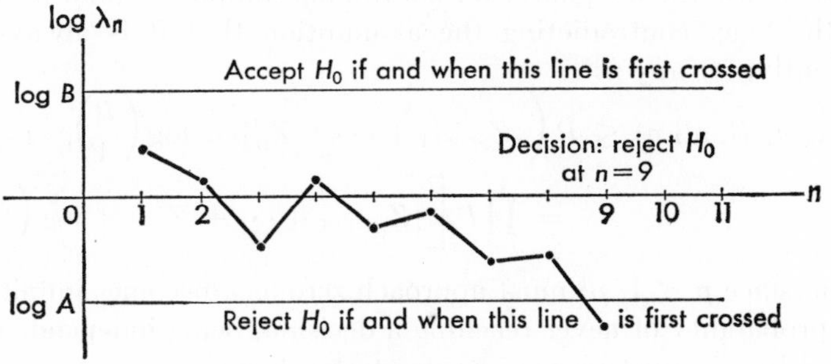

Figure 7–13

It is conceivable that the procedure as described might never terminate, but this contingency has probability zero, as will now be shown. Let

$$Z_i = \log\left[\frac{f_0(X_i)}{f_1(X_i)}\right]$$

for $i = 1, 2, \ldots$. This is a sequence of independent random variables because the X's are independent. Its partial sums are the logarithms of the likelihood ratios:

$$\log \lambda_n = Z_1 + \cdots + Z_n.$$

Now choose an integer r such that

$$\text{var}\,(Z_1 + \cdots + Z_r) = r\,\text{var}\,Z_i > \left[\log\left(\frac{B}{A}\right)\right]^2.$$

Then, since (by Problem 2–53) for any random variable Y with standard deviation $\sigma_Y > K$, $P(|Y| < K) < 1$, it follows that

$$p \equiv P\left(|Z_1 + \cdots + Z_r| < \left|\log\left(\frac{B}{A}\right)\right|\right) < 1.$$

Given any n that is a multiple of r, say, $n = kr$, the Z's that make up $\log \lambda_n$ are collected into groups of r each:

$$\log \lambda_{kr} = (Z_1 + \cdots + Z_r) + \cdots + (Z_{kr-r+1} + \cdots + Z_{kr}).$$

No group of r Z's in this sum could exceed $|\log(B/A)|$ in magnitude if all λ_n fall within the range for continuing sampling, that is, if the sampling process never terminates. For, if the "continue-sampling" inequality were always satisfied, and if the jth group of Z's were greater than $\log(B/A)$, then

$$\log \lambda_{jr} = \log \lambda_{jr-r} + (Z_{jr-r+1} + \cdots + Z_{jr}) > \log A + \log\left(\frac{B}{A}\right) = \log B.$$

On the other hand, if the jth group were less than $-\log(B/A)$, then

$$\log \lambda_{jr} < \log B - \log\left(\frac{B}{A}\right) = \log A.$$

So, in either case the inequality for continuing sampling would be violated at the (jr)th stage, contradicting the assumption that it is always satisfied. Consequently, for any k:

$$\begin{aligned} P(A < \lambda_n < B, \text{all } n) &\le P\left(|Z_{jr-r+1} + \cdots + Z_{jr}| < \log\left(\frac{B}{A}\right),\quad j = 1, \ldots, k\right) \\ &= \prod_{j=1}^{k} P\left[|Z_{jr-r+1} + \cdots + Z_{jr}| < \log\left(\frac{B}{A}\right)\right] = p^k. \end{aligned}$$

But, then, since $p < 1$, p^k must approach zero as k becomes infinite. Therefore the probability of never reaching a decision, being independent of k and dominated by p^k, must be zero, as was to be shown.

Error sizes for the sequential likelihood ratio test are easily expressed, formally, in terms of the numbers A and B which define the test:

$$\begin{cases} \alpha = P_{H_0}(\lambda_1 \leq A) + P_{H_0}(A < \lambda_1 < B \text{ and } \lambda_2 \leq A) + \cdots; \\ \beta = P_{H_1}(\lambda_1 \geq B) + P_{H_1}(A < \lambda_1 < B \text{ and } \lambda_2 \geq B) + \cdots. \end{cases}$$

Although easy to write down, these expressions are by no means easily computed. Moreover, one could not hope to *solve* these equations for A and B in terms of given α and β, despite the desirability of being able to do so in setting up a test to meet specified protection. Another approach is fortunately more fruitful. To present this approach, we must resort to a suggestive argument, the actual substantiation being beyond our scope.

It has been seen that with probability 1, sample sequences terminate after a finite number of observations. These terminating sequences can be considered in two sets: S, the set of finite sample sequences that terminate in a decision to reject H_0; and T, the set of such sequences that terminate in a decision to accept H_0. Thus, $P(S) + P(T) = 1$, and

$$\alpha = P_{H_0}(S) = \sum_S f_0(\mathbf{x}) \leq A \sum_S f_1(\mathbf{x}) = AP_{H_1}(S) = A(1 - \beta).$$

Similarly,

$$\beta = P_{H_1}(T) \leq \frac{1}{B} P_{H_0}(T) = \frac{1 - \alpha}{B}.$$

Thus lower limits have been found for A and $1/B$ to achieve a given degree of protection:

$$A \geq \frac{\alpha}{1 - \beta} \quad \text{and} \quad \frac{1}{B} \geq \frac{\beta}{1 - \alpha}.$$

(The catch in the above argument is that the "sums" used are not really sums, since the number of sequences in S or T is not necessarily countable, and that the f's are not probabilities in the continuous case.)

Since *in*equalities are obtained in this derivation simply because λ_n does not usually attain *exactly* the value A or the value B, the inequalities are almost equalities. Indeed, in practice, A and B are taken to be *equal* to $\alpha/(1 - \beta)$ and $(1 - \alpha)/\beta$, respectively. Doing so, of course, means that the test actually carried out has error sizes somewhat different from those specified. Let α' and β' denote the actual sizes of the type I and type II errors of the test defined by the limits $A = \alpha/(1 - \beta)$ and $B = (1 - \alpha)/\beta$. According to the above inequalities, then,

$$\frac{\beta'}{1 - \alpha'} \leq \frac{1}{B} = \frac{\beta}{1 - \alpha} \quad \text{and} \quad \frac{\alpha'}{1 - \beta'} \leq A = \frac{\alpha}{1 - \beta}.$$

Multiplying these through to eliminate denominators and adding the results, one obtains

$$\alpha' + \beta' \leq \alpha + \beta.$$

It could not be, therefore, that *both* $\alpha' > \alpha$ and $\beta' > \beta$; so, at most one of the error sizes will be larger than specified when using the approximate formulas for A and B. Further, it follows from the inequalities obtained that for small α and β,

$$\alpha' \leq \frac{\alpha'}{1-\beta'} \leq \frac{\alpha}{1-\beta} \doteq \alpha(1+\beta),$$

and

$$\beta' \leq \frac{\beta'}{1-\alpha'} \leq \frac{\beta}{1-\alpha} \doteq \beta(1+\alpha).$$

Thus the one error size that does increase does not increase by more than a factor of about $(1 + \alpha)$ or $(1 + \beta)$. For example, if both α and β are 0.05, the α' and β' actually achieved by using A and B as specified above are bounded by about 0.0525.

Although using the approximate values of A and B results in error sizes that are not appreciably larger than specified, it is possible that they are *smaller* than specified. This would only be disturbing in the sense that the statistician could get away with less sampling and still be within the desired α and β. This effect should be as slight as is the increase in α and β, since both are caused by the discontinuity of the sample number necessary to reach a decision. If one could imagine a continuous sample number, the formulas for A and B would be correct. Wald shows (in Reference [20], pages 65–69) that the change in sample size is at most slight; in certain common cases it amounts to at most one or two in small samples and around 1 or 2 per cent in larger samples.

Example 7–17. It is desired to test H_0: $p = 0.5$ against H_1: $p = 0.2$ in a Bernoulli population, using a sequential test with $\alpha = 0.1$ and $\beta = 0.2$. The likelihood ratio after n independent observations is

$$\lambda_n = \frac{(0.5)^f(0.5)^{n-f}}{(0.2)^f(0.8)^{n-f}},$$

where f is the number of successes in n independent trials. Thus,

$$\lambda_{n+1} = \begin{cases} (5/2)\lambda_n, & \text{if success occurs in the } (n+1)\text{st trial,} \\ (5/8)\lambda_n, & \text{if failure occurs in the } (n+1)\text{st trial.} \end{cases}$$

A success raises the value of λ_n, and a failure lowers it. If λ_n falls below the value $A = 0.1/(1 - 0.2) = 1/8$, H_0 is rejected in favor of the lower value $p = 0.2$. If λ_n reaches $B = (1 - 0.1)/0.2 = 9/2$, H_0 is accepted. Otherwise sampling is continued.

If a sequence of observations turns out to be $T, H, H, T, H, T, H, H, T, T, \ldots$, the corresponding λ_n's are

$$0.625,\ 1.54,\ 3.91,\ 2.44,\ 6.10,\ 3.82,\ 9.53,\ 23.8,\ 14.9,\ 9.30,\ \ldots.$$

At the fifth observation H_0 is accepted and the sampling stopped (despite the return at the sixth observation to the region between A and B, since this observation would not have been obtained in practice).

PROBLEMS

7–22. Construct and carry out a test for $p = 1/3$ against the alternative $p = 1/2$, where p is the probability that a die falls 1 or 2.

7–23. Construct the sequential likelihood ratio test for $\mu = \mu_0$ against $\mu = \mu_1$ in a normal population with given variance σ^2. Express the inequality for continuing sampling in terms of the sample sum, and determine the nature of the curves bounding the region in which this inequality is satisfied. Sketch these curves for the particular values $\mu_0 = 4$, $\mu_1 = 6$, $\alpha = \beta = 0.05$, and $\sigma^2 = 9$. Observe the change in the curves corresponding to a change in error sizes to $\alpha = 0.1$ and $\beta = 0.2$, and also corresponding to a change in μ_1 to 10. What are the curves like if one considers the sample *mean* instead of the sample sum?

7–24. Discuss the sequential likelihood ratio test for the problem of choosing between two specific values of the parameter θ in the negative exponential density $\theta \exp(-\theta x)$, $x > 0$.

7.3.2 Average Sample Number. The sample size needed to reach a decision in a sequential or a multiple sampling plan is a random variable. The distribution of this random variable depends on the distribution that actually obtains during the sampling process; that is, on the actual state of nature. In this section we study the expected value of this random sample size in the case of the sequential likelihood ratio test for choosing between two states of nature corresponding to two specific values of a population parameter.

It is observed first that the expected value of $\log \lambda_n$ is rather easily approximated, if n denotes the sample number at which a decision is reached. For, when a decision is reached, λ_n is approximately equal either to A or to B, according as the decision is to reject or to accept H_0. Thus, λ_n is approximately a Bernoulli variable with values A or B, and

$$\begin{aligned} E(\log \lambda_n) &\doteq (\log A)\ P(\log \lambda_n = \log A) + (\log B)\ P(\log \lambda_n = \log B) \\ &= (\log A)\ P(\text{reject } H_0) + (\log B)\ P(\text{accept } H_0). \end{aligned}$$

In this expression the expectation and the probabilities are all computed assuming a given state of nature. For example, if H_0 is true,

$$E(\log \lambda_n) = (\log A)\alpha + (\log B)(1 - \alpha).$$

This apparently tangential computation of $E(\log \lambda_n)$ is actually relevant, for we have seen that $\log \lambda_n$ is a sum of identically distributed variables:

$$\log \lambda_n = Z_1 + Z_2 + \cdots + Z_n,$$

where Z_i is the logarithm of the likelihood ration for the ith observation:

$$Z_i = \log \left[\frac{f_0(X_i)}{f_1(X_i)}\right].$$

If n were fixed, it would immediately follow that $E(\log \lambda_n) = nE(Z_i)$. But n is random, and it might reasonably be expected that changing n to $E(n)$ would salvage this relationship; one could then *solve* for $E(n)$. This hope is not in vain, as will be shown next.

Suppose for the moment that $Z, Z_1, Z_2, \ldots$ are independent, identically distributed random variables, and that n is a random variable with values $1, 2, \ldots$ such that the event $\{n \geq i\}$ is independent of any events involving $Z_i, Z_{i+1}, \ldots$. Let Y_i be 0 if $n < i$ and 1 if $n \geq i$. Then

$$E(Z_1 + \cdots + Z_n) = E\left\{\sum_{i=1}^{\infty} Y_i Z_i\right\} = \sum_{i=1}^{\infty} E(Y_i Z_i)$$

$$= E(Z) \sum_{i=1}^{\infty} E(Y_i).$$

provided the interchange of summation and expectation operations is valid. Now

$$\sum_{i=1}^{\infty} E(Y_i) = \sum_{i=1}^{\infty} P(n \geq i) = \sum_{i=1}^{\infty} \sum_{j=i}^{\infty} P(n = j)$$

$$= \sum_{j=1}^{\infty} \sum_{i=1}^{j} P(n = j) = E(n),$$

which gives the desired expression for $E(\log \lambda_n)$, namely, $E(Z)E(n)$. The interchange employed *is* valid if the following series is convergent:

$$\sum_{i=1}^{\infty} |E(Y_i Z_i)| \leq \sum_{i=1}^{\infty} E(|Y_i|)E(|Z_i|) = E(|Z|)E(n).$$

It will be convergent if $E(|Z|)$ is finite and $E(n)$ is finite. It is known that all moments of n are finite (C. Stein, "A note on cumulative sums," *Annals of Math. Stat.* (17) 1946, pages 489–499); and so, if $E(|Z|)$ is finite, the average sample number is

$$E(n) = \frac{E(\log \lambda_n)}{E(Z)} \doteq \frac{(\log A)\ P(\text{rej. H}_0) + (\log B)\ P(\text{acc. H}_0)}{E(\log [f_0(X)/f_1(X)])}.$$

All probabilities and expectations in this formula are, of course, computed on the basis of a common, assumed state of nature. This state is either H_0 or H_1 (with corresponding densities f_0 and f_1) if it is really these simple hypotheses that are being tested. If H_0 and H_1 correspond to conveniently chosen values of a parameter θ, say, θ_0 or θ_1, one might well be interested in the ASN for values of θ other than just those two corresponding to H_0 and H_1.

In general, then, the ASN is a function of θ. One of the annoying features of the sequential likelihood ratio test, when it is used to test a one-sided situation such as $H_0: \theta \leq \theta'$ against $H_1: \theta > \theta'$ is the following: The test would be set up by choosing θ_0 in H_0 (that is, $\theta_0 < \theta'$) and θ_1 in H_1 ($\theta_1 > \theta'$), the zone between θ_0 and θ_1 being an "indifference zone." And yet, if the actual population is described by a θ in this indifference zone (that is, near θ'), the ASN tends to be largest. Thus the test tends to take longer to reach a decision when θ is near the point θ' where there is perhaps little concern as to which way the test turns out. It is certainly intuitively reasonable that it should not take so long to discover that a population is violently of one kind or the other as it does to discover which kind it is when it is near the borderline. What is annoying, then, is that in the borderline case, wrong decisions are likely not to be very costly anyway, and it seems a shame to invest the effort or cost in the large sample required to reach a decision. This matter has received study, and ways of altering the sequential testing procedure have been proposed, but these are not taken up here.

Although the ASN is finite, it can be very large in any single experiment—much larger than one might want to tolerate. In practice, one establishes a bound n_0 beyond which he refuses to go; if no decision is reached by the (n_0)th stage, sampling is stopped anyway, with H_0 accepted if $\lambda_{n_0} > 1$ and rejected if $\lambda_{n_0} < 1$. The effect of such a modification, which surely alters the error sizes of the test, has been studied in Reference [20], and is slight if n_0 is large.

Graphically, the stopping rule just described amounts to altering the decision lines from those shown in Figure 7–13 to those shown in Figure 7–14.

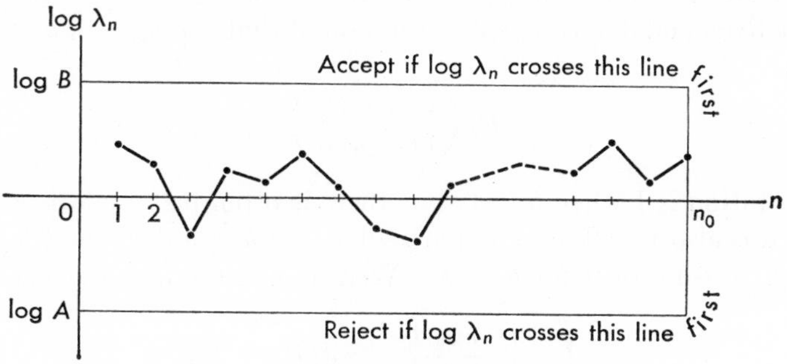

Figure 7–14

Example 7–18. Consider testing $\mu = 0$ against $\mu = 1$ in a normal population with unit variance, using $\alpha = \beta = 0.01$. Then $A = 1/99$ and $B = 99$. If H_0 is the actual state of nature,

$$E(Z_n) = (\alpha) \log \left(\frac{1}{99}\right) + (1 - \alpha) \log 99.$$

To compute $E(Z)$, first compute Z:

$$Z = \log \left[\frac{f_0(X)}{f_1(X)}\right] = \log \left\{\frac{\exp(-X^2/2)}{\exp[-(X-1)^2/2]}\right\} = \frac{1}{2} - X,$$

and obtain $E(Z) = E(1/2 - X) = 1/2$ under H_0. The ASN is then

$$E(n) = \frac{E(Z_n)}{E(Z)} \doteq 9$$

under H_0. [Note that since the logarithm in Z is a natural logarithm, natural logs must be used in computing $E(Z_n)$.]

Similarly, under H_1 it is found that $E(Z) = -1/2$, and

$$E(Z_n) = (1 - \beta) \log \left(\frac{1}{99}\right) + \beta \log 99.$$

Again $E(n)$ is about 9. It is of interest to see that in a best test of fixed sample size, for the same error sizes $\alpha = \beta = 0.01$, n turns out to be about 22, considerably greater than the ASN of 9 for the sequential test.

7.3.3 The Operating Characteristic. The operating characteristic (probability of accepting H_0) of a sequential likelihood ratio test can be obtained, somewhat indirectly, as follows: Consider a test defined by given constants A and B, with $A < 1 < B$, to test $H_0\colon f_0(x)$ against $H_1\colon f_1(x)$. If one considered f_0 and f_1 to be the only possible states of nature, there would be little point to an "operating characteristic." However, the population is frequently one of a family $f(x;\theta)$, with $f_1(x) = f(x;\theta_1)$ and $f_0(x) = f(x;\theta_0)$ used as convenient states for defining the test, the real interest lying in distinguishing $\theta \leq \theta^*$ from $\theta > \theta^*$. In such a case one *is* interested in the operating characteristic as a function of all possible values of θ.

Let θ be fixed and determine as a function of that θ a value of h other than 0 for which

$$E_\theta\left(\left\{\frac{f(x;\theta_0)}{f(x;\theta_1)}\right\}^h\right) = 1.$$

This expectation is 1 when $h = 0$, but there is often just one other value of h for which it is also 1. Observe in particular that $h = 1$ does the trick if $\theta = \theta_1$ and that $h = -1$ works for $\theta = \theta_0$. Writing out the above expected value,

$$\int_{-\infty}^{\infty} \left\{\frac{f(x;\theta_0)}{f(x;\theta_1)}\right\}^h f(x;\theta)\, dx = 1,$$

we see that the integrand function can be thought of as a density function:

$$f^*(x;\theta) = \left\{\frac{f(x;\theta_0)}{f(x;\theta_1)}\right\}^h f(x;\theta).$$

Consider now the auxiliary problem of testing

$$H^*: f^*(x;\theta) \quad \text{against} \quad H: f(x;\theta),$$

which are simple hypotheses for fixed h and θ. Using the constants A^h and B^h in the inequality for continuing sampling in testing H^* against H:

$$A^h < \prod \frac{f^*(X_i;\theta)}{f(X_i;\theta)} = \prod \left\{\frac{f(X_i;\theta_0)}{f(X_i;\theta_1)}\right\}^h < B^h,$$

we find, upon taking the $1/h$ power (assume $h > 0$), the same inequality as that used for continuing sampling in testing H_0 against H_1. (If $h < 0$, the lower boundary could have been taken as B^h and the upper one as A^h, with the same net result.) Consequently

$$P_\theta(\text{accept } H_0) = P_\theta(\text{accept } H^*) = P_H(\text{accept } H^*) = \beta^*,$$

where β^* is the size of the type II error for the auxiliary problem. This can be expressed in terms of the cease-sampling limits for the *auxiliary* problem:

$$OC(\theta) = P_\theta(\text{accept } H_0) = \beta^* = \frac{1 - A^h}{B^h - A^h}.$$

Thus the operating characteristic is expressed in terms of h. But θ, too, depends on h, and these two relations define the operating characteristic curve $OC(\theta)$ parametrically: Each choice of h determines a θ and a value of $P(\text{accept } H_0)$, that is, a point on the OC curve.

The expression relating h and θ does not define θ for $h = 0$, since it is automatically satisfied for any θ; however, the point on the operating characteristic curve corresponding to $h = 0$ can be determined by passing to the limit as $h \to 0$. Similarly, the expression for $OC(\theta)$ is indeterminate for $h = 0$, but it can be evaluated by means of l'Hospital's rule, with the result

$$OC(\theta)\big|_{h=0} = \frac{-\log A}{\log B - \log A}.$$

The values $h = 1$ and $h = -1$ have been seen to correspond to $\theta = \theta_1$ and $\theta = \theta_0$, respectively, and of course $OC(\theta_1) = \beta$, and $OC(\theta_0) = 1 - \alpha$. As $h \to \infty$, the operating characteristic clearly tends to 0, and as $h \to -\infty$, it tends to 1. Thus there are five convenient points, which frequently suffice to furnish an adequate sketch of the OC curve:

h	$-\infty$	-1	0	1	∞
θ		θ_0		θ_1	
OC	1	$1 - \alpha$	$\dfrac{-\log A}{\log B - \log A}$	β	0

Example 7–19. Consider testing $p = p_0$ against $p = p_1 > p_0$ in a Bernoulli population. Here $f(x;p) = p^x(1-p)^{1-x}$, $x = 0, 1$, so that

$$E_p\left\{\left[\frac{f(X;p_0)}{f(X;p_1)}\right]^h\right\} = \left[\frac{(1-p_0)}{(1-p_1)}\right]^h(1-p) + \left(\frac{p_0}{p_1}\right)^h p.$$

Setting this equal to 1 and solving for p, we obtain

$$p = \frac{1 - [(1-p_0)/(1-p_1)]^h}{(p_0/p_1)^h - [(1-p_0)/(1-p_1)]^h}.$$

As $h \to 0$, this becomes

$$\frac{-\log\,[(1-p_0)/(1-p_1)]}{\log\,(p_0/p_1) - \log\,[(1-p_0)/(1-p_1)]}.$$

Taking the particular values $p_0 = 0.5$, $p_1 = 0.9$, $\alpha = \beta = 0.05$, we obtain these points on the operating characteristic curve (shown in Figure 7–15):

h	$-\infty$	-1	0	1	∞
p	0	0.5	0.733	0.9	1
OC	1	0.95	0.5	0.05	0

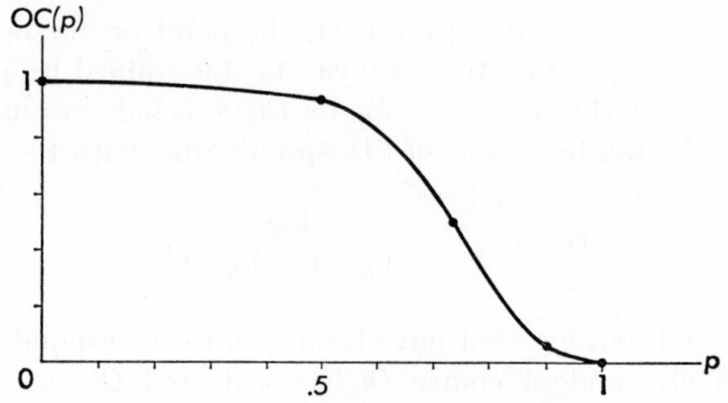

Figure 7–15

PROBLEMS

7–25. Determine the ASN under H_0 and H_1 for Problem 7–23, using $\alpha = 0.01$ and $\beta = 0.05$.

7–26. Determine the ASN under H_0 for Problem 7–22, using $\alpha = \beta = 0.05$.

7–27. Consider testing θ_0 against $\theta_1 < \theta_0$, as in Problem 7–24. Determine the operating characteristic and ASN curves as functions of θ. Use $\theta_0 = 2$ and $\theta_1 = 1$, with $\alpha = 0.05$ and $\beta = 0.10$.

7–28. Determine the relation between h and μ in a sequential likelihood ratio test for the mean μ of a normal population with given variance. Sketch the *OC* curve in a particular case.

8/Some Distribution Theory

Before taking up the detailed study of the various particular statistical problems of the following chapters, we pause to present some needed mathematical computations. It has already been seen that a discussion of statistical procedures requires a knowledge of the distributions of the statistics used, and it is some of these distributions that are to be derived in this chapter.

In general the distribution of a statistic depends on the distribution of the population from which the sample is taken. Some of the computations of this chapter yield distributions of certain statistics in the important case in which the sample is taken from a normal population. Others simply give expressions in terms of an unspecified population distribution.

8.1 Order Statistics and Related Distributions

The joint distribution of the ordered observations in a random sample from a continuous population with density $f(x)$ will now be derived.

Let $\boldsymbol{\nu}$ denote one of the $n!$ possible permutations of the integers 1, 2, ..., n:

$$\boldsymbol{\nu} = (\nu_1, \nu_2, \ldots, \nu_n).$$

Each of these permutations defines a region of sample points $\boldsymbol{x}$:

$$R_\nu = \{\text{set of } \boldsymbol{x} \text{ such that } x_{\nu_1} < x_{\nu_2} < \cdots < x_{\nu_n}\}.$$

Let R denote the region R_ν in which $\boldsymbol{\nu}$ is the particular permutation $(1,2,\ldots,n)$:

$$R = \{\text{set of } \boldsymbol{x} \text{ such that } x_1 < x_2 < \cdots < x_n\}.$$

The $n!$ sets $\{R_\nu\}$ together make up the space of sample points $\boldsymbol{x}$, except for the boundaries, which have probability zero under the assumption of a continuous population.

Each permutation $\boldsymbol{\nu}$ defines a linear transformation $\boldsymbol{y} = T_\nu \boldsymbol{x}$, where $y_k = x_{\nu_k}$. Such a transformation has the property that det $T_\nu = \pm 1$, and the inverse is just another permutation transformation. Under such a transformation the region R_ν of points $\boldsymbol{x}$ such that $x_{\nu_1} < \cdots < x_{\nu_n}$ is carried into the region R of points $\boldsymbol{y}$ such that $y_1 < \cdots < y_n$. Further, since the joint density of the random sample $\boldsymbol{X}$ is a symmetric function of the coordinates of $\boldsymbol{x}$, it is unchanged by $\boldsymbol{y} = T_\nu \boldsymbol{x}$:

$$f(\boldsymbol{x}) \equiv \Pi f(x_k) = \Pi f(x_{\nu_k}) = \Pi f(y_k) = f(\boldsymbol{y}).$$

Therefore,

$$P(R_\nu) = \int_{R_\nu} f(\boldsymbol{x})\, d\boldsymbol{x} = \int_R f(\boldsymbol{y})\, d\boldsymbol{y} = P(R),$$

which means that each R_ν has the probability $1/n!$.

Consider now the order statistic

$$\boldsymbol{Y} = t(X_1,\cdots,X_n) = (X_{(1)},\cdots,X_{(n)})$$

This function $t(\boldsymbol{x})$ carries each $\boldsymbol{x}$ into a point in R, and so induces a measure in R which is the probability distribution of the ordered observations. This distribution has zero density outside R, but for any set A in R, the probability that $\boldsymbol{Y}$ is in A can be computed. Let A_ν denote the set of those points in R_ν whose coordinates when ordered yield a point in A. Then

$$P(\boldsymbol{Y} \text{ in } A) = P(\boldsymbol{X} \text{ in } \sum_\nu A_\nu) = \sum_\nu P(\boldsymbol{X} \text{ in } A_\nu) = \sum_\nu \int_{A_\nu} f(\boldsymbol{x})\, d\boldsymbol{x}$$

$$= \sum_\nu \int_A f(\boldsymbol{y})\, d\boldsymbol{y} = n!P(\boldsymbol{X} \text{ in } A).$$

Therefore,

$$f_{\boldsymbol{Y}}(\boldsymbol{y}) = \begin{cases} n!\, f(\boldsymbol{y}), & \text{if } \boldsymbol{y} \text{ is in } R, \\ 0, & \text{otherwise.} \end{cases}$$

That is, the joint density is essentially unchanged in R, being only multiplied by $n!$ to take into account the requirement that the total probability be 1.

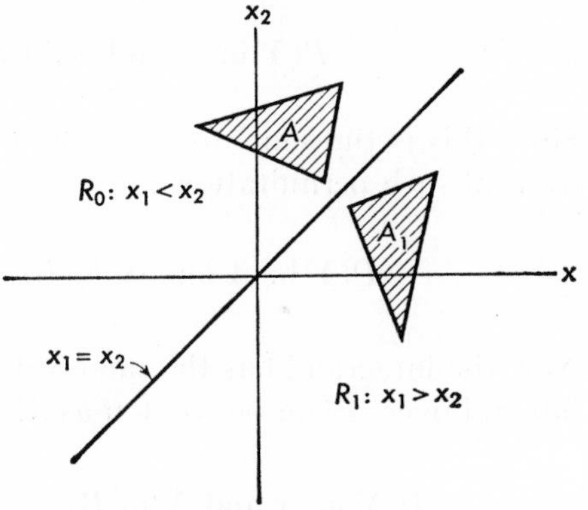

Figure 8–1

Example 8–1. It is perhaps helpful to write out some of these relations for the simple case $n = 2$. There are just two permutations of (1,2); call them *0*: (1,2), and *1*: (2,1). The regions $R_0 = R$ and R_1 are the half-planes in which $x_1 < x_2$ and $x_2 < x_1$, respectively, as shown in Figure 8–1. Shown also is a set A of points in R and the set A_1 of points in R_1 which are carried into A under the transformation $y_1 = x_2$, $y_2 = x_1$. The order statistic $(X_{(1)},X_{(2)})$ has "values" only in R and takes each point (where $x_1 \neq x_2$) into a point in R. For instance, both (4,1) and (1,4) would be carried into (1,4), which is in R; and

$$P[(X_{(1)},X_{(2)}) \text{ in } A] = P(\boldsymbol{X} \text{ in } A_0) + P(\boldsymbol{X} \text{ in } A_1)$$

$$= 2P(\boldsymbol{X} \text{ in } A_0) = \int_{A_0} 2f(x_1)f(x_2)\, dx_1\, dx_2.$$

The joint density of $X_{(1)}$ and $X_{(2)}$ is zero at any point in R_1 and is just twice the joint density of X_1 and X_2 in R_0.

8.1.1 Sufficiency of the Order Statistic. It will be shown next that the conditional distribution in the space of sample points, given the order statistic, does not depend on the population distribution. Specifically, it will be shown that this conditional distribution assigns probability $1/n!$ to each of the $n!$ sample points whose coordinates are permutations of a given point in R. This would then mean that for any family of densities $f(x;\theta)$ of the continuous type, the order statistic based on a random sample is a sufficient statistic.

Consider a set B of sample points and a set A of possible "values" of the order statistic $\mathbf{Y}$; that is, A lies in R, the set of $\mathbf{x}$ such that $x_1 < \cdots < x_n$. Then

$$\begin{aligned} P(\mathbf{Y} \text{ in } A \text{ and } \mathbf{X} \text{ in } B) &= P(\mathbf{X} \text{ in } \tilde{A}B) \\ &= \int_{\tilde{A}} \phi_B(\mathbf{x}) f(\mathbf{x})\, d\mathbf{x}, \end{aligned}$$

where $\tilde{A}$ denotes the union of all A_ν as defined earlier, and $\phi_B(x)$ is the "indicator function" of B, the function that is 1 for $\mathbf{x}$ in B and 0 for $\mathbf{x}$ in $\bar{B}$. Since a permutation transformation T_ν would not alter the set $\tilde{A}$ (which already contains all permutations of any point in it), such a change of variable in the integral above yields

$$P(\mathbf{Y} \text{ in } A \text{ and } \mathbf{X} \text{ in } B) = \int_{\tilde{A}} \phi_B(T_\nu \mathbf{x}) f(\mathbf{x})\, d\mathbf{x}.$$

Since this is the same for each permutation ν, it is the same as the average over all such permutations:

$$P(\mathbf{Y} \text{ in } A \text{ and } \mathbf{X} \text{ in } B) = \int_{\tilde{A}} \frac{1}{n!} \sum_\nu \phi_B(T_\nu \mathbf{x}) f(\mathbf{x})\, d\mathbf{x}.$$

Now the integrand has the same values in any A_ν as in A, and therefore this integral over $\tilde{A}$ can be written as $n!$ times the integral over A:

$$P(\mathbf{Y} \text{ in } A \text{ and } \mathbf{X} \text{ in } B) = \int_A \left[\frac{1}{n!} \sum_\nu \phi_B(T_\nu \mathbf{y})\right] n! f(\mathbf{y})\, d\mathbf{y}.$$

This can be interpreted as the integral with respect to the distribution of $\mathbf{Y}$ of the conditional probability of $\mathbf{X}$ given $\mathbf{Y} = \mathbf{y}$. That is,

$$P(\mathbf{X} \text{ in } B \,|\, \mathbf{Y} = \mathbf{y}) = \frac{1}{n!} \sum_\nu \phi_B(T_\nu \mathbf{y}).$$

Since $\phi_B(\mathbf{x}) = 1$ for $\mathbf{x}$ in B and zero otherwise, the sum here is just the number of permutations of $\mathbf{y}$ that are in B. In particular, if B is a single point that is one of the permutations of $\mathbf{y}$ in R, the conditional probability is $1/n!$, as claimed. That is, the various permutations that could have led to a given order statistic are equally likely to have been the original sample point.

8.1.2 Distributions of the Components of the Order Statistic. It is possible to derive (in principle) the distribution of the individual components of the order statistic or the joint distribution of several of them from the distribution of the complete order statistic. Consider instead the following more elementary approach. The distribution function of the kth smallest observation is

$$P[X_{(k)} \leq y] = P(k \text{ or more of the } n \text{ observations are } \leq y)$$
$$= \sum_{j=k}^{n} \binom{n}{j} [F(y)]^j [1 - F(y)]^{n-j},$$

the individual terms in this sum being probabilities that in n independent trials precisely j result in an observation that does not exceed y. [The individual trials are of the Bernoulli type with $p = F(y)$.]

The density function of $X_{(k)}$ can be obtained from the above distribution function by differentiating with respect to y:

$$f_{X_{(k)}}(y) = \sum_{j=k}^{n} \binom{n}{j} j[F(y)]^{j-1} f(y)[1 - F(y)]^{n-j}$$
$$+ \sum_{j=k}^{n} \binom{n}{j} (n - j)[F(y)]^j [1 - F(y)]^{n-j-1}[-f(y)]$$
$$= nf(y)\left\{ \sum_{j=k}^{n} \binom{n-1}{j-1} [F(y)]^{j-1}[1 - F(y)]^{n-j} \right.$$
$$\left. - \sum_{j=k}^{n-1} \binom{n-1}{j} [F(y)]^j [1 - F(y)]^{n-j-1} \right\}.$$

Letting $j = m - 1$ in the second sum results in terms identical with those in the first sum, but from $m = k + 1$ to n. These then cancel except for the term $j = k$ in the first sum:

$$f_{X_{(k)}}(y) = nf(y)\binom{n-1}{k-1}[F(y)]^{k-1}[1 - F(y)]^{n-k}.$$

Putting $k = n$, one obtains the distribution and density functions for the largest observation $X_{(n)}$:

$$F_{X_{(n)}}(y) = [F(y)]^n, \qquad f_{X_{(n)}}(y) = n[F(y)]^{n-1} f(y),$$

and putting $k = 1$, the distribution and density functions of $X_{(1)}$:

$$F_{X_{(1)}}(y) = 1 - [1 - F(y)]^n, \qquad f_{X_{(1)}}(y) = n[1 - F(y)]^{n-1} f(y).$$

8.1.3 Joint Distribution of the Smallest and Largest. With a little more work one can obtain the joint distribution of any pair of the ordered observations. The extra work is perhaps a minimum in the case of the smallest and largest observations, whose joint distribution function is

$$F_{X_{(1)},\, X_{(n)}}(u,v) = P[X_{(1)} \le u \text{ and } X_{(n)} \le v].$$

To evaluate this, first observe that

$$\{X_{(n)} \le v\} = \{X_{(1)} \le u \text{ and } X_{(n)} \le v\} + \{X_{(1)} > u \text{ and } X_{(n)} \le v\}.$$

The events on the right are disjoint, so the probability of the sum is the sum of the probabilities; transposing the second term, then, one obtains

$$\begin{aligned} F_{X_{(1)},X_{(n)}}(u,v) &= P[X_{(n)} \le v] - P[X_{(1)} > u \text{ and } X_{(n)} \le v] \\ &= [F(v)]^n - P(\text{all } X_i \text{ lie between } u \text{ and } v) \\ &= \begin{cases} [F(v)]^n - [F(v) - F(u)]^n, & \text{if } u \le v, \\ [F(v)]^n, & \text{if } u > v. \end{cases} \end{aligned}$$

The joint density is found by differentiation:

$$f_{X_{(1)},X_{(n)}}(u,v) = \begin{cases} n(n-1)[F(v) - F(u)]^{n-2} f(u) f(v), & \text{if } u \le v, \\ 0, & \text{if } u > v. \end{cases}$$

The distributions of statistics based on the smallest and largest observations can be obtained by using this joint density function. For instance, the average

$$A = \tfrac{1}{2}[X_{(1)} + X_{(n)}]$$

is sometimes useful in location problems. Its distribution function is

$$\begin{aligned} F_A(x) &= P(A \le x) = P[X_{(1)} + X_{(n)} \le 2x] \\ &= \int_R \int f(u,v)\, du\, dv, \end{aligned}$$

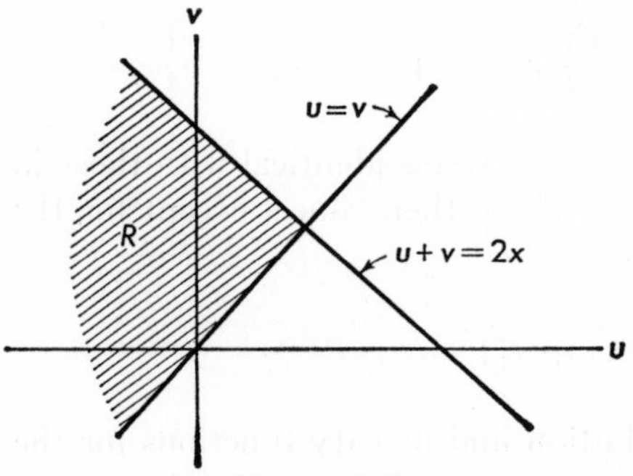

Figure 8–2

where R denotes the region (Figure 8–2) in the uv plane defined by the inequalities $u + v \le 2x$ and $u \le v$, and $f(u,v)$ denotes the joint density of $X_{(1)}$ and $X_{(n)}$. Making the change of variable $u = s$ and $v = t - s$, we obtain

$$F_A(x) = \int_{-\infty}^{2x} \int_{-\infty}^{t/2} f(s, t-s)\, ds\, dt.$$

The derivative with respect to x, which appears only in the upper limit of the outer integral, is the inner integral evaluated at $t = 2x$ times the derivative of $2x$ with respect to x:

$$\begin{aligned} f_A(x) &= 2\int_{-\infty}^{x} f(s, 2x - s)\, ds, \\ &= 2n(n-1)\int_{-\infty}^{x} [F(2x - s) - F(s)]^{n-2} f(s) f(2x - s)\, ds. \end{aligned}$$

Example 8–2. Let X be uniformly distributed on $[a,b]$. Then for $x < a$, the $f(s)$ in the above integral for $f_A(x)$ vanishes, since $s < x$. For $x > b$, $2x - s > x > b$ when $s < x$, and therefore $f(2x - s)$ vanishes. So, for $x < a$ or $x > b$, the density $f_A(x)$ is zero. For x on $[a,b]$, it is soon discovered that different calculations are required in the left and right halves of the interval.

For $a < x < (a + b)/2$, one has $a < s < x < b$ and also $a < x < 2x - s < a + b - s < b$. Thus, both s and $2x - s$ are on the interval where the uniform density is $1/(b - a)$, and where the cumulative distribution function is $(x - a)/(b - a)$. Consequently, for these x's:

$$f_A(x) = \frac{2n(n-1)}{(b-a)^2}\int_a^x \left[\frac{2x - s - a}{b - a} - \frac{s - a}{b - a}\right]^{n-2} ds$$

$$= \frac{n2^{n-1}}{(b-a)^n}(x - a)^{n-1}.$$

On the interval $(a + b)/2 < x < b$, one finds $2x - b > a$, which means that the s-integral really starts at $2x - b$ instead of at a, $f(2x - s)$ being zero for $2x - s > b$ or $s < 2x - b$. Further, on the interval $2x - b < s < x$ over which the s-integral is now seen to extend, one has $b > 2x - s > x > (a + b)/2$ and $a < 2x - b < s < x < b$, so that both s and $2x - s$ are on the interval where $F(x) = (x - a)/(b - a)$. Hence,

$$f_A(x) = \frac{2n(n-1)}{(b-a)^n}\int_{2x-b}^x \left[\frac{2x - s - a}{b - a} - \frac{s - a}{b - a}\right]^{n-2} ds$$

$$= \frac{n2^{n-1}}{(b-a)^n}(b - x)^{n-1}.$$

This is the reflection about the midpoint of the interval $[a,b]$ of the earlier formula for the left-hand half.

PROBLEMS

8–1. Compute the expected values of the smallest, the largest, and the average of the smallest and largest observations in a random sample of size n from a population uniform on $[a,b]$.

8–2. Compute the covariance of the smallest and largest observations of a random sample of size n from a uniform distribution on $[0,1]$.

8–3. Compute the variance of the average of the smallest and largest observations in a random sample of size n from a population uniform on $[a,b]$.

8–4. Consider a random sample of four observations from a uniform distribution on $[0,1]$. From the joint distribution of the ordered observations obtain the joint density function of the smallest and next smallest observations by integrating out the unwanted variables. Check to see that your result is a density function.

8–5. Compute the expected value of the second smallest observation in Problem 8–4.

8.1.4 The Sample Range. The sample range, $R = X_{(n)} - X_{(1)}$, can also be treated using the joint distribution of the smallest and largest observations. Its distribution function is

$$F_R(r) = P[X_{(n)} - X_{(1)} \le r] = \int_S\int f(u,v)\, du\, dv,$$

where $f(u,v)$ is the joint density as before, and S is the region in the uv plane defined by $0 < v - u < r$. Then

$$F_R(r) = \int_{-\infty}^{\infty} \int_{u}^{u+r} f(u,v)\,dv\,du,$$

and the density function is the derivative of this with respect to r:

$$f_R(r) = \int_{-\infty}^{\infty} f(u,u+r)\,du$$

$$= n(n-1)\int_{-\infty}^{\infty} [F(u+r) - F(u)]^{n-2} f(u)f(u+r)\,du,$$

which is valid for $r > 0$. If $r < 0$, both $F_R(r)$ and $f_R(r)$ are zero.

Example 8–3. Consider again the uniform distribution on $[a,b]$. Since the density function vanishes outside $[a,b]$, the product $f(u)f(u+r)$ vanishes outside $[a,b-r]$. On this latter interval both $f(u)$ and $f(u+r)$ are equal to $1/(b-a)$, and

$$F(u+r) - F(u) = \int_{u}^{u+r} \frac{1}{b-a}\,du = \frac{r}{b-a}.$$

Hence,

$$f_R(r) = \frac{n(n-1)}{(b-a)^n} r^{n-2}(b-r-a), \quad \text{for } 0 < r < b-a.$$

Example 8–4. Consider a normal population with mean μ and variance σ^2. Although in general the choice of population parameter values would affect the distribution of the sample range, one might expect that in the normal case (in which the choice of population mean does not affect the dispersion) the range distribution would not depend on μ. Not only is this so, but the dependence on σ is especially simple. Instead of R, consider $W = R/\sigma$, whose density function is

$$f_W(w) = \sigma f_R(\sigma w).$$

Putting the normal density function into the expression for the density function of the sample range and making two substitutions of the usual type, $y = (x - \mu)/\sigma$, one obtains

$$f_W(w) = \frac{n(n-1)}{(2\pi)^{n/2}} \int_{-\infty}^{\infty} e^{-[y^2+(y+w)^2]/2} \left\{\int_{y}^{y+w} e^{-v^2/2}\,dv\right\}^{n-2} dy.$$

Since this is independent of μ and σ, a single table suffices for the distribution of W, for each sample size. (Table V, Appendix).

8.1.5 The Transformation $F(X)$. Let X again be continuous with distribution function $F(x)$, and let x_u denote the maximum of the possible inverses $F^{-1}(u)$. Then, if $U = F(X)$ and if $0 \le u \le 1$,

$$F_U(u) = P[F(X) \le u] = P(X \le x_u) = F(x_u) = u.$$

For $u < 0$, $F_U(u) = 0$, and for $u > 1$, $F_U(u) = 1$. Thus U is uniformly distributed on $[0,1]$.

Now let each of the ordered observations in a random sample from X be transformed in this way: $U_i = F(X_{(i)})$, yielding new random variables $(U_1,\ldots,U_n)$. The Jacobian of this transformation is

$$\frac{\partial(u_1, \ldots, u_n)}{\partial(y_1, \ldots, y_n)} = f(y_1)\cdots f(y_n),$$

and so the joint density of $(U_1,\ldots,U_n)$ is

$$f_U(u) = \begin{cases} n!, & \text{if } 0 < u_1 < u_2 < \cdots < u_n < 1 \\ 0, & \text{otherwise.} \end{cases}$$

That is, $(U_1,\ldots,U_n)$ is a set of ordered observations from a population that is uniform on [0,1].

The distribution function of the sample $(X_1,\cdots,X_n)$ is

$$F_n(x) = \frac{k}{n}, \quad \text{for } X_{(k)} \le x < X_{(k+1)}.$$

But then, since $F(x)$ is monotonic,

$$F_n(F^{-1}(u)) = \frac{k}{n}, \quad \text{if } F(X_{(k)}) \le F(x) < F(X_{(k+1)}) \text{ or } U_k \le u < U_{k+1}.$$

This is just the distribution function of the sample from the uniform population whose order statistic is $(U_1,\cdots,U_n)$; call this $F_n{}^*(u)$. This fact is useful in showing that a statistic of the form

$$\int_{-\infty}^{\infty} G[F_n(x),F(x)]\, dF(x),$$

to be encountered in Chapter 9, has a distribution independent of $F(x)$. For, making the change of variable $y = F(x)$, the integral becomes

$$\int_0^1 G[F_n{}^*(u),u]\, du.$$

The random variable $F(X_{(k)})$ is the area under the population density to the left of the kth smallest observation. Its distribution is just the distribution of the kth smallest observation from a population that is uniform on [0,1]; the density of this distribution can be found in §8.1.2, putting $F(y)$ there equal to y:

$$f_{U_k}(u) = n\binom{n-1}{k-1}u^{k-1}(1-u)^{n-k},$$

for $0 < u < 1$. From this one can readily compute

$$E(U_k) = \int_0^1 n\binom{n-1}{k-1}u^k(1-u)^{n-k}\, du = \frac{k}{n+1},$$

using the integration formula given in Example 5–20, page 184.

The area between two successive ordered observations is then found to have the expected value:

$$E[F(X_{(k)}) - F(X_{(k-1)})] = E(U_k - U_{k-1}) = \frac{k}{n+1} - \frac{k-1}{n+1} = \frac{1}{n+1}.$$

That is, the expected area under the population density curve between two successive ordered observations is $1/(n+1)$; the ordered observations thus tend to divide the area under the density curve into $n+1$ equal areas.

The quantity $Z = U_n - U_1 = F(X_{(n)}) - F(X_{(1)})$ is used in construction of "tolerance intervals." It is the area under the population density curve between the smallest and largest observations in a random sample. The joint density of (U_1, U_n) was found in §8.1.3 to be (writing it for a uniform population)

$$f(u,v) = n(n-1)(v-u)^{n-2}, \quad \text{for } v > u.$$

Using this, one obtains for $0 < z < 1$:

$$\begin{aligned} F_Z(z) &= P(U_n - U_1 \le z) \\ &= \iint_{0<v-u<z} n(n-1)(v-u)^{n-2}\,du\,dv \\ &= \int_0^z \int_0^v n(n-1)(v-u)^{n-2} du\,dv + \int_z^1 \int_{v-z}^v n(n-1)(v-u)^{n-2} du\,dv. \end{aligned}$$

The density of Z is the derivative of this, namely,

$$f_Z(z) = n(n-1)(1-z)\,z^{n-2}, \quad \text{for } 0 < z < 1.$$

This is independent of the population distribution function $F(x)$.

Example 8-5. Suppose that it is desired to find a sample size n such that at least 99 per cent of a certain population will lie, with probability 0.95, between the smallest and largest sample observations. That is, n is to be chosen so that

$$\begin{aligned} 0.95 &= P[F(X_{(n)}) - F(X_{(1)}) > 0.99] \\ &= P(U_n - U_1 > 0.99) = n(n-1)\int_{0.99}^1 (1-z)z^{n-2}\,dz \\ &= 1 - (0.99)^{n-1}(0.01n + 0.99). \end{aligned}$$

This yields an n of about 475. [Note $(0.99)^{n-1} \doteq e^{-0.01(n-1)}$.] In about 95 per cent of samples of size 475, the extreme values of the sample will include 99 per cent of the population, or more.

8.1.6 The Sample Percentiles. Unless np is an integer, there is a unique $100p$th percentile of the sample distribution function of a sample of size n. It is, to be specific, the kth smallest observation $X_{(k)}$, where $k = [np] + 1$, the quantity $[np]$ denoting the greatest integer not exceeding np. If np is an integer, the 100pth percentile is not uniquely defined and can be taken to be any value between $X_{(np)}$ and $X_{(np+1)}$. When the percentile is uniquely defined, it is one of the ordered observations whose density function has been given in §8.1.2 in terms of the population density. It is shown in Reference [4], page 367 ff., that the *asymptotic* distribution is normal with mean x_p, the corresponding population percentile, and variance

$$\frac{1}{[f(x_p)]^2}\frac{p(1-p)}{n},$$

where $f(x)$ is the population density function, assumed to have a continuous derivative in the neighborhood of x_p.

Example 8–6. The median of a sample is the sample 50th percentile. The asymptotic normal distribution of the sample median then has $x_{0.5}$, the population median, as its expected value, and the variance is $[4nf^2(x_{0.5})]^{-1}$. If the population is normal (μ,σ^2), the sample median is asymptotically normal $(\mu, \pi\sigma^2/2n)$, since then

$$f(x_{0.5}) = f(\mu) = \frac{1}{\sqrt{2\pi}\,\sigma}\exp\left[-\frac{1}{2\sigma^2}(\mu-\mu)^2\right] = \frac{1}{\sqrt{2\pi}\,\sigma}.$$

PROBLEMS

8–6. Compute the expected value and variance of the distribution of the range of a random sample from a uniform population.

8–7. Carry out the changes of variable suggested in Example 8–4 to determine the density of R/σ.

8–8. Compute the variance of U_k.

8–9. Compute the probability that the smallest and largest observations will include between them 99 per cent of the population distribution for a sample of size two.

8–10. Given the following joint density function of U_r and U_s, where $r < s$, $u < v$:

$$f(u,v) = \frac{n!}{(r-1)!(s-r-1)!(n-s)!}u^{r-1}(v-u)^{s-r-1}(1-v)^{n-s},$$

determine the probability that at least 95 per cent of a probability distribution falls between the second smallest and second largest of 200 observations in a random sample.

8.2 Distributions Related to Normal Populations. Statistical problems involving normal populations have been intensively and extensively treated for many years. This is perhaps partly because normal models have been found very useful in many applications and partly because the mathematical form of the normal density function lends itself to explicit, detailed development. As a result, procedures for normal problems have come to be considered as "standard" procedures with which new procedures are compared. This section is devoted to the development of some of the distribution theory for sampling from normal populations.

8.2.1 The Gamma and Beta Functions. In evaluating certain constants, it will be convenient to have the notation

$$\Gamma(t) = \int_0^\infty e^{-x}x^{t-1}\,dx.$$

The value of this definite integral, when it converges, depends on the parameter t. As a function of this parameter the integral is called the *gamma function*. This integral is an improper integral—the range of integration is infinite, and the integrand is discontinuous at $x = 0$ if $t < 1$. It can be verified, however, that the integral is convergent for $t > 0$. (The domain of definition of the gamma function is sometimes extended to other values of t but not by means of the above integral; we shall not require this extension.)

One interesting property of the gamma function is that it can be considered as a "factorial" function—its value at a positive integer is a factorial. To see how this comes about, integrate by parts (recalling that t is a positive real number):

$$\Gamma(t) = \int_0^\infty e^{-x}x^{t-1}\,dx = \left.\frac{e^{-x}x^t}{t}\right|_0^\infty + \int_0^\infty \frac{x^t}{t}e^{-x}\,dx$$
$$= 0 + \frac{1}{t}\Gamma(t+1),$$

or

$$\Gamma(t+1) = t\Gamma(t).$$

By carrying out the integration for $t = 1$, it is easily seen that $\Gamma(1) = 1$, and then for any positive integer n:

$$\begin{aligned}\Gamma(n+1) &= n\Gamma(n) = n(n-1)\Gamma(n-1)\\ &= \cdots = n(n-1)\cdots3\cdot2\cdot1\cdot\Gamma(1) = n!.\end{aligned}$$

Other integral formulas involving $\Gamma(t)$ are obtained by change of variable in the integral. In particular, these will be useful:

$$\int_0^\infty e^{-ax}x^{t-1}\,dx = \frac{1}{a^t}\Gamma(t), \qquad a > 0,$$

and

$$\int_0^\infty x^{2t-1}e^{-x^2/2}\,dx = 2^{t-1}\Gamma(t).$$

Example 8–7. Even-order moments of a normal distribution can be expressed in terms of gamma functions. For, if X has the standard normal distribution,

$$\begin{aligned}E(X^{2k}) &= \frac{1}{\sqrt{2\pi}}\int_{-\infty}^\infty x^{2k}e^{-x^2/2}\,dx\\ &= \sqrt{\frac{2}{\pi}}\int_0^\infty x^{2k}e^{-x^2/2}\,dx = \frac{2^k}{\sqrt{\pi}}\Gamma\left(k+\frac{1}{2}\right),\end{aligned}$$

the last expression obtained either from a substitution $x^2/2 = u$ or from the formula given above. In particular, with $k = 0$:

$$1 = E(X^0) = \frac{1}{\sqrt{\pi}}\Gamma\left(\frac{1}{2}\right) \quad \text{or} \quad \Gamma\left(\frac{1}{2}\right) = \sqrt{\pi}.$$

From this, by successive application of $\Gamma(t+1) = t\Gamma(t)$, it follows that

$$\Gamma\left(k + \frac{1}{2}\right) = (2k-1)(2k-3)\cdots 5 \cdot 3 \cdot 1 \frac{\sqrt{\pi}}{2^k},$$

whence

$$E(X^{2k}) = (2k-1)(2k-3)\cdots 5 \cdot 3 \cdot 1.$$

The "beta function" arises in considering the product of two gamma functions (using the form involving $e^{-x^2/2}$):

$$\begin{aligned}\Gamma(s)\Gamma(t) &= \int_0^\infty \int_0^\infty \left(\frac{u^2}{2}\right)^{s-1}\left(\frac{v^2}{2}\right)^{t-1} e^{-(u^2+v^2)/2} uv\, du\, dv \\ &= \int_0^{\pi/2}\int_0^\infty \left(\frac{r^2}{2}\right)^{s+t-1} 2(\cos\theta)^{2s-1}(\sin\theta)^{2t-1} e^{-r^2/2} r\, dr\, d\theta \\ &= \int_0^\infty w^{s+t-1}e^{-w}dw \int_0^{\pi/2} 2(\cos\theta)^{2s-1}(\sin\theta)^{2t-1}d\theta \\ &= \Gamma(s+t)\mathrm{B}(s,t),\end{aligned}$$

where, then,

$$\begin{aligned}\mathrm{B}(s,t) &= 2\int_0^{\pi/2} \cos^{2s-1}\theta \sin^{2t-1}\theta\, d\theta = \frac{\Gamma(s)\Gamma(t)}{\Gamma(s+t)} \\ &= \int_0^1 x^{s-1}(1-x)^{t-1}\, dx = \int_0^1 (1-y)^{s-1}y^{t-1}dy = \mathrm{B}(t,s).\end{aligned}$$

This symmetric function of s and t is called the *beta function* (the B is a capital "beta").

Example 8–8. The derivation of $\mathrm{B}(s,t)$ given above is along the same lines as the calculation in §2.5.4 of the integral of the normal density, and the latter is a special case of the present formula, with $s = t = 1/2$:

$$\begin{aligned}\Gamma(\tfrac{1}{2})\Gamma(\tfrac{1}{2}) &= \mathrm{B}(\tfrac{1}{2},\tfrac{1}{2})\Gamma(1) \\ &= 2\int_0^{\pi/2} \cos^0\theta \sin^0\theta\, d\theta = \pi.\end{aligned}$$

Example 8–9. The following density function defines the *gamma distributions:*

$$f(x) = \frac{\lambda^\alpha}{\Gamma(\alpha)} x^{\alpha-1}e^{-\lambda x}, \quad \text{for } x > 0,$$

where α and λ are positive parameters. The characteristic function corresponding to the density is

$$\begin{aligned}\phi(t) &= \frac{\lambda^\alpha}{\Gamma(\alpha)}\int_0^\infty e^{-x(\lambda - it)}x^{\alpha-1}\, dx \\ &= \left(1 - \frac{it}{\lambda}\right)^{-\alpha}.\end{aligned}$$

Substitution of $t = 0$ shows, incidentally, that the proper multiplying constant was chosen in $f(x)$; its integral is 1. A special case already treated earlier, the negative exponential distribution, is obtained by setting $\alpha = 1$.

Example 8–10. The family of *beta distributions* is defined by the density

$$f(x) = \frac{1}{B(r,s)} x^{r-1}(1-x)^{s-1}, \quad \text{for } 0 < x < 1,$$

where r and s are positive parameters. The kth moment about zero is readily computed:

$$\frac{1}{B(r,s)} \int_0^1 x^k x^{r-1}(1-x)^{s-1}\, dx = \frac{B(r+k,s)}{B(r,s)}.$$

In particular, the expected value is obtained by setting $k = 1$:

$$\frac{B(r+1,s)}{B(r,s)} = \frac{r}{r+s}.$$

8.2.2 The Chi-Square Distribution. The chi-square distribution is defined as the distribution of a sum of squares of independent standard normal variables. Beginning with the special case of the square of a *single* standard normal variable, let X be normally distributed with zero mean and unit variance. The characteristic function of X^2 is then

$$E(e^{itX^2}) = \frac{1}{\sqrt{2\pi}} \int_{-\infty}^{\infty} \exp(itx^2 - x^2/2)\, dx = (1 - 2it)^{-1/2}.$$

From this can be obtained the distribution of a sum of squares of k independent standard normal variables $X_1, \ldots, X_k$:

$$\chi^2 = X_1^2 + X_2^2 + \cdots + X_k^2.$$

The characteristic function of the distribution of χ^2 is the kth power of the characteristic function of a single term:

$$\phi_{\chi^2}(t) = (1 - 2it)^{-k/2}.$$

This is the characteristic function of a gamma distribution (given in Example 8–9) with $\alpha = k/2$. Since the characteristic function uniquely defines the distribution, the density function of χ^2 is the corresponding gamma density:

$$f_{\chi^2}(x) = \frac{1}{2^{k/2}\Gamma(k/2)} x^{k/2-1} e^{-x/2}, \qquad x > 0.$$

A distribution with this density function is called a *chi-square distribution,* and the parameter k is called the number of *degrees of freedom* of the distribution.

The mean and variance of a chi-square distribution can be read from the series expansion for the characteristic function:

$$\phi_{\chi^2}(t) = (1 - 2it)^{-k/2} = 1 + k(it) + (k^2 + 2k)\frac{(it)^2}{2!} + \cdots.$$

They are as follows:

$$E(\chi^2) = k, \qquad \text{and} \qquad \operatorname{var} \chi^2 = 2k.$$

In Figure 8–3 are sketched the graphs of the chi-square density functions for several values of the parameter k. Observe that for $k = 1$, the density is infinite at $x = 0$, and that for $k = 2$, the density is that of the negative exponential distribution. As k increases, the mean shifts to the right and the variance increases. As $k \to \infty$, the *shape* approaches that of the normal density, for according to the central limit theorem the distribution of the sum of k independent, identically distributed variables is asymptotically normal. The mean and variance of this asymptotic distribution are, respectively, k and $2k$.

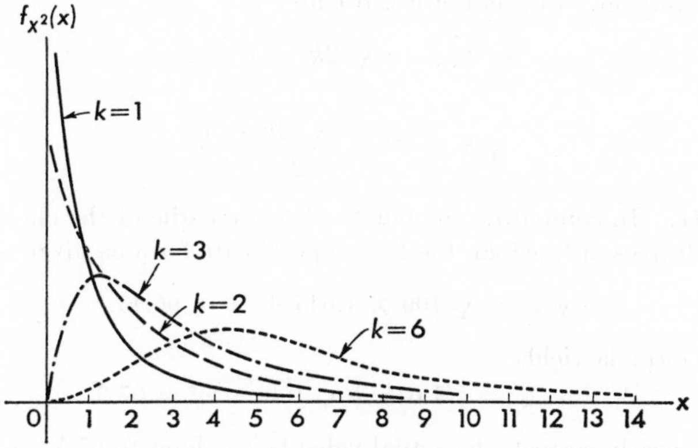

Figure 8–3

Tables of chi-square percentiles (like Table II, Appendix) take advantage of the fact that the distribution is asymptotically normal. Chi-square percentiles can be approximated, using normal percentiles as follows: For any given probability p,

$$p = P(\chi^2 < \chi_p^2) = P\left(\frac{\chi^2 - k}{\sqrt{2k}} < \frac{\chi_p^2 - k}{\sqrt{2k}}\right)$$

$$\doteq P\left(Z < \frac{\chi_p^2 - k}{\sqrt{2k}}\right),$$

where Z is standard normal. Thus, if z_p is the 100 pth percentile of the standard normal distribution,

$$z_p \doteq \frac{\chi_p^2 - k}{\sqrt{2k}} \quad \text{or} \quad \chi_p^2 \doteq \sqrt{2k}\, z_p + k.$$

A somewhat better approximation results from a modification using the variable

$$Y = \sqrt{2\chi^2} - \sqrt{2k - 1}.$$

This has the distribution function

$$P(Y < x) = P(\sqrt{2\chi^2} < \sqrt{2k-1} + x)$$
$$= P\left(\chi^2 < \frac{(2k-1)}{2} + x\sqrt{2k-1} + \frac{x_2}{2}\right)$$
$$\doteq P(\chi^2 < k + \sqrt{2k}\,x) = P\left(\frac{\chi^2 - k}{\sqrt{2k}} < x\right).$$

The approximation holds for large k, and Y has asymptotically the standard normal distribution. So, as before, for any p,

$$\sqrt{2\chi_p^2} - \sqrt{2k-1} \doteq z_p,$$

or finally

$$\chi_p^2 \doteq \frac{(z_p + \sqrt{2k-1})^2}{2}.$$

Example 8–11. In computing the ninety-fifth percentile of the chi-square distribution with 50 degrees of freedom, the first approximate formula given above yields

$$\chi_{0.95}^2 = \sqrt{100} \times 1.645 + 50 = 66.45.$$

The modified formula yields

$$\chi_{0.95}^2 = \tfrac{1}{2}(1.645 + \sqrt{100-1})^2 = 67.2,$$

which is more nearly correct, the actual value being closer to 67.5.

The chi-square distribution has many uses in normal problems, the major one in connection with the distribution of the variance of a normal population. For the present, consider the following possibly unrealistic example.

Example 8–12. Let X have a normal distribution whose mean μ is known. The maximum likelihood estimate of the variance σ^2 is

$$s^2 = \frac{1}{n}\sum(X_i - \mu)^2.$$

Observe, then, that

$$\frac{ns^2}{\sigma^2} = \sum\left(\frac{X_i - \mu}{\sigma}\right)^2,$$

a sum of squares of n independent, standard normal variables. Therefore, ns^2/σ^2 has the chi-square distribution with n degrees of freedom.

PROBLEMS

8–11. Compute the following:

(a) $\Gamma(6)$; (b) $\Gamma(11/2)$; (c) $B(2, 3/2)$;

(d) $\int_0^1 (-\log_e u)^{5/2} u\, du$ (Let $u = e^{-x}$); (e) $\int_0^\infty e^{-3x} x^4\, dx$;

(f) $\int_0^1 x^5(1-x)^9\, dx$; (g) $\int_0^{\pi/2} \cos^4\theta \sin^6\theta\, d\theta$.

8–12. Using a normal approximation, estimate:

(a) The eightieth percentile of a chi-square distribution with 60 degrees of freedom.

(b) $P(\chi^2 > 60)$, where χ^2 has the chi-square distribution with 50 degrees of freedom.

8–13. Suppose that Y/σ^2 has a chi-square distribution with ten degrees of freedom. Determine the density function, mean, and variance of Y.

8–14. Let Y have the distribution of Y in Problem 8–13, and determine a 90 per cent confidence interval for σ^2 based on a single observation of Y.

8–15. Let Y be defined as in Problem 8–14 and determine the power function of the test defined by the critical region $Y > 40$.

8–16. Show that the gamma distributions (and hence chi-square distributions) belong to the exponential family, and also that Y in Problem 8–14 has a distribution in this family.

8–17. Show that a sum of independent chi-square variables has again the chi-square distribution, the number of degrees of freedom of the sum being the sum of the numbers of degrees of freedom of the summands.

8–18. Show that if U is uniform on $[0,1]$, the variable $-2 \log U$ has a chi-square distribution with two degrees of freedom.

8–19. Show that if $\mathbf{X}$ is multivariate normal with mean vector $(0,\ldots,0)$ and convariance matrix $\mathbf{M}$, the quantity $\mathbf{X}'\mathbf{M}^{-1}\mathbf{X}$ has a chi-square distribution with n degrees of freedom. (Use the fact that $\mathbf{X}$ can be written as $\mathbf{AY}$, where $\mathbf{Y}$ has independent, standard normal components.)

8.2.3 A Partitioning Theorem. A kind of converse of the addition theorem for chi-square distributions given in Problem 8–17 will now be taken up. It is basically a theorem of algebra, and so it is not out of order to do some algebra first.

Consider the linear transformation from $(u_1,\ldots,u_n)$ to $(L_1,\ldots,L_m)$ defined by the matrix A:

$$\begin{cases} L_1 = a_{11}u_1 + \cdots + a_{1n}u_n \\ \quad\vdots \qquad\qquad\qquad \vdots \\ L_m = a_{m1}u_1 + \cdots + a_{mn}u_n \end{cases}$$

Let Q denote the sum of squares of these linear combinations of u's:

$$Q = L_1^2 + \cdots + L_m^2.$$

Let r denote the *rank* of the matrix L (that is, the number of rows in the largest nonsingular square submatrix of A). This number will be called the *number of degrees of freedom* of Q, and indicates the largest number of L's among which there is no linear relation. If it is assumed that the nonsingular matrix of rank r comes from the first r rows of A (which can be arranged by renumbering, if necessary), the quantities $L_{r+1}, \ldots, L_m$ can each be expressed as linear combinations of the first r L's in the sum of squares Q, resulting in a quadratic expression involving just the first r L's:

$$Q = \sum_{j=1}^{r} \sum_{i=1}^{r} b_{ij} L_i L_j = \boldsymbol{L}'\boldsymbol{B}\boldsymbol{L},$$

where $\boldsymbol{L}$ is the column matrix with entries $L_1, \ldots, L_r$ and B is the symmetric matrix of b_{ij}'s. Since Q is clearly positive definite (as a quadratic form in the L's), $\boldsymbol{B}$ is nonsingular.

Now, the crux of the whole argument is that Q is expressible as a sum of exactly r squares of linear combinations of the u's, and this fact is obtained as follows: As in the two-dimensional case in which a rotation of axes eliminates the cross-product term, so in the n-dimensional case there is an orthogonal transformation of coordinates that will eliminate the cross-product terms in a quadratic form, leaving only the squared terms. The matrix of the new form is diagonal and can be written as $\boldsymbol{P}'\boldsymbol{B}\boldsymbol{P}$, where $\boldsymbol{B}$ is the original matrix and $\boldsymbol{P}$ is the transformation matrix. Then, after elimination of the cross-product terms, a further change of scale along the various axes will give each squared term a coefficient 1, so that the matrix of the new form is the identity matrix. Combining the two transformations, then, it is possible to find a (nonsingular) matrix $\boldsymbol{P}$ with the property that $\boldsymbol{P}'\boldsymbol{B}\boldsymbol{P}$ is the identity matrix.[1]

With the matrix $\boldsymbol{P}$ determined in this way, so that $\boldsymbol{P}'\boldsymbol{B}\boldsymbol{P} = \boldsymbol{I}$, let $\boldsymbol{v} = \boldsymbol{P}^{-1}\boldsymbol{L}$, or $\boldsymbol{L} = \boldsymbol{P}\boldsymbol{v}$, and substitute this in Q:

$$Q = \boldsymbol{L}'\boldsymbol{B}\boldsymbol{L} = \boldsymbol{v}'\boldsymbol{P}'\boldsymbol{B}\boldsymbol{P}\boldsymbol{v} = \boldsymbol{v}'\boldsymbol{v} = v_1^2 + \cdots + v_r^2,$$

which represents Q as a sum of r linear combinations of u's, as was claimed to be possible. That is, the v's, being linear combinations of L's, are then linear combinations of the u's.

This result will now be applied. Suppose that $U_1, \ldots, U_n$ are independent, standard, normal random variables, and that

$$\sum_{i=1}^{n} U_i^2 = Q_1 + Q_2 + \cdots + Q_k,$$

where *each* Q_i is a sum of squares of linear combinations of the U's. Let r_i denote the number of degrees of freedom (rank), as defined for Q above, of the term Q_i. It is now known that Q_i is expressible as the sum of exactly r_i squares of linear combinations of U's:

$$\begin{cases} Q_1 = W_1^2 + \cdots + W_{r_1}^2 \\ Q_2 = W_{r_1+1}^2 + \cdots + W_{r_1+r_2}^2 \\ \cdot \end{cases}$$

[1]Cf. F. Hohn, *Elementary Matrix Algebra*, Macmillan, New York, 1958, pp. 228 ff.

where there are, all-in-all, $r_1 + r_2 + \cdots + r_k$ W's or linear combinations of U's involved. If, then, this sum of the ranks is n, one has

$$\sum_{i=1}^{n} U_i^2 = \boldsymbol{U}'\boldsymbol{U} = W_1^2 + \cdots + W_n^2 = \boldsymbol{W}'\boldsymbol{W}.$$

But, since each W_i is a linear combination of U's, $\boldsymbol{W} = \boldsymbol{CU}$; and

$$\boldsymbol{U}'\boldsymbol{U} = (\boldsymbol{CU})'(\boldsymbol{CU}) = \boldsymbol{U}'\boldsymbol{C}'\boldsymbol{CU}.$$

Clearly, $\boldsymbol{C}'\boldsymbol{C} = \boldsymbol{I}$, and since $\boldsymbol{C}$ is square and $\boldsymbol{C}^{-1} = \boldsymbol{C}'$, then also $\boldsymbol{CC}' = \boldsymbol{I}$. But, if $\boldsymbol{U}$ is multivariate normal with mean vector $(0,0,\ldots,0)$ and covariance matrix $\boldsymbol{I}$, $\boldsymbol{W} = \boldsymbol{CU}$ is multivariate normal, with mean vector $(0,0,\ldots,0)$ and covariance matrix $\boldsymbol{CIC}' = \boldsymbol{I}$. That is, $W_1, W_2, \ldots$, and W_n are independent, standard, normal variables, which means that $Q_1,\ldots Q_k$ are independent chi-square variables, with $r_1, \ldots, r_k$ degrees of freedom, respectively. In summary, then, we have "Cochran's theorem"[1]:

Let $U_1, \ldots, U_n$ be independent and normally distributed with means zero and unit standard deviations. Let

$$\sum_{i=1}^{n} U_i^2 = Q_1 + \cdots + Q_k,$$

where each Q_i is a sum of squares of linear combinations of $U_1, \ldots, U_n$, with r_i "degrees of freedom." Then, if

$$r_1 + \cdots + r_k = n,$$

the quantities $Q_1, \ldots, Q_k$ are independent chi-square variables with $r_1, \ldots, r_k$ degrees of freedom, respectively.

This result will be applied to situations in which $X_1, \ldots, X_n$ are independent, normal variables with $E(X_i) = \mu$ and var $X_i = \sigma^2$, and

$$\sum_{i=1}^{n} \left(\frac{X_i - \mu}{\sigma}\right)^2 = Q_1 + \cdots + Q_k,$$

each Q being a sum of squares of linear combinations of X's. Of course a linear combination

$$L_i = a_{i1}X_1 + \cdots + a_{in}X_n$$

is automatically a linear function of U's, with $U_i = (X_i - \mu)/\sigma$:

$$L_i = b_1U_1 + \cdots + b_nU_n + c$$

[1]Cochran's theorem is frequently given in a slightly different but equivalent form in which each Q is simply assumed to be a quadratic form in the $\boldsymbol{U}$'s: $Q = \boldsymbol{U}'\boldsymbol{BU}$, rather than a sum of squares of linear combinations. In the version given here the $\boldsymbol{B}$ is $\boldsymbol{A}'\boldsymbol{A}$, and it can be shown that the rank of $\boldsymbol{A}$ is the same as that of $\boldsymbol{A}'\boldsymbol{A}$. Therefore the rank condition can be investigated for either $\boldsymbol{A}$ or $\boldsymbol{B}$. In the applications to be made in this book the Q will arise as a sum of squares of linear combinations; hence the given version seems simpler to use.

and is homogenous if $c = 0$. But since $E(L_i) = c$, it is only necessary to verify that $E(L_i) = 0$ and examine the rank in the linear dependence of the L's on the X's.

For each Q the rank of the corresponding matrix A can be determined by looking for the determinant of highest order that does not vanish, or more simply in many instances as follows: If there are j linear relations among the m L's, the rank of A is at most $m - j$. Then the fact that the rank of a sum of quadratic forms is no larger than the sum of the ranks (a theorem from matrix theory)[1] can often be exploited to conclude that the rank of A is exactly $m - j$. This point will be illustrated in the following example.

Example 8–13. Let $X_1, \ldots, X_n$ be independent and normally distributed with common mean μ and common variance σ^2. Since for each i the variable $(X_i - \mu)/\sigma$ is standard normal, the following sum of squares has a chi-square distribution with n degrees of freedom:

$$\sum \left(\frac{X_i - \mu}{\sigma}\right)^2 = \sum \left(\frac{X_i - \bar{X}}{\sigma}\right)^2 + n\left(\frac{\bar{X} - \mu}{\sigma}\right)^2$$

$$= \qquad Q_1 \qquad + \qquad Q_2,$$

where the partitioning into the two Q's is essentially the parallel axis theorem. The term Q_2 is a square of a single linear combination of the standard normal variables $(X_i - \mu)/\sigma$, and the rank is just 1. The term Q_1 is the sum of squares of $L_1, \ldots, L_n$, where

$$L_i = \frac{(X_i - \bar{X})}{\sigma} = \frac{(X_i - \mu)}{\sigma} - \frac{1}{n}\sum \frac{(X_j - \mu)}{\sigma}.$$

That is, $L = AU$, where $U_i = (X_i - \mu)/\sigma$, and

$$A = \begin{pmatrix} 1 - 1/n & -1/n & -1/n & \cdots & -1/n \\ -1/n & 1 - 1/n & -1/n & \cdots & -1/n \\ \vdots & \vdots & \vdots & \vdots & \vdots \\ -1/n & -1/n & -1/n & \cdots & 1 - 1/n \end{pmatrix}$$

Since the sum of the L's is zero (a linear relation among them), the rank of A does not exceed $n - 1$. The rank of the sum is n, so that $n \leq \text{rank } A + 1$, or rank $A \geq n - 1$. But then if the rank of A is neither greater than nor less than $n - 1$, it must be $n - 1$. Consequently the ranks of the Q's do add up to n, and Cochran's theorem applies: The Q's have independent chi-square distributions with $n - 1$ degrees of freedom for Q_1 and 1 degree of freedom for Q_2. (The distribution of Q_2 is obvious from the start, of course; the new information is the distribution of Q_1 and the fact that Q_1 and Q_2 are independent random variables.)

[1]Hohn, *op., cit.* p. 240.

PROBLEMS

8–20. Let $\boldsymbol{L} = \boldsymbol{AU}$, where

$$\boldsymbol{L} = \begin{pmatrix} L_1 \\ L_2 \\ L_3 \end{pmatrix}, \quad \boldsymbol{U} = \begin{pmatrix} U_1 \\ U_2 \\ U_3 \\ U_4 \end{pmatrix}, \quad \boldsymbol{A} = \begin{pmatrix} 3 & 4 & 1 & 5 \\ 2 & 2 & 0 & 3 \\ 1 & 2 & 1 & 2 \end{pmatrix}.$$

(a) Show that the rank of $\boldsymbol{A}$ is 2, and express the third row of $\boldsymbol{A}$ as a linear combination of its first two rows. (That is, express L_3 as a linear combination of L_1 and L_2).

(b) Rewrite $L_1^2 + L_2^2 + L_3^2$ as a quadratic form in L_1 and L_2, and give the matrix $\boldsymbol{B}$ of this form.

(c) Show that $\boldsymbol{P'BP} = \boldsymbol{I}$, where

$$\boldsymbol{P} = \begin{pmatrix} 1/\sqrt{6} & 1/\sqrt{2} \\ -1/\sqrt{6} & 1/\sqrt{2} \end{pmatrix}.$$

(d) Show that if

$$\begin{pmatrix} L_1 \\ L_2 \end{pmatrix} = \boldsymbol{P}\begin{pmatrix} V_1 \\ V_2 \end{pmatrix},$$

then

$$L_1^2 + L_2^2 + L_3^2 = V_1^2 + V_2^2.$$

(Verify this on two levels: by expressing the V's in terms of the L's, and then by expressing both V's and L's in terms of the U's.)

8–21. Let X_{ij}, $i = 1, \ldots, m$ and $j = 1, \ldots, n$, be independent and normally distributed, each with mean μ and variance σ^2. Let

$$\bar{X}_{i\cdot} = \frac{1}{n}\sum_{j=i}^{n} X_{ij}, \qquad \bar{X} = \frac{1}{mn}\sum_{i=1}^{m}\sum_{j=1}^{n} X_{ij}.$$

(a) Show that

$$\sum_i \sum_j (X_{ij} - \bar{X})^2 = \sum_i \sum_j (X_{ij} - \bar{X}_{i\cdot})^2 + n\sum_i (\bar{X}_{i\cdot} - \bar{X})^2.$$

(b) What is the distribution of the left hand side of the equation in (a)?

(c) Determine the ranks of the quadratic forms in the right-hand side of the equation in (a) and draw a conclusion concerning the distributions of those forms.

8–22. Referring to Problem 8–21, and thinking of $\bar{X}_{1\cdot}, \ldots, \bar{X}_{m\cdot}$ as a random sample of size m from a normal population with mean μ and variance σ^2/n, show (without Cochran's theorem) that the second term on the right of the equation in (a), when divided by σ^2, has a chi-square distribution. What additional information is given by Cochran's theorem?

8.2.4 The Noncentral Chi-Square Distribution. A sum of squares of independent normal variables, each with unit variance but with possibly nonzero means, has what is called a *noncentral chi-square* distribution. The derivation to be presented relies on an appreciation of orthogonal transformations.

A matrix $\boldsymbol{U}$ is called *orthogonal* if it is square and has an inverse that is the same as its transpose: $\boldsymbol{UU'} = \boldsymbol{U'U} = \boldsymbol{I}$. Writing out these relations in terms of the matrix elements, one finds:

$$\begin{cases} u_{i1}^2 + u_{i2}^2 + \cdots + u_{in}^2 = 1 \\ u_{1j}^2 + u_{2j}^2 + \cdots + u_{nj}^2 = 1 \end{cases}$$

and for $i \neq k \neq j$,

$$\begin{cases} u_{i1}u_{k1} + \cdots + u_{in}u_{kn} = 0 \\ u_{1j}u_{1k} + \cdots + u_{nj}u_{nk} = 0. \end{cases}$$

These state that the rows $(u_{i1}, \ldots, u_{in})$ constitute a set of mutually orthogonal vectors of unit length, as do the columns. [The vector $(a_1, \ldots, a_n)$ is *orthogonal* to $(b_1, \ldots, b_n)$ if $a_1b_1 + \cdots + a_nb_n = 0$. For $n = 2$ or 3, this means that they are perpendicular in the usual geometrical sense. The *length* of $(a_1, \ldots, a_n)$ is $a_1^2 + \cdots + a_n^2$, again the geometrical length for $n = 2$ or 3.]

An orthogonal matrix defines an orthogonal transformation—what in two or three dimensions is a rigid rotation of axes. This is a nonsingular transformation that preserves lengths. That is, if $\boldsymbol{U}$ is orthogonal and $\boldsymbol{w} = \boldsymbol{Uz}$, then

$$w_1^2 + \cdots + w_n^2 = \boldsymbol{w'w} = \boldsymbol{z'U'Uz} = \boldsymbol{z'z} = z_1^2 + \cdots + z_n^2.$$

Another fact to be used is that given any unit vector (a vector of unit length), $n - 1$ additional unit vectors can be found which, with the given one, make up a set of mutually orthogonal unit vectors; these can then be used as rows of an orthogonal matrix. This is clear in three dimensions and will be assumed to hold in general (which it does).

Consider now the independent normal random variables $Z_1, \ldots, Z_n$, each with unit variance and with means $E(Z_i) = \mu_i$. The vector

$$\boldsymbol{a} = \left(\frac{\mu_1}{\sqrt{\sum \mu_i^2}}, \ldots, \frac{\mu_n}{\sqrt{\sum \mu_i^2}} \right)$$

has unit length. Then let $\boldsymbol{V}$ denote an orthogonal matrix with the elements of $\boldsymbol{a}$ in its first row:

$$\boldsymbol{V} = \begin{pmatrix} a_1 & \cdots & a_n \\ u_{21} & \cdots & u_{2n} \\ \vdots & & \\ u_{n1} & \cdots & u_{nn} \end{pmatrix}.$$

Then, if $\boldsymbol{W} = \boldsymbol{VZ}$,

$$\sum W_i^2 = \boldsymbol{W'W} = \boldsymbol{Z'V'VZ} = \boldsymbol{Z'IZ} = \boldsymbol{Z'Z} = \sum Z_i^2.$$

Further, being obtained by a linear transformation of normal variables, $\boldsymbol{W}$ has a multivariate normal distribution, with

$$E(\boldsymbol{W}) = E(\boldsymbol{VZ}) = \boldsymbol{V}E(\boldsymbol{Z}) = \boldsymbol{V\mu} = \begin{pmatrix} \sqrt{\sum \mu_i^2} \\ 0 \\ \vdots \\ 0 \end{pmatrix}.$$

The covariance matrix of $\boldsymbol{W}$ is $\boldsymbol{V'M_ZV} = \boldsymbol{V'V} = \boldsymbol{I}$. Therefore $W_1, \ldots, W_n$ are independent random variables, and $W_2, \cdots, W_n$ are, in addition, standard normal.

The sum of squares of the Z's can now be expressed as follows:

$$\chi'^2 = \sum_{i=1}^{n} Z_i^2 = \sum_{i=1}^{n} W_i^2 = W_1^2 + Y,$$

where

$$Y = W_2^2 + \cdots + W_n^2.$$

The variables W_1 and Y are independent, the former being normal with mean $\sqrt{\sum \mu_i^2}$ and variance 1, and the latter being chi-square with $n - 1$ degrees of freedom.

The distribution of χ'^2 can then be obtained in the usual way from the joint distribution of W_1 and Y. The density of this joint distribution is

$$f_{Y,W_1}(u,v) = \frac{u^{(n-3)/2}e^{-u/2}}{2^{(n-1)/2}\Gamma[(n-1)/2]} \cdot \frac{1}{\sqrt{2\pi}} \exp[-\tfrac{1}{2}(v - \sqrt{\textstyle\sum \mu_i^2})^2].$$

Then

$$P(\chi'^2 \le x) = \iint\limits_{u+v^2<x} f_{Y,W_1}(u,v)\, du\, dv$$

$$= \iint\limits_{\rho<\sqrt{x}} 2\rho^2(\cos\theta) f_{Y,W_1}(\rho^2\cos^2\theta,\ \rho\sin\theta)\, d\rho\, d\theta,$$

the change of variable being $v = \rho \sin\theta$, $u = \rho^2 \cos^2\theta$. Substituting the joint density of Y and W_1, and differentiating with respect to x, one obtains the following expression for the density of χ'^2:

$$f_{\chi'^2}(x) = \frac{x^{(n-2)/2}e^{-\lambda}e^{-x/2}}{\sqrt{\pi}2^{n/2}\Gamma(\frac{1}{2}n - \frac{1}{2})} \int_{-\pi}^{\pi} \cos^{n-2}\theta \exp[\sqrt{2\lambda x}\sin\theta]\, d\theta,$$

where λ denotes the "noncentrality parameter": $\lambda = \sum \mu_i^2/2$. Putting into the integrand the Maclaurin expansion for the exponential and evaluating the resulting integrals as beta functions, one obtains:

$$f_{\chi'^2}(x) = \frac{x^{(n-2)/2}e^{-\lambda-x/2}}{\sqrt{2^n\pi}} \sum_{m=0}^{\infty} \frac{(2\lambda x)^m \Gamma(m + \frac{1}{2})}{(2m)!\,\Gamma(\frac{1}{2}n + m)}.$$

When $\lambda = 0$ (that is, when $\mu_1 = \cdots = \mu_n = 0$), this reduces to the ordinary "central" chi-square density with n degrees of freedom. (Incidentally, the final formula is also valid for $n = 1$, even though it was implicit in the derivation that $n > 1$.)

It is perhaps worth noting explicitly that although the variables that make up χ'^2 involve n parameters, the distribution of the sum of squares depends only on the single noncentrality parameter λ.

The expression finally obtained above for the noncentral chi-square density is still not especially pleasant to behold or to work with. However, various tables are available; for example, E. Fix, "Tables of Noncentral χ^2," *Univ. Calif. Publ. Statistics*, Vol. 1, 1949, pages 15–19.

8.2.5 F and t Distributions. In the problem of comparing normal populations with respect to their variances, as well as in a variety of other problems, it will be necessary to know the distribution of the ratio of two chi-square random variables.

Let U and V denote independent chi-square variables with, respectively, m and n degrees of freedom. The joint distribution of U and V is defined by the joint density, which is obtained by multiplying together the densities of U and V:

$$f_{U,V}(u,v) = \frac{2^{-(m+n)/2}}{\Gamma(\frac{1}{2}m)\Gamma(\frac{1}{2}n)} u^{m/2-1}v^{n/2-1}e^{-(u+v)/2},$$

which holds for $u > 0$ and $v > 0$. Consider then the ratio $W = U/V$: This random variable has the distribution function (for $w > 0$)

$$\begin{aligned} F_W(w) &= P(W < w) = P\left(\frac{U}{V} < w\right) \\ &= \iint\limits_{u/v<w,\,u>0} f_{U,V}(u,v)\,du\,dv \\ &= \int_0^\infty \int_0^{vw} f_{U,V}(u,v)\,du\,dv \\ &= \frac{2^{-(m+n)/2}}{\Gamma(m/2)\Gamma(n/2)} \int_0^\infty e^{-v/2}v^{n/2-1} \int_0^{vw} e^{-u/2}u^{m/2-1}\,du\,dv. \end{aligned}$$

The density function is then

$$\begin{aligned} f_W(w) = \frac{d}{dw}F_W(w) &= \frac{2^{(m+n)/2}}{\Gamma(m/2)\Gamma(n/2)} \int_0^\infty e^{-(v+vw)/2}v^{n/2+m/2-1}dv \\ &= \frac{\Gamma(\frac{1}{2}[m+n])}{\Gamma(\frac{1}{2}m)\Gamma(\frac{1}{2}n)} w^{m/2-1}(1+w)^{-(m+n)/2}, \end{aligned}$$

for $w > 0$. The fact that the integral of this density over $(0, \infty)$ must be 1 provides a convenient integration formula, one that could be put in the form of a beta function by means of the change of variable $w = u/(1 - u)$.

The F distribution is now defined as the distribution of the ratio of two independent chi-square variables, each divided by the corresponding number of degrees of freedom:

$$F = \frac{U/m}{V/n} = \frac{n}{m} W.$$

The density function of F is obtained at once from the density of W:

$$f_F(x) = \frac{m}{n} f_W\left(\frac{m}{n} x\right).$$

The expected value of W is readily obtained by using the integration formula mentioned in the preceding paragraph:

$$E(W) = \int_0^\infty w f_W(w)\, dw = \frac{\Gamma(m/2 + 1)\Gamma(n/2 - 1)}{\Gamma(m/2)\Gamma(n/2)} = \frac{m}{n - 2},$$

and from this one obtains

$$E(F) = E\left(\frac{nW}{m}\right) = \frac{nE(W)}{m} = \frac{n}{(n - 2)}.$$

The variance of F is obtainable in much the same fashion.

The percentiles of the F distribution are available in tables (cf. Table IV Appendix), but it is customary to give only the lower or the higher percentiles, not both. For instance, if $F_{0.05}$ is given, then $F_{0.95}$ need not be listed because it is contained elsewhere in the table of fifth percentiles. For,

$$\begin{aligned} 0.05 = P(F < F_{0.05}) &= 1 - P(F > F_{0.05}) \\ &= 1 - P\left(\frac{1}{F} < \frac{1}{F_{0.05}}\right), \end{aligned}$$

and therefore $1/F_{0.05}$ is the ninety-fifth percentile of the distribution of $1/F$. But $1/F$ is again a random variable with an F distribution, n degrees of freedom in the numerator, and m in the denominator (if F itself has m degrees of freedom in the numerator and n in the denominator).

The *t distribution* with n degrees of freedom can be defined as that of a random variable symmetrically distributed about 0 whose square has the F distribution with 1 and n degrees of freedom in numerator and denominator, respectively. Let T denote such a random variable, so that T^2 has the F density

$$f_{T^2}(x) = \frac{\Gamma(\frac{1}{2}[1 + n])}{\Gamma(\frac{1}{2})\Gamma(\frac{1}{2}n)n} \left(\frac{x}{n}\right)^{1/2-1} \left(1 + \frac{x}{n}\right)^{-(1+n)/2}, \qquad x > 0.$$

Then, for $x > 0$,

$$f_{|T|}(x) = \frac{d}{dx} P(|T| < x) = \frac{d}{dx} P(T^2 < x^2) = 2x f_{T^2}(x^2).$$

But since T is symmetrically distributed, its distribution density is obtained from that of $|T|$ as follows:

$$f_T(\pm x) = \tfrac{1}{2} f_{|T|}(|x|) = |x| f_{T^2}(x^2)$$
$$= \frac{\Gamma([n+1]/2)}{\sqrt{n\pi}\,\Gamma(n/2)}\left(1 + \frac{x^2}{n}\right)^{-(n+1)/2}.$$

This is the desired density function of a t distribution.

The symmetry of the t distribution about $x = 0$ implies that the mean value of T, if it exists, must be 0. The integral defining the mean is clearly absolutely convergent for $n > 1$, and so for those values of n, $E(T) = 0$. For $n = 1$, the density of T reduces to what has been called the *Cauchy density*, having no absolute moments of any integral order. For $n > 2$ the integral defining $E(T^2)$ is absolutely convergent, and so for those values of n, var $T = E(T^2) = n/(n-2)$, as derived above for the F distribution.

As $n \to \infty$, the density function of T approaches that of a standard normal variate. For,

$$\left(1 + \frac{x^2}{n}\right)^{-(n+1)/2} = \left\{\left(1 + \frac{x^2}{n}\right)^{n/x^2}\right\}^{-x^2/2}\left(1 + \frac{x^2}{n}\right)^{-1/2} \to e^{-x^2/2}.$$

Moreover, of course, the constant factor tends to $1/\sqrt{2\pi}$. This can be seen using "Stirling's formula" (cf. Reference [4], page 128):

$$\Gamma(p) \sim \sqrt{\frac{2\pi}{p}}\left(\frac{p}{e}\right)^p \qquad \text{(large } p\text{)},$$

which implies that

$$\frac{\Gamma(p+h)}{\Gamma(p)} \sim p^h \qquad \text{(large } p\text{)}.$$

This approach to normality accounts for the fact that in t tables (such as Table III, Appendix), there is often a sequence of entries for $n = \infty$, which are simply the corresponding points on a standard normal distribution.

"Noncentral" F and t distributions are required for power functions of certain tests concerning normal populations. A ratio of chi-square variates, each divided by the corresponding number of degrees of freedom, has a noncentral F distribution if the numerator has a noncentral chi-square distribution that is independent of the central chi-square distribution in the denominator. The noncentral t-distribution is the distribution of the ratio of a normal random variable with mean μ and variance 1 to the square root of a central chi-square variable divided by its number of degrees of freedom. Tables of these distributions are available: Lieberman and Resnikoff, *Tables of the Non-central t-distribution*, Stanford Univ. Press, 1957; and M. Fox, "Charts of the Power of the F-test," *Ann. Math. Stat.*, 27(1956), pages 484–497.

PROBLEMS

8–23. Carry out the computation of the variance of the F distribution.

8–24. Show that the F distribution becomes a beta distribution under a suitable transformation.

8–25. Show that the t distribution with one degree of freedom is a Cauchy distribution.

8–26. Determine the first percentile of an F distribution with 15 and 8 degrees of freedom, respectively, in numerator and denominator.

8–27. Determine which columns in the F tables are squares of which columns in the t table.

8–28. Show that the distribution of the ratio of the variances of two independent samples from normal populations with the same population variances is obtainable from the F distribution.

9/*Some One-Sample Problems*

Certain decision problems involving a single population and procedures based on a sample from that population will be considered in this chapter. When the set of possible states of nature is a "parametric class," specified by a distribution function $F(x;\theta)$ depending on a parameter θ, procedures can frequently be tailored for that class. Most estimation problems and many hypothesis-testing problems are like this. Procedures are discussed here for the Bernoulli, Poisson, negative exponential, and normal families.

When the possible states of nature are not so conveniently identified, the problems are both harder to state correctly and harder to solve. The problem may be one of "location," involving perhaps the mean or the median of the population; such problems are considered in §§9.4 and 9.5. For problems expressed in terms of the population distribution function, "goodness of fit" tests and related procedures are used, as discussed in §9.1. The problem of "randomness" is taken up in §9.6.

9.1 Goodness of Fit

Goodness of fit tests are used to test the hypothesis that nature is in a certain specified state when the alternative hypothesis is the general one that nature is not in that state, or that nature is in one of a family of states when the alternative is that the state of nature is not one of that family.

In the case of a discrete random variable X with a finite number of possible values $x_1, \ldots, x_k$ with corresponding probabilities $p_1, \ldots, p_k$, the null hypothesis is

$$H_0: \quad p_1 = \pi_1, \quad \ldots, \quad \text{and} \quad p_k = \pi_k,$$

where $\pi_1, \ldots, \pi_k$ are specified numbers on the interval [0,1] whose sum is 1. The basis for testing H_0 is a random sample of n observations on X, usually presented in a tabulation such as this:

Value	x_1	x_2	$\cdots$	x_k
Frequency	f_1	f_2	$\cdots$	f_k

The statistic $(f_1, \ldots, f_k)$ is sufficient, inasmuch as the joint probability function of a random sample is

$$f(\mathbf{x};\mathbf{p}) = p_1^{f_1} p_2^{f_2} \cdots p_k^{f_k},$$

which depends on the observations $(X_1, \ldots, X_n)$ only through the frequencies $f_1, \ldots, f_k$.

A likelihood ratio test for $\mathbf{p} = \boldsymbol{\pi}$ against $\mathbf{p} \neq \boldsymbol{\pi}$ is constructed as follows: The likelihood function is the above joint probability function, considered as a function of $\mathbf{p}$ for given f's:

$$L(\mathbf{p}) = p_1^{f_1} \cdots p_k^{f_k}.$$

Its maximum on the simple hypothesis $\mathbf{p} = \boldsymbol{\pi}$ is just $L(\boldsymbol{\pi})$. Its maximum on $H_0 + H_1$ was found in Example 6–14 to be achieved for $\mathbf{p} = \hat{\mathbf{p}}$, where $\hat{p}_i = f_i/n$. Therefore,

$$\lambda = \frac{L(\boldsymbol{\pi})}{L(\hat{\mathbf{p}})} = \frac{\pi_1^{f_1} \cdots \pi_k^{f_k}}{(f_1/n)^{f_1} \cdots (f_k/n)^{f_k}} = n^n \prod_{i=1}^{k} \left(\frac{\pi_i}{f_i}\right)^{f_i}.$$

The likelihood ratio test is then to reject H_0 for $\lambda <$ constant. The value of the constant to use is determined by an assignment of an α from the distribution of λ under H_0. Problem 7–20 illustrates the fact that even for small samples, the calculation of the distribution of λ under H_0 may not be trivial. Thus the large sample distribution of $-2 \log \lambda$ is useful. Here, $-2 \log \lambda$ is asymptotically chi-square with $k - 1$ degrees of freedom, and the rejection limit is simply the $100(1 - \alpha)$th percentile of that distribution. (The numerator of λ is a maximum over a space of dimension 0; the denominator is a maximum over a space of dimension $k - 1$, since the k parameters $p_1, \ldots, p_k$ are restricted by the condition that $p_1 + \cdots + p_k = 1$.)

Example 9–1. To test the equal likelihood of the six faces of a die, the die is cast 120 times with the following results:

Face	1	2	3	4	5	6
Frequency	18	23	16	21	18	24

The quantity $-2 \log \lambda$ is computed to be

$$-2 \log \lambda = -2[120 \log 120 + 120 \log(\tfrac{1}{6}) - 18 \log 18 - 23 \log 23 - \cdots - 24 \log 24] \doteq 2.9.$$

The 5 per cent rejection limit is 11.1 (the ninety-fifth percentile of the chi-square distribution with five degrees of freedom), and so at the 5 per cent level, the null hypothesis of equal likelihood of the faces is accepted.

It should be pointed out that in this discrete problem and in the test, there is no need for a numerical coding of the possible outcomes, and that if there is one inherent in the problem, this is not used.

The null hypothesis that a population distribution is given by a certain density function $f_0(x)$ can be tested approximately by discretizing the population and applying the above procedure. The range of possible values of X can be divided into a finite number of "class intervals" or "cells" $S_1, \ldots, S_k$. Each cell has a certain probability under the assumption that the state is $f(x)$:

$$p_i = P(X \text{ in } S_i) = \int_{S_i} f(x)\,dx,$$

and the test for $\mathbf{p} = \boldsymbol{\pi}$ [with $\pi_i = P_{H_0}(X \text{ in } S_i)$] is an approximate test of $f(x) = f_0(x)$ against $f(x) \neq f_0(x)$. The designation of the cells is not unique. Further, the distribution of a random variable involves a definite ordering of its values, which does not enter at all into this kind of test.

Another approach to the problem of testing $f(x) = f_0(x)$ against $f(x) \neq f_0(x)$ is to consider the discrepancy between the observed sample distribution function and the distribution function corresponding to $f_0(x)$. The ordering of the values is brought in, and no classification into cells is required in using such an approach. A variety of tests result from the different ways in which the "discrepancy" can be measured. This approach is taken up in §9.1.2 and §9.1.3.

A goodness-of-fit test is usually employed when the alternative is not very well defined, so that the notion of power is not especially helpful in selecting a test. When the alternative *is* rather clear cut, it is usually the case that other tests are more powerful. For instance, a goodness-of-fit test can be used to test $\mu = \mu_0$ in a normal population with given variance; but if the alternative is that $\mu = \mu_1 > \mu_0$, a test of the form $\bar{X} > K$ is most powerful.

A somewhat disconcerting aspect of goodness-of-fit tests (shared by tests in other cases in which H_0 is simple and the composite H_1 includes states that are arbitrarily close in some sense to H_0) is that if these tests are consistent, a sufficiently large sample would almost surely call for rejection of H_0. That is, the actual state of nature is almost certainly not precisely the one set up as H_0, even though it may be practically close enough so that one would really want to accept H_0 (act as though H_0 were true). The point is that, usually, testing a simple hypothesis against a highly composite alternative is not exactly the problem that should be posed.

9.1.1 The Classical Chi-Square Test. It is natural to consider the differences $(f_i - n\pi_i)$ as related to the goodness of fit of the observed frequencies f_i to the expected frequencies $n\pi_i$. If these differences are larger than sampling fluctuations would ordinarily produce, there would be reason to reject π's as the true cell probabilities. K. Pearson introduced in 1900 the following measure, which is large when the differences $(f_i - n\pi_i)$ are large:

$$\chi^2 = \sum_{i=1}^{k} \frac{(f_i - n\pi_i)^2}{n\pi_i}.$$

Aside from intuitive arguments that can and have been proposed for this statistic, one of its virtues is that its asymptotic distribution is known under H_0. This asymptotic distribution, in fact, is identical with that of $-2 \log \lambda$, namely, the chi-square distribution with $k - 1$ degrees of freedom. (A derivation of this fact is found, for instance, in Reference [4], pages 417 ff.)

The asymptotic distribution of χ^2 is suggested intuitively by the following reasoning (suggested by R. A. Fisher). The joint distribution of the frequencies $(f_1, \ldots, f_k)$ is multinomial:

$$P(f_1 = \nu_1, \ldots, f_k = \nu_k) = \frac{n!}{f_1! \cdots f_k!} p_1^{\nu_1} \cdots p_k^{\nu_k}.$$

But these probabilities also give the conditional distribution of k independent Poisson variables $Y_1, \ldots, Y_k$ with parameters $np_1, \ldots, np_k$ (where $p_1 + \cdots + p_k = 1$), given that $Y_1 + \cdots + Y_k = n$. The standardized variables $Z_i = (Y_i - np_i)/\sqrt{np_i}$ are then asymptotically normally (and independently) distributed, so that $\sum (Y_i - np_i)^2/np_i$ is asymptotically the sum of k squares of standard normal variables. According to Problem 9–7, then, the *conditional* distribution of such a sum, given $Z_1 + \cdots + Z_k = 0$, is the chi-square distribution with $k - 1$ degrees of freedom. The linear restriction reduces the number of degrees of freedom by one.

Example 9–2. Given the problem and data of Example 9–1:

Face	1	2	3	4	5	6
Frequency	18	23	16	21	18	24

The statistic χ^2 is computed as follows:

$$\chi^2 = \tfrac{1}{20}[(18 - 20)^2 + (23 - 20)^2 + \cdots + (24 - 20)^2] \doteq 2.5.$$

The value of $-2 \log \lambda$ was given in Example 9–1 as 2.9.

In order that the asymptotic distribution apply with reasonable accuracy, it would seem necessary that the expected frequencies (which are the Poisson parameters in the above intuitive argument) should be large. Experience has suggested that when there are several classes, a few of them can have relatively small expected frequencies, even below 1. But generally the classes should be chosen so that not all expected frequencies are that small and should be, say, five or more. A detailed discussion of the selection of class intervals is found in the expository article by W. G. Cochran, "The χ^2 Test of Goodness of Fit," *Ann. Math. Stat.*, 23(1952), pages 315–345. See also Reference [18], pages 221 ff.

A modification of the chi-square test can be used to test a distribution in which the class expected frequencies depend on unknown parameters. The statistic used is

$$\chi^2 = \sum_{k=1}^{k} \frac{[f_i - np_i(\hat{\theta})]^2}{np_i(\hat{\theta})},$$

where $p_i(\hat{\theta}) = P_\theta(X = x_i)$ and $\hat{\theta}$ is an estimate of θ based on the sample. It can be shown (Reference [4], pp. 424 ff.) that if $\hat{\theta}$ is a BAN estimate of θ, the limiting distribution of the test statistic is again of the chi-square type, but now with $k - l - r$ degrees of freedom, where r is the dimension of θ (that is, the number of real parameters being estimated). Reduction of the number of degrees of freedom pulls in the critical boundary so that χ^2 has to be smaller for acceptance at a given level. This should not be unexpected, inasmuch as the fit is bound to be better when values from the sample are used for the parameters. Indeed, a *perfect* fit ($\chi^2 = 0$) can be achieved by estimating each cell probability (as a population "parameter") with the corresponding sample relative frequency; this would mean that $r = k - 1$, and no degrees of freedom would be left to test goodness of fit. But as long as there are at least two more cells than unknown parameters, there is residual information in the sample with which to test goodness of fit, after estimation of the parameters.

Example 9–3. Five "coins" with identical but unknown values of $p = P(\text{Heads})$ are tossed together 100 times to test the hypothesis that the number of Heads per toss follows a binomial distribution. (Perhaps some kind of dependence is introduced in the tossing process.) The results are given as follows:

Number of heads	0	1	2	3	4	5
Frequency	3	16	36	32	11	2

The maximum likelihood estimate of p is the mean number of Heads per five coins divided by five, which turns out to be 0.48. Using this to calculate the cell probabilities by the binomial formula, one obtains the following expected frequencies:

4.0, 17.9, 32.6, 29.6, 13.5, 2.4.

The value of χ^2 is then found to be

$$\chi^2 = \frac{(3 - 4)^2}{4} + \cdots + \frac{(2 - 2.4)^2}{2.4} \doteq 1.53.$$

The 5 per cent rejection limit would be the ninety-fifth percentile of the chi-square distribution with $6 - 1 - 1 = 4$ degrees of freedom, which is 9.49. Since $1.53 < 9.49$, the null hypothesis is accepted.

There is a point that should be mentioned in connection with using a chi-square test of a continuous distribution with an unknown parameter. For instance, one might want to test the null hypothesis that a population is normal. The mean and variance must then be estimated from the sample, and the natural inclination is to use the sample mean and sample variance, since these are joint maximum likelihood estimates. Then the question arises: Should one use the sample mean and variance as computed from the original data, or from the frequency tabulation after regrouping? The answer is that neither of these procedures will guarantee an asymptotic chi-square distribution for χ^2, and that what is required is to use the maximum likelihood estimates based on the likelihood function

$$L(\mu,\sigma^2) = [p_1(\mu,\sigma^2)]^{f_1}\cdots[p_k(\mu,\sigma^2)]^{f_k}.$$

The maximizing μ and σ^2 are, to say the least, somewhat awkward to obtain, and it happens that in the normal case one doesn't go far wrong in using either of the naïve estimates mentioned. There are cases, however, in which one can go appreciably astray. (Cf. H. Chernoff and E. L. Lehmann, "The Use of the Maximum Likelihood Estimates in χ^2 Tests of Goodness of Fit," *Ann. Math. Stat.*, 25(1954), page 573.)

PROBLEMS

9–1. Use the chi-square test for the hypothesis that $P(\text{Heads}) = 0.5$ on the basis of 640 tosses of a coin, of which 339 turn out to be Heads.

9–2. Show that the chi-square test for a particular Bernoulli model (as in Problem 9–1) is equivalent to a two-sided test based on the number of Heads in a random sample.

9–3. Test the hypothesis that X has a binomial distribution with $n = 4$ on the basis of these results:

x_i	0	1	2	3	4
f_i	6	38	58	47	11

9–4. Given the following data, test the hypothesis that the distribution involved is normal with mean 32 and variance 3.24:

Class Interval	Frequency
26.75–28.25	2
28.25–29.75	1
29.75–31.25	16
31.25–32.75	27
32.75–34.25	19
34.25–35.75	11
35.75–37.25	4

9–5. Test the hypothesis that the population is normal, using the data in Problem 9–4.

9–6. Mistakes in the first printing of a certain book were found distributed as follows:

Number of mistakes on a page	0	1	2	3 or more
Number of pages	221	34	11	1

9–7. Show that if $X_1, \ldots, X_k$ are independent, standard, normal variables, the conditional distribution of $X_1^2 + \cdots + X_k^2$, given $X_1 + \cdots + X_k = 0$, is chi-square with $k - 1$ degrees of freedom. (*Hint*: Let $\boldsymbol{U} = \boldsymbol{AX}$, where $\boldsymbol{A}$ is orthogonal and $a_{1i} = 1/\sqrt{k}$. Apply Cochran's theorem to conclude that $X_1^2 + \cdots + X_k^2 - U_1^2$ is chi-square with $k - 1$ degrees of freedom and is independent of U_1.)

9.1.2 The Kolmogorov-Smirnov Statistic. The sample distribution function:

$$F_n(x) = \frac{j}{n}, \quad \text{for} \quad X_{(j)} \leq x < X_{(j+1)}, \qquad j = 0, \ldots, n,$$

(with $X_{(0)} = -\infty$ and $X_{(n+1)} = \infty$) will generally differ from the population distribution function. But if it differs from an assumed distribution $F(x)$ by "too much," this may serve as grounds to reject the hypothesis that $F(x)$ is the population distribution function. That is, the amount of the difference between the empirical and assumed distribution functions should be a useful statistic in determining whether or not to accept the assumed distribution function as correct.

It is the actual numerical difference $|F_n(x) - F(x)|$ that is used in the Kolmogorov-Smirnov test. More precisely, since this difference depends on x, the Kolmogorov-Smirnov statistic is taken to be the least upper bound of such differences:

$$D_n = \sup_{\text{all } x} |F_n(x) - F(x)|.$$

The distribution of D_n is independent of $F(x)$. For, if x_y denotes the maximum of the inverses of y, so that $F(x_y) = y$,

$$\begin{aligned} D_n = \sup_{\text{all } x} |F_n(x) - F(x)| &= \sup_{f(x)\neq 0} |F_n(x) - F(x)| \\ &= \sup_{0\leq y\leq 1} |F_n(x_y) - F(x_y)| \\ &= \sup_{0\leq y\leq 1} |F_n^*(y) - y|, \end{aligned}$$

where $F_n^*(y)$ is the sample distribution function of a random sample from a uniform population (as discussed in §8.1.5).

Thus, for a given n, a single table is required for the distribution function of D_n and can be used for any $F(x)$. This table can be computed through the use of recursion formulas, and has been computed for various sample sizes (Table VI, Appendix). Asymptotic percentiles can be computed from the limiting distribution:

$$\lim_{n\to\infty} P\left(D_n < \frac{z}{\sqrt{n}}\right) = 1 - 2\sum_{j=1}^{\infty}(-1)^{j-1}e^{-2j^2z^2}$$

$$\doteq 1 - 2\exp(-2z^2).$$

The statistic D_n is a two-sided statistic in that departures of $F_n(x)$ from $F_0(x)$ on either side tends to increase its value. The critical region $D_n > K$ would then be appropriate for a class of alternatives including distribution functions on either side of $F_0(x)$.

Example 9–4. Consider testing the hypothesis that a distribution is normal with mean 32 and variance 3.24, using the ten observations: 31.0, 31.4, 33.3, 33.4, 33.5, 33.7, 34.4, 34.9, 36.2, 37.0. The sample distribution function and the population distribution function being tested are sketched in Figure 9–1. The maximum deviation is about 0.56.

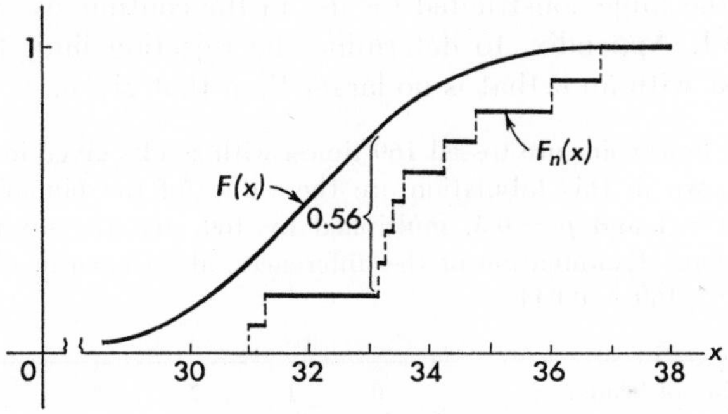

Figure 9–1

According to Table VI, Appendix, the ninety-fifth percentile of the distribution of D_{10} is 0.409. Since $0.56 > 0.409$, the distribution being tested is rejected at the 5 per cent level.

It is not possible to talk about a power "function," since the alternatives are too numerous to be indexed by even a finite number of parameters. One known result concerning the power of the K–S test is shown in Figure 9–2. For each value of Δ, there is given a lower bound on the power among the class of alternatives $F_1(x)$ for which

$$\Delta = \sup_{\text{all } x} |F_1(x) - F_0(x)|.$$

One curve gives this bound for the test $D_n > K$ where K is chosen so that $\alpha = 0.05$, and the other curve corresponds to $\alpha = 0.01$. Experiments described in the article from which the curves are taken indicate that the lower bounds given are usually quite conservative. It is also shown in that article that the K–S test is consistent and biased.

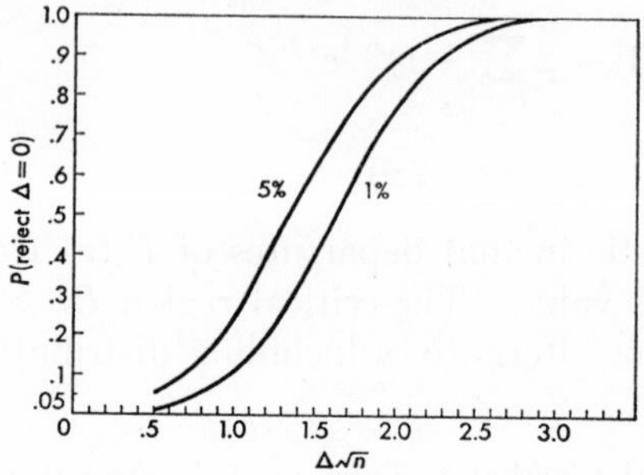

Figure 9–2

Reproduced from "The Kolmogorov-Smirnov Test for Goodness of Fit." by F. J. Massey, Jr., *Journal of the American Statistical Association*, 46 (1951), 68–78.

It has been assumed so far that the populations in question are continuous. However, it happens that in the case of a population that is not of the continuous type, the probability of rejecting H_0 is no larger (under H_0) than that given in the table constructed for use in the continuous case. That is, using Table VI, Appendix, to determine the rejection limit for a given α results in a test with an α that is no larger than that given.

Example 9–5. Four coins are tossed 160 times, with results given in the tabulation below. Also shown in this tabulation are the values of the binomial distribution function with $n = 4$ and $p = 0.5$. multiplied by 160, and the sample cumulative frequency function. Examination of the differences, also shown in the table, yields the value of D_n: $7/160 \doteq 0.044$.

Number of heads	0	1	2	3	4
Frequency	10	33	61	43	13
Sample cum. frequency	10	43	104	147	160
Cum. frequency under H_0	10	50	110	150	160
Differences	0	7	6	3	0

The 20 per cent rejection limit for a continuous population is

$$\frac{1.07}{\sqrt{160}} \doteq 0.085.$$

The test $D_n > 0.085$ in the present problem has then an α that does not exceed 0.20. Thus, at a level not exceeding 0.20, the null hypothesis is accepted, since D_n turned out to be 0.044, which does not exceed the rejection limit 0.085.

Since D_n is based on the notion of a distribution function, the values of the random variable X and their ordering play an essential role, as opposed to the circumstances of a chi-square test, in which any ordering of outcomes is not taken into account. In order to apply the K–S test to an experiment in which the outcomes are not inherently numerical, one would first have to set up an arbitrary coding of outcomes with numbers. This coding is not unique, and maximum deviations D_n can be different for different codings, as seen in the following example. This phenomenon suggests that the K–S test should not be used in such cases.

Example 9–6. To test the equal likelihood of the six faces of a die, it is cast 120 times, with the following resulting frequencies of the six faces: 18, 23, 16, 21, 18, 24. The sample distribution function has step heights proportional to 0, 18, 41, 57, 78, 96, 120, as compared with the step heights of the H_0 distribution, which are proportional to 0, 20, 40, 60, 80, 100, 120. The maximum discrepancy is $4/120 \doteq 0.033$, which is smaller than the 10 per cent rejection limit from Table VI, $1.22/\sqrt{120} = 0.111$. Thus, acceptance of H_0 is called for.

Suppose, however, that the following code is used: one dot = 2, two dots = 5, three dots = 1, four dots = 4, five dots = 3, and six dots = 6. Using the same sample of 120 tosses as above, we now find that the sample distribution function has step heights above the horizontal proportional to 16, 34, 52, 73, 96, 120. The maximum departure from the null distribution function is now $8/120 \doteq 0.067$, considerably closer to the rejection limit than with the original coding, even though the same experimental results have been used.

A one-sided $K-S$ statistic is sometimes employed to test $F_0(x)$ against the one-sided alternative $F(x) \geq F_0(x)$, with $F(x) \not\equiv F_0(x)$. The statistic used is

$$D_n{}^+ = \sup_{\text{all } x} [F_n(x) - F_0(x)].$$

The distribution of this statistic under the null hypothesis is defined by

$$P(D_{n^+} > u) = \sum_{0 \leq k \leq n(1-u)} \binom{n}{k} \left(u + \frac{k}{n}\right)^{k-1} u \left(1 - u - \frac{k}{n}\right)^{n-k}.$$

(Cf. Birnbaum and Tingey, "One-sided Confidence Contours for Distribution Functions," *Ann. Math. Stat.*, 22(1951), page 592; or Reference [18], pages 69–71.) The asymptotic formula

$$P\left(D_n{}^+ < \frac{x}{\sqrt{n}}\right) \doteq 1 - e^{-2x^2}$$

was obtained earlier by Smirnov.

An exposition of Kolmogorov-Smirnov tests and of the Cramer-von Mises tests to be considered in the next section is given in a paper by Darling.[1]

[1]D. A. Darling, "The Kolmogorov-Smirnov, Cramer-von Mises tests," *Ann. Math. Stat.* 28 (1957), p. 823.

This includes a consideration of what is and is not known concerning the relative power of such tests. For some kinds of alternatives the *K–S* test has a power advantage over the chi-square test. For testing a specific normal population against the alternative of a mean shifted to one side, the power of *K–S* does not compare favorably with that of the usual uniformly most powerful test. Chapman[1] considers the relative powers of various one-sided tests including that based on D_n^+.

No general treatment of a *K–S* type of test for the composite hypothesis $F_0(x;\theta)$ with θ unknown is available. However, it has been shown[2] that the *K–S* statistic, with (μ,σ^2) estimated by $(\bar{X},s_x^2)$, yields a test for normality which is more powerful than the chi-square test. Of course, even in general, if one used the rejection limit for D_n, a value of D_n in excess of that limit should certainly call for rejection when estimates of parameters based on the sample are used in its computation, since adjusting the theoretical distribution on the basis of the sample would tend to improve the fit.

9.1.3 Other Tests. Other measures of discrepancy between two distribution functions lead to corresponding statistics for testing goodness of fit. Given a non-negative weight function $G(y)$, the statistic

$$n\int_{-\infty}^{\infty} [F_n(x) - F(x)]^2 G[F(x)]\, dF(x),$$

like the *K–S* statistic, is distribution-free—its distribution does not depend on $F(x)$. (This was pointed out in §8.1.5.) Using such a statistic was proposed by Cramer and by von Mises; the particular form with weighting function $G \equiv 1$ was proposed by Smirnov, who then also obtained an expression for its limiting distribution. With $G \equiv 1$, the statistic reduces to

$$n\omega_n^2 = n\int_{-\infty}^{\infty} [F_n(x) - F(x)]^2\, dF(x) = n\int_0^1 [F_n^*(y) - y]^2\, dy.$$

Some of the percentiles of its asymptotic distribution are as follows[3]:

$P(n\omega_n^2 \leq x)$	0.80	0.85	0.90	0.95	0.98	0.99
x	0.241	0.284	0.347	0.461	0.620	0.743

[1]D. G. Chapman, "A comparative study of several one-sided goodness-of-fit tests," *Ann. Math. Stat.* 29 (1959), p. 655.

[2]Kac, Kieffer, and Wolfowitz, "On Tests of Normality and Other Tests of Fit Based on Distance Methods," *Ann. Math. Stat.*, 25 (1955) p. 189.

[3]These entries come from an article by Anderson and Darling, "Asymptotic Theory of Certain 'Goodness of Fit' Criteria Based on Stochastic Processes," *Ann. Math. Stat.*, 23 (1952), page 193. Computations by A. W. Marshall (*Ann. Math. Stat.*, 29(1958), page 307) indicate that the convergence to the asymptotic distribution is very rapid, the asymptotic expressions being useful even for n as small as three or four.

For computations in samples that are not too large, the following formula is useful (it is obtained by carrying out the integration indicated in $n\omega_n^2$):

$$n\omega_n^2 = \frac{1}{12n} + \sum_{j=1}^{n} \left\{ \frac{2j-1}{2n} - F(X_{(j)}) \right\}^2,$$

where $X_{(1)}, \ldots, X_{(n)}$ are the ordered observations and $F(x)$ the distribution function of the null hypothesis.

Example 9–7. Consider the ten observations of Example 9–4 for use in testing (as in that example) a normal distribution with mean 32 and standard deviation 1.8. For $X_{(1)}$,

$$F(X_{(1)}) = F(31) = N\left(\frac{31-32}{1.8}\right) \doteq 0.29,$$

and

$$\left\{\frac{2-1}{20} - 0.29\right\}^2 \doteq 0.057.$$

Proceeding in this fashion, one finds $n\omega_n^2$ to be about 0.88, whereas for $\alpha = 0.05$, the rejection limit is 0.461 (from the table of the asymptotic distribution given above). The null hypothesis that the distribution is normal with mean 32 and standard deviation 1.8 is rejected at the 5 per cent level.

A test of the Cramer-von Mises type for the null hypothesis $F(x;\theta)$, where θ is an unknown parameter and estimated from the sample, has been constructed by Darling.[1] The test statistic is again $n\omega_n^2$ except that the value of θ used is a sample estimate of θ. If this estimate is properly chosen, the asymptotic distribution of the test statistic can be determined under H_0 and for certain problems is distribution-free.

The effect of grouping data in K–S and C–vM tests has been studied in a series of Russian papers.[2]

A somewhat different measure of discrepancy between theoretical and empirical distribution functions has been proposed by Sherman[3]:

$$\sum_{i=1}^{n+1} \left| F(X_{(i)}) - F(X_{(i-1)}) - \frac{1}{n+1} \right|,$$

where $X_{(0)} = -\infty$ and $X_{(n+1)} = \infty$. This statistic is suggested by the fact that the expected area under the population density curve between a pair of successive ordered observations is $1/(n+1)$, as shown in §8.1.5. The exact distribution is given by Sherman, who also shows that it is asymptotically normal.

[1]D. A. Darling, "The Cramer-Smirnov Test in the Parametric Case," *Ann. Math. Stat.* 26 (1955), p. 1.

[2]Cf. the survey paper by Darling referred to in §9.1.2 (footnote 1, p. 303) for references.

[3]*Ann. Math. Stat.* 21 (1950), p. 339.

PROBLEMS

9–8. Test: X is binomial, $p = \frac{1}{2}$, using D_n and the data of Prob. 9–3.

9–9. Carry out the details in Example 9–7.

9–10. Show that the following statistic is distribution-free:

$$\sup_{\text{all } x} |F_n(x) - F(x)| \sqrt{F(x)}.$$

9–11. Compute the power of the test $|\bar{X} - \mu_0| > K$, with K chosen so that $\alpha = 0.05$ and $n = 25$, at the alternative $\mu = \mu_0 + .6$ in a problem involving normal populations with known variance $\sigma^2 = 1$. Compare this with the lower bound (given by the curve in Figure 9–2) for the power of the K–S test.

9–12. Discuss the construction of a confidence band about $F_n(x)$ based on the distribution of the K–S statistic. [A confidence band at level α would be defined by a pair of functions $A(x)$ and $B(x)$ such that $P[A(x) < F(x) < B(x)] = 1 - \alpha$, where A and B are determined by $F_n(x)$.]

9.2 Some Special One-Parameter Models

In this section are collected the various estimates and tests that have been considered for three important one-parameter models. Since there is a single parameter, both location and scale depend on that parameter—as opposed to the situation in the normal case, to be considered in §9.3, in which location and scale are adjustable independently.

9.2.1 The Bernoulli Model—Sampling Without Replacement. The Bernoulli model is appropirate in describing an actual population consisting of two kinds of objects. More generally, it is used in describing the result of any experiment of chance that has just two outcomes, whether or not the experiment consists of actually drawing an object from a population of real objects.

In the case of an actual population there are at least two alternative methods of experimentation to obtain data for inference or decision, namely, drawing with replacement and mixing and drawing without replacement. The latter is considered first.

Suppose that there are N objects of which M are "Black" and $N - M$ are "White." Let X_i be 0 or 1, according as the ith object drawn is White or Black. For sampling *without* replacement, the probability function of a sample $\mathbf{X}$ is

$$P(\mathbf{X} = \mathbf{k}) = \frac{\binom{M}{k}\binom{N-M}{n-k}}{\binom{N}{n}\binom{n}{k}}, \qquad k_i = 0 \text{ or } 1, \quad k = k_1 + \cdots + k_n,$$

(as in Example 1–35). Because this depends on $(k_1, \ldots, k_n)$ only through the sum of those coordinates, the statistic $X_1 + \cdots + X_n$ (the number of Black objects drawn among the n) is sufficient for the Bernoulli family:

$p^x(1-p)^{1-x}$. Further, it is minimal sufficient because the ratio of $P(\mathbf{X} = \mathbf{k})$ to $P(\mathbf{X} = \mathbf{m})$ depends on the state parameter M if and only if $\sum k_i = \sum m_i$.

The distribution of this statistic $K = X_1 + \cdots + X_n$ is hypergeometric:

$$P(K = k) = \frac{\binom{M}{k}\binom{N-M}{n-k}}{\binom{N}{n}},$$

with mean and variance

$$E(K) = \frac{nM}{N}, \qquad \text{var } K = n\frac{M}{n}\left(1 - \frac{M}{n}\right)\frac{N-n}{n-1}.$$

This hypergeometric distribution of K can be approximated (as discussed in §2.4.3) by the binomial distribution, if the size of the sample is small compared with the size of the population. A further approximation by the Poisson distribution (§2.4.5) is useful if the proportion of Black objects is small, or by the normal distribution (§4.3.4) if the sample size exceeds, say, 20, with $nM/N \geq 5$.

With a monotone loss function, the uniformly most powerful test of $M \leq M_0$ against $M > M_0$ is given by the critical region $K >$ constant, since the hypergeometric distribution has the monotone likelihood ratio property (cf. Problem 2–79), and the power function for this test is monotone increasing. Such a test is perhaps most often applied in the field of acceptance sampling "by attributes." In this application the desirability of "accepting" a lot of articles (passing it on for consumption or distribution) depends on the quality of the articles in the lot, and the quality of an individual article is judged to be either "good" or "defective." The lot quality could be determined by testing each item in the lot, but it is usually more economical to use a statistical procedure, basing the decision between accepting and rejecting the lot on the quality of a sample. (If the testing is destructive, of course, a sampling procedure is absolutely essential.)

For the test $K > c$, the number c is called the *acceptance number*, since the lot is to be accepted if the sample contains c or fewer defectives. The custom is to use the operating characteristic rather than the power function; this operating characteristic is the probability that the lot is accepted as a function of lot quality:

$$L(M) = P_M(K \leq c) = \sum_{k=0}^{c} p(k;M),$$

where $p(k;M)$ is the probability (hypergeometric, or an approximation) that the sample contains k defectives if the population contains M. The operating characteristic is monotone *decreasing* in M.

Example 9–8. A test with acceptance number $c = 1$ in samples of size four from lots of size eight would have the following operating characteristic:

$$L(M) = \sum_{k=0}^{1} \frac{\binom{M}{k}\binom{8-M}{4-k}}{\binom{8}{4}}, \qquad M = 0, 1, \ldots, 8.$$

The values of this function are as follows:

M	0	1	2	3	4	5	6,7,8
$L(M)$	1	1	$\frac{55}{70}$	$\frac{35}{70}$	$\frac{17}{70}$	$\frac{5}{70}$	0

The expected quality of lots that are passed under a given sampling inspection scheme is naturally of interest. To determine this, the plan must be specified more completely, with an agreement as to what is done about defectives that are located. One possible scheme is to replace each defective found with an article known to be good, in lots that are passed and also in lots that are rejected. The number of defectives remaining in lots that are shipped is then M, $M - 1$, ..., $M - c$, or 0, the 0 arising in the case of a lot that is initially rejected by the plan and then completely inspected. The expected proportion of defectives in shipped lots is therefore

$$AOQ = \sum_{k=0}^{c} \frac{M-k}{N} p(k;M),$$

the "average outgoing quality." For large M this will be small, since in lots of poor quality the defectives would tend to be weeded out; for small M this AOQ will also be small, since the quality is good even before inspection. There will then be an intermediate value of M for which the AOQ is a maximum; this maximum value is called the "average outgoing quality limit," or $AOQL$. (Another definition of $AOQL$ is given in Problem 9–18.)

PROBLEMS

9–13. Given numbers M_1 and M_2 such that acceptance of the lot is strongly preferred if $M \leq M_1$ and strongly regretted if $M \geq M_2$, determine corresponding sizes of type I and type II errors in terms of the operating characteristic function. (These are termed, respectively, *producer's risk* and *consumers risk.*)

9–14. Determine the probability that a producer who has his production process "in control" at level p_0 (putting out articles with a constant probability p_0 of a defective) will have a lot rejected. (This is another definition of "producer's risk.")

9–15. Given a sample of size 50 and an acceptance number $c = 0$, determine the probabilities of accepting a lot that is 5 per cent defective for $N = 10{,}000$, 1000 and 100.

9–16. Given an acceptance number $c = 0$, sketch operating characteristics (on one graph) for samples of size twenty with $N = 50, 100, 400$, and ∞.

9–17. Given an acceptance number $c = 0$, sketch on one graph operating characteristics for 20 per cent samples from populations of size $N = 25, 100$, and 400.

9–18. Given a production process "in control" at level p_0 (cf. Prob. 9–14), derive the formula

$$AOQ = p_0 \frac{N-n}{N} \sum_{k=0}^{c} \binom{n}{k} p_0^{\,k}(1-p_0)^{n-k}$$

for the expected proportion defective in inspected lots. Compute this for the situation of Example 9–8, and compare its maximum with the *AOQL* determined from the point of view given just following that example.

9.2.2 The Bernoulli Model—Sampling with Replacement. A random sample (with replacement, if there is an actual finite population) from a Bernoulli population consists of a sequence of independent observations or trials, each with the population distribution. The joint probability function of the sample observations is as follows:

$$P(\mathbf{X} = \mathbf{k}) = p^k(1-p)^{n-k}, \qquad k_i = 0 \text{ or } 1,\ k = k_1 + \cdots + k_n.$$

The sum $K = X_1 + \cdots + X_n$, or the number of outcomes of one type, is minimal sufficient (Example 5–29). It is binomially distributed and happens also to be the maximum likelihood estimate (MLE) of np, since K/n is the MLE of p (Problem 6–13). Further, it is efficient and consistent.

The Bayes estimate of p depends as usual on the assumed prior distribution and on the loss function. For a uniform prior distribution on $[0,1]$ and a quadratic regret, the Bayes estimate is $(K+1)/(n+2)$, and for a prior weighting of the form $p^{-1}(1-p)^{-1}$, it is K/n. (Cf. Example 5–22 and Problem 5–42.)

An approximate confidence interval for p can be constructed, using the fact that the binomial variable K is asymptotically normal (np, npq), as follows: Let c denote the $100(\eta + 1)/2$ percentile of the standard normal distribution; then

$$P(|K - np| < c\sqrt{npq}) \doteq \eta.$$

The inequality here is equivalent to one of the form $A < p < B$, in which A and B are then the desired 100η percent confidence limits. To obtain these, square both sides of the inequality:

$$|K - np|^2 < c^2np(1-p),$$

collect terms according to powers of p:

$$p^2\left(1 + \frac{c^2}{n}\right) - 2p\left(\bar{X} - \frac{c^2}{2n}\right) + \bar{X}^2 < 0,$$

(where $\bar{X} = K/n$), and then observe that the expression on the left *is* negative when p lies between the points where the expression is zero. These points are the confidence limits:

$$\frac{n}{n+c^2}\left\{\bar{X}+\frac{c^2}{2n}\pm c\sqrt{\frac{\bar{X}(1-\bar{X})}{n}+\frac{c^2}{4n^2}}\right\}.$$

A further approximation is useful for quite large n:

$$\bar{X}+c\sqrt{\frac{\bar{X}(1-\bar{X})}{n}}=\bar{X}\pm\frac{cs_x}{\sqrt{n}}.$$

Example 9–9. If in a sample of 400 observations 220 are of the type whose probability is p, the 95 per cent confidence limits for p are approximately

$$0.55\pm 2\sqrt{\frac{0.55(1-0.55)}{400}},$$

or about 0.50 and 0.60. Using the more precise formula obtained first does not give appreciably different confidence limits, since $c^2/(2n) = 0.005$, which is quite small relative to $\bar{X}$. For a sample of, say, 40 observations, however, the more precise formula would be used, even though $n = 40$ is large enough for an assumption of the normality of $\bar{X}$ to be adequate. (Cf. Problem 9–20).

The Bernoulli distribution belongs to the exponential family of distributions:

$$p^x(1-p)^{1-x}=(1-p)\,e^{x\log[p/(1-p)]},$$

where $Q(p) = \log[p/(1-p)]$ is a monotone increasing function of p. For monotone regrets, then, the test $K >$ constant is UMP for $p \leq p_0$ against $p > p_0$; the power function is monotone increasing.

For the problem of testing $p = p_0$ against $p \neq p_0$, there is no UMP test, although $|K - np_0| >$ constant approximates a test that is uniformly most powerful among the class of unbiased tests (cf. Reference [12], pages 128 ff.). If different actions are called for, depending on whether p is on the high or the low side of p_0, the problem is a three-action one, and for a monotone loss function the monotone procedure of taking (say) action 1 for $K < C$, action 2 for $C < K < D$, and action 3 for $K > D$ is appropriate.

The sequential likelihood ratio test of p_0 against p_1 calls for continuing sampling until the following inequality is violated (accepting p_0 if the upper inequality is violated and p_1 if the lower is violated):

$$\log A < K\log\left(\frac{p_0}{p_1}\right)+(n-K)\log\left(\frac{1-p_0}{1-p_1}\right)<\log B,$$

where K is the number of successes among the first n trials, and

$$A=\frac{\alpha}{(1-\beta)},\qquad B=\frac{(1-\alpha)}{\beta},$$

α and β being specified type I and type II error sizes. The power function for this test, when all p on $[0,1]$ are possible states, is given parametrically as follows:

$$\begin{cases} \pi(h) = \dfrac{B^h - 1}{B^h - A^h}, \\ p(h) = \dfrac{1 - [(1 - p_0)/(1 - p_1)]^h}{(p_0/p_1)^h - [(1 - p_0)/(1 - p_1)]^h}, \end{cases}$$

as obtained in Example 7–19. The expected sample size is then

$$E(n) = \frac{(\log A)\pi + (\log B)(1 - \pi)}{E[\log f_0(x) - \log f_1(x)]},$$

where the denominator is

$$E\left\{\log \frac{f_0(x)}{f_1(x)}\right\} = \log\left(\frac{1 - p_0}{1 - p_1}\right) + p \log\left(\frac{p_0(1 - p_1)}{p_1(1 - p_0)}\right).$$

Example 9–10. Testing between $p_0 = 0.5$ and $p_1 = 0.9$ with $\alpha = \beta = 0.05$, one finds $A = 1/19$, $B = 19$, and the inequality for continuing sampling:

$$1.34 + 0.733n < K < 1.34 + 0.733n.$$

The operating characteristic for this test is shown in Figure 7–15. From it one can compute corresponding points on the ASN curve, as follows:

p	0	0.5	0.733	0.9	1
$E(n)$	1.83	5.19	18.33	7.2	5.02

The point $p = 0.733$ is that for which $E(Z_n) = 0$. Since the numerator of $E(n)$ is also zero for that p, the evaluation of an indeterminate form is required, with the result as shown.

A different scheme of gathering data for inference in a Bernoulli population is that of "inverse sampling." This calls for sampling until a specified number of successes has been attained. Suppose, for instance, sampling is to continue until five successes have been attained. A sequence of outcomes might look like this:

F, S, F, F, F, S, F, F, F, F, S, S, F, F, S.

The total number of trials (15, in this case) cannot be predicted ahead of time, but the number of successes is fixed. Now, prior to each success there is a certain number of consecutive failures; this number, between any pair of successive successes, has a geometric distribution:

$$P(k \text{ failures between successive successes}) = p(1 - p)^k,$$

and the outcome of the trials can be thought of as a sample of size five from this geometric distribution. For the sequence shown above, these five spacings are 1, 3, 4, 0, and 2 (measured by numbers of failures between successes). So, considered as a sample from the geometric population, the sample size is fixed.

Denoting by k_i the number of failures between the $(i - 1)$st and the ith successes (except that k_1 is the number prior to the first success), we find the likelihood function corresponding to $(k_1, \ldots, k_M)$ to be

$$L(\hat{p}) = \prod_{i=1}^{M} p(1-p)^{k_i} = p^M(1-p)^{\Sigma k_i}.$$

The sum $\sum k_i$ is a minimal sufficient statistic, and the likelihood function is maximized by the MLE of p:

$$\hat{p} = \frac{M}{M + \sum k_i},$$

which, incidentally, is the ratio of the number of successes to the total number of Bernoulli trials in the experiment.

Even though the sampling can be interpreted as having a fixed sample size, the number of Bernoulli trials required is random, with expectation

$$E(M + \sum k_i) = M + \sum E(k_i) = M + M\left(\frac{q}{p}\right) = \frac{M}{p},$$

and variance

$$\text{var}\,(M + \sum k_i) = \sum \text{var}\, k_i = \frac{Mq}{p^2},$$

(where, as usual, $q = 1 - p$).

PROBLEMS

9–19. Determine the Bayes estimate of p based on n independent trials, a quadratic regret function, and a prior weighting $g(p) = p(1 - p)$.

9–20. Compare the confidence limits obtained with the crude and with the more precise formulas, given 22 successes out of 40 trials. Use a 5 per cent level.

9–21. Consider testing $p = 1/3$ against $p = 1/2$, using $\alpha = \beta = 0.10$. Determine the ASN of the sequential likelihood ratio test.

9–22. Show that with inverse sampling, the Bayes estimate of p with quadratic regret, and a uniform prior distribution—is given by $(M + 1)/(M + K + 2)$, where M is the "sample size" and K is the total number of failures preceding the Mth success.

9–23. Show that with inverse sampling, the quadratic regret $(p\text{-}a)^2$ leads to the same Bayes estimate for p as in the case of a fixed number of repeated trials.

9.2.3 The Poisson Model. The Poisson probability function is

$$P(X = k) = \frac{e^{-m}e^{k \log m}}{k!}, \qquad k = 0, 1, \cdots,$$

which belongs to the exponential family with $Q(m) = \log m$, a monotone increasing function of m. In a random sample $\mathbf{X}$ the sample sum $K = X_1 +$

$\cdots + X_n$ is minimal sufficient and has also a Poisson distribution, with parameter nm (cf. Problem 4–14). The maximum likelihood estimate of m (according to Problem 6–14) is K/n, which is unbiased, efficient, and consistent as an estimate of m. The Bayes estimate with quadratic regret and uniform prior distribution for m is seen in Problem 9–24 to be $(K + 1)/n$; for a prior distribution with density $g(m) = \lambda \exp(-\lambda m)$, $m > 0$, the Bayes estimate is $(K + 1)/(\lambda + n)$, which tends to $(K + 1)/n$ as $\lambda \to 0$ (Problem 9–28).

Because the distribution of X is in the exponential family, a UMP test for $m \leq m_0$ against $m > m_0$ is defined by the critical region $K >$ constant, and the power function for this test is monotone increasing [the $Q(m)$ is monotone increasing].

The sequential likelihood ratio test for $m = m_0$ against $m = m_1$ $(m_1 > m_0)$ is defined by the following inequality for continuing sampling, based on K_n, the sum of the observations up through the nth:

$$\frac{\log A - n(m_1 - m_0)}{\log (m_1/m_0)} < K_n < \frac{\log B - n(m_1 - m_0)}{\log (m_1/m_0)},$$

where A and B are defined as usual in terms of α and β. The power function is defined parametrically:

$$\pi(h) = \frac{B^h - 1}{B^h - A^h}, \qquad m(h) = \frac{(m_1 - m_0)h}{1 - (m_0/m_1)^h}.$$

In many instances in which the Poisson distribution is applicable, there is a corresponding distribution of the *spacing* between failures. This distribution, of the negative exponential type, depends on the same parameter as the corresponding Poisson distribution, although differently, and so decision problems can be set up in terms of this spacing, a matter discussed in the next section. (The relationship is quite analogous to that between sampling and "inverse sampling" in a Bernoulli problem. Recall that the negative exponential distribution is the analogue of the geometric distribution.)

9.2.4 The Negative Exponential Model. Consider now problems relating to the family of distributions defined by the density function $\theta \exp(-\theta x)$, $x > 0$, with mean $1/\theta$ and variance $1/\theta^2$. The joint density function of the observations in a random sample $\mathbf{X}$ is

$$f(\mathbf{x};\theta) = \theta^n \exp\{-\theta \textstyle\sum x_i\},$$

which belongs to the exponential family. The statistic $\sum X_i$ is minimal sufficient.

The likelihood function $L(\theta) = f(\mathbf{X};\theta)$ is easily seen to be maximized by $\theta = 1/\bar{X}$, and the MLE of the mean $1/\theta$ is therefore $\bar{X}$. A Bayes estimate of θ, using a quadratic regret function and a uniform prior distribution on θ, is given by $(n + 1)/\sum X_i$.

A large sample confidence interval for θ can be constructed by using the fact that $\bar{X}$ is asymptotically normal with parameters $(1/\theta, 1/n\theta^2)$. Relating c and η as usual by the standard normal distribution, one has

$$P\left(\left|\bar{X} - \frac{1}{\theta}\right| < \frac{c}{\sqrt{n\theta^2}}\right) \doteq \eta.$$

The inequality here is equivalent to

$$\bar{X}^2 - \frac{2\bar{X}}{\theta} + \frac{1}{\theta^2} < \frac{c^2}{n\theta^2},$$

$$\theta^2\bar{X}^2 - 2\theta\bar{X} + \left(1 - \frac{c^2}{n}\right) < 0.$$

The zeros of the left-hand member are $(1 \pm c/\sqrt{n})/X$, which are therefore the confidence limits.

Because the distribution of X belongs to the exponential family with $Q(\theta) = -\theta$, a decreasing function of θ, the UMP test for $\theta \leq \theta_0$ against $\theta > \theta_0$ is defined by the critical region $\sum X_i <$ constant. The (monotone) power function of this test is given by the distribution of the sum $\sum X_i$, which is a gamma distribution (cf. Example 4–6).

The sequential likelihood ratio test of θ_0 against θ_1 is defined by the following inequality for continuing sampling $(\theta_1 > \theta_0)$:

$$\frac{\log A + n \log (\theta_1/\theta_0)}{\theta_1 - \theta_0} < \sum X_i < \frac{\log B + n \log (\theta_1/\theta_0)}{\theta_1 - \theta_0},$$

with acceptance of θ_1 or θ_0 according as the lower or upper inequality is first violated.

Because of the nature of many applications of the negative exponential distribution, in which the random variable represents elapsed time, there are certain unusual aspects of sampling. Several observations can take a great deal of time, especially if performed one after another. A procedure sometimes used is to have several items under test simultaneously. Even in this case, however, one of them might have an extremely long life and inordinately delay the conclusion of the test. Because of this, the procedure is cften modified by calling a halt to the testing after a certain length of time or after a certain number of those items on test have failed. A further modification is to replace those that have failed with good ones, as they fail. Such matters are discussed in Reference [12], pages 56 and 111, and in an article by Epstein and Sobel, "Some Theorems Relevant to Life Testing from an Exponential Distribution," *Ann. Math Stat.*, (25), page 371, and in greater detail in a forthcoming book by B. Epstein.

PROBLEMS

9–24. Determine the Bayes estimate of the parameter of a Poisson population, using a quadratic regret and a uniform prior weighting.

9–25. Determine the distribution of the sample sum from a negative exponential distribution and show that it is in the exponential family.

9–26. Construct the likelihood ratio test for $\theta = \theta_0$ against $\theta \neq \theta_0$ for a negative exponential population, using a random sample of n.

9–27. Construct the uniformly most powerful test of $m \leq 2$ against $m > 2$ in a Poisson population, having the property that the probability of accepting $m \leq 2$ when $m = 2.2$ and the probability of accepting $m > 2$ when $m = 1.8$ are each 0.01. (That is, determine the sample size and critical boundary.)

9–28. Determine the Bayes estimate of the Poisson parameter m, assuming a quadratic regret and the prior density $g(m) = \lambda \exp(-\lambda m)$, $m > 0$.

9–29. Sketch the power function for the sequential likelihood ratio test of $m_0 = 1$ against $m_1 = 2$ in a Poisson population, with $\alpha = \beta = 0.05$.

9.3 Normal Populations.

Statistical problems involving normal distributions arise in many applications in which a population is adequately (if sometimes only approximately) represented by a normal distribution. The mathematics involved in treating normal populations is especially tractable and therefore highly developed, and procedures derived on the assumption of normality frequently turn out to be "robust"—their applicability is somewhat insensitive to moderate departures from normality. (However, robustness is a matter that is beyond our scope and not yet fully explored.)

The joint density functions of the observations in a random sample X from a normal population is

$$f(x;\mu,\sigma^2) = (2\pi\sigma^2)^{-n/2} \exp\left\{-\sum \frac{(x_i - \mu)^2}{2\sigma^2}\right\}.$$

A minimal sufficient statistic for this family (which is included in the two-parameter exponential family) is given by the sum and the sum of squares of the observations: $(\sum X_i, \sum X_i^2)$, or equivalently, by the sample mean and sample variance. (Cf. Example 5–30.) The sample mean and sample variance are joint maximum likelihood estimates of the population variance, and they are jointly asymptotically efficient (an extension to the two-parameter case of the notion of asymptotic efficiency of Chapter 6; cf. Reference [4], page 495).

9.3.1 The Variance. If the mean of the population is known, the maximum likelihood estimate of the population is the statistic

$$s^2 = \frac{1}{n}\sum_{i=1}^{n}(X_i - \mu)^2.$$

This is unbiased, consistent, and efficient. The normal family with given mean belongs to the one-parameter exponential family, with $Q(\sigma^2) = -1/(2\sigma^2)$, which is monotone increasing. Thus, s^2 is minimal sufficient, and the test $s^2 >$ constant is UMP for $\sigma^2 \leq \sigma_0^2$ against $\sigma^2 > \sigma_0^2$. The distribution of s^2 is obtainable from the chi-square distribution; specifically, ns^2/σ^2 has the chi-square distribution with n degrees of freedom, being the sum of n squares of independent standard normal variables.

The usual situation, though, is that the population variance is not known, and second moments that are to provide information about variability must be moments about some sample quantity. As pointed out above, $(\bar{X}, s_x^2)$ is minimal sufficient, and so the pertinent second moment is that about the sample mean.

The sample variance s_x^2 has a distribution depending only on the population variance. To be specific, ns_x^2/σ^2 has a chi-square distribution with $n - 1$ degrees of freedom. Consequently the mean of s_x^2 is $[(n - 1)/n]\sigma^2$ and the variance is $2(n - 1)\sigma^4/n^2$. As an estimate of σ^2 the sample variance s_x^2 is consistent. Since it is biased, its efficiency for a finite sample size is not defined, but as mentioned above, it is with $\bar{X}$ jointly asymptotically efficient.

Other estimates based on the sample sum of squares and the sample mean are used. The unbiased form $\sum(X_i - \bar{X})^2/(n - 1)$ is preferred by some, but the best multiple of $\sum(X_i - \bar{X})^2$ uses a constant multiplier $1/(n + 1)$, if by "best" is meant having minimum mean squared deviation about σ^2 (which is an appropriate criterion if a quadratic regret is used.) (Cf. Problem 9–32.)

In estimating the standard deviation σ, the statistic s_x suggests itself. The distribution of s_x can easily be derived from that of s_x^2, and in particular the rth moment is obtained as follows:

$$E(s_x^r) = E\left[\left(\frac{ns_x^2}{\sigma^2}\right)^{r/2}\right]\frac{\sigma^r}{n^{r/2}}$$

$$= \frac{\sigma^r}{n^{r/2}2^{(n-1)/2}\Gamma[(n-1)/2]}\int_0^\infty x^{r/2}x^{(n-3)/2}e^{-x/2}\,dx$$

$$= \frac{\Gamma[(n+r-1)/2]}{\Gamma[(n-1)/2]}\left(\frac{2}{n}\right)^{r/2}\sigma^r$$

Putting $r = 1$ and $r = 2$, one obtains

$$E(s_x) = \alpha_n\sigma, \qquad \text{var}\ s_x = \beta_n^2\sigma^2,$$

where

$$\alpha_n = \sqrt{\frac{2}{n}}\,\frac{\Gamma(n/2)}{\Gamma[(n-1)/2]}, \qquad \beta_n^2 = 1 - \frac{1}{n} - \alpha_n^2.$$

The statistic s_x/α_n is unbiased and has variance

$$\text{var}\ (s_x/\alpha_n) = \left[\frac{n-1}{n}\alpha_n^{-2} - 1\right]\sigma^2.$$

Since as n becomes infinite α_n tends to 1, s_x/α_n is a consistent estimate of σ (as is s_x, for that matter).

A somewhat less efficient but useful estimate of σ is provided by the sample range R. In Example 8–4 it was seen that the distribution of R/σ is independent of (μ,σ^2). This distribution, its mean a_n and variance b_n^2 are tabulated for various small sample sizes in Table V, (Appendix). The statistic R/a_n is an unbiased estimate of σ with variance:

$$\text{var}\left(\frac{R}{a_n}\right) = \left(\frac{b_n}{a_n}\right)^2 \sigma^2.$$

Table V provides percentiles w_p of $W = R/\sigma$ from which confidence limits for σ can be computed. For, since

$$P\left(w_{\alpha/2} < \frac{R}{\sigma} < w_{1-\alpha/2}\right) = 1 - \alpha,$$

the confidence limits at level α for the parameter σ (as obtained by solving the inequality for σ) are given by

$$\frac{R}{w_{1-\alpha/2}} < \sigma < \frac{R}{w_{\alpha/2}}.$$

Example 9–11. The efficiency of the unbiased estimate R/a_n relative to the unbiased estimate s_x/α_n is the ratio of the variance of the latter to the variance of the former. For $n = 10$, the computation is as follows: $\alpha_n = 0.925$, $\alpha_n^2 = 0.853$, $\beta_n^2 = 1 - 0.1 - 0.853 = 0.047$. From Table V one obtains $a_{10} = 3.078$ and $b_{10} = 0.797$. Then

$$\text{var}\left(\frac{s_x}{\alpha_n}\right) = \frac{\beta_n^2\sigma^2}{\alpha_n^2} = \frac{0.047}{0.853}\sigma^2 = 0.0508\sigma^2,$$

$$\text{var}\left(\frac{R}{a_n}\right) = \frac{b_n^2\sigma^2}{a_n^2} = \left(\frac{0.797}{3.078}\right)^2\sigma^2 = 0.067\sigma^2,$$

and the efficiency is then

$$\frac{\text{var}\ (s_x/\alpha_n)}{\text{var}\ (R/a_n)} = \frac{0.0508}{0.067} = 0.76.$$

Example 9–12. Consider the following nine readings of inlet oil temperature, assumed to be normally distributed: 99, 93, 99, 97, 90, 96, 93, 88, 89. The range is $R = 11$ and the standard deviation is 3.97. The range divided by $a_9 = 2.97$ yields an estimate of 3.71 for σ. The standard deviation divided by $\alpha_9 = 0.913$ yields 4.35. The confidence interval based on R is obtained by dividing 11 by $w_{0.025} = 1.55$ and by $w_{0.975} = 4.70$ to obtain: (2.34, 7.10).

Testing between two specific values of σ^2, say, v_0 and $v_1 > v_0$, is *not* a problem with two states of nature and a corresponding most powerful test, since specification of the variance does not determine completely a normal population. A likelihood ratio test can be constructed:

$$\lambda^* = \frac{L(\bar{X},v_0)}{L(\bar{X},v_1)} = \left(\frac{v_0}{v_1}\right)^{n/2} \exp\left[\frac{-ns_x^2}{2}(1/v_0 - 1/v_1)\right] < \text{constant}.$$

This is equivalent to $s_x^2 >$ constant. The power function of this test is obtained by using the fact that ns_x^2/σ^2 has a chi-square distribution with $n - 1$ degrees of freedom:

$$\pi(\sigma^2) = P(s_x^2 > c) = P\left(\frac{ns_x^2}{\sigma^2} > \frac{nc}{\sigma^2}\right)$$
$$= 1 - F\left(\frac{nc}{\sigma^2}\right),$$

where F denotes the chi-square distribution function with $n - 1$ degrees of freedom. This is clearly an increasing function of σ^2, and so the test is at least unbiased for a problem in which the σ^2 in H_0 are to the left of those in H_1.

A corresponding test based on sample range is given by the critical region $R > c$. The power function for this test is

$$\pi(\sigma) = P_\sigma(R > c) = 1 - F_W\left(\frac{c}{\sigma}\right),$$

where $W = R/\sigma$, and F_W is given in Table V, Appendix.

Example 9–13. In Figure 9–3 are plotted power functions for the test $s_x^2 > 6.48$ and for the test $R > 7.66$, based on a sample of size 15. These were constructed to have the same power of 0.30 at $\sigma^2 = 4$. (If H_0 were $\sigma^2 \leq 4$, these tests would have

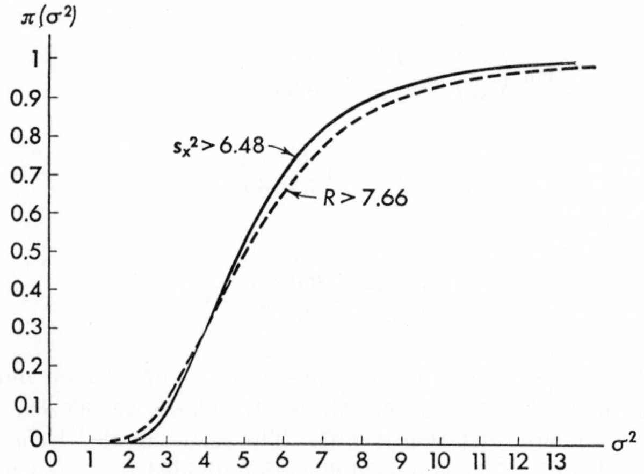

Figure 9–3

the same $\alpha = 0.30$). Notice that the test based on s_x is slightly more powerful than that based on R. Indeed, the former strictly dominates the latter, but the degree of dominance is not overwhelming.

PROBLEMS

9–30. Outside diameters of 70 supposedly identical parts are given in the following frequency table:

Diameter (inches)	Frequency
1.0950	2
1.0945	2
1.0940	9
1.0935	15
1.0930	26
1.0925	10
1.0920	6

Construct a 90 per cent confidence interval for the population variance, assuming normality.

9–31. Sketch the power function of the test whose critical region is $s_x^2 > 7$, based on a sample of size 30 from a normal population.

9–32. Determine the value of A that minimizes the risk (with quadratic regret), using the estimator $A\sum(X_i - \bar{X})^2$ for the variance of a normal population.

9–33. Compute the efficiency as in Example 9–11 but for various other sample sizes—say, $n = 2, 5, 8, 15$. Is the result for $n = 2$ to be expected?

9–34. In Example 9–13, what rejection limits would be used if the tests based on s_x^2 and on R are to have the same power of 0.2 at $\sigma^2 = 10$?

9.3.2 The Mean. In estimating the mean of a normal population, the sample mean $\bar{X}$ appears to be the best estimator from many points of view. Assuming a quadratic regret, the sample mean is the best multiple of the sample sum in the sense of minimizing the risk among the class of such multiples. It is the maximum likelihood estimate of μ, when σ^2 is known; and it is the maximum likelihood estimate of μ, jointly with s_x^2 for σ^2, when σ^2 is unknown. It is unbiased and consistent. If σ^2 is known, $\bar{X}$ is an efficient estimate of μ; if σ^2 is unknown, it is asymptotically efficient for μ, jointly with s_x^2 for σ^2.

The distribution of $\bar{X}$ is readily available, being normal with parameters $(\mu,\sigma^2/n)$, but the dependence of its variance on the population variance complicates matters. The reliability of $\bar{X}$ in representing the population mean depends on an unrelated parameter, σ^2.

The sample median can also be used to estimate the mean of a normal population. It can be shown (cf. Reference [4], page 367 ff.) that the sample 100 pth percentile is asymptotically normally distributed with parameters

$$\left(\zeta_p, \frac{p(1-p)}{nf^2(\zeta_p)}\right),$$

where ζ_p is the 100pth population percentile, and $f(x)$ is the population density function. In particular, then, the median of a sample from a normal population is asymptotically normal $(\mu,\pi\sigma^2/2n)$. It is therefore consistent and has an asymptotic efficiency of $2/\pi$, or about 64 per cent, relative to the sample mean.

Another location statistic, which can be useful because of the simplicity of its computation, is the average of the largest and smallest observations: $A = [X_{(1)} + X_{(n)}]/2$. The distribution of this random variable is derived in §8.1.3 in terms of an arbitrary population distribution. In the normal case, one obtains by means of a pair of substitutions like those in Example 8–4:

$$f_B(z) = \frac{n(n-1)}{\pi} \int_{-\infty}^{z} \left\{ \int_t^{2z-t} \frac{e^{-v^2/2}}{2\pi}\, dv \right\}^{n-2} \exp\left[\frac{-t^2}{2} - \frac{(2z-t)^2}{2}\right] dt,$$

where $B = (A - \mu)/\sigma$. Since B is symmetrically distributed about 0, it follows that $E(A) = \mu$, and so A is an unbiased estimate of μ. Its efficiency relative to the sample mean would be $\text{var}\,\bar{X}/\text{var}\,A$ or $1/(n\,\text{var}\,B)$.

A likelihood ratio test can be constructed for testing the hypothesis $\mu = \mu_0$ against the two-sided alternative $\mu \neq \mu_0$. The numerator of the likelihood ratio λ is the maximum of $L(\mu,\sigma^2)$ over σ^2 holding $\mu = \mu_0$, achieved when σ^2 is $\sum(X_i - \mu_0)^2/n$. The denominator is $L(\bar{X},s_x^2)$, the maximum when both μ and σ^2 are allowed to vary; and therefore the likelihood ratio is

$$\lambda = \frac{L(\mu_0, \sum(X_i - \mu_0)^2)}{L(\bar{X},s_x^2)} = \left\{1 + \left(\frac{\bar{X} - \mu_0}{s_x}\right)^2\right\}^{-n/2}.$$

The critical region $\lambda <$ constant is clearly equivalent to

$$t^2 = \frac{(n-1)(\bar{X} - \mu_0)^2}{s_x^2} < \text{constant}.$$

The quantity t^2 can be written in the form

$$t^2 = \frac{\left(\dfrac{\bar{X} - \mu_0}{\sigma/\sqrt{n}}\right)^2}{\dfrac{ns_x^2}{\sigma^2(n-1)}},$$

in which the numerator is a chi-square variable with one degree of freedom, under H_0, and the denominator is a chi-square variable with $n - 1$ degrees of freedom (under any state in $H_0 + H_1$) divided by that number of degrees of freedom. Since numerator and denominator are independent, t^2 has under H_0 the F distribution with parameters $(1,n-1)$. Under H_1 the numerator is no longer a central chi-square variable but, for $E(X) = \mu$, has a noncentral chi-square distribution with noncentrality parameter $(\mu - \mu_0)^2/2$. The power function of the test can therefore be obtained from the noncentral F distribution.

A two-sided confidence interval for μ can be constructed using t^2, with μ_0 replaced by a general μ. For instance, a 95 per cent confidence interval is obtained from the F-distribution with $(1, n-1)$ degrees of freedom:

$$P(t^2 < F_{0.95}) = 0.95,$$

or

$$P\left\{-\sqrt{F_{0.95}} < \sqrt{n-1}\,\frac{\bar{X}-\mu}{s_x} < +\sqrt{F_{0.95}}\right\} = 0.95.$$

Since $\sqrt{F_{0.95}} = t_{0.975}$ and $-\sqrt{F_{0.95}} = t_{0.025}$ (percentiles of the t distribution with $n - 1$ degrees of freedom), the confidence interval can be written in the form

$$\bar{X} - t_{0.975}\frac{s_x}{\sqrt{n-1}} < \mu < \bar{X} + t_{0.975}\frac{s_x}{\sqrt{n-1}}.$$

The symmetrically distributed square root of t^2 (using $\mu = \mu_0$),

$$t = \frac{\sqrt{n-1}(\bar{X} - \mu_0)}{s_x},$$

can be used as the basis of a test for the one-sided hypothesis $\mu \leq \mu_0$ against $\mu > \mu_0$. The power function of the test $t > K$ is

$$\pi(\mu) = P_\mu(t > K) = P_\mu\left[\sqrt{n-1}\,\frac{\bar{X}-\mu_0}{s_x} > K\right],$$

which can be computed from the noncentral t distribution function with noncentrality parameter $(\mu - \mu_0)^2/2$.

9.3.3 Confidence Regions for Mean and Variance. A region of (μ,σ^2) values can be constructed from the $(\bar{X},s_x^2)$ of a given sample, which with a specified probability will cover the actual (μ,σ^2), as follows: Let z_p and χ_p^2 denote percentiles of the standard normal distribution and of the chi-square distribution with $n - 1$ degrees of freedom, respectively. Given a confidence level α, choose δ and ϵ such that $1 - \alpha = (1 - 2\delta)(1 - 2\epsilon)$. Then

$$P\left\{\left(\frac{\bar{X}-\mu}{\sigma/\sqrt{n}}\right)^2 < z_{1-\delta}^2 \text{ and } \chi_\epsilon^2 < \frac{ns_x^2}{\sigma^2} < \chi_{1-\epsilon}^2\right\}$$

$$= P\left\{\left(\frac{\bar{X}-\mu}{\sigma/\sqrt{n}}\right)^2 < z_{1-\delta}^2\right\} P\left\{\chi_\epsilon^2 < \frac{ns_x^2}{\sigma^2} < \chi^2_{1-\epsilon}\right\}$$

$$= (1 - 2\delta)\ (1 - 2\epsilon)\ = 1 - \alpha.$$

The inequalities whose probability is given here define a region of the (μ,σ^2) plane, depending on $(\bar{X},s_x^2)$, which is the desired confidence region.

This confidence region is not just the rectangle defined by the confidence intervals constructed for μ alone and for σ alone. Strictly speaking, these confidence intervals could not be combined by intersection to obtain a confidence rectangle whose level is the product of the individual levels, since the statistics t and s_x^2 on which the intervals are based are not independent. The figure in the following example shows, however, that the rectangular region would not be too bad an approximation for the actual confidence region.

Example 9–14. Suppose that it is desired to construct a 90 per cent confidence region on the basis of a sample of size 20, in which $\bar{X} = 11.2$ and $s_x^2 = 6.8$. Since $0.90 \doteq 0.95 \times 0.95$, let $\delta = \epsilon = 0.05$. The inequalities defining the confidence region are then

$$(11.2 - \mu)^2 < (1.96)^2 \frac{\sigma^2}{20} \qquad \text{and} \qquad 8.91 < \frac{136}{\sigma^2} < 32.9.$$

The boundaries of this region are the curves defined by making the inequalities into equalities, and are the parabola and horizontal lines shown in Figure 9–4. Also shown in that figure are the 95 per cent confidence intervals for μ and σ^2 alone.

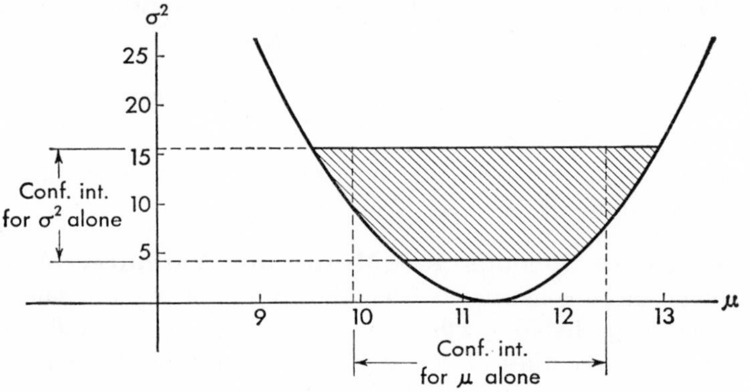

Figure 9–4

PROBLEMS

9–35. Given these observations from a normal population:

4.28, 4.32, 4.32, 4.29, 4.31, 4.35, 4.29
4.32, 4.33, 4.28, 4.37, 4.38, 4.28, 4.32,

construct 90 per cent confidence intervals for μ and for σ^2 and an 80 per cent confidence region for (μ, σ^2).

9–36. Assuming σ^2 to be known, determine (in terms of K, σ^2, and n) the large sample power function $\pi(\mu)$ of the test having as a critical region $m > K$, where m is the sample median.

9–37. Construct the likelihood ratio λ^* for testing $\mu = \mu_0$ against $\mu = \mu_1$. Show that the test $\lambda^* < 1$ is equivalent to $\bar{X} > (\mu_0 + \mu_1)/2$, if $\mu_1 > \mu_0$. Does $(\lambda^*)^{n/2}$ have a distribution which is familiar? Obtain an expression for the power function of the test $\lambda^* < 1$.

9.4 A Large Sample Test for the Mean

Given any population with second moments, the mean of a random sample is asymptotically normal $(\mu,\sigma^2/n)$, and so is a consistent estimate of the population mean. The statistic

$$Z = \frac{(\bar{X} - \mu_0)}{\sigma/\sqrt{n}}$$

is asymptotically a standard normal variable, if $\mu = \mu_0$, and so the obvious test for $\mu = \mu_0$ against $\mu \neq \mu_0$ when σ^2 is known is $|Z| >$ constant; one-sided critical regions would be appropriate for one-sided hypotheses. However, even though a significance level can be determined for such tests, their justification on other than these intuitive grounds is not possible without further assumptions about the population.

When the population variance is not known and the sample size is rather large (say, at least 100), the value of Z is not appreciably different if the sample standard deviation s_x is used in place of σ. In the same spirit an approximate confidence interval is given by the limits $\bar{X} \pm ks_x/\sqrt{n}$, k being determined by the confidence coefficient as in the case of a normal population.

9.5 Location as Measured by the Median

A problem involving the location of a population can sometimes be expressed in terms of the population median, which is a measure of location. Let X be a continuous random variable, and let m denote its median:

$$P(X > m) = P(X < m) = \tfrac{1}{2}.$$

Since the sample median is asymptotically normal with mean m and variance $[4nf^2(m)]^{-1}$, where $f(x)$ is the population density function, the sample median is at least a consistent estimate of the population median. But, since the variance of the sample median depends on the unknown $f(m)$, the obvious tests based on the sample median are not readily analyzed. The following "sign test" is available, instead.

Suppose that it is desired to test the hypothesis that $m = m_0$. If m_0 is actually the median, approximately half of the observations in a random sample would be expected to lie on either side of m_0. This suggests using the number of sample observations to the right of m_0 (or equivalently, the number to the left) as the test statistic. Too many or too few observations on one side of m_0 would be used as a basis for rejecting $m = m_0$.

The distribution of the number of observations to the right of m_0 is binomial with parameter

$$p = P(X > m_0).$$

Under H_0: $m = m_0$, the value of p is $\frac{1}{2}$, and the expected number of observations on each side is $n/2$. The power (probability of rejecting H_0) would be the same for all alternative states having a given p, and this $\pi(p)$ can be computed from the binomial distribution or from the normal distribution if n is large.

Example 9–15. Consider a test that rejects $m = m_0$ when more than 15 or fewer than 5 of 20 observations in a random sample fall to the right of m_0. The α for this test is the probability of the critical region under $p = 1/2$:

$$\frac{\left[\binom{20}{0} + \cdots + \binom{20}{4} + \binom{20}{16} + \cdots + \binom{20}{20}\right]}{2^{20}} \doteq 0.012.$$

The power function is given approximately by

$$\begin{aligned}\pi(p) &= 1 - P_p(5, 6, \ldots, \text{ or } 15 \text{ obs. to right of } m_0)\\ &\doteq 1 - \left[N\left(\frac{15.5 - 20p}{\sqrt{20pq}}\right) - N\left(\frac{4.5 - 20p}{\sqrt{20pq}}\right)\right].\end{aligned}$$

Given the following 20 observations:

37.0, 31.4, 34.4, 33.3, 34.9, 31.6, 31.3, 34.6, 32.6, 31.6,
36.2, 31.0, 33.5, 33.7, 33.4, 34.4, 32.1, 33.3, 32.7, 31.5,

to test $m = 32$ against $m \neq 32$, the following pattern of signs yields the desired statistic, + indicating an observation above and − an observation below the value 32:

$$\begin{matrix} + & - & + & + & + & - & - & + & + & - \\ + & - & + & + & + & + & + & + & + & - \end{matrix}$$

There are 14 plus signs, not enough for rejection of $m = 32$ at the level 0.012.

A confidence interval for the population median can be constructed as follows. Let $X_{(1)}, \ldots, X_{(n)}$ denote the observations in a random sample arranged in numerical order. Then if $r < s$,

$$\begin{aligned}P[X_{(r)} < m < X_{(s)}] &= P(\text{exactly } r, r+1, \ldots, \text{ or } s-1 \text{ observations} < m)\\ &= \sum_{k=r}^{s-1} \binom{n}{k} \left(\frac{1}{2}\right)^n.\end{aligned}$$

The random interval from the rth smallest to the sth smallest observation is therefore a confidence interval for m with confidence coefficient given by the above sum of binomial probabilities.

Example 9–16. In the case of 20 observations, the interval from the fourth smallest to the sixteenth smallest observation will include m with probability 0.993, according to the calculation of Example 9–15. For the 20 observations in that example, the fourth and sixteenth observations (in order of size) are 31.5 and 34.6. These are then 99.3 per cent confidence limits.

PROBLEMS

9–38. In a table of "random normal numbers" taken from a population with expectation 2 and variance 1, 88 out of 150 entries are found to be larger than 2. Would you accept $\mu = 2$ on this basis?

9–39. In testing H_0: $m = 20$ against H_1: $m > 20$, consider the rule that if more than 8 out of 10 observations exceed 20, H_0 is rejected. Compute α, and also the probability that if $P(X > 20) = 2/3$, H_0 is accepted.

9–40. Determine the probability that m is included between the fortieth and sixtieth observations (in numerical order) of a random sample of 100 observations from a continuous population.

9.6 Randomness

A random sample was defined in Chapter 5 as a sequence of identically distributed, independent random variables—a sequence of independent observations on a certain "population." If there is any reason to suspect that the process of obtaining a "random sample" might *not* fit the mathematical model of a random sample, it would be in order to test the hypothesis

$$H_0\colon\ F(x_1, \ldots, x_n) = F(x_1) \cdots F(x_n),$$

where $F(x_1, \ldots, x_n)$ is the joint distribution function of the sample observations $(X_1, \ldots, X_n)$ and $F(x)$ is a fixed (but unknown) univariate distribution function, namely, the population distribution function.

The statistical problem is not completely posed until there is specified an alternative to H_0, and herein lies one of the major obstacles to an adequate treatment of this problem of "randomness." The most inclusive alternative hypothesis would be that the observations are *not* independent replicas of a population variable—in other words, that H_0 is not true. This class of alternatives is rather unwieldy. For instance, given *any* test with a critical region of specified size under H_0, there would be many states not in H_0 for which the power of that test is zero. (Any multivariate distribution with zero mass on the critical region and dependent marginals would serve as such a state.) Thus, it is better to consider a more restricted class of alternative states which are especially feared, and then to look for a test which has reasonably high power for this restricted class, not worrying about *all* conceivable alternatives to randomness.

One way to restrict the class of alternatives is to keep the assumption of independence of the observations, allowing the distribution function to vary from observation to observation. In particular, a *trend* alternative is one in which the joint distribution function of the observations is assumed to be of the form

$$F(x_1, \ldots, x_n) = \prod_{i=1}^{n} F[x_i - g(i)].$$

With this assumption the distributions for the various observations are identical in shape but shifted in location, as would be the case if the mean of a normal population were gradually changing as the observations were taken, for example.

The principles sometimes used to derive procedures (minimax, likelihood, Bayes) appear to be especially difficult to apply in the problem of randomness, even when the class of alternatives is restricted. For one thing, costs would ordinarily be rather difficult to assess when tests of randomness are used to decide whether or not to proceed with a method of collecting data in another statistical test. The tests to be discussed here are proposed on an intuitive basis, and the discussion will include at most the derivation of the distribution of the test statistic under the null hypothesis.

9.6.1 Run Tests. A *run* in a sequence of symbols is a group of consecutive symbols of one kind preceded and followed by (if anything) symbols of another kind. For example, in the sequence

$$+ + + - + + - - - - + + - -$$

the runs can be exhibited by putting vertical bars at the changes of symbol:

$$+ + + \mid - \mid + + \mid - - - - \mid + + \mid - -$$

Here there are a run of three +'s, a run of one −, a run of two +'s, and so on. There are altogether six runs, three runs of +'s and three of −'s.

Consider now a sequence of observations from a continuous population, and let each observation be assigned the letter "a" if it is above the median of the observations and the letter "b" if it is below. The sample sequence then defines a sequence of a's and b's. If, to simplify the discussion, it is agreed to ignore the median observation when the number of observations is odd, the sequence of a's and b's will have an even number of terms—say, $2m$ terms, of which then m are a's and m are b's. In this sequence there will be a certain number of runs of a's and a certain number of runs of b's; let these numbers be denoted by r_a and r_b, respectively, and let $r = r_a + r_b$ denote the total number of runs. Run tests are then based on the intuitive notion that an unusually large or an unusually small value of r would suggest lack of randomness.

For instance, if a downward trend is present, the a's will tend to come at the beginning and the b's at the end of the sequence of a's and b's, resulting in a relatively small number of runs. Also, one could imagine certain kinds of dependences among the observations which would result in a systematic bouncing back and forth from one side of the median to the other, producing an unusually large number of runs.

The distributions of r, r_a, and r_b can be readily computed under the null hypothesis of randomness. Under this hypothesis the $(2m)!$ arrangements of the observations are equally likely to have produced a given order statistic (cf. Chapter 8, page 270). Each arrangement leads to a sequence of a's and b's, and the distinct arrangements of m a's and m b's are then also equally likely since each one comes from $(m!)^2$ arrangements of the observations. So the probability of a given run configuration can be computed as the ratio of the number of the arrangements of a's and b's having that configuration to the total number $\binom{2m}{m}$.

To compute the joint probability that $r_a = x$ and $r_b = y$, then, it is only necessary to count the number of arrangements of a's and b's having this property and divide by $\binom{2m}{m}$. In counting arrangements for the numerator there are three cases to be considered: either (i) $x = y + 1$, (ii) $x = y - 1$, or (iii) $x = y$. The probability that r_a differs from r_b by *more* than 1 is zero, so all possibilities are covered in these three cases.

In case (i) the sequence of a's and b's begins with an a and ends with an a. To divide the a's into x separated groups, slots for the b's are inserted in $x - 1$ places selected from the $m - 1$ spaces between the m a's. This can be done in $\binom{m-1}{x-1}$ ways. Having decided where to put the b's one partitions them into y (or $x - 1$) groups, just as the x's were partitioned, in one of $\binom{m-1}{y-1}$ ways, and puts the groups of b's into the prepared slots. The arrangement then has x runs of a's and y runs of b's and could have been accomplished in $\binom{m-1}{x-1}\binom{m-1}{y-1}$ ways.

Case (ii) is exactly analagous to case (i), and the number of arrangements is the same. In case (iii), in which $x = y$, the sequences begin with a and end with b, or else they begin with b and end with a. In either instance the number of ways, computed as for case (i), is again $\binom{m-1}{x-1}\binom{m-1}{y-1}$; the total for case (iii) is twice that number. Finally, then, given the order statistic one has

$$P(r_a = x \text{ and } r_b = y) = \begin{cases} 2\binom{m-1}{x-1}\binom{m-1}{y-1}\Big/\binom{2m}{m}, & \text{if } x = y \\ \binom{m-1}{x-1}\binom{m-1}{y-1}\Big/\binom{2m}{m}, & \text{if } x = y \pm 1, \\ 0, \quad \text{if } |x - y| > 1. \end{cases}$$

Since this is the same for any order statistic it is also the absolute probability of $r_a = x$ and $r_b = y$, and the condition has been omitted from the notation.

The probability function for the total number of runs can be computed from the above joint probability function as follows:

$$P(r = z) = \sum_{x+y=z} P(r_a = x \text{ and } r_b = y).$$

If z is an even number, $z = 2k$, the sum has only one term—that in which $x = y = k$. If z is odd, $z = 2k + 1$, there are two terms in the sum, one in which $x = k$ and $y = k + 1$ and one in which $x = k + 1$ and $y = k$. Hence,

$$P(r = z) = \begin{cases} 2\binom{m-1}{k-1}\binom{m-1}{k-1}\Big/\binom{2m}{m}, & \text{if } z = 2k, \\ 2\binom{m-1}{k}\binom{m-1}{k-1}\Big/\binom{2m}{m}, & \text{if } z = 2k+1, \end{cases}$$

for $z = 2, 3, \ldots, 2m$. The corresponding cumulative distribution function is readily computed from this and is available in tables.[1]

Example 9–17. In samples of size six from a continuous population there will be three observations above and three observations below the sample median. That is, $m = 3$. The number of runs can vary from two to six, and the distribution function of this number r is as follows (computed from the formulas given above):

z	2	3	4	5	6
$F_r(z)$	.1	.3	.7	.9	1.0

It is evident that a test which calls for rejecting randomness when fewer than three runs occur has a significance level

$$\alpha = P_{H_0}(\text{reject } H_0) = P_{H_0}(2 \text{ runs}) = .1.$$

It can be shown that the mean and variance of the distribution of r are

$$E(r) = m + 1, \quad \text{var } r = \frac{m(m-1)}{2m-1},$$

and that for large samples r is approximately normally distributed.[2] Using a continuity correction and the approximation

$$\text{var } r \doteq \tfrac{1}{4}(2m - 1)$$

[1]Swed, F. and Eisenhart, C., "Tables for testing randomness of grouping in a sequence of alternatives," *Annals of Math. Stat.*, 14 (1943), 66–87.

[2]For these results see A. M. Mood, "The distribution theory of runs," *Annals of Math. Stat.*, 11 (1940), 367–92.

one finds the percentiles of r to be obtained from those of the standard normal distribution as follows:

$$r_p = \tfrac{1}{2}(2m + 1 + z_p\sqrt{2m - 1}),$$

where r_p and z_p denote, respectively, the $100p$ percentiles of the distribution of r and of a standard normal variate.

Another type of run test employs the signs of the differences of successive observations. If the population mean has a rising trend, for instance, there would be a tendency for observations to increase from one observation to the next, and +'s would more often occur in groups than with no trend. A given sequence of n observations defines a sequence of $n - 1$ signs of differences of successive pairs of observations; let s denote the total number or runs of +'s and −'s in such a sequence. Various aspects of the distribution of s under the null hypothesis of randomness have been studied.[1] The mean and variance of s are

$$E(s) = \frac{2n - 1}{3}, \quad \text{var } s = \frac{16n - 29}{90},$$

and the large sample distribution of s is known to be approximately normal.

Example 9–18. In samples of size fifty the mean and variance of the total number of runs up and down, under H_0, are

$$E(s) = 33 \quad \text{and} \quad \text{var } s \doteq 8.57.$$

The fifth percentile of the distribution of s under H_0 is then

$$s_{.05} \doteq 33 - 1.64\sqrt{8.57} \doteq 27.2.$$

Thus, twenty-seven or fewer runs would be considered significant in testing against the presence of a trend, at the 5 per cent level, and would call for rejection of randomness.

PROBLEMS

9–41. Compute $P(r = z)$, $z = 2, \ldots, 6$, for samples of size six, and verify the tabulation of the distribution function of r given in Example 9–17. Verify also the formulas for $E(r)$ and var r in this case.

9–42. Write out the twenty distinct arrangements of three a's and three b's determine the number of runs in each, and thereby verify directly the probabilities computed in Problem 9–41. Given the order statistic (4, 5, 6, 7, 8, 9) write out some of the thirty-six sample sequences which lead to a specific sequence of a's and b's—say, to the sequence (a, a, b, a, b, b).

9–43. The following thirty observations are taken from a table of "random sampling numbers" (which should exhibit randomness, if anything should):

15 77, 01, 64, 69, 69, 58, 40, 81, 16, 60, 20, 00, 84, 22
28, 26, 46, 66, 36, 86, 66, 17, 34, 49, 85, 40, 51, 40, 10

Would you accept randomness on the basis of the number of runs above and below the median? On the basis of runs up and down?

[1]See papers by J. Wolfowitz and H. Levene in *Annals of Math. Stat.*, 15 (1944), p. 58 and 163.

9.6.2 Mean Square Successive Difference. Another test[1] for randomness is based on the statistic

$$r = \frac{d^2}{s^2},$$

where d^2 denotes the mean square successive difference:

$$d^2 = \frac{1}{2(n-1)}\sum_{i=1}^{n-1}(X_{i+1} - X_i)^2,$$

and s^2 is the sample variance (unbiased version). For each i the difference $X_{i+1} - X_i$ has mean zero and variance $2\sigma^2$ under the null hypothesis that $(X_1, \ldots, X_n)$ is a random sample with variance σ^2. The expected value of d^2 is then σ^2 under H_0. If a trend is present d^2 is not altered nearly so much as the variance estimate s^2, which increases greatly. Thus, the critical region $r <$ constant is employed in testing against the alternative of a trend.

In order to use this test, of course, it is necessary to know the distribution of r. It can be shown that in the case of a *normal* population

$$E(r) = 1 \quad \text{and} \quad \text{var } r = \frac{1}{n+1}\left(1 - \frac{1}{n-1}\right),$$

and that r is approximately normal for large samples (say, $n > 20$).

Example 9–19. Consider the following observations from a normal population:

39 42 38 53 51 30 40 40 28 43 46 53 55 29 24
34 53 66 43 42 38 34 57 26 33,

listed in the order of observations. From these can be computed the values $d^2 \doteq 97$ and $s^2 \doteq 111.5$, so that $r \doteq .87$. The fifth percentile of r (for $n = 25$) is approximately

$$\mu_r - 1.64\sigma_r \doteq 1 - 1.64\sqrt{\frac{1}{26}\left(1 - \frac{1}{24}\right)} \doteq .685,$$

and randomness would be accepted at the five percent level, since $.87 > .685$.

9.6.3 Other Tests. Whereas the test based on the mean square successive difference requires a knowledge of the population distribution under H_0 even to evaluate the significance level, a "randomization" technique (due to R. A. Fisher) provides a test whose level is independent of the distribution which is assumed to be common to the observations under H_0. A test based on this technique is called a *permutation test*, and is constructed as follows in the problem at hand.

If $(X_1, \cdots, X_n)$ is a random sample from a population with distribution function $F(x)$, the conditional probabilities of the $n!$ permutations of the

[1]See B. I. Hart, "Significance levels for the ratio of the mean square successive difference to the variance," *Annals of Math. Stat.*, 13 (1942), 445–7, and references given there.

observations, given the order statistic, are each $1/n!$. Then, if for each order statistic there is defined a critical region consisting of k of the $n!$ permutations, one has

$$\alpha = P_{H_0}(\text{reject randomness}) = \frac{k}{n!}.$$

To decide which permutations to put into the critical region one computes the value of some pertinent statistic T for each permutation, assuming that this permutation gives the order in which the observations occurred, and orders the permutations according to their T-values. The k permutations having the most "extreme" T-values make up the critical region, where the specification of what is "extreme" depends on the alternatives to randomness.

For instance, one might compute the mean square successive difference d^2 for each permutation and use this for ordering them, putting permutations with the smallest values of d^2 into the critical region when testing against trend. More generally, (see Problem **9-47**), one might use a "serial correlation" of the form

$$R_h = \sum_{i=1}^{n-h} X_i X_{i+h}$$

for some fixed h. Again the critical values of R_h and now also the value of h would be chosen (perhaps intuitively) in light of the alternatives to randomness.

Certain other tests for randomness are based on a consideration of *ranks* of the observations. The rank t_i of the observation X_i is its position in the order statistic (i.e., one more than the number of observations less than X_i in the sample). In the case of a continuous population each sample $(X_1, \ldots, X_n)$ defines a sequence of ranks $(t_1, \ldots, t_n)$ which is one of the $n!$ permutations of the integers $(1, 2, \ldots, n)$. Under the null hypothesis of randomness these are equally likely, and again a critical region is constructed by putting into it rank sequences ordered according to some function of the ranks, $T(t_1, \ldots, t_n)$. Two of the many rank-order statistics[1] which have been proposed are

$$\sum_{i=1}^{n} i\, t_i, \quad \text{and} \quad \sum_{i=1}^{n} E[Z_{(i)}]t_i,$$

where $Z_{(i)}$ denotes the ith smallest among n observations from a standard normal population.

Another test for randomness[2] is based on the number of inequalities $X_j < X_k$ for $j < k$ (for downward trend alternatives). This shares with the run, permutation, and rank tests the property of being "distribution free,"

[1]Such statistics are studied by A. Stuart, "The asymptotic relative efficiences of distribution-free tests of randomness against normal alternatives," *J. Amer. Stat. Assn.*, 49 (1954), 147–57; by I. R. Savage, "Contributions to the theory of rank order statistics—the 'trend' case," *Annals of Math. Stat.*, 28 (1957), 968–77; and in [*12*], page 258.

[2]H. B. Mann, "Nonparametric tests against trend," *Econometrica*, 13 (1945), 245.

the distribution of the statistic under the null hypothesis being independent of the population distribution.

Example 9–20. Suppose that in a sample of five from a continuous population the results are (1, 3, 9, 4, 7). There are 5! or 120 permutations of these numbers. Some of them, together with values of $T = \sum_{i=1}^{n-1} (X_{i+1} - X_i)^2$, the corresponding rank sequence, and the values of $\sum i\, t_i$ are listed below. (Of course for each entry listed the permutation with numbers reversed would have the same T-value; for instance, $T(9,7,4,3,1) = 18$.)

Permutation	T	Ranks	$\sum i\, t_i$
1 3 4 7 9	18	1 2 3 4 5	55
3 1 4 7 9	26	2 1 3 4 5	54
1 4 3 7 9	30	1 3 2 4 5	54
4 1 3 7 9	33	3 1 2 4 5	52
1 3 4 9 7	34	1 2 3 5 4	54
3 1 4 9 7	42	2 1 3 5 4	53
4 3 1 7 9	45	3 2 1 4 5	51
1 3 7 9 4	49	1 2 4 5 3	52
3 4 1 7 9	50	2 3 1 4 5	52
1 4 3 9 7	50	1 3 2 5 4	53
1 3 9 7 4	53	1 2 5 4 3	51
4 1 3 9 7	53	3 1 2 5 4	51
1 3 7 4 9	54	1 2 4 3 5	54
1 4 9 7 3	54	1 3 5 4 2	48

These are listed in order of increasing T-values, but observe that they would be ordered differently using the rank statistic $\sum i\, t_i$. For a test based on T with $\alpha = .1$ the twelve permutations with smallest T-values would make up the critical region; that is, randomness would be rejected for $T \leq 42$. The sequence given at the outset as the list of observations in the sample has a T-value of 74, and would therefore call for acceptance of randomness.

PROBLEMS

9–44. Test the data of Problem **9–43** for randomness using d^2/s^2.

9–45. Add k to the $(k + 1)^{st}$ observation, $k = 1, \ldots, 25$, in Example 9–19 and test the resulting sequence of numbers of randomness using the number of runs above and below the median; using the number of runs up and down; and using d^2/s^2.

9–46. Given var $d^2 = (3n - 4)\sigma^4/(n - 1)^2$ in the case of a normal population (no trend), determine the efficiency of d^2 relative to s^2 as an estimate of the variance σ^2.

9–47. Show that using the statistic d^2 is almost equivalent to using the serial correlation R_h with $h = 1$, when ordering permutations of the numbers in the order statistic. Compute R_1 for the permutations of Example 9–20.

9–48. Compute the value of the statistic $\sum t_i E[Z_{(i)}]$ for the permutations of Example 9–20.

10/*Comparisons*

Many statistical problems arise because of a need to make a comparison between two populations with respect to some characteristic. It may be that one wants to know if the quality of an agricultural, industrial, or sociological product with one kind of production (or treatment) is different from another, and possibly how much different. If quality is random, a measure of quality for each kind of production could be taken to be the expected value of the quality of a single item, and the comparison desired would be a comparison of the expected values. A comparison of variabilities might be desired where uniformity is wanted, but the different treatments do not affect the level or average quality.

Although one might occasionally want to *estimate* a difference in quality or the probability that an item produced in one way is better than one produced the other way, the more common statistical problem of comparison is that of *testing* the null hypothesis of little or no difference against the alternative of an appreciable difference. This null hypothesis is sometimes given as a hypothesis of identical distributions:

$$H_0: \quad F_X(\lambda) = F_Y(\lambda),$$

but sometimes (in parametric cases) it is just the hypothesis of equal means or of equal variances. The alternative hypothesis is sometimes rather vague, although frequently the context of the problem does suggest a particular class of alternatives as including those most feared. In general the most sensitive tests can be constructed for situations in which the alternative hypotheses are those in a special restricted class. One commonly employed alternative to identical distributions is that one distribution is "shifted" from the other:

$$H_1: \quad F_X(\lambda) = F_Y(\lambda - \theta), \qquad \theta \neq 0,$$

(or, in the continuous case, $f_X(\lambda) = f_Y(\lambda - \theta)$). If θ is restricted to positive or to negative values, the problem is one-sided. If different actions are appropriate, according as θ is near zero, appreciably positive, or appreciably negative, the problem is a three-action one, not included under the "testing of hypotheses" classification.

Decision procedures for comparing two populations are based on two samples, one drawn from each population, not necessarily of the same size. Although the samples may be actual independent samples from the corresponding populations, sometimes comparisons are made on the basis of "paired" or "related" samples. In such cases observations come paired, each pair consisting of an observation using one treatment and an observation using the other treatment; the observations do not necessarily constitute two samples, one from each population, since the values corresponding to one treatment may be affected by other factors than the treatment. The point of pairing in these cases is to nullify the effect of those other factors, and in effect the result is a single sample of differences (or of whatever quantity is used in comparing observations.) Thus a comparison problem may call for a one-sample procedure.

Example 10–1. Pipes of two different alloys are to be compared as to corrosion resistance. To avoid the influencing of results by differences in composition of the earth, $2n$ pipes are buried in pairs; the extraneous factors are different from pair to pair but the same for each pair. The null hypothesis of no difference in alloys would be equivalent to the hypothesis that the probability is one-half that one pipe in a given pair will outlast the other. If corrosion is indicated by a numerical measure which is, say, normally distributed, the null hypothesis would be that the means for the two alloys are equal, or that their difference is zero. The sample would then be considered a sample of size n from a normal population with mean zero. The observations would be the n differences for the n pairs, and a t test with $n - 1$ degrees of freedom could be used.

When factors influence the observations that are not under test, and which cannot be canceled out by matching the observations, it is necessary to conduct the test in their presence through the use of more complicated designs than those to be taken up in this chapter. Such designs are introduced in Chapter 11.

10.1 Comparisons Based on Sample Distribution Functions

Different populations have different distribution functions, and it is expected that samples from these different populations will have sample distribution functions that differ. Of course random sampling fluctuations can introduce a difference in sample distribution functions even though the samples be from the same population, but a very large discrepancy between sample distribution functions might reasonably serve as the basis for an inference that the populations are different.

Tests based on the discrepancy between sample distribution functions are ordinarily employed when the alternatives to the null hypothesis of identical populations include all ways in which the populations can differ, as opposed to problems in which the shift alternatives, say, are relevant. Different ways of measuring discrepancies between sample distribution functions lead to different tests. The two-sample Kolmogorov-Smirnov test (or the Smirnov test) is based on the statistic D, defined as follows:

$$D = \sup_{\text{all } x} |F_m(x) - G_n(x)|,$$

where $F_m(x)$ is the sample distribution function of a sample of size m from X and $G_n(x)$ is the sample distribution function of a sample of size n from Y. Smirnov has shown that for large samples of sizes m and n:

$$P_{H_0}\left(D > z\sqrt{\frac{1}{m} + \frac{1}{n}}\right) \doteq 2 \sum_{k=1}^{\infty} (-1)^{k-1} \exp[-2k^2z^2],$$

the same function appearing on the right as showed up in the one-sample K–S test. Again the first-term approximation is very good and on the safe side. Using this, the above probability is seen to be approximately α if $z = \sqrt{-(\log \alpha/2)/2}$, and so a test with level α is obtained by rejecting H_0 for

$$D > \sqrt{-\frac{1}{2}\left(\frac{1}{m} + \frac{1}{n}\right) \log \frac{\alpha}{2}}.$$

Values of this asymptotic rejection limit for $\alpha = 0.05$ and $\alpha = 0.01$ are given in Table VII, Appendix, along with small-sample rejection limits for these two levels.

Example 10–2. Consider the two samples of size 60 given in the accompanying frequency tabulations. The maximum absolute difference in cumulative relative frequencies is 0.1 and the 5 per cent rejection limit from Table VII is about 0.25. The null hypothesis of identical distributions is accepted.

x_i	Frequencies		Cumulative Frequencies	
	Sample 1	Sample 2	Sample 1	Sample 2
0	5	6	5	6
1	9	2	14	8
2	4	5	18	13
3	5	7	23	20
4	7	8	30	28
5	2	4	32	32
6	8	4	40	36
7	4	9	44	45
8	9	6	53	51
9	7	9	60	60

The test just described is two-sided, since either positive or negative differences are counted. A one-sided test is provided by the one-sided statistic

$$D^+ = \sup_{\text{all } x} [F_m(x) - G_n(x)],$$

which would intuitively be appropriate for a one-sided class of alternatives, say, $F_Y(\lambda) < F_X(\lambda)$. The large sample distribution of D^+ was shown by Smirnov to be defined by

$$P\left(D^+ > z\sqrt{\frac{1}{m} + \frac{1}{n}}\right) = \exp(-2z^2), \qquad z \geq 0.$$

From this it is evident that the large sample distribution of

$$\frac{4(D^+)^2mn}{(m+n)}$$

is given by

$$P\left[\frac{4(D^+)^2mn}{(m+n)} < u\right] = 1 - \exp\left(\frac{-u}{2}\right), \qquad u \geq 0,$$

which is of the negative exponential type and happens also to be the chi-square distribution function with two degrees of freedom.

Example 10–3. Had the data been gathered as in Example 10–2, but to test instead the hypothesis that the population distributions are identical against the alternative that population 2 is shifted to the right, the one-sided D^+ should be used. Since for the data obtained all the differences between the sample distribution functions are positive, $D^+ = D = 0.1$. Then, since

$$\frac{4(D^+)^2mn}{(m+n)} = 1.2 < 5.99,$$

where 5.99 is the ninety-fifth percentile of the chi-square distribution with two degrees of freedom, the null hypothesis would be accepted at the 5 per cent level.

10.2 Large Sample Comparison of Means

Consider independent samples from populations having second moments, one sample of size m with mean $\bar{X}$ and variance s^2 from a population X with mean μ and variance σ^2, and the other of size n with mean $\bar{Y}$ and variance t^2 from a population Y with mean ν and variance τ^2. The difference $\bar{X} - \bar{Y}$ is asymptotically normal with mean $\mu - \nu$ and variance $\sigma^2/m + \tau^2/n$, no matter what the population distributions. Thus, if σ^2 and τ^2 are *known*, the statistic

$$Z = \frac{\bar{X} - \bar{Y}}{\sqrt{\sigma^2/m + \tau^2/n}}$$

is approximately a standard normal variable under the null hypothesis of identical distributions of X and Y, or under the hypothesis of equal means.

The rejection region $Z >$ constant would be used against the one-sided alternative $\mu > \nu$, and $|Z| >$ constant against the two-sided alternative $\mu \neq \nu$. The choice of constant for given alternative is made using the standard normal table. Given an alternative with $\mu - \nu \neq 0$, the power is approximately $\pi(\mu - \nu) = P(Z^2 > \text{constant})$, in the case of the two-sided test, which can be evaluated approximately from the noncentral chi-square distribution with one degree of freedom and noncentrality parameter $(\mu - \nu)^2/2$.

Of course the population variances would be seldom known, but because in large samples the sample variances are ordinarily very close to the population variances, the modified statistic

$$Z^* = \frac{\bar{X} - \bar{Y}}{\sqrt{s^2/m + t^2/n}}$$

will differ little from Z and can be used in place of Z with reasonable success.

Example 10–4. Given $m = 100$, $\bar{X} = 42.3$, $s^2 = 18.5$, $n = 400$, $\bar{Y} = 42.9$, $t^2 = 17.6$, the estimate of the variance of $\bar{X} - \bar{Y}$ is

$$\frac{18.5}{100} + \frac{17.6}{400} = 0.229,$$

and therefore

$$Z^2 = \frac{(42.9 - 42.3)^2}{0.229} = 1.57.$$

Since this is less than 2.71, the ninetieth percentile of the chi-square distribution with one degree of freedom, equality of means would be accepted at the 10 per cent level. An approximate 90 per cent confidence interval for $\mu - \nu$ would be given by the limits

$$(\bar{X} - \bar{Y}) \pm 1.64\sqrt{0.229},$$

or 0.6 ± 0.79. That this confidence interval contains the value 0 corresponds to the acceptance, above, of $\mu = \nu$ at the 10 per cent level. (Indeed, the constant 1.645 is the square root of the chi-square constant 2.71.)

10.3 Bernoulli Populations

Comparison of two Bernoulli populations is a matter of comparison of their values of the parameter p. The two-sided problem would be that of testing $H_0\colon p_1 = p_2$ against $H_1\colon p_1 \neq p_2$, for which problem a likelihood ratio test can be constructed. On the basis of a random sample of size m from the population with parameter p_1 and an independent random sample of size n from the population with parameter p_2, the likelihood function is

$$L(p_1,p_2) = p_1^J(1 - p_1)^{m-J}p_2^K(1 - p_2)^{n-K},$$

where J and K are the numbers of successes in the two samples. The likelihood function is maximized over H_0 by the values $p_1 = p_2 = \hat{p}$, where

$\hat{p} = (J + K)/(m + n)$. Over $H_0 + H_1$ the maximum is achieved for $p_1 = J/m$ and $p_2 = K/n$. The likelihood ratio is therefore

$$\lambda = \frac{(J + K)^{J+K}(m + n - J - K)^{m+n-J-K}m^m n^n}{J^J K^K (m - J)^{m-J}(n - K)^{n-K}(m + n)^{m+n}}.$$

The quantity $-2 \log \lambda$ has asymptotically a chi-square distribution with one degree of freedom (H_0 is one-dimensional and $H_0 + H_1$ is two-dimensional).

Example 10–5. Consider 50 independent trials of each of two Bernoulli experiments, with the results: 24 out of 50 successes in the first experiment and 30 out of 50 in the second. With these data,

$$\lambda = \left(\frac{27}{24}\right)^{24}\left(\frac{27}{30}\right)^{30}\left(\frac{23}{26}\right)^{26}\left(\frac{23}{20}\right)^{20} \doteq 0.484.$$

The value of $-2 \log \lambda$ is then about 1.453, which is less than the critical value of 2.71 at the 10 per cent level. Equality of p's is therefore accepted at that level.

Consider next "Fisher's exact test" for equality of p's. This is usually conducted with the data arranged in the following "fourfold table":

	Successes	Failures	
Population 1	J	$m - J$	m
Population 2	K	$n - K$	n
	$J + K$	$m + n - J - K$	$N = m + n$

Denoting $J + K$ by S and $j + k$ by s, we have under $p_1 = p_2 = p$,

$$P(J = j,\ K = k \mid S = s) = \frac{P(J = j,\ K = k, \text{ and } S = s)}{P(S = s)}$$

$$= \frac{\binom{m}{j}p^j(1 - p)^{m-j}\binom{n}{k}p^k(1 - p)^{n-k}}{\binom{N}{s}p^s(1 - p)^{N-s}}$$

$$= \frac{\binom{m}{j}\binom{n}{k}}{\binom{N}{s}} = \frac{\binom{j+k}{j}\binom{N-j-k}{m-j}}{\binom{N}{m}}.$$

Each configuration of outcomes J and K corresponds to a certain fourfold table, and the above probability is the probability of a particular fourfold table, given that it is one of those with certain common marginal totals; that is, given $J + K = s$ (which fixes also the value of $m + n - J - K$).

The test is now constructed as follows: For each number s, the fourfold tables with $S = s$ are arranged according to the value of J. A set A_s of these tables is selected whose total conditional probability, given $S = s$, is as close as possible to a specified level α without exceeding it. The decision rule now calls for rejecting H_0 (equal p's) if the observed fourfold table is one of those included in some A_s. For this rule,

$$P_{H_0}(\text{reject H}_0) = \sum_{s=0}^{N} P(\text{reject } H_0 | S = s) P(S = s)$$

$$= \sum_{s=0}^{N} P(A_s | S = s) P(S = s) \le \alpha \sum_{s=0}^{N} P(S = s) = \alpha.$$

Which fourfold tables are put into A_s depends on the alternatives. For testing against $p_1 < p_2$, the tables with the smallest values of J should be used in A_s. For the alternative $p_1 \neq p_2$, put into A_s first the fourfold tables for $j = 0$ and $j = m$; then, those for $j = 1$ and $j = m - 1$, and so on, until no more can be put into A_s without exceeding α.

Example 10–6. Suppose that in testing $p_1 \ge p_2$ against $p_1 < p_2$ one obtains the following results:

	Success	Failure	
From pop. 1	3	5	8
From pop. 2	7	5	12
	10	10	20

The fourfold tables with these same marginal totals but with fewer successes from population 1 are as follows:

2	6	8
8	4	12
10	10	20

1	7	8
9	3	12
10	10	20

0	8	8
10	2	12
10	10	20

The probabilities of these results, given 10 successes among the 20 trials of the experiments, are as follows, under H_0: 0.075, 0.0095, and 0.0004. A test of level at most 0.05 would call for rejection of $p_1 \ge p_2$ if either of the last two tables resulted, and a test of level at most 0.10 is any of the three most extreme tables resulted. Since the table actually obtained is not among these three most extreme cases, the null hypothesis is accepted at the 5 per cent level.

In large samples the asymptotic normal distribution can be used to approximate the hypergeometric probabilities. That is, the distribution of J, given $S = s$ (which is used to determine the critical region), is hypergeometric with mean and variance as follows:

$$\text{Mean: } s\frac{m}{m+n} \qquad \text{Variance: } s\frac{m}{m+n}\left(1 - \frac{m}{m+n}\right)\frac{m+n-s}{m+n-1},$$

and so the following quantity has asymptotically the chi-square distribution with one degree of freedom:

$$\chi^2 \equiv \frac{\left(J - \dfrac{ms}{m+n}\right)^2}{\dfrac{ms}{m+n}\left(1 - \dfrac{m}{m+n}\right)\dfrac{m+n-s}{m+n-1}} = \frac{(J/m - K/n)^2}{\dfrac{J+K}{m+n}\left(1 - \dfrac{J+K}{m+n}\right)\dfrac{m+n}{mn}} \cdot \frac{m+n-1}{m+n}.$$

The test that rejects H_0 for too large or too small values of J amounts, then (in large samples), to rejecting H_0 if χ^2 is too large—how large being determined from the chi-square distribution with one degree of freedom.

Notice that χ^2 has the same asymptotic distribution as $-2 \log \lambda$; this is no accident, for it can be shown that they are asymptotically equal. The following example bears this out.

Example 10–7. If the data of Example 10–5 (24 and 30 successes in 50 trials) are used in a computation of χ^2, the result is

$$\chi^2 = \frac{(24/50 - 30/50)^2 \cdot (50 + 50 - 1)}{(24 + 30)(100 - 54)/2500} \doteq 1.44,$$

whereas $-2 \log \lambda \doteq 1.45$.

PROBLEMS

10–1. Discuss the first-term approximation and the statement that it is on the safe side, for the distribution of D in §10.1.

10–2. Verify the claim in §10.1 concerning the large sample distribution of $4(D^+)^2mn/(m+n)$.

10–3. Measurements of viscosity for a certain substance were made with the following results:

First day	37.0, 31.4, 34.4, 33.3, 34.9
	36.2, 31.0, 33.5, 33.7, 33.4
	34.8, 30.8, 32.9, 34.3, 33.3
Second day	28.4, 31.3, 28.7, 32.1, 31.9
	32.8, 30.2, 30.2, 32.4, 30.7

Would you say the population has changed from one day to the next?

10–4. If 40 per cent of 80 patients given a placebo experience relief, and 60 per cent of 140 patients given a certain drug experience relief, would you say that the drug is effective? If the figures are 40 per cent of 10 and 60 per cent of 20, would you reach the same conclusion?

10–5. In a problem of comparing Bernoulli populations, show the minimal sufficiency of the numbers of successes (J, K) among the m trials and n trials, respectively, from the two populations.

10–6. Show that (in the notation of §10.3) $J/m - K/n$ is a consistent estimate of $p_1 - p_2$.

10–7. Construct an approximate confidence interval for $p_1 - p_2$, using the data of Example 10–5.

10.4 Normal Populations

When the populations from which two samples are drawn are both normal, a natural way to compare them is with respect to the parameters. Usually the problem calls for a comparison with respect to just one of the parameters—either with respect to means (or location parameters) or with respect to variances (or scale parameters). The latter is the simpler problem (as in the case of single sample problems), since the distributions of the variances of the samples do not involve the population means.

The notation to be used in this section is as follows:

Population	Mean	Variance	Sample Size	Sample Mean	Sample Variance
X	μ	σ^2	m	$\bar{X}$	s^2
Y	ν	τ^2	n	$\bar{Y}$	t^2

10.4.1 Variances. Consider first the following two-sided problem of hypothesis-testing:

$$H_0:\ X \text{ and } Y \text{ are independent and normal, with } \sigma^2 = \tau^2,$$
$$H_1:\ X \text{ and } Y \text{ are independent and normal, with } \sigma^2 \neq \tau^2.$$

The likelihood ratio test for this problem is constructed as follows: The likelihood function (for random samples) has the logarithm

$$\log L(\mu, \nu; \sigma^2, \tau^2) = -\frac{m+n}{2}\log 2\pi - \frac{m}{2}\log \sigma^2 - \frac{n}{2}\log \tau^2 - \frac{1}{2\sigma^2}\sum_{i=1}^{m}(X_i - \mu)^2 - \frac{1}{2\tau^2}\sum_{j=1}^{n}(Y_j - \nu)^2.$$

Allowing all four parameters to vary, differentiating with respect to each one in turn, and setting the derivatives equal to zero, one obtains the following solutions, which are then the joint maximum likelihood estimates:

$$\hat{\mu} = \bar{X}, \quad \hat{\nu} = \bar{Y}, \quad \hat{\sigma}^2 = s^2, \quad \hat{\tau}^2 = t^2.$$

(It is readily seen that $(\bar{X}, \bar{Y}, s^2, t^2)$ is sufficient for the problem.)

The numerator of the likelihood ratio is the maximum of the likelihood function with the restriction of H_0, namely, that $\sigma^2 = \tau^2$. Holding these equal to the value v, allowing v, μ, and ν to vary, setting the derivatives with respect to v, μ, and ν equal to zero, and solving simultaneously the resulting equations, one obtains

$$\mu = \bar{X}, \quad \hat{\nu} = \bar{Y}, \quad \hat{v} = \frac{1}{m+n}(ms^2 + nt^2).$$

The estimate $\hat{v}$ is a "pooled variance," the average sum of squared deviations of the observations each about the mean of the sample to which it belongs:

$$\hat{v} = \frac{1}{m+n}\left\{\sum_{i=1}^{m}(X_i - \bar{X})^2 + \sum_{j=1}^{n}(Y_j - \bar{Y})^2\right\}.$$

The likelihood ratio is now obtained by dividing the maximum of the likelihood function subject to H_0 by its maximum without restriction. These maxima are, respectively,

$$L(\bar{X},\bar{Y};\hat{v},\hat{v}) = (2\pi)^{-(m+n)/2}\left(\frac{m+n}{ms^2+nt^2}\right)^{(m+n)/2}\exp[-\tfrac{1}{2}(m+n)],$$

and

$$L(\bar{X},\bar{Y};s^2,t^2) = (2\pi)^{-(m+n)/2}s^{-m}t^{-n}\exp[-\tfrac{1}{2}(m+n)].$$

The likelihood ratio is then

$$\lambda = \frac{L(\bar{X},\bar{Y};\hat{v},\hat{v})}{L(\bar{X},\bar{Y};s^2,t^2)} = (m+n)^{(m+n)/2}\cdot\frac{(s^2)^{m/2}(t^2)^{n/2}}{(ms^2+nt^2)^{(m+n)/2}}$$

$$= \frac{(m+n)^{(m+n)/2}}{m^{m/2}n^{n/2}}\cdot\frac{Z^{m/2}}{(1+Z)^{(m+n)/2}},$$

where

$$Z = \frac{(ms^2)}{(nt^2)} = \frac{\sum(X_i - \bar{X})^2}{\sum(Y_j - \bar{Y})^2}.$$

The critical region $\lambda <$ constant defines a critical region for Z which calls for rejecting equality of variances if Z is either too large or too small. This is seen in Figure 10–1, in which the distribution of Z is sketched (schematically) beneath the sketch of the functional relationship between λ and Z. The two shaded regions, whose total area is the probability of rejecting H_0 with the test $\lambda < \lambda_0$, are not necessarily of equal area, but it is convenient to choose modified limits for Z such that they would be of equal area. Such a modification yields a test that is not the same as the likelihood ratio test—but which is not radically different.

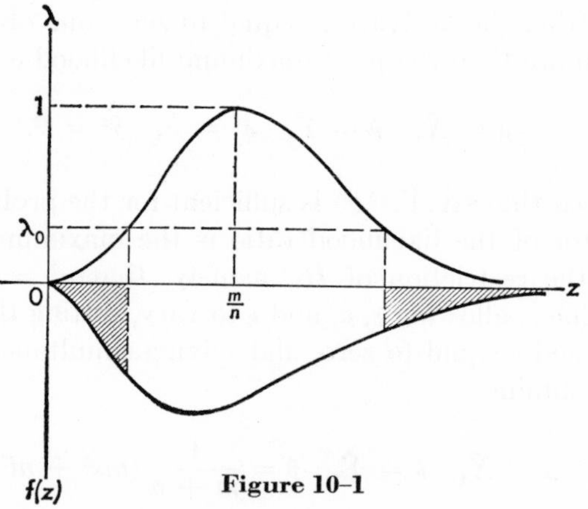

Figure 10–1

In practice, it is the ratio of the unbiased variance estimates,

$$F \equiv \frac{n-1}{m-1} Z = \frac{\sum(X_i - \bar{X})^2/(m-1)}{\sum(Y - \bar{Y})^2/(n-1)} = \frac{\tilde{s}^2}{\tilde{t}^2},$$

which is used in place of Z. This ratio has the F distribution with parameters $(m-1, n-1)$, independent of the values of the population means. (Indeed, the cogent reason for using F in place of Z is that the F tables are available and can be used directly.)

Example 10–8. To test $\sigma^2 = \tau^2$ against the alternative of unequal variances, samples of sizes $m = 25$ and $n = 20$ are obtained, respectively, from X and Y. If the significance level is to be $\alpha = 0.10$, the test used calls for accepting equality of variances if the ratio of the unbiased sample variances falls between the fifth and ninety-fifth percentiles of the F distribution with parameters (24,19). From the F table (Table IV, Appendix) it is found that

$$F_{0.95}(24,19) = 2.11 \qquad \text{and} \qquad F_{0.05}(24,19) = \frac{1}{F_{0.95}(19,24)} = 0.485.$$

If $\tilde{s}^2/\tilde{t}^2$ exceeds 2.11 or is less than 0.485, equality of variances is rejected.

For testing the one-sided hypothesis $\sigma^2 \leq \tau^2$ against $\sigma^2 > \tau^2$, it would seem reasonable to adopt the test with critical region $F >$ constant. The power function of this test is a function of the ratio τ^2/σ^2:

$$\begin{aligned} P(F > k) &= 1 - P(F < k) \\ &= 1 - P\left(\frac{\tilde{s}^2/\sigma^2}{\tilde{t}^2/\tau^2} < \frac{\tau^2}{\sigma^2} k\right) = 1 - F\left(\frac{\tau^2}{\sigma^2} k\right), \end{aligned}$$

where $F(\lambda)$ is the distribution function of the random variable F. Since this distribution function is monotone increasing, the power function is a monotone decreasing function of the ratio τ^2/σ^2, and the test is at least unbiased. It can be shown that there is no uniformly most powerful test for even this one-sided problem. (Cf. Reference [12], page 117.)

10.4.2 Means. Comparison of the means of two normal populations is a simpler problem when the variances (if unknown) can be assumed to be equal than it is when they are not equal. The case of *equal variances* will therefore be considered first.

Using the notation established above, the maximum likelihood estimates of the means μ and ν and of the common variance σ^2 are (as shown in §10.4.1)

$$\hat{\mu} = \bar{X}, \quad \hat{\nu} = \bar{Y}, \quad \hat{\sigma}^2 = \frac{1}{m+n}(ms^2 + nt^2),$$

which happen to be minimal sufficient for the normal family considered. Using these estimates in the likelihood function, one obtains the maximum over all states:

$$L(\bar{X}, \bar{Y}, \hat{\sigma}^2) = (2\pi\hat{\sigma}^2)^{-(m+n)/2} \exp[-\tfrac{1}{2}(m+n)].$$

For a likelihood ratio test of $\mu = \nu$ against the two-sided alternative $\mu \neq \nu$, the maximum of the likelihood function subject to the restriction $\mu = \nu$ is required. The maximizing values of $\mu = \nu$ and σ^2 are found to be

$$\tilde{\mu} = \frac{m\bar{X} + n\bar{Y}}{m+n}, \quad \tilde{\sigma}^2 = \frac{1}{m+n}\left\{\sum(X_i - \tilde{\mu})^2 + \sum(Y_j - \tilde{\mu})^2\right\}.$$

Substitution in the likelihood function again produces $-(m+n)/2$ in the exponent, and the likelihood ratio becomes

$$\lambda = \left(\frac{\hat{\sigma}^2}{\tilde{\sigma}^2}\right)^{(m+n)/2}.$$

Then

$$\begin{aligned}\left(\frac{1}{\lambda}\right)^{2/(m+n)} &= \frac{\tilde{\sigma}^2}{\hat{\sigma}^2} \\ &= \frac{\sum(X_i - \bar{X})^2 + \sum(Y_j - \bar{Y})^2 + m(\bar{X} - \tilde{\mu})^2 + n(\bar{Y} - \tilde{\mu})^2}{\sum(X_i - \bar{X})^2 + \sum(Y_j - \bar{Y})^2} \\ &= 1 + \frac{1}{m+n-2} T^2,\end{aligned}$$

where

$$T^2 = mn\left(\frac{m+n-2}{m+n}\right)\frac{(\bar{X} - \bar{Y})^2}{ms^2 + nt^2} = \frac{Z^2}{Q/(m+n-2)}$$

and

$$Z^2 = \frac{(\bar{X} - \bar{Y})^2}{\sigma^2(1/m + 1/n)}, \qquad Q = \frac{ms^2 + nt^2}{\sigma^2}.$$

Under H_0 the quantity Z^2 has a chi-square distribution with one degree of freedom, and Q has a chi-square distribution with $m + n - 2$ degrees of freedom. Further, they are independent, and so under H_0 the ratio T^2 has the F distribution with parameters $(1, m + n - 2)$, independent of the value of the common variance σ^2. The value of the constant would be determined by specification of α, using Table IV, or equivalently from the table of the t distribution, since the symmetrically distributed square root T of T^2 has the t distribution.

Example 10–9. Consider the following data, taken from independent normal populations with equal (but unknown) variances: $s^2 = 0.4$, $t^2 = 0.3$, $\bar{X} = 2.3$, $\bar{Y} = 2.8$, and $m = n = 10$. Then

$$T^2 = 100 \cdot \frac{18}{20} \cdot \frac{(0.5)^2}{4+3} = 1.875,$$

and from Table IVa one finds $F_{0.95}(1.18) = 4.41$. Since $1.875 < 4.41$, equality of means would be accepted at the 5 per cent level.

When it is not assumed that $\mu = \nu$, the distribution of T^2 is noncentral F, the numerator Z^2 being then noncentral chi-square with noncentrality parameter $(\mu - \nu)^2/2\sigma^2$. Thus the power of the test $T^2 > k$ can be expressed as a function of $(\mu - \nu)/\sigma$:

$$\pi\left(\frac{\mu - \nu}{\sigma}\right) = P(T^2 > k) = 1 - F(k),$$

where $F(\cdot)$ denotes the noncentral F distribution function.

A two-sided confidence interval is readily constructed by using the fact that

$$T^2 = \frac{[\bar{X} - \bar{Y} - (\mu - \nu)]^2}{(m + n)(ms^2 + nt^2)}\, mn(m + n - 2)$$

has the F distribution with parameters $(1, m + n - 2)$.

A test of $\mu \leq \nu$ against $\mu > \nu$ is provided by the critical region $T >$ constant, where

$$T = (\bar{X} - \bar{Y})\sqrt{\frac{mn(m + n - 2)}{(m + n)(ms^2 + nt^2)}}.$$

The power function of this test would involve the noncentral t distribution.

Next consider the case of *unequal variances*. The problem of comparing means of two normal populations when the variances are unknown and possibly unequal is called the *Behrens-Fisher problem*. It has an extensive history of controversy, and there are still unsettled aspects of the problem. The difficulty lies in the fact that the ratio T^2 used above for the case of equal variances no longer has a distribution under H_0 which is independent of population parameters.

Considerations of invariance have served to suggest that the critical region of a test ought to be of the form (for the one-sided case):

$$\frac{\bar{Y} - \bar{X}}{\sqrt{ms^2 + nt^2}} \geq h\left(\frac{nt^2}{ms^2}\right),$$

for a suitably chosen function h. It is not known whether there is an h such that the probability of the critical region is a given α under H_0, for all values of the common mean and for all values of τ/σ, although a test with approximately this property is available (cf. B. L. Welch, "The Generalization of Student's Problem when Several Different Population Variances Are Involved," *Biometrika*, 34(1947), pages 28–35).

We give here a test proposed by Scheffé ("On solutions of the Behrens-Fisher Problem, Based on the t-Distribution," *Ann. Math. Stat.*, 14(1943), pages 35–44). It is assumed for definiteness that $m < n$. The statistic used is

$$S = \frac{\bar{X} - \bar{Y}}{\sqrt{Q}} \sqrt{m(m-1)},$$

where

$$Q = \sum_{i=1}^{m} (U_i - \bar{U})^2, \qquad U_i = X_i - \sqrt{\frac{m}{n}}\, Y_i, \qquad i = 1, \ldots, m.$$

Under the null hypothesis that $\mu = \nu$, the statistic S has a t distribution with $m - 1$ degrees of freedom, independent of the population variances. To see why this is so, put

$$d_i = X_i - \sqrt{\frac{m}{n}}\, Y_i + \sum_{i=1}^{m} \frac{Y_i}{\sqrt{mn}} - \bar{Y}, \qquad i = 1, \ldots, m.$$

Being linear combinations of the normally distributed observations, the d's have a multivariate normal distribution, with means

$$E(d_i) = E(X_i) - \sqrt{\frac{m}{n}}\, E(Y_i) + \frac{mE(Y)}{\sqrt{mn}} - E(Y) = \mu - \nu,$$

and covariances

$$\text{cov}(d_i, d_j) = \begin{cases} 0, & \text{if } i = j, \\ \sigma^2 + (m/n)\tau^2, & \text{if } i \neq j. \end{cases}$$

That is, the d's may be thought of as making up a random sample of size m from a normal population with mean $\mu - \nu$ and variance $\sigma^2 + (m/n)\tau^2$. The mean of this sample, $\bar{d} = \bar{X} - \bar{Y}$, is then normally distributed; further, it is independent of the variance of the sample consisting of the d's, and the following ratio has the t distribution with $m - 1$ degrees of freedom:

$$S^* = \sqrt{m(m-1)}\, \frac{\bar{d} - (\mu - \nu)}{\sqrt{Q}},$$

where again

$$Q = \sum_{i=1}^{m} (U_i - \bar{U})^2 = \sum_{i=1}^{m} (d_i - \bar{d}^2).$$

Then, under H_0 the variable S^* is S, which has the distribution claimed.

Example 10–10. Consider the following data from two normal populations:

From X: 17, 21, 19, 23, 18, 22;
From Y: 21, 19, 23, 26, 20, 22, 24, 21.

Here $m = 6$, $n = 8$, $\sqrt{m/n} = 0.866$, $\bar{X} = 20$, and $\bar{Y} = 22$. The U's are as follows: -1.2, 4.5, -0.9, 0.5, 0.7, 2.9. From these are obtained $\bar{U} = 1.083$ and $Q = 24.63$; and then

$$S = \sqrt{6 \times 5}\,\frac{(20 - 22)}{\sqrt{24.63}} = -2.21.$$

Since this is less than -2.01, the fifth percentile of the t distribution with $m - 1 = 5$ degrees of freedom, the hypothesis of equal population means would be rejected in favor of unequal means at the 10 per cent level. A two-sided 90 per cent confidence interval would be given as follows:

$$-2 - 2.01\sqrt{\frac{24.63}{30}} < \mu - \nu < -2 + 2.01\sqrt{\frac{24.63}{30}},$$

or $(-3.82, -0.18)$, which does not contain 0.

This test of Scheffé has certain desirable properties. It is based on the readily accessible t tables; the distribution of the test statistic under the null hypothesis is independent of the population variances; and (as shown by Scheffé) the confidence interval that results has a property of minimum length among the class of procedures based on linear combinations of the observations. However, the test statistic is *not* independent of the ordering of the observations—it is not symmetric in the X's and in the Y's. Indeed, if the original ordering is lost, the test must be applied to a randomly selected one of the possible orderings of the observations in the order statistic. It is also noted that if the population variances *are* equal, the t test discussed first would apply and is based on $n + m - 2$ degrees of freedom; the fact that only $m - 1$ degrees of freedom are available in using the Scheffé procedure suggests that the latter is not so good as might be hoped for.

PROBLEMS

10–8. Show that $(\bar{X}, \bar{Y}, s^2, t^2)$ is minimal sufficient for problems involving two independent normal populations with unknown parameters.

10–9. If the data of Example 10–9 has been obtained to test equality of variances, what conclusion would be drawn?

10–10. Determine the power function of the test defined in Example 10–8 (as a function of the ratio of population variances).

10–11. Would equality of means be accepted on the basis of the data in Example 10–10 if it could be assumed that the population variances are equal? Construct a confidence interval for $\mu - \nu$ under this assumption.

10–12. Varify the computation of $\text{cov}(d_i, d_j)$ in the development of the Scheffé test.

10–13. Compute the value of the Scheffé statistic for the data of Example 10–10, but using a different ordering of the Y values (for instance, let $Y_i \to Y_{i+1}$, and $Y_8 \to Y_1$).

10.5 Nonparametric Comparison of Locations

In this section are considered various tests (by no means all that have been proposed) for the null hypothesis that two populations have the same locations. That is, the tests to be discussed are particularly sensitive to alternatives that are shifts in the population distribution, whether such shifts be measured by means, medians, or just by a shifted distribution function. The particular parametric cases involving normal and Bernoulli families were considered separately in §§10.3 and 10.4; the tests of this section are "nonparametric," being applied in cases in which the population is not known to be one of a certain parametric class. Consequently a general treatment of power is somewhat awkward. Sometimes power is computed for certain specific alternatives, members of a parametric class, in which case a test especially designed for the particular parametric class in question is usually available for comparison.

10.5.1 The Sign Test. The term *sign test*, used in §9.5, is used here again because again the problem will be reduced to testing $p = \frac{1}{2}$ in a Bernoulli population.

The observations in a random sample from X of size n and those in a random sample from Y of the same size n are paired according to the order of observation: (X_i, Y_i), $i = 1, \ldots, n$. For each pair a plus sign $(+)$ or a minus sign $(-)$ is recorded according as the Y exceeds or is exceeded by the X. Assume for the present that the distribution of (X, Y) is continuous so that ties have probability zero. If the probability that Y exceeds X is denoted by p: $p = P(Y > X)$, the null hypothesis that X and Y are identically distributed yields the value $p = \frac{1}{2}$. Of course p can be $\frac{1}{2}$ even though X and Y are not identically distributed, and it is really the hypothesis $p = \frac{1}{2}$ that the sign test is designed for.

The test statistic used is the number of $+$ signs or the number of pairs of observations in which Y exceeds X. Considering each pair (X_i, Y_i) as a trial of a Bernoulli experiment, the statistic is simply the number of successes in n independent trials, which has been seen to be minimal sufficient for problems involving p. The statistic has the binomial distribution with parameters (n,p).

Pairing the observations makes the two-sample problem into a one-sample problem—indeed, into a parametric one-sample problem, which has already been studied. The potential disadvantage in the requirement of equal sample sizes is offset by the fact that X and Y do not have to be independent; the test can be used in comparing twins, or right- and left-hand characteristics in individual, or two sides of a tire, etc. In fact, all that is required is that the probability $P(Y_i > X_i)$ remain fixed.

Even though the populations be assumed continuous, ties *do* occur in practice owing to round-off. Rather than make half of the ties $+$ and half $-$, or to assign + and − by the toss of a coin, the best procedure for handling ties appears to be to ignore them (cf. Reference [12], §4.7, and J. Hemelryk, "A theorem on the sign test when ties are present," Proc. Kon. Ned. Akad. sect. of sciences A 55, page 322). That is, the test is applied, using only those pairs in which there is not a tie. Using this procedure results in a significance level that is at most as large as that used in determining the critical region based on the assumption of continuous populations. For, with the critical region C determined for each m so that under the null hypothesis

$$P(C \mid m \text{ nonzero differences}) \leq \alpha,$$

it follows that

$$\begin{aligned} P_{H_0}(C) &= \sum_{m=0}^{n} P_{H_0}(C \mid m \text{ nonzero differences}) P_{H_0}(m \text{ nonzero differences}) \\ &\leq \sum_{m=0}^{n} \alpha P_{H_0}(m \text{ nonzero differences}) = \alpha. \end{aligned}$$

Of course, with an agreement as to how to handle ties, the sign test can be used even if the populations are discrete. The null hypothesis in this case would be that $P(X < Y) = P(X > Y)$, or that $P(X < Y \mid X \neq Y) = \frac{1}{2}$.

It would appear intuitively that since the sign test does not exploit the magnitudes of the observations except in a crude way, there might be more efficient methods of comparison. In a sense this is so in some cases but to what extent depends on the nature of the populations. Pitman (Columbia lecture notes, 1949) has introduced the notion of asymptotic efficiency of one test relative to another in the case of a parametric family of alternatives. For comparisons, with $m = n$, the asymptotic efficiency of a procedure d relative to a procedure d^* is the limit of the ratio n^*/n, where n and n^* are the sample sizes under d and d^* required to achieve the same power β for the same alternative, if this ratio has a limit independent of α and β as $n \to \infty$. Pitman showed that the relative asymptotic efficiency of the sign test with respect to the t test is $8\sigma^2 f^2(0)$, in the case of shift alternatives: $F_X(\lambda) = F_Y(\lambda - \theta)$, where f denotes the density of $F_{X-Y}(\lambda)$ and $X - Y$ is symmetrical about 0. This relative asymptotic efficiency does not have a positive lower bound; for normal alternatives it reduces to $2/\pi \doteq 0.63$. (For small samples the efficiency is greater than this.)

The sign test has the feature of being applicable to situations in which comparisons are qualitative; for these, tests like the t test, which depend on numerical comparisons, cannot be applied.

Example 10–11. Returning to the pipes buried in pairs, Example 10–1, it is very likely that comparisons of corrosion in each pair are made qualitatively. Suppose that there are altogether four dozen pipes and that when they are compared in pairs, there are six ties, and pipes of alloy A fared better than those of alloy B in 13 of the remaining 18 pairs. The probability of five or fewer minus' or five or fewer plus' among 18 observations is about 0.096 under the hypothesis of no difference in alloys, or $p = 1/2$. A two-sided test at the level 0.096 therefore calls for rejection of equal corrosion resistance of the two alloys. (Here is a situation in which a three-action problem would better represent actual practice. No doubt different action would be called for if $p < 1/2$ than if $p > 1/2$.)

10.5.2 The Median Test. Again consider the null hypothesis that two populations X and Y are identical and that a test is to be based on a random sample from each—one of size m from X and one of size n from Y. It is now required that X and Y be independent.

The median test is again designed to detect shifts in location and is constructed as follows: The $m + n$ independent observations in the two random samples are arranged in numerical order, and the median of this combination of the two samples is determined. The test statistic is then the number of observations from X which lie to the left of this median. (Alternatively one could use the number of observations from Y or count the number to the right of the median.) Selection of this statistic is based on the intuitive notion that it will tend to be abnormally large when Y is located to the right of X and abnormally small when Y is located to the left of X. If the populations are identical (or if only they have the same median), one would expect to find close to half of the X observations and half of the Y observations on either side of the median of the combined sample.

The distribution of M_1, the number of observations from X which lie to the left of the median of the combined sample, is readily obtained under the null hypothesis. To avoid fussiness of detail, assume that $m + n = N = 2K$, where K is an integer. Then, under the null hypothesis, the combined sample is a sample of size N from the common population. Given the order statistic of this combined sample, there are $N!$ samples that could have led to it, and these are equally likely to have done so (according to §8.1.1). To determine the conditional probability of m_1 observations to the left of the median, given the order statistic, it is only necessary to count the sample configurations in which $M_1 = m_1$ and divide by $N!$. The number of arrangements of m X's and n Y's in which m_1 X's lie to the left of the median, is

$$\binom{m}{m_1}\binom{n}{K - m_1} K!\,K!,$$

and dividing this by $N!$ yields the desired probability:

$$P(M_1 = m_1 \,|\, \text{order statistic}) = \frac{\binom{m}{m_1}\binom{n}{K - m_1}}{\binom{N}{K}}.$$

Because this is independent of the condition, it is also the absolute probability of m_1 X's to the left of the median (under H_0).

The statistic M_1 determines also the number of observations from X to the right of the median, as well as the numbers of observations from Y to the right and to the left of the median. These four numbers can be thought of in a fourfold table with fixed marginal totals:

	Number from X	Number from Y	Totals
Left of median	M_1	N_1	$N/2 = K$
Right of median	M_2	N_2	$N/2 = K$
Total	m	n	N

The probability (under H_0) of this table has been found to be hypergeometric, as it was in §10.3 where fourfold tables with fixed marginal totals arose in comparing Bernoulli populations. For a two-sided test, the quantity χ^2 defined in §10.3, which is asymptotically chi-square with one degree of freedom, can be used as the basis of the test, rejecting H_0 for large values of χ^2.

In the small sample case it is usually necessary to randomize in order to achieve a desired level α exactly, since the test statistic is discrete (cf. §7.1.2). It is shown by Tocher (in "Extension of the Neyman-Pearson Theory of Tests to Discontinuous Variates," *Biometrika*, 39(1950), pages 130–144) that the randomized test obtained in this way is most powerful in the one-sided case.

Example 10–12. Wire B is to be replaced by wire A if the resistance per unit length is not significantly lower. Twenty tests on each type of wire were conducted, with the following results (in ohms):

Wire A	Wire B	Wire A	Wire B
0.051	0.054	0.049	0.057
0.047	0.051	0.051	0.051
0.049	0.052	0.053	0.054
0.048	0.051	0.050	0.051
0.048	0.051	0.053	0.052
0.049	0.055	0.047	0.052
p.049	0.049	0.049	0.050
0.049	0.049	0.050	0.052
0.049	0.051	0.051	0.052
0.051	0.052	0.049	0.048

Listing these 40 observations in a single-ordered sequence, it is found that there are at least 14 observations from wire A to the left of the combined median (the ambiguity arising because of ties introduced by rounding-off). The value of X^2 corresponding to $m_1 = 14$ is

$$\frac{20(20 \cdot 14 - 20 \cdot 6)^2(20 + 20 - 1)}{(14 + 6) \cdot 20 \cdot 20 \cdot (20 + 20 - 14 - 6)} = 6.24.$$

The 97.5 percentile of the chi-square distribution with one degree of freedom is 5.02, and so a one-sided test at the 2.5 per cent level rejects the null hypothesis of no difference.

It is shown by Mood ("On the Asymptotic Efficiency of Certain Nonparametric Two Sample Tests," *Ann. Math. Stat.*, 25(1954), pages 514–522) that for normal shift alternatives, the asymptotic efficiency of the median test relative to the t test is the same as that of the sign test, namely, $2/\pi$, or about 0.63.

PROBLEMS

10–14. One puppy is fed diet A and another diet B in each of 30 pairs of puppies, each pair taken from a single litter. If diet A puppies fare better (according to some specified mode of comparison) in 16 of the 30 pairs and fare worse in 10 pairs, is this sufficient evidence to assert that diet A is superior?

10–15. Apply the sign test to the data of Example 10–12. For this application, assume that H_0 (which calls for using wire A) is that $p \geq 0.4$ and that H_1 (which calls for using wire B) is that $p < 0.4$, where p is the probability that in a pair of measurements, one on A and one on B, the result for A exceeds that for B.

10–16. Determine the power function of the test in Problem 9–15 that calls for using wire B if fewer than six plus' turn up in 20 comparisons; also determine the value of α for this test.

10–17. Apply the median test to the following data:

From X: 16, 21, 15, 18, 19, 13, 20, 22
From Y: 12, 18, 17, 14, 18, 10.

10.5.3 The Wilcoxon-Mann-Whitney Test. Tests based on ranks for the hypothesis of no difference in location against shift alternatives are motivated (as was the median test) by the notion that if there is no difference, there should not be a preponderance of observations from one population in either end of the combined order statistic.

Consider the sequence of observations as they appear in the order statistic, noting only which population an observation comes from. For each Y observation count the number of X observations preceding it, and let U_Y denote the total of these numbers. That is, for each pair of observations X_i and Y_j define

$$Z_{ij} = \begin{cases} 1, & \text{if } X_i < Y_j, \\ 0, & \text{if } X_i > Y_j. \end{cases}$$

The sum of these Z's is the statistic U_Y:

$$U_Y = \sum_{i=1}^{m} \sum_{j=1}^{n} Z_{ij}.$$

A similar sum with 1 and 0 reversed can be used in defining U_X as the total number of X inversions; that is, the total of the numbers of Y observations preceding the X observations. Since there are mn terms in the summation of Z_{ij}, and since interchanging 0's and 1's in U_Y produces U_X, it is evident that $U_X + U_Y = mn$.

of the $N!$ sample points that lead to a given order statistic; but then, since these $N!$ sample points are equally likely, the conditional distribution of a given sequence of X's and Y's with subscripts dropped is just

$$\frac{n!(N-n)!}{N!} = \frac{1}{\binom{N}{n}}.$$

Since this is independent of the condition, it is also the absolute probability; that is, the various possible sequences of n Y's and $m = N - n$ X's are equally likely.

A test based on Y ranks will have an α that is just $1/\binom{N}{n}$ times the number of arrangements of X's and Y's in the critical region. The different rank tests used result from different ways of filling up the critical region. The Wilcoxon test calls for putting into the critical region those points for which the sum of the Y ranks is largest (or smallest, depending on the alternative direction of the shift), and a test is constructed by putting into the critical region first the arrangement with largest rank sum, then the one with the next largest rank sum, and so on, until the number of arrangements divided by $\binom{N}{n}$ is just equal to α, or (because of the discreteness) perhaps slightly less.

The Fisher-Yates c_1 test calls for putting arrangements into the critical region according to the size of

$$c_1 = \frac{1}{n}\sum_{i=1}^{n} E(Z_{s_i}),$$

where $Z_1, \ldots, Z_N$ are the ordered observations in a random sample from a standard normal population, and $s_1, \ldots, s_n$ is the sequence of Y ranks in the combined order statistic of X's and Y's. For one-sided shift alternatives, the critical region is $c_1 >$ constant (or $c_1 <$ constant, depending on the direction of the shift), and it can be shown that this test is most powerful in the case of normal alternatives for sufficiently small shifts. (Cf. Reference [12], page 236 ff.) It is also known that in terms of the concept introduced by Pitman (§10.5.1), the asymptotic efficiency of the c_1 test relative to the t test is always at least 1 for shift alternatives and is equal to 1 only in the normal case. (Cf. H. Chernoff and I. R. Savage, "Asymptotic normality and efficiency of certain nonparametric test statistics," *Ann. Math. Stat.*, 29(1958), page 972.) Further, c_1 is asymptotically normal as m and n become infinite with a nonzero, finite limiting ratio, with mean zero and variance

$$\frac{m}{nN(N-1)} \sum_{i=1}^{N} a_{N_i}{}^2,$$

where $a_{Ni} = E(Z_i)$.

Tables of a_{Ni} are available in *Biometrika Tables for Statisticians*, Vol. 1 (Cambridge Univ. Press), 1954, and in a paper by Teichrow in *Ann. Math. Stat.* 27(1956), page 410. A short version appears here as Table IX, Appendix.

Example 10–14. Consider the c_1 test based on samples of sizes $m = 4$ and $n = 6$. The values of $a_{10,i}$ found in one of the tables mentioned are as follows: -1.539, -1.001, -0.656, -0.376, -0.123, 0.123, 0.376, 0.656, 1.001, and 1.539. The sequences having largest c_1 values are then found to be those listed:

Sequence	Y Ranks	$6c_1 = \sum_{i=1}^{6} a_{10,s_i}$
$XXXXYYYYYY$	5 6 7 8 9 10	3.57
$XXXYXYYYYY$	4 6 7 8 9 10	3.32
$XXXYYXYYYY$	4 5 7 8 9 10	3.07
$XXYXXYYYYY$	3 6 7 8 9 10	3.04
$XXXYYYXYYY$	4 5 6 8 9 10	2.82
$XXYXYXYYYY$	3 5 7 8 9 10	2.79
$XYXXXYYYYY$	2 6 7 8 9 10	2.69
$XXYXYYXYYY$	3 5 6 8 9 10	2.54
$XXYYXXYYYY$	3 4 7 8 9 10	2.54
$XXXYYYYXYY$	4 5 6 7 9 10	2.54
$XYXXYXYYYY$	2 5 7 8 9 10	2.45
$XXYYXYXYYY$	3 4 6 8 9 10	2.30
$XXYXYYYXYY$	3 5 6 7 9 10	2.26

For $\alpha = 0.05$ there would be $0.05 \times \binom{10}{4} = 10.5$ points in the critical region; rather, $\theta = 0$ would be accepted for $c_1 \leq 2.30$, rejected for $c_1 \geq 2.54$, and rejected or accepted according to the toss of a suitably chosen "coin" if $c_1 = 2.45$, the value that puts α just over the desired 0.05.

If the result of sampling is as follows: 22, 25, 27, 30, from X, and 24, 29, 32, 33, 35, 36, from Y, the corresponding sequence of X's and Y's in the combined order statistic is $XYXXYXYYYY$, with $c_1 = 2.45$. This is the boundary point of the 5 per cent critical region.

It is interesting to compute the critical value of c_1 which comes from the asymptotic distribution; the approximate variance is 0.0587, and for $\alpha = 0.05$ the critical value would be $1.645\sqrt{0.0587} = 0.4$, or $6c_1 = 2.4$, which is approximately what was obtained above. Similarly, for $\alpha = 0.025$, $1.96\sqrt{0.0587} = 0.475$, or $6c_1 = 2.85$. This would put the first four points into the critical region, with $\alpha = 4/\binom{10}{4} = 0.019$. The agreement is fairly good, considering the small sample sizes.

10.5.5 The Van der Waerden Test. Van der Waerden has proposed the following test based on ranks: reject $F_X(\lambda) = F_Y(\lambda)$ in favor of a shift $F_Y(\lambda) = F_X(\lambda - \theta)$ with $\theta > 0$ if the value of

$$\mathcal{Y} = \sum_{j=1}^{n} \Psi\left(\frac{s_j}{N+1}\right)$$

is too large, where again $s_1, \ldots, s_n$ are the Y ranks, and Ψ is the inverse of the standard normal distribution function: $\Psi(N(x)) = x$. The corresponding sum for X ranks $r_1, \ldots, r_m$:

$$\mathcal{X} = \sum_{i=1}^{m} \Psi\left(\frac{r_i}{N+1}\right)$$

is just equal to $-\mathcal{Y}$, since

$$\mathcal{X} + \mathcal{Y} = \sum_{k=1}^{N} \Psi\left(\frac{k}{N+1}\right) = 0.$$

[This follows from the relation $\Psi(t) = -\Psi(1-t)$].

The mean and variance of $\mathcal{Y}$ are respectively $E(\mathcal{Y}) = 0$ and

$$\operatorname{var} \mathcal{Y} = \frac{mn}{N(N-1)} \sum_{k=1}^{N} \Psi^2\left(\frac{k}{N+1}\right).$$

Tables of critical values and the average sum of squares needed for var $\mathcal{Y}$ are available (B. L. van der Waerden and E. Nievergelt, *Tafeln zum Vergleich zweier Stickproben mittels X-test und Zeichentest*, Springer-Verlag, 1956.)

Again the level of the test is the ratio of the number of distinct sequences of X's and Y's in the critical region to $\binom{N}{n}$, and the test given is another scheme for deciding which points to put into the critical region first, and how many.

The properties of asymptotic normality and asymptotic efficiency are the same as those of the c_1 statistic of §10.5.4, again following from the theorem of Chernoff and Savage referred to there.

Example 10–15. Again consider (as in Example 10–14) the case $m = 4$ and $n = 6$. The necessary values of $\Psi(k/11)$ are as follows: -1.34, -0.91, -0.60, -0.35, -0.11, 0.11, 0.35, 0.60, 0.91, 1.34, for $k = 1, 2, \ldots, 10$, in that order. The rank sequences given in Example 10–14 are repeated below, this time with the value of $\mathcal{Y}$:

Y Ranks	$\mathcal{Y}$	
5 6 7 8 9 10	3.20	
4 6 7 8 9 10	2.96	
4 5 7 8 9 10	2.74	
3 6 7 8 9 10	2.71	
4 5 6 8 9 10	2.50	
3 5 7 8 9 10	2.49	
2 6 7 8 9 10	2.40	
3 5 6 8 9 10	2.25	
3 4 7 8 9 10	2.25	
4 5 6 7 9 10	2.25	
2 5 7 8 9 10	2.18	
3 4 6 8 9 10	2.01	
3 5 6 7 9 10	2.00	($6c_1 = 2.26$)
4 5 6 7 8 10	1.94	($6c_1 = 2.20$)
2 5 6 8 9 10	1.94	($6c_1 = 2.20$)
1 6 7 8 9 10	1.97	($6c_1 = 2.16$)

Although there are minor differences in ordering at the bottom of this list, the test for $\alpha = 0.05$ would be exactly the same as in the case of the c_1 test.

10.5.6 A Permutation Test. Again consider m observations from X and n observations from Y, obtained for the purpose of testing $\Delta = 0$, where

$$F_X(y - \Delta) = F_Y(y).$$

It is assumed that all $m + n$ observations are independent, and under the null hypothesis they can be considered as making up a random sample of size $m + n$ from a population with distribution function $F_Y(y)$. Given the order statistic corresponding to these $m + n$ observations, the $(m + n)!$ permutations which would yield that order statistic are equally likely. A critical region is then constructed, with probability $1/(m + n)!$ for each permutation put into it, according to the value of $\bar{X} - \bar{Y}$, $\bar{X}$ denoting the average of the first m observations and $\bar{Y}$ the average of the last n. For the alternative $\Delta > 0$ permutations with the largest values of $\bar{X} - \bar{Y}$ are used in the critical region.

Actually, since $\sum(X_i + Y_j)$ is given, and

$$\bar{X} - \bar{Y} = \frac{1}{m}\sum(X_i + Y_j) - \frac{m+n}{mn}\sum Y_j,$$

the value of $\sum Y_j$ (or equally well, $\sum X_i$) can be used instead of $\bar{X} - \bar{Y}$ to code the permutations. Further, the ordering among the X's and the ordering among the Y's does not play a role, so that for the purpose of comparing values of $\sum Y_j$, only $\binom{m+n}{m}$ combinations (equally likely, of course) need be considered.

Example 10–15. Suppose that three observations are from X and two from Y, and that the observed combined order statistic is (4, 6, 7, 8, 9). There are (5/3) or ten possible combinations and corresponding values of $\sum Y_j$, as shown in the following tabulation:

X's	Y's	$\sum Y_j$
4, 6, 7	8, 9	17
6, 4, 8	7, 9	16
4, 7, 8	6, 9	15
4, 6, 9	7, 8	15
4, 7, 9	6, 8	14
6, 7, 8	4, 9	13
4, 8, 9	6, 7	13
6, 7, 9	4, 8	12
6, 8, 9	4, 7	11
7, 8, 9	4, 6	10

If the permutations yielding $\sum Y_j = 10$ or 11 are put into the critical region, the level of the test is $\alpha = 2/10$. An actual sample of (6, 9, 8) from X and (7, 4) from Y would call for rejection of the null hypothesis of no difference in locations at the twenty percent level.

This test is discussed with respect to properties of optimality and asymptotic behaviour for large samples in [12], §5.7 and §5.8.

PROBLEMS

10–18. Apply Wilcoxon's test to the data of Problem 10–17.

10–19. Compute the Pitman asymptotic efficiency of the Wilcoxon test relative to the t test for the case of shift alternatives and a basic uniform population.

10–20. Data are obtained as follows. From X: 12.9, 12.4, 14.7 ,13.8, 15.4, 11.8, 14.2, 13.3, 12.1, and from Y: 13.0, 15.1, 13.7, 16.6, 15.2, 12.3, 14.8, 15.8, 14.3, 13.4, 14.0 . Apply Wilcoxon's test for identical distributions of X and Y against $F_X(\lambda) = F_X(\lambda - \theta)$, for $\theta > 0$.

10–21. Compute the sum of the ranks for the sequences listed in Example 10–14, and notice whether the Wilcoxon statistic would imply the same order of putting points into a critical region.

10–22. Apply the c_1 test and the Van der Waerden test to the data of Example 10–13 (use the exact distributions).

10–23. Apply the c_1 test to the situation of Problem 10–20, using the asymptotic distribution to determine the critical region.

10–24. Derive the formula for the variance of the Van der Waerden statistic. [*Hint:* Let $a_i = \Psi(i/[N+1])$. Then for each $j = 1, \ldots, n$, a_{s_j} is a random variable with values $a_1, \ldots, a_N$ each with probability $1/N$. Compute $E(a_{s_j})$, var a_{s_j}, $E(a_{s_j}a_{s_k})$, and then var $\mathcal{Y}$. Use the fact that $\sum a_i = 0$ and therefore $(\sum a_i)^2 = 0$ to express $\sum a_i a_j$ in terms of $\sum a_i^2$.]

10–25. Apply the permutation test to the results of sampling given in Example 10–14.

11/Linear Models and Analysis of Variance

The problems to be considered in this chapter are concerned with the means of several normal populations, generalizing the situation of §10.4.2. A null hypothesis will again be equality of means, but there are new features to be treated. In some cases it is not really expected that the means will be equal, and one is interested in determining the functional dependence of the means on a numerical index of the populations (regression problems). In other cases the means depend on several non-numerical factors, and it is desired to test a hypothesis of no effect on the means from one factor in the presence of the other factors (analysis of variance problems). Some problems involve dependence of the mean both on a numerical index and on non-numerical factors (analysis of covariance problems). The models to be considered in this discussion are those in which the dependence on parameters is linear in the parameters—linear models. All the problems mentioned above can be treated in the framework of a general linear hypothesis model, an introduction to which will close the chapter.

The material to be presented is but an introduction to an important and highly developed field of problems to which complete books are devoted (cf. References [5], [11], [14], and [17], to name but a few). Although power functions will be touched upon, space will not permit discussion of optimality of procedures (cf. Chapter 7 of Reference [12]).

11.1 Regression

Consider a nonrandom variable z that depends on a "controlled variable" t in some way. That is, t is an independent variable that can be preset, and z depends on t: $z = g(t)$. It is desired to measure this dependence, but the measured value of z includes a random error. Let X_t denote the *measured* value corresponding to t, and let ϵ_t be the measurement error:

$$X_t = g(t) + \epsilon_t.$$

Let n measurements be made, corresponding to preselected values of t, with the results (t_1,X_1), . . ., (t_n,X_n), where

$$X_j = X_{t_j} = g(t_j) + \epsilon_j,$$

ϵ_j denoting the measurement error ϵ_{t_j} at t_j.

It is assumed throughout that the measurement errors are all independent random variables, normally distributed; that $E(\epsilon_t) = 0$ so that $E(X_t) = g(t)$; and that there is a common variance σ^2 for all measurement errors. That is, $(\epsilon_1, \ldots, \epsilon_n)$ is assumed to have a multivariate normal distribution with mean vector $(0,0,\ldots,0)$ and covariance matrix $\sigma^2 I$, where I denotes the $n \times n$ identity matrix.

The main problem considered is that in which the mean function or "regression function" $g(t)$ has a known form but with certain undetermined coefficients or parameters. For instance, $g(t)$ might be: $\alpha + \beta t$, $a + bt + ct^2 + dt^3$, Ke^{at}, At^p, $A \sin \omega t$, etc. The first would be called a linear regression; the next, a cubic; and so on. In the case of linear regression, cubic regression, and indeed, any polynomial regression, the regression function is *linear in the parameters*. In the exponential, power, and trigonometric cases listed, this dependence on the parameters is not linear. However, in the exponential case one can write $\log z = \log K + at$, which is linear in the parameters a and $\log K$ as well as linear in t; and in the case of At^p, $\log z = \log A + p \log t$, which is linear in the parameters $\log A$ and p.

Linear regression, with $g(t) = \alpha + \beta t$, will be the main topic of discussion. A similar development is possible whenever the regression function is linear in the parameters. Further, the linear regression case includes the exponential and power cases if the error can be assumed to be additive and normal in the logarithmic forms. Multiple regression problems, in which z is a function of more than one controlled variable, will not be treated.

11.1.1 Linear Regression. It soon becomes evident in a linear regression problem that it is advantageous to use the form $\alpha + \beta(t - \bar{t})$ for the regression function, where $\bar{t}$ is the arithmetic mean of the t values used, and this form will be used from the beginning.

There are three unknown parameters: α, β, and σ^2, and the likelihood function is as follows, given observations (t_1,X_1), . . ., (t_n,X_n):

$$L(\alpha,\beta,\sigma^2) = (2\pi)^{-n/2}(\sigma^2)^{-n/2} \exp\left\{-\frac{1}{2\sigma^2}\sum_{i=1}^{n}[X_i - (\alpha + \beta[t_i - \bar{t}])]^2\right\}.$$

The partial derivatives of $\log L(\alpha,\beta,\sigma^2)$ with respect to α, β, and σ^2 are then

$$\frac{\partial \log L}{\partial \alpha} = -\frac{1}{2\sigma^2}\sum(-2)\{X_i - (\alpha + \beta[t_i - \bar{t}])\},$$

$$\frac{\partial \log L}{\partial \beta} = -\frac{1}{2\sigma^2}\sum(-2[t_i - \bar{t}])\{X_i - (\alpha + \beta[t_i - \bar{t}])\},$$

$$\frac{\partial \log L}{\partial \sigma^2} = -\frac{n}{2\sigma^2} + \frac{1}{2\sigma^4}\sum\{X_i - (\alpha + \beta[t_i - \bar{t}])\}^2.$$

Setting these equal to zero and solving simultaneously, one finds the maximum likelihood estimates:

$$\hat{\alpha} = \bar{X}, \quad \hat{\beta} = \frac{s_{tx}}{s_t^2}, \quad \hat{\sigma}^2 = \frac{1}{n}\sum[X_i - \hat{\alpha} - \hat{\beta}(t_i - \bar{t})]^2,$$

where

$$s_{tx} = \frac{1}{n}\sum X_i(t_i - \bar{t}) = \frac{1}{n}\sum(X_i - \bar{X})(t_i - \bar{t}),$$

and

$$s_t^2 = \frac{1}{n}\sum t_i(t_i - \bar{t}) = \frac{1}{n}\sum(t_i - \bar{t})^2.$$

(Observe that although the notation might suggest it, s_{tx} and s_t^2 are not "sample second moments" in the usual sense, since the t's are not observations but fixed values of the controlled variable t. The quantity s_t^2 is therefore not random, and in s_{tx} the randomness enters only through the X_i.)

Several facts about these maximum likelihood estimates are of interest. First, they are functions of a minimal sufficient statistic (cf. Problem 11–1): $(\sum X_i, \sum t_i X_i, \sum X_i^2)$. Second, the estimates $\hat{\alpha}$ and $\hat{\beta}$ are "least squares" estimates; they are precisely the values of $\tilde{\alpha}$ and $\tilde{\beta}$ which minimize the average of the squared deviations of the observations about an estimated regression function:

$$\frac{1}{n}\sum(X_i - \tilde{\alpha} - \tilde{\beta}[t_i - \bar{t}])^2.$$

The minimum value of this average is $\hat{\sigma}^2$, obtained by using $\hat{\alpha}$ and $\hat{\beta}$. The two likelihood equations for $\hat{\alpha}$ and $\hat{\beta}$ are just what are called the *normal equations* of the least squares problem:

$$\begin{cases} \sum[X_i - \hat{\alpha} - \hat{\beta}(t_i - \bar{t})] = 0 \\ \sum(t_i - \bar{t})[X_i - \hat{\alpha} - \hat{\beta}(t_i - \bar{t})] = 0. \end{cases}$$

Third, the estimate $\hat{\alpha} + \hat{\beta}(t - \bar{t})$ of the regression function $\alpha + \beta(t - \bar{t})$ has the smallest variance of all unbiased linear estimates of the regression function. This will be demonstrated in §11.1.2. For the present, it is noted that $\hat{\alpha}$ and $\hat{\beta}$ are indeed linear combinations of the observations and that they are unbiased:

$$E(\hat{\alpha}) = E(\bar{X}) = \frac{1}{n}\sum E(X_i) = \frac{1}{n}\sum(\alpha + \beta[t_i - \bar{t}]) = \alpha,$$

and

$$E(\hat{\beta}) = \frac{1}{ns_t^2}\sum E(X_i)(t_i - \bar{t}) = \beta.$$

Hence,

$$E(\hat{\alpha} + \hat{\beta}[t - \bar{t}]) = \alpha + \beta[t - \bar{t}].$$

The fact that $\hat{\alpha}$ and $\hat{\beta}$ are *linear* combinations of the independent variables $X_1, \ldots, X_n$ permits ready computation of their variances:

$$\text{var } \hat{\alpha} = \text{var } \bar{X} = \frac{1}{n^2} \sum \text{var } X_i = \frac{\sigma^2}{n},$$

and

$$\text{var } \hat{\beta} = \frac{1}{n^2 s_t^4} \sum (t_i - \bar{t})^2 \text{ var } X_i = \frac{\sigma^2}{n s_t^2}.$$

It is seen directly from these expressions (as well as from the fact that $\hat{\alpha}$ and $\hat{\beta}$ are maximum likelihood estimates) that $\hat{\alpha}$ and $\hat{\beta}$ are consistent estimates of α and β. It is seen also from the expression for the variance of $\hat{\beta}$ that this slope estimate is most reliable when the points $t_1, \ldots, t_n$ have as much spread as possible so that s_t^2 is large. It is clear that at least two distinct values of t must be used in order to obtain an estimate of slope.

The joint distribution of $(\hat{\alpha}, \hat{\beta})$ is bivariate normal, since $\hat{\alpha}$ and $\hat{\beta}$ are linear combinations of $(X_1, \ldots, X_n)$. The covariance of $\hat{\alpha}$ and $\hat{\beta}$ is readily shown to be zero, implying independence of $\hat{\alpha}$ and $\hat{\beta}$ in their bivariate normal distribution. (This independence will become evident a bit later.)

If the value of α is held fixed at α_0, the maximum of the likelihood function is found to be

$$L(\alpha_0, \hat{\beta}, \hat{\sigma}_0^2) = (2\pi\hat{\sigma}_0^2)^{-n/2} \exp\left[\frac{-n}{2}\right],$$

where

$$\hat{\sigma}_0^2 = \frac{1}{n} \sum [X_i - \alpha_0 - \hat{\beta}(t_i - \bar{t})]^2.$$

The maximum of L over all α, β, and σ^2 is

$$L(\hat{\alpha}, \hat{\beta}, \hat{\sigma}^2) = (2\pi\hat{\sigma}^2)^{-n/2} \exp\left[\frac{-n}{2}\right],$$

and so the likelihood ratio test for $\alpha = \alpha_0$ against $\alpha \neq \alpha_0$ has the critical region

$$\frac{L(\alpha_0, \hat{\beta}, \hat{\sigma}_0^2)}{L(\hat{\alpha}, \hat{\beta}, \hat{\sigma}^2)} = \left[\frac{\hat{\sigma}_0^2}{\hat{\sigma}^2}\right]^{-n/2} < \text{constant},$$

or equivalently,

$$\left(\frac{\hat{\alpha} - \alpha_0}{\hat{\sigma}/\sqrt{n}}\right)^2 > \text{constant}.$$

Similarly, the likelihood ratio critical region for $\beta = \beta_0$ against $\beta \neq \beta_0$ is given by

$$\left(\frac{\hat{\beta} - \beta_0}{\hat{\sigma}/\sqrt{n s_t^2}}\right)^2 > \text{constant}.$$

That is, if $\hat{\alpha}$ differs from α_0 by too much, $\alpha = \alpha_0$ is rejected—"too much" being measured with respect to the standard deviation of $\hat{\alpha}$, estimated by

$\hat{\sigma}/\sqrt{n}$. How much is "too much" is determined from a prescribed size of type I error and the distribution of the statistic used.

To obtain the distributions of the statistics that have emerged, Cochran's theorem will be used. The identity

$$(X_i - \alpha - \beta[t_i - \bar{t}]) = (X_i - \hat{\alpha} - \hat{\beta}[t_i - \bar{t}]) + (\hat{\beta} - \beta)(t_i - \bar{t}) + (\hat{\alpha} - \alpha)$$

is squared, summed on i, and divided by σ^2 with the following result:

$$\sum_{i=1}^{n} \left(\frac{X_i - \alpha - \beta[t_i - \bar{t}]}{\sigma} \right)^2 = \frac{n\hat{\sigma}^2}{\sigma^2} + \frac{(\hat{\beta} - \beta)^2}{\sigma^2/ns_t^2} + \frac{(\hat{\alpha} - \alpha)^2}{\sigma^2/n}.$$

In the process of squaring, three cross-product terms appear; these vanish when the summation is performed, one because the sum of $(t_i - \bar{t})$ is zero and the others because $\hat{\alpha}$ and $\hat{\beta}$ satisfy the likelihood equations (or the normal equations of the least squares process). Now, the sum on the left is a sum of squares of independent standard normal variables, a chi-square variable with n degrees of freedom. It is represented in the form $Q_1 + Q_2 + Q_3$, where the Q's are sums of squares of linear combinations of the standardized X's. In Q_1 there are n terms, but there are two linear relations among the linear combinations in that sum of squares (namely, the normal equations), which means that the rank of Q_1 is at most $n - 2$. Both Q_2 and Q_3 are of rank 1, and so the rank of Q_1 is at least $n - 2$, and therefore exactly $n - 2$. These ranks add up properly: $(n - 2) + 1 + 1 = n$; and so, according to Cochran's theorem, Q_1, Q_2, and Q_3 have independent chi-square distributions with, respectively, $n - 2$, 1, and 1 degree of freedom. (The distributions of Q_2 and Q_3 were apparent without Cochran's theorem, but now it is clear that they are independent.) It should be noticed that the distribution of Q_1, and hence of $\hat{\sigma}^2$, is independent of the values of α and β.

The distributions of the statistics arising from the likelihood ratio technique can now be discussed. Except for a constant factor, they were as follows:

$$(n - 2)\,\frac{(\hat{\beta} - \beta_0)^2}{\hat{\sigma}^2/s_t^2} \quad \text{and} \quad (n - 2)\,\frac{(\hat{\alpha} - \alpha_0)^2}{\hat{\sigma}^2},$$

and these have each the F distribution with $(1, n - 2)$ degrees of freedom, provided $\beta = \beta_0$ and $\alpha = \alpha_0$. If $\alpha \neq \alpha_0$, the numerator of the corresponding ratio is no longer a central chi-square variable but a noncentral one, with noncentrality parameter $(\alpha - \alpha_0)^2/2$. The power functions of the likelihood ratio tests for $\alpha = \alpha_0$ and $\beta = \beta_0$ can therefore be obtained from the noncentral F distribution.

Confidence intervals can be constructed for α and for β. Let $-k$ denote the $100\gamma/2$ percentile of the t distribution with $n - 2$ degrees of freedom, or equivalently, $k^2 = F_{1-\gamma}(1,n-2)$. Then

$$P\left\{(n-2)\frac{(\hat{\alpha}-\alpha)^2}{\hat{\sigma}^2} < k^2\right\} = 1-\gamma,$$

or

$$P\left(\hat{\alpha} - \frac{k\hat{\sigma}}{\sqrt{n-2}} < \alpha < \hat{\alpha} + \frac{k\hat{\sigma}}{\sqrt{n-2}}\right) = 1-\gamma.$$

Similarly, a confidence interval for β is found to have the limits

$$\hat{\beta} \pm \frac{k\hat{\sigma}}{\sqrt{(n-2)s_t^2}}.$$

Example 11–1. Suppose that calculations for a given set of 100 points (t_i,X_i) yield $s_t^2 = 9.7$, $\hat{\alpha} = 1.1$, $\hat{\beta} = 0.02$, and $\hat{\sigma}^2 = 0.0036$. The normal distribution can be used to approximate the t distribution with 98 degrees of freedom, so that for $\gamma = 0.10$, $k = 1.645$. The 90 per cent confidence intervals for α and β are, respectively,

$$1.1 \pm 1.645 \times \frac{0.06}{\sqrt{98}} \qquad \text{or} \qquad (1.0990, 1.1010),$$

and

$$0.02 \pm 1.645 \times \frac{0.06}{\sqrt{98 \times 9.7}} \qquad \text{or} \qquad (0.0168, 0.0232).$$

The likelihood ratio test of $\beta = \beta_0$ is equivalent to the rule of rejecting β_0 if the confidence interval for β does not include it. According to this test, the value $\beta = 0$ (equality of means) would be rejected because the confidence interval obtained does not include it.

It should be pointed out that although inferences can be made concerning α without any assumptions on β, and vice versa, the statistics used for these two parameters are not independent, and care should be taken in making statements about α and β jointly. For instance, the 90 per cent confidence intervals for α and β cannot be used to assert that both α and β lie in the corresponding confidence intervals with probability 0.90×0.90. On the other hand, a simultaneous confidence region can be constructed, taking the ratio of the *sum* of the second and third terms in the chi-square partitioning to the first term; the numerator would be chi-square with 2 degrees of freedom, and the ratio would then have the F distribution with $(2,n-2)$ degrees of freedom. That is, with k and γ related as above:

$$P\left\{\frac{(\hat{\alpha}-\alpha)^2 + s_t^2(\hat{\beta}-\beta)^2}{\hat{\sigma}^2} < F_{1-\gamma}(2,n-2)\right\} = 1-\gamma.$$

The inequality is satisfied (for given $\hat{\alpha}$, $\hat{\beta}$, and $\hat{\sigma}^2$) by the points (α,β) in an ellipse. This elliptical region, which depends on the observations and is therefore random, is the confidence region.

It is perhaps instructive to view the tests derived for α and β in the following intuitive way: The quantities

$$\frac{n\hat{\sigma}^2}{n-2}, \quad ns_t^2(\hat{\beta}-\beta_0)^2, \quad \text{and} \quad n(\hat{\alpha}-\alpha_0)^2$$

are, under the hypothesis that $\alpha = \alpha_0$ and $\beta = \beta_0$, unbiased estimates of σ^2; the ratio of any two of these should be around 1, on the average at least. But

$$\begin{aligned} E[n(\hat{\alpha}-\alpha_0)^2] &= E[n(\hat{\alpha}-\alpha)^2] + n(\alpha-\alpha_0)^2 + 2(\alpha-\alpha_0)E[n(\hat{\alpha}-\alpha)] \\ &= \sigma^2 + n(\alpha-\alpha_0)^2, \end{aligned}$$

so that if $\alpha \neq \alpha_0$, the estimate $n(\hat{\alpha}-\alpha_0)^2$ tends to be higher than when $\alpha = \alpha_0$. The distribution of $\hat{\sigma}^2$, on the other hand, is not affected by the value of α, and so the ratio used for tests on α tends to be higher for $\alpha \neq \alpha_0$ than for $\alpha = \alpha_0$. The rejection rule that was derived thus appears to be intuitively quite reasonable.

Problems concerning the common variance σ^2 are handled just as in the simpler case of a sample from a single normal population, using $\hat{\sigma}^2$, except that here only $n-2$ degrees of freedom are available, two having been "used up" in the estimation of the two parameters α and β.

PROBLEMS

11–1. Determine the minimal sufficient statistic, given $(t_1,X_1), \ldots, (t_n,X_n)$, for the normal family of §11.1.1.

11–2. Construct a 90 per cent confidence interval for σ^2, using the data in Example 11–1.

11–3. Determine the line that best fits the following points in the least squares sense, minimizing the sum of squares of vertical deviations: (0,2), (1,1), (4,3), (5,2).

11–4. Construct 95 per cent confidence intervals for α, for β, and for σ^2 based on the following data from a sample of size 50: $\bar{t} = 8.2$, $s_t^2 = 10.24$, $\hat{\alpha} = 6.31$, $\hat{\beta} = 0.092$, $\hat{\sigma}^2 = 4.6$. Also test $\beta = 0$ at the level 0.01.

11–5. Construct a 90 per cent confidence region for α and β, using the data of Problem 11–4.

11–6. Compute the covariance of $\hat{\alpha}$ and $\hat{\beta}$ directly from their definitions.

11.1.2 The Minimum Variance Linear Unbiased Estimate. We pause to verify the claim made in the preceding section that the maximum likelihood (least squares) estimate $\hat{\alpha} + \hat{\beta}(t-\bar{t})$ of the regression line $\alpha + \beta(t-\bar{t})$ at t is the linear unbiased estimate with smallest variance. Consider, then, any unbiased linear estimate U:

$$U = c_1X_1 + \cdots + c_nX_n.$$

The condition that U be unbiased implies that

$$E(U) = \sum c_i E(X_i) = \sum c_i[\alpha + \beta(t_i - \bar{t})] = \alpha + \beta(t - \bar{t}),$$

or that

$$\sum c_i = 1 \quad \text{and} \quad \sum c_i(t_i - \bar{t}) = t - \bar{t}.$$

The variance of U is

$$\text{var}\, U = \text{var}\{\sum c_i X_i\} = \sigma^2 \sum c_i^2.$$

The U with minimum variance is then given by that choice of $c = (c_1, \ldots, c_n)$ that minimizes $\sum c_i^2/2$ subject to the restrictions that $\sum c_i = 1$ and $\sum c_i(t_i - \bar{t}) = t - \bar{t}$. Using the method of Lagrange multipliers, we minimize (cf. Example 6–7):

$$\frac{\sum c_i^2}{2} - \lambda(\sum c_i - 1) - \mu[\sum c_i(t_i - \bar{t}) - (t - \bar{t})]$$

as a function of the $n + 2$ variables $c_1, \ldots, c_n$, λ, and μ. Setting derivatives of this with respect to these variables equal to zero yields

$$\begin{cases} c_j - \lambda - \mu(t_j - \bar{t}) = 0, & j = 1, \ldots, n, \\ \sum c_j = 1, \\ \sum c_j(t_j - \bar{t}) = t - \bar{t}. \end{cases}$$

Elimination of λ and μ then gives the desired coefficients:

$$c_j = \frac{1}{n} + \frac{(t - \bar{t})(t_j - \bar{t})}{n s_t^2},$$

so that the minimum variance estimate is

$$\sum c_j X_j = \bar{X} + \frac{s_{tx}(t - \bar{t})}{s_t^2}.$$

This is precisely the maximum likelihood estimate of $E(X_t)$.

This phenomenon is a special case of the Gauss-Markov theorem, which will be stated in more general form in discussing the general linear model in §11.3.

11.1.3 Testing Linearity. There was nothing in the development of §11.1.1 that ruled out the possibility that some of the t's might be alike, and so the results there apply to a situation in which n_1 observations are taken at $t = t_1, \ldots,$ and n_k observations at $t = t_k$. But the notation requires some revision (as it did when going to grouped data in a single sample):

Controlled Variable	Observations	Sample Mean	Population Mean	Sample Size
t_1	$X_{11}, \ldots, X_{1n_1}$	$\bar{X}_1$	$g(t_1)$	n_1
$\vdots$	$\vdots$	$\vdots$	$\vdots$	$\vdots$
t_k	$X_{k1}, \ldots, X_{kn_k}$	$\bar{X}_k$	$g(t_k)$	n_k

If as before n denotes the total number of observations, then $\sum n_i = n$. The mean of the t's is now a weighted average of the distinct t's, with a similar modification for s_t^2:

$$\bar{t} = \frac{1}{n}\sum n_i t_i, \qquad s_t^2 = \frac{1}{n}\sum n_i(t_i - \bar{t})^2.$$

The over-all mean of the observations X_{ij} can be expressed in terms of the means at the individual t's:

$$\bar{X} = \frac{1}{n}\sum_{i=1}^{k}\sum_{j=1}^{n_i} X_{ij} = \frac{1}{n}\sum_{i=1}^{k} n_i\bar{X}_i, \qquad \bar{X}_i = \frac{1}{n_i}\sum_{j=1}^{n_i} X_{ij}.$$

The revised formulas for $\hat{\alpha}$, $\hat{\beta}$, and $\hat{\sigma}^2$ are then

$$\hat{\alpha} = \bar{X}, \qquad \hat{\beta} = \frac{\sum n_i\bar{X}_i(t_i - \bar{t})}{ns_t^2},$$

and

$$\hat{\sigma}^2 = \frac{1}{n}\sum\sum[X_{ij} - \hat{\alpha} - \hat{\beta}(t_i - \bar{t})]^2,$$

single sums on j extending from 1 to n_i; single sums on i, from 1 to k; and double sums from $j = 1$ to $j = n_i$ and from $i = 1$ to k.

With the assumption that $g(t) = \alpha + \beta(t - \bar{t})$, tests and estimates for α, β, and σ^2 are available as in §11.1.1 but with the computation formulas modified as shown here. But it is now possible to test for linearity of the regression function, with the aid of a further breakup of $\hat{\sigma}^2$. Let the empirical regression function be denoted by $\tilde{X}_t$, with $\tilde{X}_i = \hat{\alpha} + \hat{\beta}(t_i - \bar{t})$, and write

$$X_{ij} - \tilde{X}_i = (X_{ij} - \bar{X}_i) + (\bar{X}_i - \tilde{X}_i).$$

Squaring and summing this over i and j gives

$$\sum\sum(X_{ij} - \tilde{X}_i)^2 = \sum\sum(X_{ij} - \bar{X}_i)^2 + \sum n_i(\bar{X}_i - \tilde{X}_i)^2,$$

the cross-product term again disappearing upon summation. The first term is a contribution to variability of the observations about the empirical regression line caused by variability of the observations about the means at the individual t values; the second term is a contribution caused by variation of these means about the empirical regression line.

Since there are k linear relations among the n quantities $(X_{ij} - \bar{X}_i)$, the sum of squares of these quantities has rank at most $n - k$. (The k linear relations are these: $\sum(X_{ij} - \bar{X}_i) = 0$ for $i = 1, \ldots, k$.) There are two linear relations among the k quantities $(\bar{X}_i - \tilde{X}_i)$, namely, the normal equations; the rank of the sum of their squares is then at most $k - 2$. With this further breakup, then, the application of Cochran's theorem in §11.1.1 would show that $\sum\sum(X_{ij} - \bar{X}_i)^2/\sigma^2$ and $\sum n_i(\bar{X}_i - \tilde{X}_i)^2/\sigma^2$ are independent chi-square variables with $n - k$ and $k - 2$ degrees of freedom, respectively, if the regression function is linear. Under this assumption, therefore, the ratio

$$\frac{\sum n_i(\bar{X}_i - \tilde{X}_i)^2/(k-2)}{\sum\sum(X_{ij} - \bar{X}_i)^2/(n-k)}$$

has the F distribution $(k - 2, n - k)$. The numerator and denominator are each unbiased estimates of σ^2 if the regression function is linear. The denominator is so, even if the regression function is *not* linear, being a weighted average of independent variance estimates at the individual t values; the latter have $n_1 - 1, \ldots, n_k - 1$ degrees of freedom, the sum of these being $n - k$.

The test that rejects linearity of the regression function for excessively large values of the above ratio is exactly the likelihood ratio test that $H_0\colon g(t_i) = \alpha + \beta(t_i - \bar{t})$, with unknown α and β, against $H_1\colon g(t_i)$ are not collinear. The level desired determines the critical value of the ratio as a percentile of the F distribution.

Example 11–2. Consider the following artificial data, made up to look more quadratic than linear:

t_i	X_{ij}	$\bar{X}_i$	n_i	$\Sigma(X_{ij} - \bar{X}_i)^2$
1	3, 4, 5	4	3	2
2	1, 3	2	2	2
3	3, 4, 5	4	3	2

It is apparent that $\hat{\beta} = 0$, so the empirical regression line is horizontal. Then $\tilde{X}_i = \hat{\alpha} = \bar{X} = 7/2$, and

$$\sum\sum\left(X_{ij} - \frac{7}{2}\right)^2 = 12 = \sum\sum(X_{ij} - \bar{X}_i)^2 + \sum n_i(\bar{X}_i - \tilde{X}_i)^2$$
$$= \qquad 6 \qquad + \qquad 6.$$

Now $n - k = 8 - 3 = 5$ and $k - 2 = 3 - 2 = 1$, and the test ratio is

$$\frac{6/1}{6/5} = 5.$$

For a 5 per cent significance level, the rejection limit is $F_{0.95}(1,5) = 6.61 > 5$. At this level, linearity is accepted, although at the 10 per cent level, the rejection limit is 4.06 and linearity would be rejected.

PROBLEMS

11–7. Given the data tabulated, and assuming normal, independent observations with constant variance σ^2:

t_i	X_{ij}
1	2, 5, 5
2	4, 6, 5
3	6, 4, 8

(a) Test for linearity of the regression function.
(b) Assuming linearity, give estimates of α, β, and σ^2.
(c) Assuming linearity, determine a 95 per cent confidence region for (α, β).

11–8. With the usual assumptions of independence, normality, and constant variance σ^2, and assuming $E(X_t) = ct^2$, determine maximum likelihood estimates of c and σ^2 based on several observations at each of k values of t. Construct a test for this quadratic type of regression function. Determine an estimate of σ^2 that will apply even if the regression function is not of the quadratic form given, and state how it can be improved if the regression function *is* ct^2.

11–9. Set up the likelihood ratio test for linearity and show that it turns out as claimed just before Example 11–2. (The denominator of λ is the maximum of the likelihood function over the $k + 1$ parameters $g(t_1), \ldots, g(t_k)$, and σ^2.)

11–10. Show that $E(\bar{X}_i - \tilde{X}_i) = 0$ if the regression function is linear.

11.1.4 Prediction. Suppose that the purpose in gathering data at various values of the controlled variable t is the prediction of the value $X_0 = X_{t_0}$ at some new value t_0. If success in prediction is measured by mean square error, the best prediction is the expected value at t_0:

$$E(X_0) = \alpha + \beta(t_0 - \bar{t}),$$

but, of course, α and β are not usually known. The problem is then to estimate this linear combination of parameters. The maximum likelihood estimate is $\hat{\alpha} + \hat{\beta}(t_0 - \bar{t})$, which was seen in §11.1.2 to be also the minimum variance linear unbiased estimate. Denote this estimate by $\tilde{X}_0$.

The deviation $d = \tilde{X}_0 - X_0$ is normally distributed with mean zero and variance

$$\sigma_d^2 = \sigma^2 + \frac{\sigma^2}{n} + \frac{\sigma^2(t_0 - \bar{t})^2}{ns_t^2},$$

the first term being present even if the regression function were known exactly, and the other terms arising because of errors in the estimates of the regression coefficients. It is evident that the closer is t_0 to $\bar{t}$, the better the prediction (from the point of view of mean square error).

A kind of "confidence interval," better described as a prediction interval, can be constructed by using the variance estimate

$$s^2 = \frac{1}{n-2} \sum \sum (X_{ij} - \bar{X}_i)^2.$$

Since d^2/σ_d^2 is chi-square with one degree of freedom, and since it is independent of $(n-2)s^2/\sigma^2$ (which is chi-square with $n-2$ degrees of freedom), the ratio

$$F = \frac{d^2/\sigma_d^2}{s^2/\sigma^2}$$

has the F distribution with $(1, n-2)$ degrees of freedom. Hence,

$$P\left\{\frac{[X_0 - \hat{\alpha} - \hat{\beta}(t_0 - \bar{t})]^2}{s[1 + 1/n + (t_0 - \bar{t})^2/(ns_t^2)]} < F_\eta(1,n-2)\right\} = \eta.$$

The inequality can be written also as follows, with $t' = \sqrt{F_\eta(1, n-2)}$:

$$P\left\{\bar{X}_0 - t's\sqrt{1 + \frac{1}{n} + \frac{(t_0 - \bar{t})^2}{ns_t^2}} < X_0 < \bar{X}_0 + t's\sqrt{1 + \frac{1}{n} + \frac{(t_0 - \bar{t})^2}{ns_t^2}}\right\} = \eta.$$

The interval within which X_0 falls with probability η is called a *prediction interval;* it as well as X_0 are random.

Another type of prediction sometimes desired is the determination of the value t_0 of the controlled variable at which a given set of observations $X_1', \ldots, X_m'$ is obtained, given the usual data for the regression problem. The maximum likelihood estimate of t_0 turns out to be

$$\hat{t}_0 = \frac{(\bar{X}' - \hat{\alpha})}{\hat{\beta}} + \bar{t}$$

Since $\bar{X}' - \hat{\alpha} - \hat{\beta}(t_0 - \bar{t})$ is normal with mean zero and variance

$$\sigma^2\left[\frac{1}{m} + \frac{1}{n} + \frac{(t_0 - \bar{t})^2}{ns_t^2}\right],$$

a confidence interval for t_0 is readily constructed.

Example 11–3. Using the data of Example 11–2, a prediction interval for X_0 at $t_0 = 6$ is set up as follows: The pooled variance s^2 is

$$\frac{1}{8-2} \sum\sum \left(X_{ij} - \frac{7}{2}\right)^2 = 2,$$

and $ns_t^2 = \sum n_i(t_i - \bar{t})^2 = 6$. Using $\eta = 0.90$, and therefore $t' = 1.94$ (since $n - 2 = 6$), the prediction interval has the limits $\bar{X}_0 \pm 1.94\sqrt{91/12} = 3.5 \pm 5.35$.

A confidence interval for determination of the value of t corresponding to some new data cannot be constructed because $\hat{\beta} = 0$, and the empirical regression line is horizontal.

11.1.5 Optimum Allocation of Observations. It was seen earlier that the estimate $\hat{\beta}$ is the unbiased linear combination of observations with the smallest variance and that this smallest variance is $\sigma^2/(ns_t^2)$. Given that n observations are permitted, it is of interest to know how best to distribute these on the axis of the controlled variable. If by "best" is meant that the variance of the slope estimate $\hat{\beta}$ is to be as small as possible, what is wanted is a distribution of observations which maximizes ns_t^2. This is accomplished by putting observations at the smallest and largest t's possible (say, t_1 and t_k), since for any other distribution the quantity ns_t^2 could be increased by moving observations farther toward t_1 or t_k (whichever is closer in each case). But if a proportion p are put at t_1 and q at t_2, with $p + q = 1$, then

$$ns_t^2 = pt_1^2 + qt_2^2 - (pt_1 + qt_2)^2 = pq(t_1 - t_2)^2.$$

This is maximized for $p = q = 1/2$, and so the best distribution is achieved by putting half of the observations at each of the values t_1 and t_2.

The problem of allocation has been considered more generally by Elfving and others (cf. "Optimum designs in regression problems," by Kiefer and Wolfowitz, *Ann. Math. Stat.* 30(1959), page 271, and references given there). Elfving showed (1952 *Ann. Math. Stat.*, page 255) by interchanging the minimizing operations (with respect to constants in the linear combination of observations and with respect to distributions of observations) that for estimation of any single linear function of parameters, exactly two t values should be used; he also gave a scheme for determining the proportions at those values.

Of course, for testing linearity, it was found desirable to have k large (the number of distinct t values) in order to make a large number of degrees of freedom in the relevant term. Different aims call for different optimum allocations.

PROBLEMS

11–11. Using the data in Problem 11–7, construct a 90 per cent prediction interval for X_t at $t = 6$, assuming a linear regression function.

11–12. Construct a 70 per cent confidence interval for t_0, the value of t at which the data 3, 7, 5 are obtained, assuming a linear regression function and the data of Problem 11–7.

11–13. Show that for a *given* linear unbiased estimator $T = \sum n_i c_i \bar{X}_i$, where var $\bar{X}_i = \sigma^2/n_i$, the allocation of n observations with n_i at t_i which minimizes the variance of T is given by

$$\frac{n_i}{n} = \frac{|c_i|}{\sum |c_i|}.$$

(Minimize var T by selecting $n_1, \ldots, n_k$ subject to $\sum n_i = n$, using the Lagrange multiplier technique.)

11.2 Analysis of Variance

Although the name "analysis of variance" does not suggest it, the topic deals with tests for equality of means, the various means of a random quantity corresponding to different "treatments," or in the case considered first, corresponding to different "levels" of a single factor that may be affecting the results of a chance experiment.

Most of the work done in the field of analysis of variance assumes normal distributions (as in regression problems), and the discussion here is restricted by this assumption. (See Chapter 16 of Mood's *Introduction to the Theory of Statistics*, and the article by Kruskal and Wallis: "Use of ranks in one-criterion variance analysis," *Jour. Amer. Stat. Assn.* 47 (1952), pages 583–621,) for discussions of nonparametric analysis of variance.)

It is assumed here that the variances of the observations are all equal. A likelihood ratio test for equality of variances of several normal populations is readily constructed (Problem 11–14).

The technique of analysis of variance is briefly as follows: Taking all the observations in samples from several populations (corresponding to several treatments), one breaks the variability about the over-all mean into components, one associated with the actual population variability and the others associated with variations in the sample means caused by the various factors involved. If the technique sounds familiar, it is because the treatment of regression problems in §11.1 employed it.

In regression problems, too, one is concerned with testing hypotheses about the means of several populations; the several populations in the regression case correspond to the chosen values of the controlled variable. That is, the populations are indexed according to the value of the controlled variable, and the concern is not only with equality of population means but (if the means are not equal) also with the functional relationship between the population mean and the indexing parameter. In the problems of "analysis of variance" the populations are not indexed by a single controlled variable, and it does not make sense to consider a regression function. In this respect, the problem is simpler. However, the real value of analysis of variance methods lies in its providing a means of studying one factor in the presence of other factors. The case of a single factor will be treated first.

11.2.1 A Single Classification Problem. Consider k independent, normally distributed populations $X_1, \ldots, X_k$ with var $X_i = \sigma^2$, and assume that data are given as follows:

Population	Sample Size	Observations	Sample Means	Pop. Mean
X_1	n_1	$X_{11}, \ldots, X_{1n_1}$	$\bar{X}_1$	μ_1
$\vdots$	$\vdots$	$\vdots$	$\vdots$	$\vdots$
X_k	n_k	$X_{k1}, \ldots, X_{kn_k}$	$\bar{X}_k$	μ_k

The maximum likelihood estimates of $\mu_1, \ldots, \mu_k$ and σ^2 are

$$\hat{\mu}_1 = \bar{X}_1, \ldots, \quad \hat{\mu}_k = \bar{X}_k, \quad \hat{\sigma}^2 = \frac{1}{n} \sum \sum (X_{ij} - \bar{X}_i)^2,$$

where $n = \sum n_i$, the total number of observations.

Now define

$$\mu = \frac{1}{n} \sum n_i \mu_i \qquad \text{and} \qquad \theta_i = \mu_i - \mu.$$

The MLE of μ is $\bar{X}$; of θ_i, $\bar{X}_i - \bar{X}$, where $\bar{X} = \sum n_i \bar{X}_i / n$. If the population means *are* identical, they are equal to μ, and then $\theta_i = 0$ for all i. And if such be the case, the n observations in all the samples make up a sample of size n from a common normal population with mean μ and variance σ^2. An estimate of variance could then be obtained from the sum of squares about $\bar{X}$: $\sum \sum (X_{ij} - \bar{X})^2$. Consider the following partition of this sum:

$$\begin{aligned} \sum \sum (X_{ij} - \bar{X})^2 &= \sum \sum [(X_{ij} - \bar{X}_i) + (\bar{X}_i - \bar{X})]^2 \\ &= \sum \sum (X_{ij} - \bar{X}_i)^2 + \sum n_i (\bar{X}_i - \bar{X})^2. \end{aligned}$$

(The cross-product term vanishes because $\sum (X_{ij} - \bar{X}_i) = 0$.) The first term on the right is $n\hat{\sigma}^2$, and is based on "within samples" variation; it will be about the same no matter what the μ_i, and its distribution is independent of the means. The second term on the right, on the other hand, will tend to be large if the means μ_i are not identical, since then the sample means $\bar{X}_i$ will tend to be more widely dispersed about $\bar{X}$ than if all population means are alike.

The distributions of these sums in the partition come from an application of Cochran's theorem. Consider the following sum of squares:

$$\sum \sum \frac{(X_{ij} - \mu)^2}{\sigma^2} = \sum \sum \frac{(X_{ij} - \bar{X}_i)^2}{\sigma^2} + \sum \frac{n_i (\bar{X}_i - \bar{X})^2}{\sigma^2} + \frac{n(\bar{X} - \mu)^2}{\sigma^2}.$$

Under the null hypothesis that $\theta_i = 0$ for all i, the sum on the left has the chi-square distribution with n degrees of freedom. On the right the ranks do not exceed $n - k$, $k - 1$, and 1, in that order. Consequently the terms on the right are independent chi-square variables with $n - k$, $k - 1$, and 1 degree of freedom, respectively—under the null hypothesis. Therefore the ratio

$$F = \frac{\frac{1}{k-1} \sum n_i (\bar{X}_i - \bar{X})^2}{\frac{1}{n-k} \sum \sum (X_{ij} - \bar{X}_i)^2}$$

has the F distribution, $(k - 1, n - k)$, under the null hypothesis, and this distribution is used to set the constant K in the test $F > K$ corresponding to a given size of type I error.

Example 11–4. Consider the following data:

n_i	X_{ij}	$\bar{X}_i$	$(X_{ij} - \bar{X}_i)^2$
4	11, 9, 13, 11	11	8
6	25, 28, 31, 27, 30, 33	29	42
5	19, 23, 19, 21, 20	20.4	11.2
$n = 15$			$61.2 = 918/15.$

The pooled variance (unbiased variance estimate based on within samples variation) is

$$s^2 = \frac{1}{15 - 3}(61.2) = 5.1.$$

The mean $\bar{X}$ of all the data is 64/3, and the total sum of squares about $\bar{X}$ divides as follows:

$$\frac{12{,}680}{15} = \frac{918}{15} + \frac{11{,}762}{15}.$$

The second term divided by $k - 1 = 2$ is much too large, in comparison with s^2 (the latter being an unbiased estimate of σ^2 even if the population means are not equal). The ratio is

$$F = \frac{\dfrac{1}{3 - 1} \cdot \dfrac{11{,}762}{15}}{\dfrac{1}{15 - 3} \cdot \dfrac{918}{15}} \doteq 77.$$

The ninety-fifth percentile of the F distribution with parameters (2,12) is 3.89, and hence the null hypothesis of no difference in population means is rejected at the 5 per cent level.

Operating characteristics have been worked out in terms of the noncentral F distribution for various analyses of variance tests, but these will not be presented here. (Cf. Eisenhart, Hastay, and Wallis (eds.), *Techniques of Statistical Analysis*, McGraw-Hill, 1947.)

PROBLEMS

11–14. Construct the likelihood ratio test for equality of variances.

11–15. Construct the likelihood ratio test for $\theta_i = 0$, $i = 1, \ldots, k$ against the alternative that at least one θ_i is not zero.

11–16. Verify that the cross-product terms in the partition of $\sum\sum(X_{ij} - \mu)^2$ vanish, and also verify the ranks given.

11–17. Apply the test for equality of means to the data in Problem 11–7. Does your conclusion agree with that based on regression theory (that is, with the result of testing $\beta = 0$)?

11.2.2 Two Factors—One Observation per Cell. A simple extension of the model discussed in the preceding section is one in which two "factors" are provided for, say, factor A and factor B. Each combination of a level of factor A and a level of factor B is referred to as a *treatment;* and corresponding to each treatment there may be several observations. Before considering this general situation in §11.2.3, consider first the case in which just one observation per treatment is available.

Denote by X_{ij} the single observation corresponding to the ith level of factor A and the jth level of factor B. These observations are assumed to be independently and normally distributed with common variance σ^2. Let $\mu_{ij} = E(X_{ij})$, and define

$$\mu_{i\cdot} = \frac{1}{n}\sum_j \mu_{ij}, \quad \mu_{\cdot j} = \frac{1}{m}\sum \mu_{ij}, \quad \mu = \frac{1}{mn}\sum_j \sum_i \mu_{ij},$$

where sums on i extend from 1 to m, the number of levels of factor A, and sums on j extend from 1 to n, the number of levels of factor B. It is assumed that μ_{ij} can be expressed in the form

$$\mu_{ij} = \mu + \theta_i + \phi_j, \quad \text{where } \sum_i \theta_i = \sum_j \phi_j = 0,$$

which implies that

$$\theta_i = \mu_{i\cdot} - \mu, \qquad \phi_j = \mu_{\cdot j} - \mu.$$

This assumption is not necessarily fulfilled; the effects of factor A and factor B may not contribute additively to the mean of X_{ij}. In general an "interaction" term would have to be included to incorporate into the model what frequently happens—the effect of factor A, say, is different when factor B is present than when it is not. This more general model can be treated when there are several observations per cell, as in §11.2.3. For the present, there is assumed to be no interaction.

The assumed model involves $m + n + 2$ parameters: $\mu, \theta_1, \ldots, \theta_m, \phi_1, \ldots, \phi_n$, and σ^2. Their maximum likelihood estimates are

$$\hat{\mu} = \bar{X}, \quad \hat{\theta}_i = \bar{X}_{i\cdot} - \bar{X}, \quad \hat{\phi}_j = \bar{X}_{\cdot j} - \bar{X}$$

and

$$\hat{\sigma}^2 = \frac{1}{mn}\sum\sum[X_{ij} - (\bar{X}_{i\cdot} - \bar{X}) - (\bar{X}_{\cdot j} - \bar{X}) - \bar{X}]^2,$$

where

$$\bar{X}_{i\cdot} = \frac{1}{n}\sum_j X_{ij}, \qquad \bar{X}_{\cdot j} = \frac{1}{m}\sum_i X_{ij},$$

and

$$\bar{X} = \frac{1}{mn}\sum\sum X_{ij} = \frac{1}{m}\sum_i \bar{X}_{i\cdot} = \frac{1}{n}\sum_j \bar{X}_{\cdot j}.$$

These estimates suggest the following partition:

$$\sum\sum(X_{ij} - \mu_{ij})^2 = mn\hat{\sigma}^2 + mn(\bar{X} - \mu)^2 + n\sum(\bar{X}_{i\cdot} - \bar{X} - \theta_i)^2 + m\sum(\bar{X}_{\cdot j} - \bar{X} - \phi_j)^2.$$

(Again all cross-product terms drop out when summed.) The ranks of the quadratic forms on the right are, respectively: $mn - m - n + 1$, 1, $m - 1$, and $n - 1$, which add up to the rank mn on the left. [The rank of $\hat{\sigma}^2$ is the number of terms, mn, less the number of linear relations; the sum of $(X_{ij} - \mu_{ij})$ from 1 to m on i yields zero for each j, and the sum from 1 to n on j yields zero for each i, but these $m + n$ relations are not completely independent. One is implied by the other $m + n - 1$, so the rank is $mn - (m + n - 1)$.] Cochran's theorem then asserts that, when divided by σ^2, the terms on the right in the partition have independent chi-square distributions with $(m - 1)(n - 1)$, 1, $(m - 1)$, and $(n - 1)$ degrees of freedom, respectively.

Likelihood ratio tests for $\theta_i = 0$ and for $\phi_j = 0$ have the critical regions $F_\theta >$ constant and $F_\phi >$ constant, respectively, where

$$F_\theta = \frac{\frac{n}{m-1}\sum(\bar{X}_{i\cdot} - \bar{X})^2}{\frac{1}{(m-1)(n-1)}\sum\sum(X_{ij} - \bar{X}_{i\cdot} - \bar{X}_{\cdot j} + \bar{X})^2}$$

and

$$F_\phi = \frac{\frac{m}{n-1}\sum(\bar{X}_{\cdot j} - \bar{X})^2}{\frac{1}{(m-1)(n-1)}\sum\sum(X_{ij} - \bar{X}_{i\cdot} - \bar{X}_{\cdot j} + \bar{X})^2}.$$

The ratio F_θ has a noncentral F distribution with $(m - 1, mn - m - n + 1)$ degrees of freedom, and under the null hypothesis that $\theta_i = 0$ for all i, it has a central F distribution. (The noncentrality parameter is $\frac{1}{2}\sum\theta_i^2$.) Thus the significance level α of the test $F_\theta >$ constant determines the constant used as a rejection limit through the F distribution, and the power function comes from the noncentral F distribution. Similar statements apply to the ratio F_ϕ and the null hypothesis that $\phi_j = 0$ for all j.

Although the test ratios are not independent, the distribution of F_θ does not depend on the ϕ's, and the distribution of F_ϕ does not depend on the θ's. Therefore, even if factor A is not the same at all levels, a test for factor B can be carried out, and vice versa.

Example 11–5. Consider two factors with three levels each, and assume that one observation per cell is obtained, with the results as shown in the following array:

		Factor B Level 1	Level 2	Level 3	$\bar{X}_{i\cdot}$	$(\bar{X}_{i\cdot} - \bar{X})$
Factor A	level 1	3	5	4	4	−7
	level 2	11	10	12	11	0
	level 3	16	21	17	18	7
	$\bar{X}_{\cdot j}$	10	12	11	$\bar{X} = 11$	
	$(\bar{X}_{\cdot j} - \bar{X})$	−1	1	0		

The sum of squared deviations about $\bar{X}$ is 312, which is decomposed as follows:

$$312 = 12 + 294 + 6.$$

The first term, 12, divided by (3 − 1)(3 − 1) = 4 gives an unbiased estimate of σ^2 whether or not θ_i and ϕ_j are zero. The second term, 294, divided by (3 − 1), related to factor A, exceeds 3 by a considerable amount. The ratio is

$$\frac{294/(3-1)}{12/4} = 49.$$

Since this exceeds 6.94, the ninety-fifth percentile of the F distribution with (2,4) degrees of freedom, the hypothesis that $\theta_i = 0$ for all i is rejected at the 5 per cent level. On the other hand, the ratio related to factor B is

$$\frac{6/(3-1)}{12/4} = 1,$$

so the hypothesis that $\phi_j = 0$ for all j is accepted at any level.

11.2.3 Two Factors with Interaction. Consider again factors A and B with m and n levels, respectively, but assume now that in the "cell" corresponding to the ith level of A and the jth level of B there are several observations:

$$X_{ij1}, X_{ij2}, \ldots, X_{ijp},$$

the same number p in each cell, for simplicity. The notation is otherwise as it was in §11.2.2 except that

$$\mu_{ij} = \mu + \theta_i + \phi_j + \psi_{ij},$$

and there is now an additional subscript to keep track of:

$$\bar{X} = \frac{1}{mnp}\sum\sum\sum X_{ijk}, \quad \bar{X}_{i\cdot\cdot} = \frac{1}{np}\sum\sum X_{ijk}, \quad \bar{X}_{ij\cdot} = \frac{1}{p}\sum X_{ijk},$$

and so on. It is assumed that

$$\sum\theta_i = \sum\phi_j = \sum_i \psi_{ij} = \sum_j \psi_{ij} = 0$$

Maximum likelihood estimates (assuming the usual normal populations with common variance σ^2) are as follows:

$$\hat{\theta}_i = \bar{X}_{i\cdot\cdot} - \bar{X}, \quad \hat{\phi}_j = \bar{X}_{\cdot j\cdot} - \bar{X}, \quad \hat{\mu} = \bar{X},$$

$$\hat{\psi}_{ij} = \bar{X}_{ij\cdot} - (\bar{X}_{i\cdot\cdot} - \bar{X}) - (\bar{X}_{\cdot j\cdot} - \bar{X}) - \bar{X},$$

$$\hat{\sigma}^2 = \frac{1}{mnp}\sum\sum\sum(X_{ijk} - \bar{X}_{ij\cdot})^2.$$

The following partition is used:

$$\begin{aligned}\sum\sum\sum(X_{ijk} - \mu_{ij})^2 = &\sum\sum\sum(X_{ijk} - \bar{X}_{ij\cdot})^2 \\ &+ p\sum\sum(\bar{X}_{ij\cdot} + \bar{X} - \bar{X}_{i\cdot\cdot} - \bar{X}_{\cdot j\cdot} - \psi_{ij})^2 \\ &+ mnp(\bar{X} - \mu)^2 + np\sum(\bar{X}_{i\cdot\cdot} - \bar{X} - \theta_i)^2 \\ &+ mp\sum(\bar{X}_{\cdot j\cdot} - \bar{X} - \phi_j)^2.\end{aligned}$$

(Once more cross-product terms drop out when summed.) Upon division by σ^2, the terms of the partition are seen to have independent chi-square distributions; the rank relationship, which also then gives the degrees of freedom in each case, is as follows:

$$mnp = mn(p - 1) + (m - 1)(n - 1) + 1 + (m - 1) + (n - 1).$$

Under the hypothesis $\psi_{ij} = 0$, the ratio

$$F_\psi = \frac{\dfrac{p}{(m-1)(n-1)} \sum\sum(\bar{X}_{ij\cdot} - \bar{X}_{i\cdot\cdot} - \bar{X}_{\cdot j\cdot} + \bar{X})^2}{\dfrac{1}{mn(p-1)} \sum\sum\sum(X_{ijk} - \bar{X}_{ij\cdot})^2}$$

has the F distribution with parameters $[(m - 1)(n - 1), mn(p - 1)]$, independent of any assumption about θ_i or ϕ_j. The denominator has a distribution depending only on σ^2 and can therefore be used as a measuring stick to determine whether the numerator is too large, indicating a presence of interaction. The test for $\psi_{ij} = 0$, for all i and j, is then to reject this hypothesis if $F_\psi >$ constant.

The denominator of F is based only on the variation of the observations in the cells about the corresponding cell means and has in it no component of cell-to-cell variation. If $\psi_{ij} = 0$, on the other hand, a more precise estimate of σ^2 can be obtained by pooling the estimates in numerator and denominator of F_ψ, to obtain

$$\frac{1}{mnp - m - n + 1} \sum\sum\sum(X_{ijk} - \bar{X}_{ij\cdot} - \bar{X}_{\cdot j\cdot} + \bar{X})^2.$$

This then could be used in place of the less precise estimate based on $\hat{\sigma}^2$ as a denominator for an F_θ or an F_ϕ to test $\theta_i = 0$ or $\phi_j = 0$. These latter tests can be carried out even in the *presence* of interaction, of course, using the same denominator as in F_ψ, which is an important feature of the technique.

11.2.4 A Model with Randomly Drawn Levels. In the models considered so far, conclusions are of the form that factor A, say, has no effect when introduced at levels 1, 2, ..., m. One has no right to infer, however, that if a different level of factor A be used, there is still no effect. For example, if factor A is the operator of a machine, and the tests used persons a, b, and c, then no conclusion can be drawn about the effect of operator when using persons d and e.

It is sometimes desirable to think of the particular operators used as a sample from a population of possible operators, in order to conclude that the operator has no effect, rather than just that the particular operators used have no effect. For a single factor, with observations $X_{i1}, \ldots, X_{in_i}$ at level i, consider the model in which it is assumed that

$$X_{ij} = \mu + Y_i + Z_{ij},$$

where $Y_1, \ldots, Y_k, Z_{11}, \ldots, Z_{kn_k}$ are independent normal variables with zero means. The quantity Z_{ij} denotes the random variation present with each observation at each level, and Y_i denotes the *random* contribution to X_{ij} associated with the factor at level i. Another instance in which this model might be appropriate is in the experimental determination of a chemical or physical property of a product that comes in batches or sheets, in which there is randomness from batch to batch or sheet to sheet and also randomness in determination of the property of a single batch or sheet, the latter caused either by the measuring process itself or by variations from point to point in the batch or sheet.

It is assumed that var $Y_i = \omega^2$ and var $Z_{ij} = \sigma^2$, so that var $X_{ij} = \omega^2 + \sigma^2$. The observations are not independent in this model, since, for instance,

$$E[(X_{11} - \mu)(X_{12} - \mu)] = E[(Y_1 + Z_{11})(Y_1 + Z_{12})] = E(Y_1^2) = \omega^2.$$

This is not zero unless it happens that $\omega^2 = 0$, which would imply that Y_i is really a constant for all observations and all levels. That is, $\omega^2 = 0$ is the hypothesis that the factor being tested has "no effect" (that is, a constant effect).

We use the following notation:

$$\bar{X}_i = \frac{1}{n_i}\sum_j X_{ij}, \quad \bar{Z}_i = \frac{1}{n_i}\sum_j Z_{ij} = \bar{X}_i - (\mu + Y_i),$$

$$n = \sum n_i, \quad \bar{Y} = \frac{1}{n}\sum_i n_i Y_i, \quad \bar{X} = \frac{1}{n}\sum_i n_i \bar{X}_i,$$

and

$$\bar{Z} = \frac{1}{n}\sum_i n_i \bar{Z}_i = \bar{X} - (\mu + \bar{Y}).$$

As in the linear model for the single classification problem, we have the identity:

$$\sum\sum(X_{ij} - \mu)^2 = \sum\sum(X_{ij} - \bar{X}_i)^2 + \sum n_i(\bar{X}_i - \bar{X})^2 + n(\bar{X} - \mu)^2.$$

However, since the X_{ij} are not independent, the quantity on the left is not in general a chi-square variable when divided by var X_{ij}. But if $\omega^2 = 0$, the X_{ij} are uncorrelated and (because they are normal) independent, with variance σ^2; division of the equation by σ^2 results in a chi-square variable on the left, with n degrees of freedom, and by Cochran's theorem, independent chi-square distributions on the right, with $n - k$, $k - 1$, and 1 degree of freedom, in that order. So, under the null hypothesis of *no* effect introduced by the factor, the ratio

$$F = \frac{\frac{1}{k-1}\sum n_i(\bar{X}_i - \bar{X})^2}{\frac{1}{n-k}\sum\sum(X_{ij} - \bar{X}_i)^2}$$

has the F distribution with parameters $(k - 1, n - k)$.

Now, since $X_{ij} - \bar{X}_i = Z_{ij} - \bar{Z}_i$, and since for each i the sum on j, $\sum(Z_{ij} - \bar{Z}_i)^2/\sigma^2$, has the chi-square distribution with $n_i - 1$ degrees of freedom (being of the form ns_z^2/σ^2 for a sample of size n_i from a normal population), it then follows that the quantity

$$\sum\sum\frac{(X_{ij} - \bar{X})^2}{\sigma^2} = \sum\sum\frac{(Z_{ij} - \bar{Z}_i)^2}{\sigma^2}$$

is the sum of k independent chi-square variables and is therefore also chi-square, with $(n_1 - 1) + \cdots + (n_k - 1) = n - k$ degrees of freedom, even if $\omega^2 \neq 0$. The denominator of F is then an estimate of F independent of the null hypothesis. The numerator, on the other hand, depends on the assumption about the variance of Y_i. Its expected value is

$$\sigma^2 + \frac{n\omega^2\,[1 - \sum(n_i/n)^2]}{k-1},$$

which is smallest when $\omega^2 = 0$. So, if the ratio F is too large as determined by a given significance level and the F table, the hypothesis of no effect from the factor is rejected.

It is interesting that the test statistic used and the critical region $F >$ constant for testing $\omega^2 = 0$ are identical with those used in the linear hypothesis model of §11.2.1. The model is different, however, and the conclusion here has to do with the population of possible operators or batches (etc.) rather than with just the particular operators or batches used in the test.

A similar model can be used in a two-factor problem. Given the observation X_{ij} corresponding to the ith level of factor A and the jth level of factor B, it would be assumed that X_{ij} can be represented in the form

$$X_{ij} = \mu + Y_i + Z_j + W_{ij},$$

where W_{ij}, Y_i, Z_j (for $i = 1, \ldots, m$ and $j = 1, \ldots, n$) are independent normal random variables with zero means. An analysis similar to that of the one-factor problem just given shows that again the F ratios used in the linear hypothesis model are appropriate. But again there is a difference in how the phrase "no effect" is interpreted. Details are omitted.

PROBLEMS

11–18. Using the data in the accompanying table, test the effects of the two factors.

		Level of Factor A				
		1	2	3	4	5
	1	53	56	45	52	49
Level of	2	47	50	47	47	53
Factor B	3	57	63	54	57	58
	4	45	52	42	41	48

11–19. Using the three observations per cell given, test for no interaction between factors. Test also the hypotheses that the factors have no effect.

		Machine			
		A	B	C	D
	1	59	61	48	47
		43	49	47	40
		63	52	58	51
	2	60	49	40	38
Operator		51	52	48	50
		48	55	56	41
	3	63	58	46	48
		60	48	53	40
		57	56	51	50

11–20. Verify the expression given in the text for the expected value of $\sum n_i(\bar{X}_i - \bar{X})^2/(k-1)$. [Write $\bar{X}_i - \bar{X} = U_i - \bar{U}$, where $U_i = Y_i + \bar{Z}_i$, and note that $\sum n_i(U_i - \bar{U})^2 = \sum n_i U_i^2 - n\bar{U}^2$, where $\bar{U} = \sum n_i U_i/n$.]

11.2.5 Other Designs. More than two factors can be considered. Indeed, additional factors must be considered if there is any chance that they are confounding the results. For the case of three factors, at m, n, and p levels, with q observations per treatment, a linear model would be of the form

$$E(X_{ijk}) = \mu + \alpha_i + \beta_j + \gamma_k + \zeta_{ij} + \xi_{jk} + \eta_{ki} + \delta_{ijk},$$

with the usual normalizing conditions that sums of these quantities (except μ) with respect to any one of the pertinent subscripts are zero. The α_i, β_j, and γ_k are factor effects, the ζ_{ij}, ξ_{ki}, and η_{jk} are second-order interactions, and δ_{ijk} is a third-order interaction—a contribution present, when all three factors are involved, which would not be present for any pair of factors. Maximum likelihood estimates are

$$\hat{\mu} = \bar{X}, \quad \hat{\alpha}_i = \bar{X}_{i\cdots} - \bar{X}, \ldots,$$

$$\zeta_{ij} = \bar{X}_{ij\cdot\cdot} - \bar{X}_{i\cdots} - \bar{X}_{\cdot j\cdot\cdot} + \bar{X}, \ldots,$$

$$\delta_{ijk} = \bar{X}_{ijk\cdot} - \bar{X}_{ij\cdot\cdot} - \bar{X}_{i\cdot k\cdot} - \bar{X}_{\cdot jk\cdot} + \bar{X}_{\cdot j\cdot\cdot} + \bar{X}_{i\cdots} + \bar{X}_{\cdot\cdot k\cdot} - \bar{X}.$$

To carry out a test for the various factors and interactions, it would be necessary to have *mnpq* observations. This could be more observations than are easily obtainable, and it is both interesting and useful that it is possible to test for one of the three factors in the presence of the other two with even fewer than the *mnp* observations that would be needed for one observation per cell. (Of course, with fewer observations, the sensitivity of the test is reduced, but the point is that there *is* a test.)

Suppose that the three factors are machines, operators, and time periods, and that there are four levels of each. Instead of obtaining a performance figure for each of the 64 combinations of machine, operator, and time period, one obtains the 16 observations as indicated in the accompanying table, each operator working once in each time period and once on each machine. The letter in the array indicates the machine to be used. An array (Latin) of the letters A, B, C, D such as is shown, with the property that no letter appears more than once in any column or in any row, is called a *Latin square;* these have been extensively studied, computed, and tabulated. (Cf. References [5] and [11].)

		Time Period 1	2	3	4
Operator	1	A	B	C	D
	2	B	C	D	A
	3	C	D	A	B
	4	D	A	B	C

The observations in a linear model are assumed to be of the form

$$X_{ij(k)} = \mu + \alpha_i + \beta_j + \gamma_k + Y_{ijk}$$

(no interactions), where the level (k) of the third factor is determined by i, j, and the particular Latin square used. The breakup used is indicated in the accompanying table.

	Sum of Squares	Degrees of Freedom
Rows	$m\Sigma(\bar{X}_{i\cdot} - \bar{X} - \alpha_i)^2$	$m - 1$
Columns	$m\Sigma(\bar{X}_{\cdot j} - \bar{X} - \beta_j)^2$	$m - 1$
"Letters"	$m\Sigma(\bar{X}_{(k)} - \bar{X} - \gamma_k)^2$	$m - 1$
Mean	$m^2(\bar{X} - \mu)^2$	1
Residual	$\Sigma\Sigma(X_{ij(k)} - \bar{X}_{i\cdot} - \bar{X}_{\cdot j} - \bar{X}_{(k)} + 2\bar{X}$	$(m - 2)(m - 1)$
Total	$\Sigma\Sigma(X_{ij(k)} - \mu_{ij})^2$	m^2

The numbers in the rightmost column denote the number of degrees of freedom of the corresponding chi-square distribution (when the term in question is divided by σ^2). The mean $\bar{X}_{(k)}$ denotes the average of all entries in the table that are taken at the kth level of the third factor (letters).

Four factors can be considered simultaneously using a "Latin-Greco square," in which the levels of factor C are entered as Latin letters and the levels of factor D are entered as Greek letters. Each level of each factor appears once with each level of each other factor. A three-by-three square of this type (corresponding to three levels of each of four factors) is shown at the right.

		Factor 2		
		1	2	3
	1	$A\alpha$	$B\beta$	$C\gamma$
Factor 1	2	$B\gamma$	$C\alpha$	$A\beta$
	3	$C\beta$	$A\gamma$	$B\alpha$

The study of designs of experiments to handle many factors while permitting testing one of them has been very extensive but will not be developed further here. These methods are characteristically different from methods in which a factor is studied by keeping all other factors at fixed levels. In the statistical approach, these other factors are allowed to vary, and the results can be exploited to make inferences concerning these other factors as well as the one of interest.

11.3 A General Linear Model

It is possible to subsume the regression, analysis of variance, and analysis of covariance problems under a rather general linear model. The estimation, testing, and distribution problems can be studied in this general model and the general results then made specific for the various applications. (Such a program is carried out in the excellent book of Scheffé [17].) It is our purpose here simply to introduce the model as a hint of what might then be done.

Consider the n observations $Y_1, Y_2, \ldots, Y_n$ and suppose that a given observation is made up as follows:

$$Y_i = x_{1i}\beta_1 + \cdots + x_{pi}\beta_p + \epsilon_i, \qquad i = 1, \ldots, n, \quad p < n.$$

Introducing the matrix notation:

$$\boldsymbol{Y} = \begin{pmatrix} Y_1 \\ \vdots \\ Y_n \end{pmatrix}, \quad \boldsymbol{X} = \begin{pmatrix} x_{11} & \cdots & x_{1n} \\ \vdots & & \\ x_{p1} & \cdots & x_{pn} \end{pmatrix}, \quad \boldsymbol{\epsilon} = \begin{pmatrix} \epsilon_1 \\ \vdots \\ \epsilon_n \end{pmatrix}, \quad \boldsymbol{\beta} = \begin{pmatrix} \hat{\beta}_1 \\ \vdots \\ \hat{\beta}_p \end{pmatrix},$$

the makeup of $\boldsymbol{Y}$ can be exhibited in this way:

$$\boldsymbol{Y} = \boldsymbol{X}'\boldsymbol{\beta} + \boldsymbol{\epsilon}.$$

It is assumed that $\boldsymbol{\epsilon}$ is multivariate normal with zero mean vector and covariance matrix $\sigma^2\boldsymbol{I}$, where $\boldsymbol{I}$ is the n-by-n identity matrix. Then $\boldsymbol{Y}$ is multivariate normal with the same covariance matrix and mean vector $\mu = EY = X'\beta$. The density function of Y is

$$f_Y(y) = (2\pi\sigma^2)^{-n/2} \exp\left[\frac{-(y-\mu)'(y-\mu)}{2\sigma^2}\right].$$

Most problems in regression and analysis of variance and covariance can be put into the above framework. In regression problems the quantities x_{ij} are functions of selected values of the controlled variable. In analysis of variance problems, they are either 1 or 0 (usually), corresponding to the presence or absence of a factor in the observation. In analysis of covariance problems there are x's of both kinds.

Example 11–6. Consider a problem of quadratic regression, in which it is assumed that $E(Y_i) = a + bt_i + ct_i^2$. (Take the simple case of one observation at each t_i.) The following identification is then made:

$$x_{1i} = 1, \quad x_{2i} = t_i, \quad x_{3i} = t_i^2, \quad a = \beta_1, \quad b = \beta_2, \quad c = \beta_3.$$

This reduces the general model to this particular regression problem.

Example 11–7. Consider a single classification analysis of variance problem with n_i observations at the ith level of the single factor. Here the observations, given earlier in a double array, are strung out:

$$Y' = (Y_{11}, Y_{12}, \ldots, Y_{1n_1}, Y_{21}, \ldots, Y_{kn_k}),$$

and

$$\epsilon = (\epsilon_{11}, \epsilon_{12}, \ldots, \epsilon_{1n_1}, \ldots, \epsilon_{kn_k}).$$

The x's are either 0 or 1. For the single classification problem it is assumed that observations are made up as follows:

$$Y_{ij} = \mu + \theta_i + \epsilon_{ij}, \quad i = 1,\ldots,k, \quad j = 1,\ldots,n_i.$$

The identification

$$\beta_1 = \theta_1, \ \ldots, \ \beta_k = \theta_k, \ \beta_{k+1} = \mu,$$

$$x_{1ij} = \begin{cases} 1 & \text{for } i = 1, j = 1, \ldots, n_1 \\ 0 & \text{for } i \neq 1, \end{cases}$$

$$\vdots \qquad \qquad \vdots$$

$$x_{kij} = \begin{cases} 1 & \text{for } i = k, j = 1, \ldots, n_k \\ 0 & \text{for } i \neq k, \end{cases}$$

$$x_{(k+1)ij} = 1$$

reduces the general model to the single classification problem. Sums from $i = 1$ to n in the general model correspond here to double sums, from $i = 1$ to k and from $j = 1$ to n_i.

Consider now the possible estimates b_i for β_i, and form $\boldsymbol{X}'\boldsymbol{b}$ as an estimate of $\boldsymbol{X}'$. The vector

$$\boldsymbol{e} = \boldsymbol{Y} - \boldsymbol{X}'\boldsymbol{b}$$

can be thought of as an estimate of the error vector $\boldsymbol{\epsilon}$, with squared "norm" given by

$$\sum_{i=1}^{n} e_i^2 = \boldsymbol{e}'\boldsymbol{e} = (\boldsymbol{Y} - \boldsymbol{X}'\boldsymbol{b})'(\boldsymbol{Y} - \boldsymbol{X}'\boldsymbol{b})$$

$$= \sum_{i=1}^{n} \left\{ Y_i - \sum_{j=1}^{p} x_{ji} b_j \right\}^2.$$

A *least squares estimate* of $\boldsymbol{\beta}$ is a value $\boldsymbol{b} = \hat{\boldsymbol{\beta}}$ which minimizes this norm. For such a value it must be that

$$\left.\frac{\partial(\boldsymbol{e}'\boldsymbol{e})}{\partial b_\nu}\right|_{b=\hat{\beta}} = -2 \sum_{i=1}^{n} \left\{ Y_i - \sum_{j=1}^{p} x_{ji}\hat{\beta}_j \right\} x_{\nu i} = 0$$

for $\nu = 1, \ldots, p$. This condition can be written in matrix form:

$$\boldsymbol{X}\boldsymbol{X}'\hat{\boldsymbol{\beta}} = \boldsymbol{X}\boldsymbol{Y}.$$

The equations represented here are called the *normal equations* of the least squares problem.

The minimum value of $\boldsymbol{e}'\boldsymbol{e}$ is achieved by putting $\boldsymbol{b} = \hat{\boldsymbol{\beta}}$, and is therefore

$$(\boldsymbol{Y} - \boldsymbol{X}')'(\boldsymbol{Y} - \boldsymbol{X}'\hat{\boldsymbol{\beta}}) = \boldsymbol{Y}'\boldsymbol{Y} - \hat{\boldsymbol{\beta}}'\boldsymbol{X}\boldsymbol{Y} - \boldsymbol{Y}'\boldsymbol{X}'\hat{\boldsymbol{\beta}} + \hat{\boldsymbol{\beta}}'\boldsymbol{X}\boldsymbol{X}'\hat{\boldsymbol{\beta}}$$

$$= \boldsymbol{Y}'\boldsymbol{Y} - \hat{\boldsymbol{\beta}}'\boldsymbol{X}\boldsymbol{Y} + [\hat{\boldsymbol{\beta}}'(\boldsymbol{X}\boldsymbol{X}'\hat{\boldsymbol{\beta}} - \boldsymbol{X}\boldsymbol{Y})]'$$

$$= \sum_{i=1}^{n} Y_i^2 - \sum_{\nu=1}^{k} \hat{\beta}_\nu \sum_{i=1}^{n} x_{\nu i} Y_i.$$

This is the *error sum of squares.*

If the rank of $\boldsymbol{X}$ is p, called the case of *full rank*, the matrix $\boldsymbol{X}\boldsymbol{X}'$ is non-singular (as well as square and symmetric) and can be inverted. The solution of the normal equations is then unique:

$$\hat{\boldsymbol{\beta}} = (\boldsymbol{X}\boldsymbol{X}')^{-1}\boldsymbol{X}\boldsymbol{Y}.$$

The covariance matrix of this least squares solution is readily computed in terms of $\boldsymbol{S} = \boldsymbol{X}\boldsymbol{X}'$:

$$\boldsymbol{M}_{\hat{\beta}} = (\boldsymbol{S}^{-1}\boldsymbol{X})\boldsymbol{M}_{\boldsymbol{Y}}(\boldsymbol{S}^{-1}\boldsymbol{X})' = \sigma^2\boldsymbol{S}^{-1}\boldsymbol{X}\boldsymbol{X}'\boldsymbol{S}^{-1} = \sigma^2\boldsymbol{S}^{-1}.$$

Example 11–8. Consider the linear regression problem with one observation at each of $x_1, \ldots, x_n$. In this problem the identification with the general model is as follows:

$$\boldsymbol{X} = \begin{pmatrix} 1 & 1 \cdots 1 \\ x_1 & x_2 \cdots x_n \end{pmatrix}, \quad \boldsymbol{\beta} = \begin{pmatrix} \alpha \\ \beta \end{pmatrix}, \quad \boldsymbol{X}' = \begin{pmatrix} 1 & x_1 \\ \vdots & \vdots \\ 1 & x_n \end{pmatrix},$$

and

$$\boldsymbol{XX'} = \begin{pmatrix} n & \sum x_i \\ \sum x_i & \sum x_i^2 \end{pmatrix}, \qquad \boldsymbol{XY} = \begin{pmatrix} \sum Y_i \\ \sum x_i Y_i \end{pmatrix}.$$

The normal equations become

$$\begin{pmatrix} na & + b\sum x_i \\ a\sum x_i & + b\sum x_i^2 \end{pmatrix} = \begin{pmatrix} \sum Y_i \\ \sum x_i Y_i \end{pmatrix}.$$

The solution $a = \hat{\alpha}$ and $b = \hat{\beta}$ is then unique ($\boldsymbol{X}$ is of full rank and $\boldsymbol{XX'}$ can be inverted) if the x_i's are not all the same:

$$(\boldsymbol{XX'})^{-1} = \frac{1}{n^2 s_x^2}\begin{pmatrix} \sum x_i^2 & -\sum x_i \\ -\sum x_i & n \end{pmatrix}.$$

With this one finds

$$\hat{\boldsymbol{\beta}} = \frac{1}{ns_x^2}\begin{pmatrix} \bar{Y}\sum x_i^2 - \bar{x}\sum x_i Y_i \\ \sum x_i Y_i - n\bar{x}\bar{Y} \end{pmatrix},$$

giving again the estimates obtained in §11.1. Their variances and covariance are found as the elements of the matrix $\sigma^2 \mathrm{S}^{-1}$:

$$\operatorname{var} \hat{\alpha} = \frac{\sigma^2 \sum x_i^2}{n^2 s_x^2}, \qquad \operatorname{var} \hat{\beta} = \frac{\sigma^2}{ns_x^2},$$

and

$$\operatorname{cov}(\hat{\alpha},\hat{\beta}) = -\frac{\sigma^2\sum x_i}{n^2 s_x^2}.$$

(Notice that if $\bar{x} = 0$, $\hat{\alpha}$ and $\hat{\beta}$ are uncorrelated.)

It is to be noted (in the full rank case, still) that the least squares estimate $\hat{\boldsymbol{\beta}}$ is a linear transformation of $\boldsymbol{Y}$. That is, each component of $\hat{\boldsymbol{\beta}}$ is a *linear* function of the observations:

$$\hat{\boldsymbol{\beta}} = (\boldsymbol{S}^{-1}\mathrm{X})\boldsymbol{Y}.$$

Further, it is an *unbiased* estimate (so that each component $\hat{\beta}_i$ is unbiased):

$$E(\hat{\boldsymbol{\beta}}) = (\boldsymbol{S}^{-1}\mathrm{X})E(\boldsymbol{Y}) = \boldsymbol{S}^{-1}\boldsymbol{XX'}\boldsymbol{\beta} = \boldsymbol{\beta}.$$

The Gauss-Markov theorem states that the least squares estimate, in the class of unbiased, linear estimates, has a minimum variance property: the variances of its components are (simultaneously) smallest. This may be seen as follows.

Consider an arbitrary linear estimate of $\boldsymbol{\beta}$ of the form $\boldsymbol{\beta}^* = \boldsymbol{AY}$, and define $\boldsymbol{B}$ by

$$\boldsymbol{\beta}^* - \hat{\boldsymbol{\beta}} = (\boldsymbol{A} - \boldsymbol{S}^{-1}\mathrm{X})\boldsymbol{Y} \equiv \boldsymbol{BY}.$$

The requirement that $\boldsymbol{\beta}^*$ be *unbiased:*

$$E(\boldsymbol{\beta}^*) = E[(\boldsymbol{B} + \boldsymbol{S}^{-1}\boldsymbol{X})\boldsymbol{Y}] = \boldsymbol{B}\boldsymbol{X}'\boldsymbol{\beta} + \boldsymbol{S}^{-1}\boldsymbol{X}\boldsymbol{X}'\boldsymbol{\beta} = \boldsymbol{B}\boldsymbol{X}'\boldsymbol{\beta} + \boldsymbol{\beta} = \boldsymbol{\beta},$$

implies that $\boldsymbol{B}\boldsymbol{X}'$ must be 0. The second moment matrix is then

$$\boldsymbol{M}_{\hat{\beta}^*} = \sigma^2(\boldsymbol{B} + \boldsymbol{S}^{-1}\boldsymbol{X})(\boldsymbol{B} + \boldsymbol{S}^{-1}\boldsymbol{X})' = \sigma^2(\boldsymbol{B}\boldsymbol{B}' + \boldsymbol{S}^{-1}).$$

Since $\boldsymbol{S}^{-1}$ is constant and the diagonal elements of $\boldsymbol{B}\boldsymbol{B}'$ are

$$(\boldsymbol{B}\boldsymbol{B}')_{ii} = b_{i1}^2 + \cdots + b_{in}^2,$$

the smallest variances of the β_i^* are clearly achieved for $\boldsymbol{B} = \boldsymbol{O}$ (which satisfies $\boldsymbol{B}\boldsymbol{X} = \boldsymbol{O}$), or $\boldsymbol{\beta}^* = \hat{\boldsymbol{\beta}}$.

It is also true (cf. Problem 11–22) that there is a unique unbiased, minimum variance, linear estimate of any linear function $\boldsymbol{c}'\boldsymbol{\beta}$ which has an unbiased linear estimate, and that this minimum variance estimate is $\boldsymbol{c}'\hat{\boldsymbol{\beta}}$, where $\hat{\boldsymbol{\beta}}$ is the least squares estimate of $\boldsymbol{\beta}$.

Obtaining the maximum likelihood estimate of $\boldsymbol{\beta}$ requires use of the distribution of the observations $\boldsymbol{Y}$, which has not been used in the above discussion of least squares, unbiasedness, and minimum variance. It was assumed at the outset that the observations were normal—that $\boldsymbol{Y}$ is multivariate normal, and the likelihood function has the logarithm

$$\log L(\boldsymbol{\beta},\sigma^2) = -\frac{n}{2}(\log 2\pi + \log \sigma^2) - \frac{1}{2\sigma^2}(\boldsymbol{Y} - \boldsymbol{X}'\boldsymbol{\beta})'(\boldsymbol{Y} - \boldsymbol{X}'\boldsymbol{\beta}).$$

It is clear from the form of this expression that minimization with respect to $(\boldsymbol{\beta},\sigma^2)$ produces maximum likelihood estimates $(\hat{\boldsymbol{\beta}},\hat{\sigma}^2)$ of which $\hat{\boldsymbol{\beta}}$ is precisely the least squares estimate, and $\hat{\sigma}^2$ is the error sum of squares divided by n:

$$\hat{\sigma}^2 = \frac{1}{n}(\boldsymbol{Y} - \boldsymbol{X}'\hat{\boldsymbol{\beta}})'(\boldsymbol{Y} - \boldsymbol{X}'\hat{\boldsymbol{\beta}}) = \frac{1}{n}\min(\boldsymbol{e}'\boldsymbol{e}).$$

Thus, least squares estimates are maximum likelihood estimates in the normal case.

We have touched briefly on some of the aspects of estimation in the general linear model. Tests of hypotheses of the kind usually encountered can be phrased in terms of linear subspaces of the parameter space. Distribution problems can be handled quite generally to include the various results obtained earlier by Cochran's theorem. (See Reference [17] for such developments.)

PROBLEMS

11–21. Verify the "degrees of freedom" results shown in the table for the Latin square problem, §11.2.5.

11–22. Using the derivation of the Gauss-Markov theorem as a guide, verify the claim made concerning the minimum variance, unbiased estimate of $\boldsymbol{c}'\boldsymbol{\beta}$, where $\boldsymbol{c}'$ is a given vector of constants.

References

[1] Anderson, T. W., *Introduction to Multivariate Statistical Analysis* (Wiley), New York, 1958.

[2] Blackwell, D., and Girshick, M., *Theory of Games and Statistical Decisions* (Wiley), New York, 1954.

[3] Chernoff, H., and Moses, L., *Elementary Decision Theory* (Wiley), New York, 1959.

[4] Cramer, H., *Mathematical Methods of Statistics* (Princeton Univ. Press), Princeton, 1946.

[5] Cochran, W., and Cox, G., *Experimental Designs*, 2nd ed. (Wiley), New York, 1957.

[6] Feller, W., *An Introduction to Probability Theory and Its Applications*, 2nd ed. (Wiley), New York, 1957.

[7] Fraser, D. A. S., *Nonparametric Methods in Statistics* (Wiley), New York, 1957.

[8] Goldberg, S., *Probability: An Introduction* (Prentice Hall), Englewood Cliffs, N. J., 1960.

[9] Hogg, R., and Craig, A., *Introduction to Mathematical Statistics* (Macmillan) New York, 1959.

[10] Hanson, M., Hurwitz, W., and Madow, W., *Sample Survey Methods and Theory* (Vol. I and Vol. II) (Wiley), New York, 1953.

[11] Kempthorne, O., *The Design and Analysis of Experiments* (Wiley), New York, 1952.

[12] Lehmann, E., *Testing Statistical Hypotheses* (Wiley), New York, 1959.

[13] Loeve, M., *Probability Theory* (Van Nostrand), New York, 1955.

[14] Mann, H. B., *Analysis of Variance and the Design of Experiments* (Dover), New York, 1949.

[15] Parzen, E., *Modern Probability Theory and Its Applications* (Wiley), New York, 1960.

[16] Savage, L. J., *The Foundations of Statistics* (Wiley), New York, 1954.

[17] Scheffe, H., *The Analysis of Variance* (Wiley), New York, 1959.

[18] Van der Waerden, B., *Mathematische Statistik* (Springer), Berlin, 1957.

[19] Wald, A., *Statistical Decision Functions* (Wiley), New York, 1950.

[20] Wald, A., *Sequential Analysis* (Wiley), New York, 1947.

[21] Wilks, S. S., *Mathematical Statistics* (Princeton Univ. Press), Princeton, 1944.

Appendix—Tables

LIST OF TABLES

Table I. Values of the Standard Normal Distribution Function

$$N(z) = \int_{-\infty}^{z} \frac{1}{\sqrt{2\pi}} e^{-u^2/2}\, du = P(Z \le z)$$

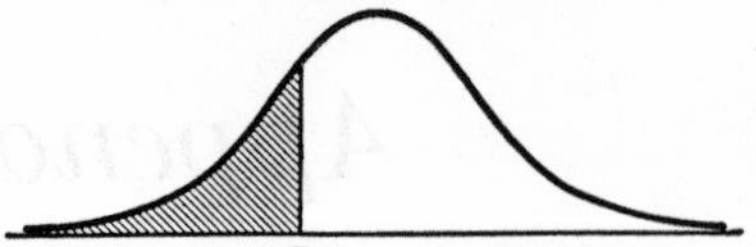

z

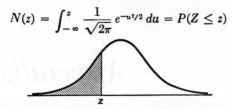

z	0	1	2	3	4	5	6	7	8	9
−3.	.0013	.0010	.0007	.0005	.0003	.0002	.0002	.0001	.0001	.0000
−2.9	.0019	.0018	.0017	.0017	.0016	.0016	.0015	.0015	.0014	.0014
−2.8	.0026	.0025	.0024	.0023	.0023	.0022	.0021	.0021	.0020	.0019
−2.7	.0035	.0034	.0033	.0032	.0031	.0030	.0029	.0028	.0027	.0026
−2.6	.0047	.0045	.0044	.0043	.0041	.0040	.0039	.0038	.0037	.0036
−2.5	.0062	.0060	.0059	.0057	.0055	.0054	.0052	.0051	.0049	.0048
−2.4	.0082	.0080	.0078	.0075	.0073	.0071	.0069	.0068	.0066	.0064
−2.3	.0107	.0104	.0102	.0099	.0096	.0094	.0091	.0089	.0087	.0084
−2.2	.0139	.0136	.0132	.0129	.0126	.0122	.0119	.0116	.0113	.0110
−2.1	.0179	.0174	.0170	.0166	.0162	.0158	.0154	.0150	.0146	.0143
−2.0	.0228	.0222	.0217	.0212	.0207	.0202	.0197	.0192	.0188	.0183
−1.9	.0287	.0281	.0274	.0268	.0262	.0256	.0250	.0244	.0238	.0233
−1.8	.0359	.0352	.0344	.0336	.0329	.0322	.0314	.0307	.0300	.0294
−1.7	.0446	.0436	.0427	.0418	.0409	.0401	.0392	.0384	.0375	.0367
−1.6	.0548	.0537	.0526	.0516	.0505	.0495	.0485	.0475	.0465	.0455
−1.5	.0668	.0655	.0643	.0630	.0618	.0606	.0594	.0582	.0570	.0559
−1.4	.0808	.0793	.0778	.0764	.0749	.0735	.0722	.0708	.0694	.0681
−1.3	.0968	.0951	.0934	.0918	.0901	.0885	.0869	.0853	.0838	.0823
−1.2	.1151	.1131	.1112	.1093	.1075	.1056	.1038	.1020	.1003	.0985
−1.1	.1357	.1335	.1314	.1292	.1271	.1251	.1230	.1210	.1190	.1170
−1.0	.1587	.1562	.1539	.1515	.1492	.1469	.1446	.1423	.1401	.1379
− .9	.1841	.1814	.1788	.1762	.1736	.1711	.1685	.1660	.1635	.1611
− .8	.2119	.2090	.2061	.2033	.2005	.1977	.1949	.1922	.1894	.1867
− .7	.2420	.2389	.2358	.2327	.2297	.2266	.2236	.2206	.2177	.2148
− .6	.2743	.2709	.2676	.2643	.2611	.2578	.2546	.2514	.2483	.2451
− .5	.3085	.3050	.3015	.2981	.2946	.2912	.2877	.2843	.2810	.2776
− .4	.3446	.3409	.3372	.3336	.3300	.3264	.3228	.3192	.3156	.3121
− .3	.3821	.3783	.3745	.3707	.3669	.3632	.3594	.3557	.3520	.3483
− .2	.4207	.4168	.4129	.4090	.4052	.4013	.3974	.3936	.3897	.3859
− .1	.4602	.4562	.4522	.4483	.4443	.4404	.4364	.4325	.4286	.4247
− .0	.5000	.4960	.4920	.4880	.4840	.4801	.4761	.4721	.4681	.4641

Table I. Values of the Standard Normal Distribution Function (Continued)

z	0	1	2	3	4	5	6	7	8	9
.0	.5000	.5040	.5080	.5120	.5160	.5199	.5239	.5279	.5319	.5359
.1	.5398	.5438	.5478	.5517	.5557	.5596	.5636	.5675	.5714	.5753
.2	.5793	.5832	.5871	.5910	.5948	.5987	.6026	.6064	.6103	.6141
.3	.6179	.6217	.6255	.6293	.6331	.6368	.6406	.6443	.6480	.6517
.4	.6554	.6591	.6628	.6664	.6700	.6736	.6772	.6808	.6844	.6879
.5	.6915	.6950	.6985	.7019	.7054	.7088	.7123	.7157	.7190	.7224
.6	.7257	.7291	.7324	.7357	.7389	.7422	.7454	.7486	.7517	.7549
.7	.7580	.7611	.7642	.7673	.7703	.7734	.7764	.7794	.7823	.7852
.8	.7881	.7910	.7939	.7967	.7995	.8023	.8051	.8078	.8106	.8133
.9	.8159	.8186	.8212	.8238	.8264	.8289	.8315	.8340	.8365	.8389
1.0	.8413	.8438	.8461	.8485	.8508	.8531	.8554	.8577	.8599	.8621
1.1	.8643	.8665	.8686	.8708	.8729	.8749	.8770	.8790	.8810	.8830
1.2	.8849	.8869	.8888	.8907	.8925	.8944	.8962	.8980	.8997	.9015
1.3	.9032	.9049	.9066	.9082	.9099	.9115	.9131	.9147	.9162	.9177
1.4	.9192	.9207	.9222	.9236	.9251	.9265	.9278	.9292	.9306	.9319
1.5	.9332	.9345	.9357	.9370	.9382	.9394	.9406	.9418	.9430	.9441
1.6	.9452	.9463	.9474	.9484	.9495	.9505	.9515	.9525	.9535	.9545
1.7	.9554	.9564	.9573	.9582	.9591	.9599	.9608	.9616	.9625	.9633
1.8	.9641	.9648	.9656	.9664	.9671	.9678	.9686	.9693	.9700	.9706
1.9	.9713	.9719	.9726	.9732	.9738	.9744	.9750	.9756	.9762	.9767
2.0	.9772	.9778	.9783	.9788	.9793	.9798	.9803	.9808	.9812	.9817
2.1	.9821	.9826	.9830	.9834	.9838	.9842	.9846	.9850	.9854	.9857
2.2	.9861	.9864	.9868	.9871	.9874	.9878	.9881	.9884	.9887	.9890
2.3	.9893	.9896	.9898	.9901	.9904	.9906	.9909	.9911	.9913	.9916
2.4	.9918	.9920	.9922	.9925	.9927	.9929	.9931	.9932	.9934	.9936
2.5	.9938	.9940	.9941	.9943	.9945	.9946	.9948	.9949	.9951	.9952
2.6	.9953	.9955	.9956	.9957	.9959	.9960	.9961	.9962	.9963	.9964
2.7	.9965	.9966	.9967	.9968	.9969	.9970	.9971	.9972	.9973	.9974
2.8	.9974	.9975	.9976	.9977	.9977	.9978	.9979	.9979	.9980	.9981
2.9	.9981	.9982	.9982	.9983	.9984	.9984	.9985	.9985	.9986	.9986
3.	.9987	.9990	.9993	.9995	.9997	.9998	.9998	.9999	.9999	1.0000

Note 1: If a random variable X is not "standard," its values must be "standardized": $Z = (X - \mu)/\sigma$. That is, $P(X \leq x) = N\left(\frac{x - \mu}{\sigma}\right)$.

Note 2: For "two-tail" probabilities, see Table Ib.

Note 3: For $z \geq 4$, $N(z) = 1$ to four decimal places; for $z \leq -4$, $N(z) = 0$ to four decimal places.

Table Ia. Percentiles of the Standard Normal Distribution

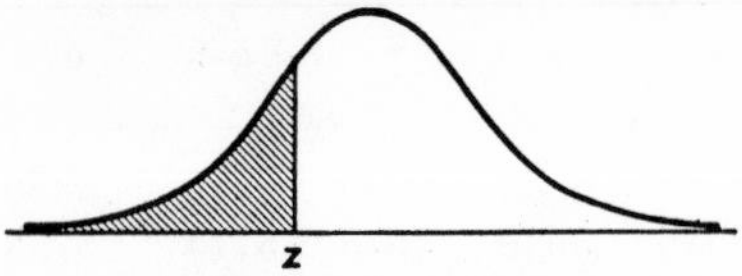

$P(Z \leq z)$	z
.001	−3.09
.005	−2.58
.01	−2.33
.02	−2.05
.03	−1.88
.04	−1.75
.05	−1.64
.10	−1.28
.15	−1.04
.20	− .84
.30	− .52
.40	− .25
.50	0
.60	.25
.70	.52
.80	.84
.85	1.04
.90	1.28
.95	1.64
.96	1.75
.97	1.88
.98	2.05
.99	2.33
.995	2.58
.999	3.09

Table Ib. Two-Tail Probabilities for the Standard Normal Distribution

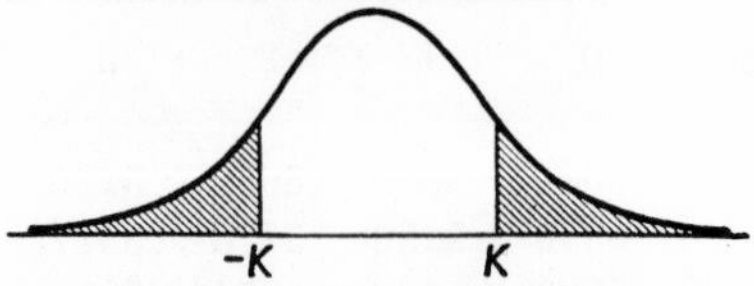

K	$P(\|Z\| > K)$
1.04	.30
1.15	.25
1.28	.20
1.44	.15
1.64	.10
1.70	.09
1.75	.08
1.81	.07
1.88	.06
1.96	.05
2.05	.04
2.17	.03
2.33	.02
2.58	.01
2.81	.005
3.09	.002
3.29	.001

Table II. Percentiles of the Chi-Square Distribution

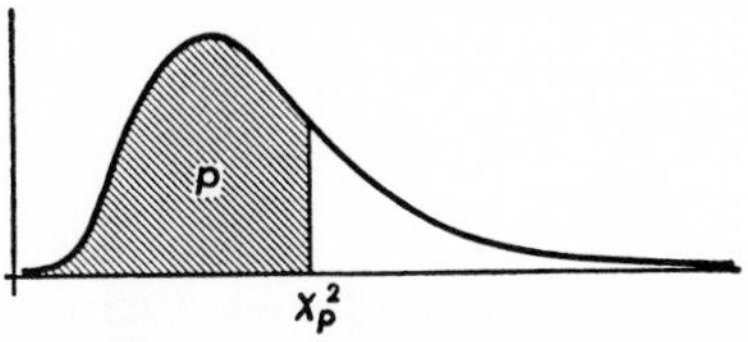

Degrees of Freedom	$\chi^2_{.005}$	$\chi^2_{.01}$	$\chi^2_{.025}$	$\chi^2_{.05}$	$\chi^2_{.10}$	$\chi^2_{.20}$	$\chi^2_{.30}$	$\chi^2_{.50}$	$\chi^2_{.70}$	$\chi^2_{.80}$	$\chi^2_{.90}$	$\chi^2_{.95}$	$\chi^2_{.975}$	$\chi^2_{.99}$	$\chi^2_{.995}$
1	.000	.000	.001	.004	.016	.064	.148	.455	1.07	1.64	2.71	3.84	5.02	6.63	7.88
2	.010	.020	.051	.103	.211	.446	.713	1.39	2.41	3.22	4.61	5.99	7.38	9.21	10.6
3	.072	.115	.216	.352	.584	1.00	1.42	2.37	3.66	4.64	6.25	7.81	9.35	11.3	12.8
4	.207	.297	.484	.711	1.06	1.65	2.20	3.36	4.88	5.99	7.78	9.49	11.1	13.3	14.9
5	.412	.554	.831	1.15	1.61	2.34	3.00	4.35	6.06	7.29	9.24	11.1	12.8	15.1	16.7
6	.676	.872	1.24	1.64	2.20	3.07	3.83	5.35	7.23	8.56	10.6	12.6	14.4	16.8	18.5
7	.989	1.24	1.69	2.17	2.83	3.82	4.67	6.35	8.38	9.80	12.0	14.1	16.0	18.5	20.3
8	1.34	1.65	2.18	2.73	3.49	4.59	5.53	7.34	9.52	11.0	13.4	15.5	17.5	20.1	22.0
9	1.73	2.09	2.70	3.33	4.17	5.38	6.39	8.34	10.7	12.2	14.7	16.9	19.0	21.7	23.6
10	2.16	2.56	3.25	3.94	4.87	6.18	7.27	9.34	11.8	13.4	16.0	18.3	20.5	23.2	25.2
11	2.60	3.05	3.82	4.57	5.58	6.99	8.15	10.3	12.9	14.6	17.3	19.7	21.9	24.7	26.8
12	3.07	3.57	4.40	5.23	6.30	7.81	9.03	11.3	14.0	15.8	18.5	21.0	23.3	26.2	28.3
13	3.57	4.11	5.01	5.89	7.04	8.63	9.93	12.3	15.1	17.0	19.8	22.4	24.7	27.7	29.8
14	4.07	4.66	5.63	6.57	7.79	9.47	10.8	13.3	16.2	18.2	21.1	23.7	26.1	29.1	31.3
15	4.60	5.23	6.26	7.26	8.55	10.3	11.7	14.3	17.3	19.3	22.3	25.0	27.5	30.6	32.8
16	5.14	5.81	6.91	7.96	9.31	11.2	12.6	15.3	18.4	20.5	23.5	26.3	28.8	32.0	34.3
17	5.70	6.41	7.56	8.67	10.1	12.0	13.5	16.3	19.5	21.6	24.8	27.6	30.2	33.4	35.7
18	6.26	7.01	8.23	9.39	10.9	12.9	14.4	17.3	20.6	22.8	26.0	28.9	31.5	34.8	37.2
19	6.83	7.63	8.91	10.1	11.7	13.7	15.4	18.3	21.7	23.9	27.2	30.1	32.9	36.2	38.6
20	7.43	8.26	9.59	10.9	12.4	14.6	16.3	19.3	22.8	25.0	28.4	31.4	34.2	37.6	40.0
21	8.03	8.90	10.3	11.6	13.2	15.4	17.2	20.3	23.9	26.2	29.6	32.7	35.5	38.9	41.4
22	8.64	9.54	11.0	12.3	14.0	16.3	18.1	21.3	24.9	27.3	30.8	33.9	36.8	40.3	42.8
23	9.26	10.2	11.7	13.1	14.8	17.2	19.0	22.3	26.0	28.4	32.0	35.2	38.1	41.6	44.2
24	9.89	10.9	12.4	13.8	15.7	18.1	19.9	23.3	27.1	29.6	33.2	36.4	39.4	43.0	45.6
25	10.5	11.5	13.1	14.6	16.5	18.9	20.9	24.3	28.2	30.7	34.4	37.7	40.6	44.3	46.9
26	11.2	12.2	13.8	15.4	17.3	19.8	21.8	25.3	29.2	31.8	35.6	38.9	41.9	45.6	48.3
27	11.8	12.9	14.6	16.2	18.1	20.7	22.7	26.3	30.3	32.9	36.7	40.1	43.2	47.0	49.6
28	12.5	13.6	15.3	16.9	18.9	21.6	23.6	27.3	31.4	34.0	37.9	41.3	44.5	48.3	51.0
29	13.1	14.3	16.0	17.7	19.8	22.5	24.6	28.3	32.5	35.1	39.1	42.6	45.7	49.6	52.3
30	13.8	15.0	16.8	18.5	20.6	23.4	25.5	29.3	33.5	36.2	40.3	43.8	47.0	50.9	53.7
40	20.7	22.1	24.4	26.5	29.0	32.3	34.9	39.3	44.2	47.3	51.8	55.8	59.3	63.7	66.8
50	28.0	29.7	32.3	34.8	37.7	41.4	44.3	49.3	54.7	58.2	63.2	67.5	71.4	76.2	79.5
60	35.5	37.5	40.5	43.2	46.5	50.6	53.8	59.3	65.2	69.0	74.4	79.1	83.3	88.4	92.0

Note: For degrees of freedom $k > 30$, use $\chi_p{}^2 = \frac{1}{2}(z_p + \sqrt{2k-1})^2$, where z_p is the corresponding percentile of the standard normal distribution.

This table is adapted from Table VIII of *Biometrika Tables for Statisticians*, Vol. 1, 1954, by E.S. Pearson and H.O. Hartley, originally prepared by Catherine M. Thompson, with the kind permission of the editor of *Biometrika*.

Table III. Percentiles of the t Distribution

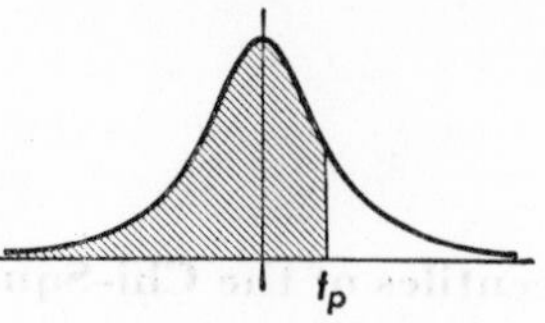

Degrees of Freedom	$t_{.55}$	$t_{.60}$	$t_{.65}$	$t_{.70}$	$t_{.75}$	$t_{.80}$	$t_{.85}$	$t_{.90}$	$t_{.95}$	$t_{.975}$	$t_{.99}$	$t_{.995}$	$t_{.9995}$
1	.158	.325	.510	.727	1.00	1.38	1.96	3.08	6.31	12.7	31.8	63.7	637
2	.142	.289	.445	.617	.816	1.06	1.39	1.89	2.92	4.30	6.96	9.92	31.6
3	.137	.277	.424	.584	.765	.978	1.25	1.64	2.35	3.18	4.54	5.84	12.9
4	.134	.271	.414	.569	.741	.941	1.19	1.53	2.13	2.78	3.75	4.60	8.61
5	.132	.267	.408	.559	.727	.920	1.16	1.48	2.01	2.57	3.36	4.03	6.86
6	.131	.265	.404	.553	.718	.906	1.13	1.44	1.94	2.45	3.14	3.71	5.96
7	.130	.263	.402	.549	.711	.896	1.12	1.42	1.90	2.36	3.00	3.50	5.40
8	.130	.262	.399	.546	.706	.889	1.11	1.40	1.86	2.31	2.90	3.36	5.04
9	.129	.261	.398	.543	.703	.883	1.10	1.38	1.83	2.26	2.82	3.25	4.78
10	.129	.260	.397	.542	.700	.879	1.09	1.37	1.81	2.23	2.76	3.17	4.59
11	.129	.260	.396	.540	.697	.876	1.09	1.36	1.80	2.20	2.72	3.11	4.44
12	.128	.259	.395	.539	.695	.873	1.08	1.36	1.78	2.18	2.68	3.06	4.32
13	.128	.259	.394	.538	.694	.870	1.08	1.35	1.77	2.16	2.65	3.01	4.22
14	.128	.258	.393	.537	.692	.868	1.08	1.34	1.76	2.14	2.62	2.98	4.14
15	.128	.258	.393	.536	.691	.866	1.07	1.34	1.75	2.13	2.60	2.95	4.07
16	.128	.258	.392	.535	.690	.865	1.07	1.34	1.75	2.12	2.58	2.92	4.02
17	.128	.257	.392	.534	.689	.863	1.07	1.33	1.74	2.11	2.57	2.90	3.96
18	.127	.257	.392	.534	.688	.862	1.07	1.33	1.73	2.10	2.55	2.88	3.92
19	.127	.257	.391	.533	.688	.861	1.07	1.33	1.73	2.09	2.54	2.86	3.88
20	.127	.257	.391	.533	.687	.860	1.06	1.32	1.72	2.09	2.53	2.84	3.85
21	.127	.257	.391	.532	.686	.859	1.06	1.32	1.72	2.08	2.52	2.83	3.82
22	.127	.256	.390	.532	.686	.858	1.06	1.32	1.72	2.07	2.51	2.82	3.79
23	.127	.256	.390	.532	.685	.858	1.06	1.32	1.71	2.07	2.50	2.81	3.77
24	.127	.256	.390	.531	.685	.857	1.06	1.32	1.71	2.06	2.49	2.80	3.74
25	.127	.256	.390	.531	.684	.856	1.06	1.32	1.71	2.06	2.48	2.79	3.72
26	.127	.256	.390	.531	.684	.856	1.06	1.32	1.71	2.06	2.48	2.78	3.71
27	.127	.256	.389	.531	.684	.855	1.06	1.31	1.70	2.05	2.47	2.77	3.69
28	.127	.256	.389	.530	.683	.855	1.06	1.31	1.70	2.05	2.47	2.76	3.67
29	.127	.256	.389	.530	.683	.854	1.05	1.31	1.70	2.04	2.46	2.76	3.66
30	.127	.256	.389	.530	.683	.854	1.05	1.31	1.70	2.04	2.46	2.75	3.65
∞	.126	.253	.385	.524	.674	.842	1.04	1.28	1.64	1.96	2.33	2.58	3.29

Note 1: For the lower percentiles, use the relation $t_\alpha = -t_{1-\alpha}$. In particular, $t_{.50} = -t_{.50} = 0$. For example, for 6 degrees of freedom, $t_{.35} = -t_{.65} = -.404$.

Note 2: For two-tail probabilities, see Table IV.

This table is abridged from Table II of Fisher and Yates, *Statistical Tables for Biological, Agricultural, and Medical Research* (5th ed.)/Fisher, *Statistical Methods for Research Workers*, published by Oliver and Boyd, Ltd., Edinburgh, by permission of the authors and publishers.

Table IVa. $F_{.95}$, Ninety-Fifth Percentiles of the F Distribution

Numerator Degrees of Freedom

Denominator Degrees of Freedom	1	2	3	4	5	6	8	10	12	15	20	24	30
1	161	200	216	225	230	234	239	242	244	246	248	249	250
2	18.5	19.0	19.2	19.2	19.3	19.3	19.4	19.4	19.4	19.4	19.4	19.5	19.5
3	10.1	9.55	9.28	9.12	9.01	8.94	8.85	8.79	8.74	8.70	8.66	8.64	8.62
4	7.71	6.94	6.59	6.39	6.26	6.16	6.04	5.96	5.91	5.86	5.80	5.77	5.75
5	6.61	5.79	5.41	5.19	5.05	4.95	4.82	4.74	4.68	4.62	4.56	4.53	4.50
6	5.99	5.14	4.76	4.53	4.39	4.28	4.15	4.06	4.00	3.94	3.87	3.84	3.81
7	5.59	4.74	4.35	4.12	3.97	3.87	3.73	3.64	3.57	3.51	3.44	3.41	3.38
8	5.32	4.46	4.07	3.84	3.69	3.58	3.44	3.35	3.28	3.22	3.15	3.12	3.08
9	5.12	4.26	3.86	3.63	3.48	3.37	3.23	3.14	3.07	3.01	2.94	2.90	2.86
10	4.96	4.10	3.71	3.48	3.33	3.22	3.07	2.98	2.91	2.85	2.77	2.74	2.70
11	4.84	3.98	3.59	3.36	3.20	3.09	2.95	2.85	2.79	2.72	2.65	2.61	2.57
12	4.75	3.89	3.49	3.26	3.11	3.00	2.85	2.75	2.69	2.62	2.54	2.51	2.47
13	4.67	3.81	3.41	3.18	3.03	2.92	2.77	2.67	2.60	2.53	2.46	2.42	2.38
14	4.60	3.74	3.34	3.11	2.96	2.85	2.70	2.60	2.53	2.46	2.39	2.35	2.31
15	4.54	3.68	3.29	3.06	2.90	2.79	2.64	2.54	2.48	2.40	2.33	2.29	2.25
16	4.49	3.63	3.24	3.01	2.85	2.74	2.59	2.49	2.42	2.35	2.28	2.24	2.19
17	4.45	3.59	3.20	2.96	2.81	2.70	2.55	2.45	2.38	2.31	2.23	2.19	2.15
18	4.41	3.55	3.16	2.93	2.77	2.66	2.51	2.41	2.34	2.27	2.19	2.15	2.11
19	4.38	3.52	3.13	2.90	2.74	2.63	2.48	2.38	2.31	2.23	2.16	2.11	2.07
20	4.35	3.49	3.10	2.87	2.71	2.60	2.45	2.35	2.28	2.20	2.12	2.08	2.04
21	4.32	3.47	3.07	2.84	2.68	2.57	2.42	2.32	2.25	2.18	2.10	2.05	2.01
22	4.30	3.44	3.05	2.82	2.66	2.55	2.40	2.30	2.23	2.15	2.07	2.03	1.98
23	4.28	3.42	3.03	2.80	2.64	2.53	2.37	2.27	2.20	2.13	2.05	2.01	1.96
24	4.26	3.40	3.01	2.78	2.62	2.51	2.36	2.25	2.18	2.11	2.03	1.98	1.94
25	4.24	3.39	2.99	2.76	2.60	2.49	2.34	2.24	2.16	2.09	2.01	1.96	1.92
30	4.17	3.32	2.92	2.69	2.53	2.42	2.27	2.16	2.09	2.01	1.93	1.89	1.84
40	4.08	3.23	2.84	2.61	2.45	2.34	2.18	2.08	2.00	1.92	1.84	1.79	1.74
60	4.00	3.15	2.76	2.53	2.37	2.25	2.10	1.99	1.92	1.84	1.75	1.70	1.65

This table is adapted from Table XVIII in *Biometrika Tables for Statisticians*, Vol. I, 1954, by E.S. Pearson and H.O. Hartley, originally prepared by M. Merrington and C.M. Thompson, with the kind permission of the editor of *Biometrika*.

Table IVb. $F_{.99}$, Ninety-Ninth Percentiles of the F Distribution

Numerator Degrees of Freedom

Denominator Degrees of Freedom	1	2	3	4	5	6	8	10	12	15	20	24	30
1	4050	5000	5400	5620	5760	5860	5980	6060	6110	6160	6210	6235	6260
2	98.5	99.0	99.2	99.2	99.3	99.3	99.4	99.4	99.4	99.4	99.4	99.5	99.5
3	34.1	30.8	29.5	28.7	28.2	27.9	27.5	27.3	27.1	26.9	26.7	26.6	26.5
4	21.2	18.0	16.7	16.0	15.5	15.2	14.8	14.5	14.4	14.2	14.0	13.9	13.8
5	16.3	13.3	12.1	11.4	11.0	10.7	10.3	10.1	9.89	9.72	9.55	9.47	9.38
6	13.7	10.9	9.78	9.15	8.75	8.47	8.10	7.87	7.72	7.56	7.40	7.31	7.23
7	12.2	9.55	8.45	7.85	7.46	7.19	6.84	6.62	6.47	6.31	6.16	6.07	5.99
8	11.3	8.65	7.59	7.01	6.63	6.37	6.03	5.81	5.67	5.52	5.36	5.28	5.20
9	10.6	8.02	6.99	6.42	6.06	5.80	5.47	5.26	5.11	4.96	4.81	4.73	4.65
10	10.0	7.56	6.55	5.99	5.64	5.39	5.06	4.85	4.71	4.56	4.41	4.33	4.25
11	9.65	7.21	6.22	5.67	5.32	5.07	4.74	4.54	4.40	4.25	4.10	4.02	3.94
12	9.33	6.93	5.95	5.41	5.06	4.82	4.50	4.30	4.16	4.01	3.86	3.78	3.70
13	9.07	6.70	5.74	5.21	4.86	4.62	4.30	4.10	3.96	3.82	3.66	3.59	3.51
14	8.86	6.51	5.56	5.04	4.69	4.46	4.14	3.94	3.80	3.66	3.51	3.43	3.35
15	8.68	6.36	5.42	4.89	4.56	4.32	4.00	3.80	3.67	3.52	3.37	3.29	3.21
16	8.53	6.23	5.29	4.77	4.44	4.20	3.89	3.69	3.55	3.41	3.26	3.18	3.10
17	8.40	6.11	5.18	4.67	4.34	4.10	3.79	3.59	3.46	3.31	3.16	3.08	3.00
18	8.29	6.01	5.09	4.58	4.25	4.01	3.71	3.51	3.37	3.23	3.08	3.00	2.92
19	8.18	5.93	5.01	4.50	4.17	3.94	3.63	3.43	3.30	3.15	3.00	2.92	2.84
20	8.10	5.85	4.94	4.43	4.10	3.87	3.56	3.37	3.23	3.09	2.94	2.86	2.78
21	8.02	5.78	4.87	4.37	4.04	3.81	3.51	3.31	3.17	3.03	2.88	2.80	2.72
22	7.95	5.72	4.82	4.31	3.99	3.76	3.45	3.26	3.12	2.98	2.83	2.75	2.67
23	7.88	5.66	4.76	4.26	3.94	3.71	3.41	3.21	3.07	2.93	2.78	2.70	2.62
24	7.82	5.61	4.72	4.22	3.90	3.67	3.36	3.17	3.03	2.89	2.74	2.66	2.58
25	7.77	5.57	4.68	4.18	3.86	3.63	3.32	3.13	2.99	2.85	2.70	2.62	2.54
30	7.56	5.39	4.51	4.02	3.70	3.47	3.17	2.98	2.84	2.70	2.55	2.47	2.39
40	7.31	5.18	4.31	3.83	3.51	3.29	2.99	2.80	2.66	2.52	2.37	2.29	2.20
60	7.08	4.98	4.13	3.65	3.34	3.12	2.82	2.63	2.50	2.35	2.20	2.12	2.03

This table is adapted from Table XVIII in *Biometrika Tables for Statisticians*, Vol. I, 1954, by E.S. Pearson and H.O. Hartley, originally prepared by M. Merrington and C.M. Thompson, with the kind permission of the editor of *Biometrika*.

Table V. Distribution of the Standardized Range $W = R/\sigma$
(Assuming a Normal Population)

	Sample Size										
	2	3	4	5	6	7	8	9	10	12	15
$E(W)$	1.128	1.693	2.059	2.326	2.534	2.704	2.847	2.970	3.078	3.258	3.472
σ_W	.853	.888	.880	.864	.848	.833	.820	.808	.797	.778	.755
$W_{.005}$	.01	.13	.34	.55	.75	.92	1.08	1.21	1.33	1.55	1.80
$W_{.01}$	.02	.19	.43	.66	.87	1.05	1.20	1.34	1.47	1.68	1.93
$W_{.025}$	.04	.30	.59	.85	1.06	1.25	1.41	1.55	1.67	1.88	2.14
$W_{.05}$	.09	.43	.76	1.03	1.25	1.44	1.60	1.74	1.86	2.07	2.32
$W_{.1}$	.18	.62	.98	1.26	1.49	1.68	1.83	1.97	2.09	2.30	2.54
$W_{.2}$	.36	.90	1.29	1.57	1.80	1.99	2.14	2.28	2.39	2.59	2.83
$W_{.3}$	.55	1.14	1.53	1.82	2.04	2.22	2.38	2.51	2.62	2.82	3.04
$W_{.4}$	.74	1.36	1.76	2.04	2.26	2.44	2.59	2.71	2.83	3.01	3.23
$W_{.5}$	.95	1.59	1.98	2.26	2.47	2.65	2.79	2.92	3.02	3.21	3.42
$W_{.6}$	1.20	1.83	2.21	2.48	2.69	2.86	3.00	3.12	3.23	3.41	3.62
$W_{.7}$	1.47	2.09	2.47	2.73	2.94	3.10	3.24	3.35	3.46	3.63	3.83
$W_{.8}$	1.81	2.42	2.78	3.04	3.23	3.39	3.52	3.63	3.73	3.90	4.09
$W_{.9}$	2.33	2.90	3.24	3.48	3.66	3.81	3.93	4.04	4.13	4.29	4.47
$W_{.95}$	2.77	3.31	3.63	3.86	4.03	4.17	4.29	4.39	4.47	4.62	4.80
$W_{.975}$	3.17	3.68	3.98	4.20	4.36	4.49	4.61	4.70	4.79	4.92	5.09
$W_{.99}$	3.64	4.12	4.40	4.60	4.76	4.88	4.99	5.08	5.16	5.29	5.45
$W_{.995}$	3.97	4.42	4.69	4.89	5.03	5.15	5.26	5.34	5.42	5.54	5.70

This table is adapted from Tables XX and XXII in *Biometrika Tables for Statisticians*, Vol. I, 1954, by E. S. Pearson and H. O. Hartley, with the kind permission of the editor of *Biometrika*.

Table VI. Acceptance Limits for the Kolmogorov-Smirnov Test of Goodness of Fit

Sample Size (n)	Significance Level .20	.15	.10	.05	.01
1	.900	.925	.950	.975	.995
2	.684	.726	.776	.842	.929
3	.565	.597	.642	.708	.829
4	.494	.525	.564	.624	.734
5	.446	.474	.510	.563	.669
6	.410	.436	.470	.521	.618
7	.381	.405	.438	.486	.577
8	.358	.381	.411	.457	.543
9	.339	.360	.388	.432	.514
10	.322	.342	.368	.409	.486
11	.307	.326	.352	.391	.468
12	.295	.313	.338	.375	.450
13	.284	.302	.325	.361	.433
14	.274	.292	.314	.349	.418
15	.266	.283	.304	.338	.404
16	.258	.274	.295	.328	.391
17	.250	.266	.286	.318	.380
18	.244	.259	.278	.309	.370
19	.237	.252	.272	.301	.361
20	.231	.246	.264	.294	.352
25	.21	.22	.24	.264	.32
30	.19	.20	.22	.242	.29
35	.18	.19	.21	.23	.27
40				.21	.25
50				.19	.23
60				.17	.21
70				.16	.19
80				.15	.18
90				.14	
100				.14	
Asymptotic Formula:	$\frac{1.07}{\sqrt{n}}$	$\frac{1.14}{\sqrt{n}}$	$\frac{1.22}{\sqrt{n}}$	$\frac{1.36}{\sqrt{n}}$	$\frac{1.63}{\sqrt{n}}$

Reject the hypothetical distribution $F(x)$ if $D_n = \max |F_n(x) - F(x)|$ exceeds the tabulated value.

(For $\alpha = .01$ and $.05$, asymptotic formulas give values which are too high—by 1.5 per cent for $n = 80$.)

This table is taken from F.J. Massey, Jr., "The Kolmogorov-Smirnov Test for Goodness of Fit," *J. Amer. Stat. Assn.* (1951), **46:** 68–78, except that certain corrections and additional entries are from Z.W. Birnbaum, "Numerical Tabulation of the Distribution of Kolmogorov's Statistic for Finite Sample Size," *J. Amer. Stat. Assn.* (1952), **47:** 425–441, with the kind permission of the authors and the *J. Amer. Stat. Assn.*

Table VII. Acceptance Limits for the Kolmogorov-Smirnov Test of H_0: $F_1(x) = F_2(x)$

Sample Size n_2	Sample Size n_1: 1	2	3	4	5	6	7	8	9	10	12	15
1	* *	* *	* *	* *	* *	* *	* *	* *	* *	* *		
2		* *	* *	* *	* *	* *	* *	7/8 *	16/18 *	9/10 *		
3			* *	* *	12/15 *	5/6 *	18/21 *	18/24 *	7/9 8/9		9/12 11/12	
4				3/4 *	16/20 *	9/12 10/12	21/28 24/28	6/8 7/8	27/36 32/36	14/20 16/20	8/12 10/12	
5					4/5 4/5	20/30 25/30	25/35 30/35	27/40 32/40	31/45 36/45	7/10 8/10		10/15 11/15
6						4/6 5/6	29/42 35/42	16/24 18/24	12/18 14/18	19/30 22/30	7/12 9/12	
7							5/7 5/7	35/56 42/56	40/63 47/63	43/70 53/70		
8								5/8 6/8	45/72 54/72	23/40 28/40	14/24 16/24	
9									5/9 6/9	52/90 62/90	20/36 24/36	
10										6/10 7/10		15/30 19/30
12											6/12 7/12	30/60 35/60
15												7/15 8/15

Reject H_0 if

$D = \max |F_{n_1}(x) - F_{n_2}(x)|$

exceeds the tabulated value. The upper value gives a level at most .05 and the lower value gives a level at most .01.

Note 1: Where * appears, do not reject H_0 at the given level.

Note 2: For large values of n_1 and n_2, the following approximate formulas may be used:

$$\alpha = .05: \quad 1.36\sqrt{\frac{n_1 + n_2}{n_1 n_2}}$$

$$\alpha = .01: \quad 1.63\sqrt{\frac{n_1 + n_2}{n_1 n_2}}$$

This table is derived from F.J. Massey, Jr., "Distribution Table for the Deviation Between Two Sample Cumulatives," *Ann. Math. Stat.* (1952), **23:** 435–441. Adapted with the kind permission of the author and the *Ann. Math. Stat.* Formulas for large sample sizes were given by N. Smirnov, "Tables for Estimating the Goodness of Fit of Empirical Distributions," *Ann. Math. Stat.* (1948), **19:** 280–281.

Table VIII. Rejection Limits for the Wilcoxon-Mann-Whitney Test

m \ n	3	4	5	6	7	8	9	10
2			0 (4.7)	0 (3.6)	0 (2.8)	0 (2.2) 1 (4.4)	0 (1.8) 1 (3.6)	0 (1.5) 1 (3.0)
3	0 (5.0)	0 (2.8)	0 (1.8) 1 (3.6)	1 (2.4) 2 (4.8)	0 (.83) 1 (1.7) 2 (3.3)	0 (.61) 2 (2.4) 3 (4.2)	0 (.45) 1 (.91) 3 (3.2) 4 (5.0)	0 (.35) 1(.70) 3(2.5) 4 (3.9)
4		0 (1.4) 1 (2.9)	0 (.79) 1 (1.6) 2 (3.2)	0 (.48) 1 (1.0) 2 (1.9) 3 (3.3)	0 (.30) 1 (.61) 3 (2.1) 4 (3.6)	1 (.40) 2 (.81) 4 (2.4) 5 (3.6)	1 (.28) 3 (.98) 5 (2.5) 6 (3.8)	2 (.40) 3 (.70) 5 (1.8) 7 (3.8)
5			0 (.40) 1 (.79) 2 (1.6) 4 (4.8)	1 (.43) 2 (.82) 3 (1.5) 5 (4.1)	1 (.25) 3 (.88) 5 (2.4) 6 (3.7)	2 (.31) 4 (.93) 6 (2.3) 8 (4.7)	3 (.35) 5 (.95) 7 (2.1) 9 (4.2)	4 (.40) 6 (.97) 8 (2.0) 11 (5.0)
6				2 (.43) 3 (.67) 5 (2.1) 7 (4.7)	3 (.41) 4 (.70) 6 (1.8) 8 (3.7)	4 (.40) 5 (.63) 8 (2.1) 10 (4.1)	5 (.38) 7 .(88) 10 (2.5) 12 (4.4)	6 (.37) 8 (2.0) 11 (2.1) 14 (4.7)
7					4 (.35) 6 (.87) 8 (1.9) 11 (4.9)	5 (.47) 7 (1.0) 10 (2.0) 13 (4.7)	7 (.39) 9 (.82) 12 (2.1) 15 (4.5)	9 (.48) 11 (.93) 14 (2.2) 17 (4.4)
8						7 (.35) 9 (.74) 13 (2.5) 15 (4.2)	9 (.39) 11 (.76) 15 (2.3) 18 (4.6)	11 (.43) 13 (.78) 17 (2.2) 20 (4.2)
9							11 (.39) 14 (.94) 18 (2.5) 21 (4.7)	13 (.38) 16 (.86) 20 (2.2) 24 (4.7)
10								16 (.45) 19 (.93) 23 (2.2) 27 (4.5)

Note: See explanations on page 403.

The four entries for each pair of sample sizes are rejection limits when it is desired to have:

a one-sided test at .5 per cent or a two-sided test at 1 per cent;
a one-sided test at 1 per cent or a two-sided test at 2 per cent;
a one-sided test at 2.5 per cent or a two-sided test at 5 per cent;
a one-sided test at 5 per cent or a two-sided test at 10 per cent.

The entries in the table are lower limits; corresponding upper limits are $mn - u$.
The number in parentheses after a value u is the probability (in per cent) that $U \leq u$.

Example If a two-sided test at 5 per cent is desired for $m = 5$ and $n = 8$, use $6 < U < 34$ as the acceptance region. For this test,

$$\alpha = P_{H_0}(U \leq 6 \text{ or } U \geq 34) = 2 \times (0.023) = 0.046,$$

which is less than 0.05 as desired.

This table is adapted from those given in H.B. Mann and D.R. Whitney, "On a Test of Whether One of the Two Random Variables Is Stochastically Larger than the Other," *The Annals of Mathematical Statistics* (1947), **18:** 50–60, with the kind permission of *The Annals of Mathematical Statistics.*

Table IX. Expected Values of Order Statistics from a Standard Normal Population

n	$E[X_{(n)}]$	$E[X_{(n-1)}]$	$E[X_{(n-2)}]$	$E[X_{(n-3)}]$	$E[X_{(n-4)}]$	$E[X_{(n-5)}]$	$E[X_{(n-6)}]$	$E[X_{(n-7)}]$	$E[X_{(n-8)}]$	$E[X_{(n-9)}]$
2	.564									
3	.846									
4	1.029	.297								
5	1.163	.495								
6	1.267	.642	.202							
7	1.352	.757	.353							
8	1.424	.852	.473	.153						
9	1.485	.932	.572	.275						
10	1.539	1.001	.656	.376	.123					
11	1.586	1.062	.729	.462	.225					
12	1.629	1.116	.793	.537	.312	.103				
13	1.668	1.164	.850	.603	.388	.190				
14	1.703	1.208	.901	.662	.456	.267	.088			
15	1.736	1.248	.948	.715	.516	.335	.165			
16	1.766	1.285	.990	.763	.570	.396	.234	.077		
17	1.794	1.319	1.030	.807	.619	.451	.295	.146		
18	1.820	1.350	1.066	.848	.665	.502	.351	.208	.069	
19	1.844	1.380	1.099	.886	.707	.548	.402	.264	.131	
20	1.867	1.408	1.131	.921	.745	.590	.448	.315	.187	.062

Adapted from Table 28 of *Biometrika Tables for Statisticians*, Vol. I, 1954, by E. S. Pearson and H. O. Hartley, with the kind permission of the editor of *Biometrika*.

Table X. Binomial Coefficients $\binom{n}{k}$

n \ k	2	3	4	5	6	7	8	9	10
2	1								
3	3	1							
4	6	4	1						
5	10	10	5	1					
6	15	20	15	6	1				
7	21	35	35	21	7	1			
8	28	56	70	56	28	8	1		
9	36	84	126	126	84	36	9	1	
10	45	120	210	252	210	120	45	10	1
11	55	165	330	462	462	330	165	55	11
12	66	220	495	792	924	792	495	220	66
13	78	286	715	1287	1716	1716	1287	715	286
14	91	364	1001	2002	3003	3432	3003	2002	1001
15	105	455	1365	3003	5005	6435	6435	5005	3003
16	120	560	1820	4368	8008	11440	12870	11440	8008
17	136	680	2380	6188	12376	19448	24310	24310	19448
18	153	816	3060	8568	18564	31824	43758	48620	43758
19	171	969	3876	11628	27132	50388	75582	92378	92378
20	190	1140	4845	15504	38760	77520	125970	167960	184756

Table XI. Exponential Functions

x	e^{-x}	e^x	$\log_{10}e^x$
.01	.9900	1.0101	.00434
.02	.9802	1.0202	.00869
.03	.9704	1.0305	.01303
.04	.9608	1.0408	.01737
.05	.9512	1.0513	.02171
.06	.9418	1.0618	.02606
.07	.9324	1.0725	.03040
.08	.9231	1.0833	.03474
.09	.9139	1.0942	.03909
.10	.9048	1.1052	.04343
.20	.8187	1.2214	.08686
.30	.7408	1.3499	.13029
.40	.6703	1.4918	.17372
.50	.6065	1.6487	.21715
.60	.5488	1.8221	.26058
.70	.4966	2.0138	.30401
.80	.4493	2.2255	.34744
.90	.4066	2.4596	.39087
1.00	.3679	2.7183	.43429
2.00	.1353	7.3891	.86859
3.00	.04979	20.0886	1.30288
4.00	.01832	54.598	1.73718
5.00	.00674	148.41	2.17147
6.00	.00248	403.43	2.60577
7.00	.000912	1096.6	3.04006
8.00	.000335	2981.0	3.47536
9.00	.000123	8103.1	3.90865
10.00	.000045	22026.0	4.34294

Table XII. Poisson Distribution Function: $F(c) = \sum_{k=0}^{c} \frac{m^k e^{-m}}{k!}$

m (Expected value)

c	.02	.04	.06	.08	.10	.15	.20	.25	.30	.35	.40
0	.980	.961	.942	.923	.905	.861	.819	.779	.741	.705	.670
1	1.000	.999	.998	.997	.995	.990	.982	.974	.963	.951	.938
2		1.000	1.000	1.000	1.000	.999	.999	.998	.996	.994	.992
3						1.000	1.000	1.000	1.000	1.000	.999
4											1.000

c	.45	.50	.55	.60	.65	.70	.75	.80	.85	.90	.95
0	.638	.607	.577	.549	.522	.497	.472	.449	.427	.407	.387
1	.925	.910	.894	.878	.861	.844	.827	.809	.791	.772	.754
2	.989	.986	.982	.977	.972	.966	.959	.953	.945	.937	.929
3	.999	.998	.998	.997	.996	.994	.993	.991	.989	.987	.984
4	1.000	1.000	1.000	1.000	.999	.999	.999	.999	.998	.998	.997
5					1.000	1.000	1.000	1.000	1.000	1.000	1.000

c	1.0	1.1	1.2	1.3	1.4	1.5	1.6	1.7	1.8	1.9	2.0
0	.368	.333	.301	.273	.247	.223	.202	.183	.165	.150	.135
1	.736	.699	.663	.627	.592	.558	.525	.493	.463	.434	.406
2	.920	.900	.879	.857	.833	.809	.783	.757	.731	.704	.677
3	.981	.974	.966	.957	.946	.934	.921	.907	.891	.875	.857
4	.996	.995	.992	.989	.986	.981	.976	.970	.964	.956	.947
5	.999	.999	.998	.998	.997	.996	.994	.992	.990	.987	.983
6	1.000	1.000	1.000	1.000	.999	.999	.999	.998	.997	.997	.995
7					1.000	1.000	1.000	1.000	.999	.999	.999
8									1.000	1.000	1.000

c	2.2	2.4	2.6	2.8	3.0	3.2	3.4	3.6	3.8	4.0	4.2
0	.111	.091	.074	.061	.050	.041	.033	.027	.022	.018	.015
1	.355	.308	.267	.231	.199	.171	.147	.126	.107	.092	.078
2	.623	.570	.518	.469	.423	.380	.340	.303	.269	.238	.210
3	.819	.779	.736	.692	.647	.603	.558	.515	.473	.433	.395
4	.928	.904	.877	.848	.815	.781	.744	.706	.668	.629	.590
5	.975	.964	.951	.935	.916	.895	.871	.844	.816	.785	.753
6	.993	.988	.983	.976	.966	.955	.942	.927	.909	.889	.867
7	.998	.997	.995	.992	.988	.983	.977	.969	.960	.949	.936
8	1.000	.999	.999	.998	.996	.994	.992	.988	.984	.979	.972
9		1.000	1.000	.999	.999	.998	.997	.996	.994	.992	.989
10				1.000	1.000	1.000	.999	.999	.998	.997	.996
11							1.000	1.000	.999	.999	.999
12									1.000	1.000	1.000

Table XII. Poisson Distribution Function *(Continued)*

c	4.4	4.6	4.8	5.0	5.2	5.4	5.6	5.8	6.0	6.2	6.4
0	.012	.010	.008	.007	.006	.005	.004	.003	.002	.002	.002
1	.066	.056	.048	.040	.034	.029	.024	.021	.017	.015	.012
2	.185	.163	.143	.125	.109	.095	.082	.072	.062	.054	.046
3	.359	.326	.294	.265	.238	.213	.191	.170	.151	.134	.119
4	.551	.513	.476	.440	.406	.373	.342	.313	.285	.259	.235
5	.720	.686	.651	.616	.581	.546	.512	.478	.446	.414	.384
6	.844	.818	.791	.762	.732	.702	.670	.638	.606	.574	.542
7	.921	.905	.887	.867	.845	.822	.797	.771	.744	.716	.687
8	.964	.955	.944	.932	.918	.903	.886	.867	.847	.826	.803
9	.985	.980	.975	.968	.960	.951	.941	.929	.916	.902	.886
10	.994	.992	.990	.986	.982	.977	.972	.965	.957	.949	.939
11	.998	.997	.996	.995	.993	.990	.988	.984	.980	.975	.969
12	.999	.999	.999	.998	.997	.996	.995	.993	.991	.989	.986
13	1.000	1.000	1.000	.999	.999	.999	.998	.997	.996	.995	.994
14				1.000	1.000	1.000	.999	.999	.999	.998	.997
15							1.000	1.000	.999	.999	.999
16									1.000	1.000	1.000

c	6.6	6.8	7.0	7.2	7.4	7.6	7.8	8.0	8.5	9.0	9.5
0	.001	.001	.001	.001	.001	.001	.000	.000	.000	.000	.000
1	.010	.009	.007	.006	.005	.004	.004	.003	.002	.001	.001
2	.040	.034	.030	.025	.022	.019	.016	.014	.009	.006	.004
3	.105	.093	.082	.072	.063	.055	.048	.042	.030	.021	.015
4	.213	.192	.173	.156	.140	.125	.112	.100	.074	.055	.040
5	.355	.327	.301	.276	.253	.231	.210	.191	.150	.116	.089
6	.511	.480	.450	.420	.392	.365	.338	.313	.256	.207	.165
7	.658	.628	.599	.569	.539	.510	.481	.453	.386	.324	.269
8	.780	.755	.729	.703	.676	.648	.620	.593	.523	.456	.392
9	.869	.850	.830	.810	.788	.765	.741	.717	.653	.587	.522
10	.927	.915	.901	.887	.871	.854	.835	.816	.763	.706	.645
11	.963	.955	.947	.937	.926	.915	.902	.888	.849	.803	.752
12	.982	.978	.973	.967	.961	.954	.945	.936	.909	.876	.836
13	.992	.990	.987	.984	.980	.976	.971	.966	.949	.926	.898
14	.997	.996	.994	.993	.991	.989	.986	.983	.973	.959	.940
15	.999	.998	.998	.997	.996	.995	.993	.992	.986	.978	.967
16	.999	.999	.999	.999	.998	.998	.997	.996	.993	.989	.982
17	1.000	1.000	1.000	.999	.999	.999	.999	.998	.997	.995	.991
18				1.000	1.000	1.000	1.000	.999	.999	.998	.996
19								1.000	.999	.999	.998
20									1.000	1.000	.999
21											1.000

Table XII. Poisson Distribution Function (*Continued*)

c	10.0	10.5	11.0	11.5	12.0	12.5	13.0	13.5	14.0	14.5	15.0
2	.003	.002	.001	.001	.001	.000					
3	.010	.007	.005	.003	.002	.002	.001	.001	.000		
4	.029	.021	.015	.011	.008	.005	.004	.003	.002	.001	.001
5	.067	.050	.038	.028	.020	.015	.011	.008	.006	.004	.003
6	.130	.102	.079	.060	.046	.035	.026	.019	.014	.010	.008
7	.220	.179	.143	.114	.090	.070	.054	.041	.032	.024	.018
8	.333	.279	.232	.191	.155	.125	.100	.079	.062	.048	.037
9	.458	.397	.341	.289	.242	.201	.166	.135	.109	.088	.070
10	.583	.521	.460	.402	.347	.297	.252	.211	.176	.145	.118
11	.697	.639	.579	.520	.462	.406	.353	.304	.260	.220	.185
12	.792	.742	.689	.633	.576	.519	.463	.409	.358	.311	.268
13	.864	.825	.781	.733	.682	.628	.573	.518	.464	.413	.363
14	.917	.888	.854	.815	.772	.725	.675	.623	.570	.518	.466
15	.951	.932	.907	.878	.844	.806	.764	.718	.669	.619	.568
16	.973	.960	.944	.924	.899	.869	.835	.798	.756	.711	.664
17	.986	.978	.968	.954	.937	.916	.890	.861	.827	.790	.749
18	.993	.988	.982	.974	.963	.948	.930	.908	.883	.853	.819
19	.997	.994	.991	.986	.979	.969	.957	.942	.923	.901	.875
20	.998	.997	.995	.992	.988	.983	.975	.965	.952	.936	.917
21	.999	.999	.998	.996	.994	.991	.986	.980	.971	.960	.947
22	1.000	.999	.999	.998	.997	.995	.992	.989	.983	.976	.967
23		1.000	1.000	.999	.999	.998	.996	.994	.991	.986	.981
24				1.000	.999	.999	.998	.997	.995	.992	.989
25					1.000	.999	.999	.998	.997	.996	.994
26						1.000	1.000	.999	.999	.998	.997
27								1.000	.999	.999	.998
28									1.000	.999	.999
29										1.000	1.000

Table XIII. Logarithms of Factorials

	0	1	2	3	4	5	6	7	8	9
00	0.0000	0.0000	0.3010	0.7782	1.3802	2.0792	2.8573	3.7024	4.6055	5.5598
10	6.5598	7.6012	8.6803	9.7943	10.9404	12.1165	13.3206	14.5511	15.8063	17.0851
20	18.3861	19.7083	21.0508	22.4125	23.7927	25.1906	26.6056	28.0370	29.4841	30.9465
30	32.4237	33.9150	35.4202	36.9387	38.4702	40.0142	41.5705	43.1387	44.7185	46.3096
40	47.9116	49.5244	51.1477	52.7811	54.4246	56.0778	57.7406	59.4127	61.0939	62.7841
50	64.4831	66.1906	67.9066	69.6309	71.3633	73.1037	74.8519	76.6077	78.3712	80.1420
60	81.9202	83.7055	85.4979	87.2972	89.1034	90.9163	92.7359	94.5619	96.3945	98.2333
70	100.0784	101.9297	103.7870	105.6503	107.5196	109.3946	111.2754	113.1619	115.0540	116.9516
80	118.8547	120.7632	122.6770	124.5961	126.5204	128.4498	130.3843	132.3238	134.2683	136.2177
90	138.1719	140.1310	142.0948	144.0632	146.0364	148.0141	149.9964	151.9831	153.9744	155.9700
100	157.9700	159.9743	161.9829	163.9958	166.0128	168.0340	170.0593	172.0887	174.1221	176.1595
110	178.2009	180.2462	182.2955	184.3485	186.4054	188.4661	190.5306	192.5988	194.6707	196.7462
120	198.8254	200.9082	202.9945	205.0844	207.1779	209.2748	211.3751	213.4790	215.5862	217.6967
130	219.8107	221.9280	224.0485	226.1724	228.2995	230.4298	232.5634	234.7001	236.8400	238.9830
140	241.1291	243.2783	245.4306	247.5860	249.7443	251.9057	254.0700	256.2374	258.4076	260.5808
150	262.7569	264.9359	267.1177	269.3024	271.4899	273.6803	275.8734	278.0693	280.2679	282.4693
160	284.6735	286.8803	289.0898	291.3020	293.5168	295.7343	297.9544	300.1771	302.4024	304.6303
170	306.8608	309.0938	311.3293	313.5674	315.8079	318.0509	320.2965	322.5444	324.7948	327.0477
180	329.3030	331.5606	333.8207	336.0832	338.3480	340.6152	342.8847	345.1565	347.4307	349.7071
190	351.9859	354.2669	356.5502	358.8358	361.1236	363.4136	365.7059	368.0003	370.2970	372.5959

Table XIV. Four-Place Common Logarithms

N	0	1	2	3	4	5	6	7	8	9
10	0000	0043	0086	0128	0170	0212	0253	0294	0334	0374
11	0414	0453	0492	0531	0569	0607	0645	0682	0719	0755
12	0792	0828	0864	0899	0934	0969	1004	1038	1072	1106
13	1139	1173	1206	1239	1271	1303	1335	1367	1399	1430
14	1461	1492	1523	1553	1584	1614	1644	1673	1703	1732
15	1761	1790	1818	1847	1875	1903	1931	1959	1987	2014
16	2041	2068	2095	2122	2148	2175	2201	2227	2253	2279
17	2304	2330	2355	2380	2405	2430	2455	2480	2504	2529
18	2553	2577	2601	2625	2648	2672	2695	2718	2742	2765
19	2788	2810	2833	2856	2878	2900	2923	2945	2967	2989
20	3010	3032	3054	3075	3096	3118	3139	3160	3181	3201
21	3222	3243	3263	3284	3304	3324	3345	3365	3385	3404
22	3424	3444	3464	3483	3502	3522	3541	3560	3579	3598
23	3617	3636	3655	3674	3692	3711	3729	3747	3766	3784
24	3802	3820	3838	3856	3874	3892	3909	3927	3945	3962
25	3979	3997	4014	4031	4048	4065	4082	4099	4116	4133
26	4150	4166	4183	4200	4216	4232	4249	4265	4281	4298
27	4314	4330	4346	4362	4378	4393	4409	4425	4440	4456
28	4472	4487	4502	4518	4533	4548	4564	4579	4594	4609
29	4624	4639	4654	4669	4683	4698	4713	4728	4742	4757
30	4771	4786	4800	4814	4829	4843	4857	4871	4886	4900
31	4914	4928	4942	4955	4969	4983	4997	5011	5024	5038
32	5051	5065	5079	5092	5105	5119	5132	5145	5159	5172
33	5185	5198	5211	5224	5237	5250	5263	5276	5289	5302
34	5315	5328	5340	5353	5366	5378	5391	5403	5416	5428
35	5441	5453	5465	5478	5490	5502	5514	5527	5539	5551
36	5563	5575	5587	5599	5611	5623	5635	5647	5658	5670
37	5682	5694	5705	5717	5729	5740	5752	5763	5775	5786
38	5798	5809	5821	5832	5843	5855	5866	5877	5888	5899
39	5911	5922	5933	5944	5955	5966	5977	5988	5999	6010
40	6021	6031	6042	6053	6064	6075	6085	6096	6107	6117
41	6128	6138	6149	6160	6170	6180	6191	6201	6212	6222
42	6232	6243	6253	6263	6274	6284	6294	6304	6314	6325
43	6335	6345	6355	6365	6375	6385	6395	6405	6415	6425
44	6435	6444	6454	6464	6474	6484	6493	6503	6513	6522
45	6532	6542	6551	6561	6571	6580	6590	6599	6609	6618
46	6628	6637	6646	6656	6665	6675	6684	6693	6702	6712
47	6721	6730	6739	6749	6758	6767	6776	6785	6794	6803
48	6812	6821	6830	6839	6848	6857	6866	6875	6884	6893
49	6902	6911	6920	6928	6937	6946	6955	6964	6972	6981
50	6990	6998	7007	7016	7024	7033	7042	7050	7059	7067
51	7076	7084	7093	7101	7110	7118	7126	7135	7143	7152
52	7160	7168	7177	7185	7193	7202	7210	7218	7226	7235
53	7243	7251	7259	7267	7275	7284	7292	7300	7308	7316
54	7324	7332	7340	7348	7356	7364	7372	7380	7388	7396
N	**0**	**1**	**2**	**3**	**4**	**5**	**6**	**7**	**8**	**9**

Table XIV. Four-Place Common Logarithms (*Continued*)

N	0	1	2	3	4	5	6	7	8	9
55	7404	7412	7419	7427	7435	7443	7451	7459	7466	7474
56	7482	7490	7497	7505	7513	7520	7528	7536	7543	7551
57	7559	7566	7574	7582	7589	7597	7604	7612	7619	7627
58	7634	7642	7649	7657	7664	7672	7679	7686	7694	7701
59	7709	7716	7723	7731	7738	7745	7752	7760	7767	7774
60	7782	7789	7796	7803	7810	7818	7825	7832	7839	7846
61	7853	7860	7868	7875	7882	7889	7896	7903	7910	7917
62	7924	7931	7938	7945	7952	7959	7966	7973	7980	7987
63	7993	8000	8007	8014	8021	8028	8035	8041	8048	8055
64	8062	8069	8075	8082	8089	8096	8102	8109	8116	8122
65	8129	8136	8142	8149	8156	8162	8169	8176	8182	8189
66	8195	8202	8209	8215	8222	8228	8235	8241	8248	8254
67	8261	8267	8274	8280	8287	8293	8299	8306	8312	8319
68	8325	8331	8338	8344	8351	8357	8363	8370	8376	8382
69	8388	8395	8401	8407	8414	8420	8426	8432	8439	8445
70	8451	8457	8463	8470	8476	8482	8488	8494	8500	8506
71	8513	8519	8525	8531	8537	8543	8549	8555	8561	8567
72	8573	8579	8585	8591	8597	8603	8609	8615	8621	8627
73	8633	8639	8645	8651	8657	8663	8669	8675	8681	8686
74	8692	8698	8704	8710	8716	8722	8727	8733	8739	8745
75	8751	8756	8762	8768	8774	8779	8785	8791	8797	8802
76	8808	8814	8820	8825	8831	8837	8842	8848	8854	8859
77	8865	8871	8876	8882	8887	8893	8899	8904	8910	8915
78	8921	8927	8932	8938	8943	8949	8954	8960	8965	8971
79	8976	8982	8987	8993	8998	9004	9009	9015	9020	9025
80	9031	9036	9042	9047	9053	9058	9063	9069	9074	9079
81	9085	9090	9096	9101	9106	9112	9117	9122	9128	9133
82	9138	9143	9149	9154	9159	9165	9170	9175	9180	9186
83	9191	9196	9201	9206	9212	9217	9222	9227	9232	9238
84	9243	9248	9253	9258	9263	9269	9274	9279	9284	9289
85	9294	9299	9304	9309	9315	9320	9325	9330	9335	9340
86	9345	9350	9355	9360	9365	9370	9375	9380	9385	9390
87	9395	9400	9405	9410	9415	9420	9425	9430	9435	9440
88	9445	9450	9455	9460	9465	9469	9474	9479	9484	9489
89	9494	9499	9504	9509	9513	9518	9523	9528	9533	9538
90	9542	9547	9552	9557	9562	9566	9571	9576	9581	9586
91	9590	9595	9600	9605	9609	9614	9619	9624	9628	9633
92	9638	9643	9647	9652	9657	9661	9666	9671	9675	9680
93	9685	9689	9694	9699	9703	9708	9713	9717	9722	9727
94	9731	9736	9741	9745	9750	9754	9759	9763	9768	9773
95	9777	9782	9786	9791	9795	9800	9805	9809	9814	9818
96	9823	9827	9832	9836	9841	9845	9850	9854	9859	9863
97	9868	9872	9877	9881	9886	9890	9894	9899	9903	9908
98	9912	9917	9921	9926	9930	9934	9939	9943	9948	9952
99	9956	9961	9965	9969	9974	9978	9983	9987	9991	9996
N	0	1	2	3	4	5	6	7	8	9

Table XV. Natural Logarithms

N	0	1	2	3	4	5	6	7	8	9
0.0		5.395	6.088	6.493	6.781	7.004	7.187	7.341	7.474	7.592
0.1	7.697 (Take tabular value — 10)	7.793	7.880	7.960	8.034	8.103	8.167	8.228	8.285	8.339
0.2	8.391	8.439	8.486	8.530	8.573	8.614	8.653	8.691	8.727	8.762
0.3	8.796	8.829	8.861	8.891	8.921	8.950	8.978	9.006	9.032	9.058
0.4	9.084	9.108	9.132	9.156	9.179	9.201	9.223	9.245	9.266	9.287
0.5	9.307	9.327	9.346	9.365	9.384	9.402	9.420	9.438	9.455	9.472
0.6	9.489	9.506	9.522	9.538	9.554	9.569	9.584	9.600	9.614	9.629
0.7	9.643	9.658	9.671	9.685	9.699	9.712	9.726	9.739	9.752	9.764
0.8	9.777	9.789	9.802	9.814	9.826	9.837	9.849	9.861	9.872	9.883
0.9	9.895	9.906	9.917	9.927	9.938	9.949	9.959	9.970	9.980	9.990
1.0	0.00000	0995	1980	2956	3922	4879	5827	6766	7696	8618
1.1	9531	*0436	*1333	*2222	*3103	*3976	*4842	*5700	*6551	*7395
1.2	0.1 8232	9062	9885	*0701	*1511	*2314	*3111	*3902	*4686	*5464
1.3	0.2 6236	7003	7763	8518	9267	*0010	*0748	*1481	*2208	*2930
1.4	0.3 3647	4359	5066	5767	6464	7156	7844	8526	9204	9878
1.5	0.4 0547	1211	1871	2527	3178	3825	4469	5108	5742	6373
1.6	7000	7623	8243	8858	9470	*0078	*0682	*1282	*1879	*2473
1.7	0.5 3063	3649	4232	4812	5389	5962	6531	7098	7661	8222
1.8	8779	9333	9884	*0432	*0977	*1519	*2058	*2594	*3127	*3658
1.9	0.6 4185	4710	5233	5752	6269	6783	7294	7803	8310	8813
2.0	9315	9813	*0310	*0804	*1295	*1784	*2271	*2755	*3237	*3716
2.1	0.7 4194	4669	5142	5612	6081	6547	7011	7473	7932	8390
2.2	8846	9299	9751	*0200	*0648	*1093	*1536	*1978	*2418	*2855
2.3	0.8 3291	3725	4157	4587	5015	5442	5866	6289	6710	7129
2.4	7547	7963	8377	8789	9200	9609	*0016	*0422	*0826	*1228
2.5	0.9 1629	2028	2426	2822	3216	3609	4001	4391	4779	5166
2.6	5551	5935	6317	6698	7078	7456	7833	8208	8582	8954
2.7	9325	9695	*0063	*0430	*0796	*1160	*1523	*1885	*2245	*2604
2.8	1.0 2962	3318	3674	4028	4380	4732	5082	5431	5779	6126
2.9	6471	6815	7158	7500	7841	8181	8519	8856	9192	9527
3.0	9861	*0194	*0526	*0856	*1186	*1514	*1841	*2168	*2493	*2817
3.1	1.1 3140	3462	3783	4103	4422	4740	5057	5373	5688	6002
3.2	6315	6627	6938	7248	7557	7865	8173	8479	8784	9089
3.3	9392	9695	9996	*0297	*0597	*0896	*1194	*1491	*1788	*2083
3.4	1.2 2378	2671	2964	3256	3547	3837	4127	4415	4703	4990
3.5	5276	5562	5846	6130	6413	6695	6976	7257	7536	7815
3.6	8093	8371	8647	8923	9198	9473	9746	*0019	*0291	*0563
3.7	1.3 0833	1103	1372	1641	1909	2176	2442	2708	2972	3237
3.8	3500	3763	4025	4286	4547	4807	5067	5325	5584	5841
3.9	6098	6354	6609	6864	7118	7372	7624	7877	8128	8379
4.0	8629	8879	9128	9377	9624	9872	*0118	*0364	*0610	*0854
4.1	1.4 1099	1342	1585	1828	2070	2311	2552	2792	3031	3270
4.2	3508	3746	3984	4220	4456	4692	4927	5161	5395	5629
4.3	5862	6094	6326	6557	6787	7018	7247	7476	7705	7933
4.4	8160	8387	8614	8840	9065	9290	9515	9739	9962	*0185
4.5	1.5 0408	0630	0851	1072	1293	1513	1732	1951	2170	2388
4.6	2606	2823	3039	3256	3471	3687	3902	4116	4330	4543
4.7	4756	4969	5181	5393	5604	5814	6025	6235	6444	6653
4.8	6862	7070	7277	7485	7691	7898	8104	8309	8515	8719
4.9	8924	9127	9331	9534	9737	9939	*0141	*0342	*0543	*0744
5.0	1.6 0944	1144	1343	1542	1741	1939	2137	2334	2531	2728
N	0	1	2	3	4	5	6	7	8	9

Table XV. Natural Logarithms (*Continued*)

N	0	1	2	3	4	5	6	7	8	9
5.0	1.6 0944	1144	1343	1542	1741	1939	2137	2334	2531	2728
5.1	2924	3120	3315	3511	3705	3900	4094	4287	4481	4673
5.2	4866	5058	5250	5441	5632	5823	6013	6203	6393	6582
5.3	6771	6959	7147	7335	7523	7710	7896	8083	8269	8455
5.4	8640	8825	9010	9194	9378	9562	9745	9928	*0111	*0293
5.5	1.7 0475	0656	0838	1019	1199	1380	1560	1740	1919	2098
5.6	2277	2455	2633	2811	2988	3166	3342	3519	3695	3871
5.7	4047	4222	4397	4572	4746	4920	5094	5267	5440	5613
5.8	5786	5958	6130	6302	6473	6644	6815	6985	7156	7326
5.9	7495	7665	7834	8002	8171	8339	8507	8675	8842	9009
6.0	9176	9342	9509	9675	9840	*0006	*0171	*0336	*0500	*0665
6.1	1.8 0829	0993	1156	1319	1482	1645	1808	1970	2132	2294
6.2	2455	2616	2777	2938	3098	3258	3418	3578	3737	3896
6.3	4055	4214	4372	4530	4688	4845	5003	5160	5317	5473
6.4	5630	5786	5942	6097	6253	6408	6563	6718	6872	7026
6.5	7180	7334	7487	7641	7794	7947	8099	8251	8403	8555
6.6	8707	8858	9010	9160	9311	9462	9612	9762	9912	*0061
6.7	1.9 0211	0360	0509	0658	0806	0954	1102	1250	1398	1545
6.8	1692	1839	1986	2132	2279	2425	2571	2716	2862	3007
6.9	3152	3297	3442	3586	3730	3874	4018	4162	4305	4448
7.0	4591	4734	4876	5019	5161	5303	5445	5586	5727	5869
7.1	6009	6150	6291	6431	6571	6711	6851	6991	7130	7269
7.2	7408	7547	7685	7824	7962	8100	8238	8376	8513	8650
7.3	8787	8924	9061	9198	9334	9470	9606	9742	9877	*0013
7.4	2.0 0148	0283	0418	0553	0687	0821	0956	1089	1223	1357
7.5	1490	1624	1757	1890	2022	2155	2287	2419	2551	2683
7.6	2815	2946	3078	3209	3340	3471	3601	3732	3862	3992
7.7	4122	4252	4381	4511	4640	4769	4898	5027	5156	5284
7.8	5412	5540	5668	5796	5924	6051	6179	6306	6433	6560
7.9	6686	6813	6939	7065	7191	7317	7443	7568	7694	7819
8.0	7944	8069	8194	8318	8443	8567	8691	8815	8939	9063
8.1	9186	9310	9433	9556	9679	9802	9924	*0047	*0169	*0291
8.2	2.1 0413	0535	0657	0779	0900	1021	1142	1263	1384	1505
8.3	1626	1746	1866	1986	2106	2226	2346	2465	2585	2704
8.4	2823	2942	3061	3180	3298	3417	3535	3653	3771	3889
8.5	4007	4124	4242	4359	4476	4593	4710	4827	4943	5060
8.6	5176	5292	5409	5524	5640	5756	5871	5987	6102	6217
8.7	6332	6447	6562	6677	6791	6905	7020	7134	7248	7361
8.8	7475	7589	7702	7816	7929	8042	8155	8267	8380	8493
8.9	8605	8717	8830	8942	9054	9165	9277	9389	9500	9611
9.0	9722	9834	9944	*0055	*0166	*0276	*0387	*0497	*0607	*0717
9.1	2.2 0827	0937	1047	1157	1266	1375	1485	1594	1703	1812
9.2	1920	2029	2138	2246	2354	2462	2570	2678	2786	2894
9.3	3001	3109	3216	3324	3431	3538	3645	3751	3858	3965
9.4	4071	4177	4284	4390	4496	4601	4707	4813	4918	5024
9.5	5129	5234	5339	5444	5549	5654	5759	5863	5968	6072
9.6	6176	6280	6384	6488	6592	6696	6799	6903	7006	7109
9.7	7213	7316	7419	7521	7624	7727	7829	7932	8034	8136
9.8	8238	8340	8442	8544	8646	8747	8849	8950	9051	9152
9.9	9253	9354	9455	9556	9657	9757	9858	9958	*0058	*0158
10.0	2.3 0259	0358	0458	0558	0658	0757	0857	0956	1055	1154
N	**0**	**1**	**2**	**3**	**4**	**5**	**6**	**7**	**8**	**9**

ANSWERS TO PROBLEMS

Chapter 1

1–1. 210

1–2. (c) 161,700

1–3. 243

1–4. 16, no

1–5. 1024, 56, 252, 36

1–6. 216, 16, 56

1–7. (a) 2,598,960, (b) 0, 1, 2, 3, 4, 5, (c) two

1–13. The numbers of outcomes in each case are as follows: (a) 9, (b) 9, (c) 6, (d) 6, (e) 5, (f) 12, (g) 4, (h) 23

1–15. (a) 1,098,240 (b) 123,552 (c) 3744 (d) 54,912 (e) 5148

1–18. null set, if $c < 0$; $\{2,4,6\}$, if $0 \leq c < 1$; whole space, if $c \geq 1$

1–20. 1/4, 3/13, 11/26, 9/13

1–21. 1/3, 1/3, 7/12, 2/3, 2/3, 1/3

1–22. 1/20

1–23. 1/6, 5/6, 11/12

1–24. 3/95

1–25. .423, .0475, .00144, .0211, .00198

1–26. .135, .632, .233

1–27. 1/2, 1/8, 3/4, $1 - \pi/16$, 3/8, 3/4, 3/4, 7/8, 0

1–28. 1/6

1–29. 1/3, 1/2

1–31. 1/26, 11/221, 6/25

1–33. 1/2, 1/2

1–36. .97, .34

1–37. .6561

1–38. 1/1024

1–41. .1225, .245, .435

Chapter 2

2–1. 0, 1/4, 1/2, 3/4, 1/4, 3/4

2–2. First decile is -1.28

2–3. .9192, .5371, .0228, .0026, .8400, .8426

2–4. .1015, 1/4, 1/4, 0

2–5. 3.7, .155, .48, .30

2–6. $p(0) = 1/3$, $p(1) = 8/15$, $p(2) = 2/15$

2–7. $p(k) = 1/5$, $k = 1, 2, 3, 4, 5$

2–8. $p(0) = 1/3$, $p(1) = 1/2$, $p(3) = 1/6$

2–9. $p(0) = 9/13$, $p(1) = \cdots = p(4) = 1/13$

2–10. $p(k) = (5/6)^{k-1}(1/6), k = 1, 2, \ldots$

2–11. $Y = 1, 2, 3$ with probabilities .6, .3, .1

$R = 2, 3, 4$ with probabilities .3, .4, .3

2–12. $f(x) = \begin{cases} 2x, & 0 < x < 1 \\ 0, & \text{elsewhere} \end{cases}$

2–13. $f(x) = [\pi(1 + x^2)]^{-1}$, $Q_3 = 1$, $P(|X| < 1) = .5$

2–14. $F(x) = \begin{cases} 0, & x < -1 \\ \frac{1}{2}(1 + x)^2, & -1 \le x \le 0 \\ 1 - \frac{1}{2}(1 - x)^2, & 0 \le x \le 1 \\ 1, & x > 1 \end{cases}$

$P(X > 0) = \frac{1}{2}$, $P(|X| > \frac{1}{2}) = \frac{1}{4}$

2–16. 1/2, 6

2–17. no, $e^{-x} \to \infty$ as $x \to -\infty$

2–18. yes, $k = \frac{1}{2}$, $F(x) = \frac{1}{2}e^{x}$ for $x < 0$, $1 - \frac{1}{2}e^{-x}$ for $x > 0$

2–19. no, $K = 1/p - 1$

2–20. $\dfrac{1}{2\sqrt{y}}$, $0 < y < 1$

2–21. Uniform on [0,1]

2–22. $Y = -2, 0, 4$ each with probability 1/3

2–23. Uniform on [0,1]

2–24. Uniform on [0,1]

2–26. 1/5, 4/5

2–27. 3

2–28. 1

2–29. 10/13

2–30. 6

2–31. 3/2, 3

2–32. 2/3

2–33. 0

2–34. 1, π

2–36. 0

2–37. 1/3

2–38. 1/2

2–39. 1/2, 1/3

2–40. Not defined

2–42. $6 = 1.5 + 4.5$

2–45. 4/25, 32/75

2–46. .45, .6

2–47. 1/18

2–48. 1/6

2–49. .96

2–51. Both 1/4

2–52. .018, 1/8

2–55. e^{tk}, $E(X^r) = k^r$, 0, 0

2–56. $E(X^k) = (k + 1)!$

2–57. $\dfrac{p}{1 - t(1 - p)}$

2–58. $e^{ibt}\, \phi_X(at)$

2–60. $\exp[itm - |at|]$

2–62. $ap + bq$, $(a - b)^2pq$, $e^{bt}[e^{(a-b)t}p + q]$

2–63. Bernoulli, $p = 1/4$

2–64. 1/16, 7/128, 7/128

2–65. $1 - (1/12)^4$

2–66. $(.9)^4$

2–67. 20, 16

2–68. 5

2–69. 16/2187

2–70. .59, .92, 5

2–72. $(n)_r\, p^r$

2–73. $p(0) = 3/66$, $p(1) = 20/66$, $p(2) = 30/66$, $p(3) = 12/66$, $p(4) = 1/66$

2–74. .0064, .0081

2–75. 1, 3

2–76. $\sum_{k=6}^{10} \binom{10}{k} (.45)^k (.55)^{10-k}$

2–78. $\binom{5}{k}\binom{15}{5-k} \Big/ \binom{20}{5}$

2–80. 6

2–81. 6, 9/2

2–82. No replacement:
$(9 - k)(8 - k)/240$, $k = 0, \ldots, 7$
Replacement:
$.3(.7)^k$, $k = 0, 1, \ldots$

2–83. q/p^2

2–84. $(k - 1)(k - 2)/240$

2–85. .57, .30, .035

2–86. .184

2–87. .147

2–88. .0803

2–89. e^{-4}, $5e^{-4}$

2–91. .973, .071

2–92. .1512

2–93. .049

2–94. 0, $\pi^2/12$, 1/2, $2/\pi$

2–95. Median = any number on [1,2]; 3/2, 13/12

2–96. $(1 + \pi)/(2\pi)$

2–98. $(\log 2)/\lambda$

2–99. .082, .543

2–100. Negative exponential, mean 5 hours

2–104. .1336

2–105. .3830

2–106. .7257, .2881

2–107. 8.65, 11.35

2–108. $(-\infty,6)$ and $(14,\infty)$: .0228
$(6,7)$ and $(13,14)$: .0440
$(7,8)$ and $(12,13)$: .0919
$(8,9)$ and $(11,12)$: .1493
$(9,10)$ and $(10,11)$: .1915

2–110. $\frac{2}{\sigma}f\left(\frac{y}{\sigma}\right)$, where $f(x)$ is the standard normal density; $\sqrt{\frac{2}{\pi}}\sigma$

2–112. 6.1 per cent, 2.6 percent, $5.33k$

Chapter 3

3–1. (a) 5/9, (c) 7/9

3–2. $1 + 3p^2 - 3p$

3–3. $\pi/4$; 1/2; 1; 7/16

3–5. $\exp(-x-y)$, for $x > 0$, $y > 0$; $1 - 1/e$; $1 - 3/e^2$; 1/2

3–6. $1 - e^{-z} - ze^{-z}$; 1

3–7. (a) $F_Z(z) = \begin{cases} 0, & z < -2 \\ \frac{1}{8}(2+z)^2, & -2 \le z \le 0 \\ 1 - \frac{1}{8}(2-z)^2, & 0 \le z \le 2 \\ 1, & z > 2 \end{cases}$
(b) $F_W(w) = \begin{cases} 0, & w < -1 \\ \frac{1}{4}(1+w)^2, & -1 \le w \le 1 \\ 1, & w > 1 \end{cases}$

3–8. $1/\pi$, 0

3–9. 1/4, 1/2, 1/4 for $x = 1, 2, 3$, and 1/3 for $y = 2, 3, 4$; 1/2; 1/2; 3/8; 8/3; 2.

3–10. 1/2; $\sqrt{4 - x^2}/(2\pi)$ for $|x| < 2$; $1/(2\sqrt{3})$ for $x^2 < 3$; $2/\sqrt{15}$; $z/4$ for $0 \le z \le 4$; $w^2/4$ for $0 \le w \le 2$

3–11. $[\exp(-\frac{1}{2}x^2)]/\sqrt{2\pi}$; $\{\exp(-[x-y]^2)\}/\sqrt{\pi}$; y; $x/2$

3–12. 1 for $0 < x < 1$; $y^{-1/2}$ for $0 < y < \frac{1}{4}$.

3–17. $\frac{1}{4\pi}\exp[-\frac{1}{4}(x^2 + y^2)]$; $1 - \exp(-\frac{1}{4}w^2)$ for $w > 0$; $1/(2\pi)$ for $0 < \theta < 2\pi$

3–18. $1 - e^{-2z} - 2ze^{-2z}$, $z > 0$

3–19. $\frac{a^2}{a^2 + b^2}$, if $a, b > 0$

3–24. 0

3–27. $-1/2$

3–30. $f_{X+h,Y+k}(u,v) = f_{X,Y}(u-h, v-k)$

3–31. $f_{X/Y}(v) = [\pi(1 + v^2)]^{-1}$

3–32. (a) $\begin{pmatrix} 1/5 & -2/5 \\ 1/5 & 3/5 \end{pmatrix}$, (c) $A^{-1}B = \begin{pmatrix} -8/5 \\ 17/5 \end{pmatrix}$

3–34. $\frac{1}{2\pi\sqrt{5}}\exp\left\{-\frac{1}{10}(9x^2 - 4x[y-4] + [y-4]^2)\right\}$

3–35. $\mu = \begin{pmatrix} 0 \\ 0 \end{pmatrix}$, $\boldsymbol{M} = \begin{pmatrix} 4/7 & 1/7 \\ 1/7 & 2/7 \end{pmatrix}$, constant $= \frac{\sqrt{7}}{2\pi}$

3–36. In independent case: ellipses with axes parallel to coordinate axes

3–40. (d) $-1/29$, 0, 0

3–41. (a) 6, (b) $6(1 - x - y)$ for $x + y \le 1$, $x \ge 0$, $y \ge 0$; $3(1-x)^2$, for $0 < x < 1$, (c) $f_{U,V,W}(u,v,w) = 6$ for $0 < u < v < w < 1$ and 0 elsewhere

3–42. $f_{\boldsymbol{X}}(\boldsymbol{x}) = n!$ for $x_1 + \cdots + x_n \le 1$, $x_i \ge 0$; and 0 elsewhere

3–44. (a) $\frac{1}{6(2\pi)^{3/2}}\exp\left[-\frac{x^2}{8} + \frac{(y-2)^2}{18} + \frac{z^2}{2}\right]$
(b) $\exp[2it - \frac{1}{2}(4s^2 + 9t^2 + u^2)]$
(c) $\boldsymbol{\mu} = \begin{pmatrix} 2 \\ 2 \end{pmatrix}$, $\boldsymbol{M} = \begin{pmatrix} 13 & 9 \\ 9 & 13 \end{pmatrix}$
(d) $\exp[(2s + 2t)i - \frac{1}{2}(13s^2 + 18st + 10t^2)]$
(e) $\frac{1}{14\pi}\exp\left\{-\frac{1}{98}[10(u-2)^2 - 18(u-2)(v-2) + 13(v-2)^2]\right\}$

3–45.

y \ x	0	1	2
0	1/36	1/9	1/9
1	1/6	1/3	0
2	1/4	0	0

3–46. $4(3/8)^4$

3–47. (b) $\sqrt{10}/5$

(c) $\begin{pmatrix} 8 \\ 0 \\ 2 \end{pmatrix}, \begin{pmatrix} 13 & 9 & 11 \\ 9 & 13 & 11 \\ 11 & 11 & 11 \end{pmatrix}$

(d) $\phi(t_1,t_2) = \exp[8t_1 i - \frac{1}{2}(13t_1^2 + 18t_1t_2 + 13t_2^2)]$

$f(y_1,y_2) = \frac{1}{2\pi\sqrt{88}}\exp\left\{-\frac{1}{176}[13(y_1-8)^2 - 18y_2(y_1 - 8) + 13y_2^2]\right\}$

(e) 2, 11

Chapter 4

4–2. $\lambda^2 w\, e^{-\lambda w}$, $w > 0$

4–3. 10, 290/17

4–4. .0046″

4–5. 1.12 miles

4–9. $(e^t - 1)^2/t^2$

4–17. .807

4–18. .159

4–19. .46, .08, .94

4–20. .19

4–21. .0026

4–22. .92

4–25. Normal, $(n/\lambda, n/\lambda^2)$

Chapter 5

5–1. He should play

5–3. Same column for θ_1, add 3 to θ_2 column, add 2 to θ_3 column

5–4. (partial ans.) $L(\theta_2,\mathbf{p}) = -3p_1 + p_3 + 2p_4$

5–5. Strategy is defined by the d. f. $F(k)$, with

$$L(\mu, F) = \int_{-\infty}^{\infty} (\mu - k)^2 dF(k)$$

5–6. (.7, .5, .2)

5–8. Pure: a_1 using loss, a_2 using regret
Mixed: (1,0) using loss, (1/3, 2/3) using regret

5–9. a_3 using loss, a_1 using regret

5–10. a_2 if $w < 2/3$, a_1 if $w > 2/3$, either if $w = 2/3$

5–11. a_1

5–12. Same as using loss (cf. Example 5–5)

5–13. (a) Pass with probability 1/3, reject with probability 2/3
(b) Pass

5–14. a_1 dominates a_2, $\frac{1}{2}(a_1 + a_4)$ dominates a_3

5–15. Mixtures of a_1 and a_4

5–17. Probability of $[X_1 = k_1, \ldots, X_4 = k_4]$ is

(a) $(.7)^{\Sigma k_i}(.3)^{4-\Sigma k_i}$

(b) $\dfrac{\binom{7}{\Sigma k_i}\binom{3}{4-\Sigma k_i}}{\binom{4}{\Sigma k_i}\binom{10}{4}}$

5–18. (a) $(b - a)^{-n}$ if $a < x_i < b$ (all i), 0 otherwise

(b) $(2\pi\sigma^2)^{-n/2} \exp\left[-\frac{1}{2\sigma^2}\Sigma(x_i - \mu)^2\right]$

(c) $p^{\Sigma x_i}(1 - p)^{n-\Sigma x_i}$, $x_i = 0, 1$

(d) $\dfrac{e^{-nm} m^{\Sigma x_i}}{\prod x_i!}$, $x_i = 0, 1, \ldots$

(e) $p^n(1 - p)^{\Sigma x_i}$, $x_i = 0, 1, \ldots$

5–19. 0, 0, 9, $\sqrt{54/5}$

5–20. ± 2

5–21. 75, 13; 75, $\sqrt{173}$

5–22. 29, 19, 6

5–24. $(n\lambda)^n x^{n-1} e^{-n\lambda x}/(n - 1)!$, $x > 0$

5–25. 0, 4.004, .0456

5–26. (a) $\frac{1}{n}[EX^{2k} - (EX^k)^2]$

(b) $E(X - \mu)^3 = EX^3 - 3\mu EX^2 + 2\mu^3$

5–27. (a) Probability 1/6 for each of (1,2), (1,3), (1,4), (2,3), (2,4), (3,4)
(b) Probabilities 1/2, 1/3, 1/6 for R = 1, 2, 3, resp.
(c) 5/2

5–28. Normal: mean σ^2, variance $\frac{1}{n}\operatorname{var}(X - \mu)^2$

5–30. $[F(\lambda)]^n$

5–31.

Decision function	Action, if data is 0 H	1 H	2 H	Risk under $p = \frac{1}{4}$	$p = \frac{3}{4}$
d_1	$\frac{1}{4}$	$\frac{1}{4}$	$\frac{1}{4}$	0	$\frac{1}{4}$
d_2	$\frac{3}{4}$	$\frac{3}{4}$	$\frac{3}{4}$	$\frac{1}{4}$	0
d_3	$\frac{3}{4}$	$\frac{3}{4}$	$\frac{1}{4}$	$\frac{15}{64}$	$\frac{9}{64}$
d_4	$\frac{3}{4}$	$\frac{1}{4}$	$\frac{3}{4}$	$\frac{5}{32}$	$\frac{3}{32}$
d_5	$\frac{1}{4}$	$\frac{3}{4}$	$\frac{3}{4}$	$\frac{7}{64}$	$\frac{1}{64}$
d_6	$\frac{3}{4}$	$\frac{1}{4}$	$\frac{1}{4}$	$\frac{9}{64}$	$\frac{15}{64}$
d_7	$\frac{1}{4}$	$\frac{3}{4}$	$\frac{1}{4}$	$\frac{3}{32}$	$\frac{5}{32}$
d_8	$\frac{1}{4}$	$\frac{1}{4}$	$\frac{3}{4}$	$\frac{1}{64}$	$\frac{7}{64}$

5–32. $1/n$, $\sqrt{2}/\sqrt{n\pi}$

5–33. $\dfrac{n}{n+1}, \dfrac{\theta^2}{n+1}$

5–34. d_5 or d_8

5–35. $b = 0$

5–36. d_3

5–38. d_5 or d_8

5–39. 1/10 and 9/10; 9/40 and 1/40; Bayes action is to choose 3/4

5–43. $[6(n+2)]^{-1}$

5–44. (a) Same as 5–18(b)
(b) Same as 5–18(d)
(c) Same as 5–18(c)
(d) $L(k) = 1/k^n$ if k exceeds all observations, 0 otherwise

5–45. Take a_1 if at most 1 defective in sample; take a_2 if 2 defective

5–46. Mode: $\bar{x}$, mean: $\dfrac{n}{n-2}\bar{x}$

5–49. $\sum X_i$

5–50. $\sum X_i$

5–51. Conditional density is $\dfrac{1}{\pi\sqrt{8}}$

$$\exp\left[-\frac{1}{4}(x_1 - x_2)^2 - \frac{1}{2}(x_3 - \mu)^2\right],$$

which is not independent of μ.

5–55. $\sum X_i$

5–57. $\sum X_i^2$

5–58. Multinomial

5–60. $d(x) = \dfrac{d(cx+k) - k}{c}$

Chapter 6

6–2. 0

6–3. $\sum a_i = 1$

6–8. $1/n$, $2/n$

6–12. $2/n$

6–13. $\hat{p} = k/n$

6–14. Sample mean

6–15. $\hat{\theta} = 1/\bar{X}$

6–16. $\hat{M} = 2$

6–17. $\hat{b}$ = smallest observation

6–18. (19.6,20.4),(19.9,20.1),(19.6,20.4), (19.84,20.16), (19.74,20.26)

6–19. 664

6–20. (1.91, 2.33)

Chapter 7

7–1. S, C, C, S, C, C, S, C

7–2. (a) (There are eight tests)
(b) Type I: 0 for no Whites, 2/5 for 1 White
Type II: 3/10 for 2 Whites, 1/10 for 3 Whites, 0 for 4 or 5 Whites
(c) Rejecting H_0 for any outcome is a test with type II error size 0.

7–3. .106, 1

7–4. (a) 86, .50 (b) 53, .64 (c) 1.64, .74

7–5. $\bar{X} > 0.80$

7–6. $\bar{X} > -0.19$

7–7. $\sum X_i >$ const.

7–8. $\sum_1^{32} X_i > 44.7$

7–9. $\bar{X} <$ const.

7–10. $\sum_1^{73} (X_i - \mu)^2 > 348$

7–11. If $Q(\theta_0) - Q(\theta_1) > 0$,
$\sum R(X_i) <$ const.
If $Q(\theta_0) - Q(\theta_1) < 0$,
$\sum R(X_i) >$ const.

7–12. $1 - 3p + 3p^2$

7–13. 104.4, 14, $\pi(\mu) = N\left(\dfrac{\mu - 104.4}{2.71}\right)$

7–14. $\left[\binom{10-M}{4} + \binom{M}{1}\binom{10-M}{3}\right] \Big/ \binom{10}{4}$

7-15. $K = .0351,\ \pi(\sigma^2) = 1 - N\left(\frac{.0351 - .99\sigma^2}{.141\sigma^2}\right)$

7-17. $\sum_1^{25} X_i^2 > 36.6$

7-18. $\sum X_i > 59,\ \pi(p) = N\left(\frac{100p - 59}{\sqrt{100pq}}\right)$

7-19. Reject H_0 when $\bar{X}\exp(-\theta_0\bar{X}) <$ constant

7-20. $\lambda = \frac{1}{8}$ with prob. $\frac{1}{4}$ and $\lambda = \frac{27}{32}$ with prob. $\frac{3}{4}$

7-21. Reject H_0 when $\hat{v}\exp(-\hat{v}/v_0) <$ constant, where $\hat{v} = \frac{1}{n}\sum(X_i - \mu)^2$

7-22. Continue sampling for $\sum X_i$ between $.415\,n - 3.32\log_{10} B$ and $.415\,n + 3.32\log_{10}(1/A)$

7-23. Continue sampling for $\sum X_i$ between (for $\mu_1 > \mu_0$):

$$\frac{n}{2}(\mu_0 + \mu_1) - \frac{\sigma^2}{\mu_1 - \mu_0}\log_e B \quad \text{and}$$

$$\frac{n}{2}(\mu_0 + \mu_1) + \frac{\sigma^2}{\mu_1 - \mu_0}\log(1/A)$$

7-24. Continue sampling for $(\theta_0 - \theta_1)\bar{X}$ between

$$\log_e(\theta_0/\theta_1) - \frac{1}{n}\log_e B \quad \text{and}$$

$$\log_e(\theta_0/\theta_1) + \frac{1}{n}\log_e(1/A)$$

7-25. 13.2 (under H_0), 18.8 (under H_1)

7-26. 47

7-27.

h	$-\infty$	-1	0	1	∞
θ	∞	2	1.44	1	0
OC	1	.95	.56	.1	0
ASN	3.25	10.3	13.5	7.74	0

7-28. $\mu(h) = \frac{1}{2}(\mu_1 + \mu_0) + \frac{1}{2}h(\mu_1 - \mu_0)$

Chapter 8

8-1. $a + \frac{b-a}{n+1},\ b - \frac{b-a}{n+1},\ \frac{1}{2}(a+b)$

8-2. $\frac{1}{(n+2)(n+1)^2}$

8-3. $\frac{(b-a)^2}{2(n+2)(n+1)}$

8-4. $12(1 - y_2)^2,\ 0 < y_1 < y_2 < 1.$

8-5. 2/5.

8-6. $\frac{n-1}{n+1}(b-a),\ \frac{2(n-1)}{(n+2)(n+1)^2}(b-a)^2$

8-8. $\frac{(n+1-k)k}{(n+1)^2(n+2)}$

8-9. .0001

8-10. .99

8-11. (a) 120 (b) $945\sqrt{\pi/32}$
(c) 4/15 (d) $\frac{15\sqrt{2\pi}}{128}$
(e) 8/81
(g) $3\pi/512$ (f) 1/30030

8-12. (a) 69.03 (b) .16

8-13. $\frac{1}{2^5 4!\sigma^2}\left(\frac{y}{\sigma^2}\right)^4 e^{-y/2\sigma^2},\ y > 0;$ $10\sigma^2;\ 20\sigma^4$

8-14. $\frac{Y}{18.3} < \sigma^2 < \frac{Y}{3.94}$

8-15. $1 - F_{\chi^2(10)}(40/\sigma^2)$

8-20. (a) $L_3 = L_1 - L_2$
(b) $B = \begin{pmatrix} 2 & -1 \\ -1 & 2 \end{pmatrix}$

8-21. (b) $\chi^2(mn - 1)$, when divided by σ^2
(c) Ranks are $mn - m,\ m - 1$; distributions are independent chi-square, when divided by σ^2

8-23. $\operatorname{var} F = \frac{2n^2(m+n-2)}{m(n-2)^2(n-4)}$, $n > 4$

8-26. .181

8-27. $F_{1-\gamma}(1,n) = [t_{1-\gamma/2}(n)]^2$

Chapter 9

9-1. $\chi^2 = 2.26$, accept $p = 1/2$ at 5% level

9-3. $\chi^2 = .95 < \chi^2_{.95}(3)$, accept at 5% level

9-4. $\chi^2 = 13.5 > \chi^2_{.95}(6)$, reject at 5% level

9-5. $\chi^2 = 5.63 < \chi^2_{.95}(4)$, accept at 5% level

9–6. $\chi^2 = 10.3 > \chi^2_{.95}(2)$, reject at 5% level

9–8. $D_n = .05 < .0957$, accept at 5% level

9–11. .85 as compared with lower bound of about .4

9–13. $1 - L(M_1)$, $L(M_2)$

9–14. $\sum_{c+1}^{n} \binom{n}{k} p_0^k(1-p_0)^{n-k}$

9–15. .082, .072, .028

9–18. 8/81, 15/112

9–19. $\dfrac{k+2}{n+4}$

9–20. Crude: (.39, .71), better: (.400, .692)

9–21. 30.9 under H_0, 29.9 under H_1

9–24. $\dfrac{K+1}{n}$, where K is the sum of n observations

9–25. Density: $\theta^n x^{n-1} e^{-\theta x}/(n-1)!$, $x > 0$

9–26. Reject H_0 if $\bar{X}\exp(-\theta_0 \bar{X}) <$ constant

9–27. $n = 257$, $K = 512$

9–28. $\dfrac{K+1}{n+\lambda}$, where K is the sum of n observations

9–29.

m	0	1	1.44	2	∞
$\pi(m)$	0	.05	.5	.95	1

9–30. $(34.9 \times 10^{-8}, 61.2 \times 10^{-8})$

9–31. $1 - F_{\chi^2(29)}(210/\sigma^2)$

9–32. $(n+2)^{-1}$

9–33. 1, .98, .95, .87

9–34. $R > 12.9$, $s_x^2 > 12.1$

9–35. (4.301,4.326); $(4.0 \times 10^{-4}, 15.2 \times 10^{-4})$; 80% confidence region: $\begin{cases}(4.314-\mu)^2 < .187\sigma^2 \\ .000402 < \sigma^2 < .00151\end{cases}$

9–36. $1 - N\left(\dfrac{K-\mu}{\sqrt{\pi}\sigma/\sqrt{2n}}\right)$

9–38. Reject using two-sided test at 5% level

9–39. .011, .90

9–40. .95

9–43. $r = 19 > 13.9 = r_{.95}$ [Reject at 10% level with two-sided rest, but one-sided test $r <$ const. would accept.] $s = 20 = E(s) + .15\sigma_s$, so accept H_0

9–44. $d^2/s^2 = 807/671 > 1$, accept H_0 against trend

9–45. $r = 8 < 8.56 = r_{.05}$; $s = 13 = s_{.05}$; $\dfrac{d^2}{s^2} = E\left(\dfrac{d^2}{s^2}\right) - 2.06\sqrt{\operatorname{var}\left(\dfrac{d^2}{s^2}\right)}$

9–46. $\dfrac{2n-2}{3n-4}$

9–47. 106, 98, 100, 91, 114, 106, 85, 123, 86, 116, 131, 112, 88, 124

9–48. 5.64, 4.97, 5.15, 3.81, 4.31, 4.97, 4.31, 3.32, 3.81, 3.98, 4.48, 3.32, 3.15, 5.15, 1.66

Chapter 10

10–3. $D = 22/30 > 15/30$, reject at 5% level

10–4. (a) $\chi^2 \doteq 8 > 3.84$, reject at 5% level
(b) Accept at 10% level

10–7. 95%: (−.08, .32)

10–9. $F = 4/3 < 3.2$, accept at 5% level

10–10. $1 - F_F(2.11\tau^2/\sigma^2) + F_F(.485\tau^2/\sigma^2)$

10–11. $\tau^2 = 18/7 < 4.75$, accept at 5% level
95% confidence interval: (−.22, 4.22)

10–13. −.663

10–14. Accept equality at any level up to .1635

10–15. Choose wire A at 5% level

10–16. Maximum $\alpha = .127$

10–17. Accept $F_X = F_Y$ at 4.24% level

10–18. Accept at 5% level, since $10 < 11 < 38$ (two-sided test)

10–19. 1

10–20. Reject $F_X = F_Y$ at 5% level

10–21. No change in order

10–22. (Either test) Accept $F_X = F_Y$ at any level up to 10/35

10–23. $c_1/\sigma_{c_1} \doteq 1.9 > 1.64$, reject $F_X = F_Y$ (one-sided test)

10–25. At 5% level, observed sample is in critical region for one-sided test

Chapter 11

11–2. $.00283 < \sigma^2 < .0050$

11–3. $53 + 6x = 34y$

11–4. $4.34 < \alpha < 8.28$, $-5.23 < \beta < .707$, $3.36 < \sigma^2 < 7.60$; Accept $\beta = 0$.

11–5. Center: (6.31,.092), semi-axes: 2.67 and 1.2

11–6. 0

11–7. (a) $F = 0$, accept linearity; (b) 5, 1, 16/9 (max. lik.) (c) Center: (5,1), semi-axes: 3.39 and 4.15.

11–8. $c = \sum \sum X_{ij} t_i^2 / \sum n_i t_i^2$

11–11. (3.41,14.59)

11–12. (.47,3.53), using $\hat{\sigma}^2$ from 11–7

11–14. $\prod_{i=1}^{k} \left\{ \frac{1}{n_i} \sum (X_{i_i} - \bar{X}_i)^2 \right\}^{n_i/2} <$ (const) $\left\{ \frac{1}{n} \sum \sum (X_{i_i} - \bar{X}_i)^2 \right\}^{n/2}$

11–15. LR-test is same as F-test given

11–17. $F = 9/8$, accept $\theta_i = 0$ at 5% level

11–18. Using 5% level: $F_A = 4.4 > 3.26$, A has effect; $F_B = 15.4 > 3.49$, B has effect

11–19. Using 5% level: $.18 < 2.51$, no interaction; $5.46 > 3.01$, machine effect present; $1.04 < 3.40$, no operator effect

Index

AUTHOR INDEX